modern trigonometry

A PROGRAM FOR SELF-INSTRUCTION

MYRA McFADDEN
Department of Mathematics
Bucknell University
Lewisburg, Pennsylvania

PROGRAM EDITORS

J. William Moore
Department of Education
Bucknell University
Lewisburg, Pennsylvania

Wendell I. Smith
Department of Psychology
Bucknell University
Lewisburg, Pennsylvania

McGRAW-HILL BOOK COMPANY

New York   St. Louis   San Francisco   Toronto   London   Sydney

modern trigonometry

A PROGRAM FOR SELF-INSTRUCTION

Preface

In a sense, the century in which we live has been, and is, a century of revolution—in particular, of revolutions in knowledge. Mathematics has been centrally involved in the revolutions in the sciences—in both the social and the natural sciences. Of equal importance to its participation in the scientific revolutions is the revolution within mathematics itself. Teachers of mathematics are rapidly becoming aware of the changing views of the appropriate content for courses in mathematics—courses bearing such familiar titles as algebra, geometry, trigonometry, and calculus. Through the impetus provided by the work of the School Mathematics Study Group, the Commission on Mathematics of the College Entrance Examination Board, the University of Illinois Committee on School Mathematics, and similar groups, text materials in modern mathematics for secondary-school and college curricula have been developed in the past half-dozen years.

What is "modern" mathematics? How does it differ from traditional mathematics? Why should we study it? What can be done with it? These are questions raised frequently by both teachers and students of the traditional mathematics. They deserve an explanation, although it is not an easy task to provide specific answers to such general questions. Much of modern mathematics is not new. Little of it was developed recently; in fact, many of the most important ideas in modern mathematics, the concepts of set, relationship, and function, for example, probably antedate man's recorded history. Further, the formal development and introduction of many of the concepts into mathematics during the nineteenth and twentieth centuries were preceded by some three hundred years of research. To mortal man, "modern" does not mean anything as old as a sixteenth-, seventeenth-, or eighteenth-century invention! The "new" mathematics is modern largely in the sense that its importance has become generally recognized by mathematicians only during this century. The great significance of the "new" mathematics has been widely recognized as a result of (1) the tremendous amount of research in mathematics and science that has been done in this century and (2) the technological revolution which goes on around us unabated.

The chief task of the creative mathematician is the development of theorems and the construction of proofs for them. In the research necessary for attaining this goal, the need for more languages which permit precise definition of terms has become apparent. Increasingly in the recent history of mathematics, the importance of formal logic has been recognized. The use of axioms, theorems, and proofs has been extended to all mathematics and not restricted simply to Euclid's geometry.

The extension of the logical system to the algebras has been particularly fruitful, since it has brought more attention to the *structure* of algebras and has helped to decrease the emphasis on an algebra as a means only of solving equations, with the accompanying reduction of overemphasis on the development of manipulative skills. This is not to imply that solving equations and manipulating a number system with skill are unimportant. On the contrary, the ability to solve and the ability to manipulate have great utility *providing they are applied with understanding.* Without understanding, one manipulates numbers and solves problems as though mathematics were a bag of tricks. The important developments in the mathematics underlying the technological revolution that has produced automation and the digital computer were not new "tricks." The increasing number of applications of mathematics in economics, biology, sociology, and psychology is not the result of transplanting old "tricks" to new subject matter.

The presentation of trigonometry in this book follows the recommendations of the Commission on Mathematics and includes the topics suggested by the School Mathematics Study Group.

Less time is given to the numerical solution of triangles and the usual work with logarithms, so that greater emphasis can be placed on the analytical and functional aspects of trigonometry, which have very important applications in science and industry.

The word *trigonometry* suggests triangle measurement (the numerical solution of triangles). Today, however, many of the most important applications of trigonometry do not involve angles or triangles specifically. The study of wave motion and periodic phenomena, such as sound waves, alternating electric currents, and business cycles, rests upon the principles developed in trigonometry, though not from the angles concept explicitly.

The geometric approach to trigonometry (through the study of angles) does make the introduction meaningful, and it is the one used in the first part of the course.

The only prerequisites which have been assumed for successful completion of this programmed text are (1) a desire to increase one's understanding of the "why" in mathematics and (2) two years of high-school algebra and one year of high-school geometry.

Graph paper, a ruler, and a compass are recommended for preparing all drawings.

HOW TO USE THIS TEXT

The material presented to you in this book is in the form of a program for self-instruction. The subject matter covered in this program has been broken into items or frames which permit you to learn efficiently by studying and answering each step or frame separately.

The material in the text will be arranged in this manner:

1 To assist the student to learn mathematics more efficiently, a self-instruction program provides units of new information in separate frames. The information is broken down into separate question-and-answer frames to make it easier for you to _____.

learn

2 Thus each program item, or _____, provides new information which you will read carefully and for which you provide an answer in writing. You will then be able to compare your answer with the correct one given below each question frame.

frame

Usually you will find that the most effective way to study a program for self-instruction is to read and study each frame carefully, covering with a sheet of paper or an index card all the material on the page below the frame which you are studying. It is best to study definitions and formulas thoroughly as you go along, so that you will be able to acquire new information, step by step, as you go through this self-instruction course.

After you have studied a question frame, write out your answer fully on a separate piece of paper. Then move the sheet of paper down the page until you uncover the correct answer below the question frame. Compare your answer with the answer given in the book. Later topics in the program build on the material covered in earlier sections; hence you will find it desirable to study again each question on which you make an error and to correct your first answer to that question.

"Optional frames" are provided throughout the book for the purpose of giving you additional experience with a concept or more difficult problems and applications. If you are in a hurry, you may skip them. If you enjoy a challenge, try them.

IMPORTANT THINGS TO REMEMBER

1. Always read the question frame first.
2. Write your answer out in complete form.
3. Compare your answer with the answer given in the answer frame of the text.
4. If you make an error, correct your answer before going on to the next question frame.
5. Learning is an active process. You must do something; that is, you must respond to each question by writing your answer before you read the answer provided.

REVIEW

To enable you to review the material in a programmed text, the author has made three provisions: (1) At intervals, *review frames* have been included. These will be recognized by the symbol ∇ preceding the frame number. Review frames are also listed in the Contents. If you are unable to answer a review frame correctly, you should reread the teaching frames immediately preceding it to be certain that you have acquired the information before proceeding to the next set of teaching frames. (2) *Self-tests* have been provided for each section in the text. The answers to the test questions are given at the back of the book. It is advisable to work through each test before proceeding to the next section. If you find that you are not able to answer most of the questions correctly, you should reread the teaching frames which contain the information needed to answer correctly any question upon which you have not succeeded. (3) An *index* to the teaching frames in which key concepts are presented is provided at the back of the book.

Unlike nearly all textbooks, a self-instructional program is developed in a manner which maximizes its ability to teach. If the program has been properly constructed, the reader who carefully *follows the directions* for its use will be able to learn its contents with no other help.

SELF-TESTS

Six self-tests are provided in this text to assist you in measuring your progress. Each test *precedes* the unit of material of which it is the assessment measure. When the text is used for self-study, it is recommended that you take the test before reading the material with which it is concerned; if your score on the test is high, you may skip that section and proceed with the next. Self-test 1 is concerned with the material contained in Frames 1-398, Self-test 2 with Frames 399-774, Self-test 3 with Frames 775-1124, Self-test 4 with Frames 1125-1384, Self-test 5 with Frames 1385-1896, and Self-test 6 with the remainder of the book.

PANELS

At several points in the text, you will be asked to refer by number to one of a set of panels. Each panel contains information required for solving or understanding problems. These panels are placed at the end of the book for your convenience.

J. William Moore
Wendell I. Smith

References

Allendoerfer, C. B., and C. O. Oakley: "Fundamentals of Freshman Mathematics," McGraw-Hill Book Company, New York, 1959.

_____ and _____: "Principles of Mathematics," 2d ed., McGraw-Hill Book Company, New York, 1963.

Brink, Raymond W.: "Plane Trigonometry," 3d ed., Appleton-Century-Crofts, Inc., New York, 1959.

Brixey, John C., and Richard V. Andree: "Fundamentals of College Mathematics," Holt, Rinehart and Winston, Inc., New York, 1961.

Dubisch, Roy: "Trigonometry," The Ronald Press Company, New York, 1955.

Fisher, Robert C., and Allen D. Zieber: "Integrated Algebra and Trigonometry," Prentice-Hall, Inc., Englewood Cliffs, N.J., 1958.

Freilich, Aaron, Henry H. Shanholt, and Joseph P. McCormak: "Plane Trigonometry," Silver Burdett Company, Morristown, N.J., 1958.

Rees, Paul D., and Fred W. Sparks: "Trigonometry," McGraw-Hill Book Company, New York, 1965.

Spitzbart, Abraham, and Ross H. Bardell: College Algebra and Plane Trigonometry," Addison Wesley Publishing Company, Inc., Cambridge, Mass., 1964.

Vance, Elbridge P.: "Modern Algebra and Trigonometry," Addison Wesley Publishing Company, Inc., Cambridge, Mass., 1962.

Wylie, C. R., Jr.: "Plane Trigonometry," McGraw-Hill Book Company, New York, 1955.

contents

Preface   v

References   x

SELF-TEST 1 (Frames 1-398)   1

PART ONE

		Frame	Page
Unit 1.	TRIGONOMETRIC FUNCTIONS	1	7
	Angles and Angle Measure	1	7
	Trigonometric Functions	104	32
	Special Angles and Their Functions	225	66
	Applications	269	80
	Reduction Formulas	283	85
	SELF-TEST 2 (Frames 399-774)		120
	Graphs of the Trigonometric Functions	399	122
	Solution of Triangles	447	138
	Review of Algebra	605	182
	Basic Trigonometric Formulas	622	189
	Three Theorems from Geometry	766	232
	SELF-TEST 3 (Frames 775-1124)		237
Unit 2.	TRIGONOMETRIC IDENTITIES	775	239

		Frame	*Page*
Unit 3.	TRIGONOMETRIC EQUATIONS	981	293
Unit 4.	MISCELLANEOUS PROBLEMS	1061	317
	SELF-TEST 4 (Frames 1125-1384)		337

PART TWO

Unit 5.	CIRCULAR FUNCTIONS	1125	341
	Circular Functions Defined	1125	341
	Graphs of Circular Functions	1204	371
	Applications	1297	409
	SELF-TEST 5 (Frames 1385-1896)		444

PART THREE

Unit 6.	VECTORS	1385	449
Unit 7.	POLAR COORDINATES	1456	475
Unit 8.	COMPLEX NUMBERS	1529	500
	SELF-TEST 6 (Frames 1897-2058)		595
Unit 9.	INVERSE TRIGONOMETRIC FUNCTIONS	1897	597

	Page
Appendix A. INTERPOLATION	637
Appendix B. EQUATIONS INVOLVING RADICALS	639
ANSWERS TO SELF-TESTS	643
PANELS	659
INDEX	671

Review frames for Part One: 17, 24, 26, 32, 53, 60, 75, 101, 116-118, 120, 131, 140, 143, 169, 173, 181, 184, 190-193, 211-214, 224, 231, 232, 242, 254-256, 280, 281, 294, 303, 304, 308, 318, 350, 369-371, 382, 383, 415, 425, 434, 464, 470, 496, 504, 547, 563, 571, 597, 600, 621, 643, 653, 663, 684, 698, 717, 735-737, 759, 787, 790, 793, 800, 808, 822, 840, 845, 847, 852, 860, 864, 868, 877, 884, 896, 902, 909, 910, 915, 920, 936, 937, 943-945, 951, 952, 966, 972, 977, 993, 1010, 1017, 1023, 1027, 1038, 1039, 1045, 1046, 1049, 1052, 1073, 1079, 1099, 1100, 1109, 1118

Review frames for Part Two: 1168, 1179, 1185, 1192, 1203, 1207, 1212, 1219, 1223, 1227, 1229, 1231, 1233, 1241, 1242, 1246, 1251, 1254, 1264-1266, 1270, 1271, 1280, 1285, 1291, 1312, 1352-1357, 1365

Review frames for Part Three: 1396, 1404, 1414, 1422, 1445-1427, 1444-1447, 1460-1462, 1469, 1474, 1475, 1481, 1486, 1487, 1506, 1507, 1546-1549, 1553, 1557, 1563, 1565, 1569, 1570, 1574, 1575, 1582-1584, 1587, 1590, 1591, 1597, 1598, 1605, 1606, 1609, 1616-1618, 1621, 1622, 1626, 1631, 1634, 1642, 1643, 1656, 1659, 1663, 1664, 1666, 1679, 1685, 1688, 1690, 1693, 1694, 1733, 1737, 1749, 1750, 1763, 1774, 1775, 1818, 1819, 1822, 1828, 1829, 1893-1896, 1908, 1909, 1919-1921, 1934, 1936, 1939, 1941, 1946, 1961, 1970, 1971, 1974, 1981-1983, 1996, 1997, 2001, 2002, 2014

SELF-TEST 1

1 (a) Which of the following are quadrantal angles? (b) Which are coterminal?
$$180°, \quad 0°, \quad -\tfrac{1}{2} \text{ rev}, \quad \tfrac{3}{8} \text{ rev}, \quad \tfrac{11}{8} \text{ rev}, \quad 1 \text{ rev}$$

2 If a central angle θ cuts off an arc of $4\pi/3$ in. on a circle having a radius of 8 in., then $\theta =$ ____ radians.

3 (a) Change $\pi/3$ radians to degrees. (b) Change $150°$ to radians.
(c) Change $225°$ to radians. (d) Change $11\pi/6$ radians to degrees.
(e) Change $10,000°$ to radians. (f) Change -7π radians to degrees.

4 One radian is approximately ____°.

X 5 What is the length of the radius of a circle if an arc of 6π in. is cut off by a central angle of $3\pi/2$ radians.

6 Find the area of a sector of a circle whose radius is 3 if the central angle is $\pi/4$.

7 On a rectangular coordinate system locate the following points:
$P_1(3, 7)$, $P_2(-1, -3)$, $P_3(4, -2)$, and $P_4(-4, 0)$.

8 (a) In terms of ordinate and abscissa of point P in the sketch, give the definitions for sine and cosine of angle θ.
(b) In terms of x, y, and r, define sine and cosine of angle θ if $P(x, y)$ is a point on the terminal side of θ and r is the distance from P to O.

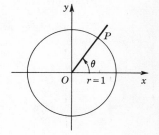

9 In which quadrants may an angle terminate if (a) the sine is negative and (b) the cosine is negative?

10 $P(6, -10)$ is a point on the terminal side of an angle θ in standard position. Sketch the angle; then find $\sin \theta$ and $\cos \theta$.

11 If $\cos \theta = -\tfrac{4}{5}$ and θ terminates in quadrant II, find (a) $\sin \theta$ and (b) $\tan \theta$. (Make a sketch.)

1

12 Two points on a circle of radius r are $P_2(x, y)$ and $P_1(r, 0)$ as shown in the sketch. Derive a formula for the length of the chord $P_2 P_1$.

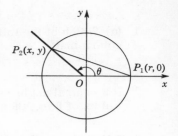

13 Fill in the following table without using Panel 1:

θ, radians	Degrees	$\sin \theta$	$\cos \theta$	$\tan \theta$
$\pi/6$				
$\pi/4$				
$\pi/2$				

14 $P(-1, \sqrt{3})$ is a point on the terminal side of a positive angle in standard position. **(a)** Sketch the angle. **(b)** Report the radian measure of this positive angle. **(c)** Find $\sin \theta$, $\cos \theta$ and $\tan \theta$.

15 Find the numerical value for $\sin 300° + (\cos 30° \cdot \sin 150°)$.

16 Find the indicated angle in each sketch. Find the tangent of each angle θ.

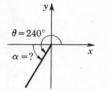

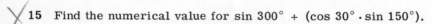

(1) **(a)** $\theta = 240°$
$\alpha =$ _____
$\tan \theta =$ _____ .

(2) **(b)** $\theta = 315°$
$\alpha =$ _____
$\tan \theta =$ _____ .

(3) **(c)** $\theta = 120°$
$\alpha =$ _____
$\tan \theta =$ _____ .

17 Given the right triangle ABC with B the right angle and the length of $BC = 12$ ft and angle $A = 50°$, find **(a)** the measure of angle C and **(b)** the length of AC.

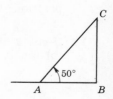

18 A tree casts a shadow 20 ft long at a time of day when the angle of elevation of the sun is 25°. How tall is the tree?

19 Simplify to a positive angle less than 360°: (a) sin 405° = sin ___, (b) cos 600° = cos ___ , (c) tan (-90°) = tan ___ , (d) sin 840° = sin ___ .

20 $\theta = 14\pi/3$. Find α, $0 \le \alpha < 2\pi$, coterminal with θ satisfying the statement $\theta = (\alpha + k \cdot 2\pi)$, k is an integer.

21 $\theta = 980°$. (a) Make a sketch of this angle in standard position. (b) Show the reference angle you should use to determine sin 980°, cos 980°, and tan 980°. (c) Consult Panel 1 and give the numerical values.

22 If sin θ = 0 and cos θ = -1, (a) find the measure of θ in radians, $0 \le \theta \le 2\pi$, and (b) give θ in degrees.

23 As θ increases from 180 to 270°, what changes take place in sin θ? (Be sure to give the maximum and minimum values of sin θ in your discussion.)

PART
ONE

UNIT 1 | Trigonometric Functions

ANGLES AND ANGLE MEASURE

1 Consider the figure formed by two half-lines (rays) r and s extending from a point O. You will recall from your study of geometry that this figure is called an *angle*. The *vertex* of the angle is the point (1)___ from which the rays are drawn and the rays (2)___ and (3)___ are called *sides* of the angle.

(1) O (2) r (3) s

2 The figure formed by two rays drawn from a fixed point is called a(n) (1)_____. The point from which the lines are drawn is called the (2)_____ of the angle; the rays are the (3)_____ of the angle.

(1) angle   (2) vertex   (3) sides

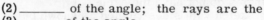

3 When we speak of a "half-line" or a "ray," we mean just the part of a line extending in one direction only through a point. Suppose you allow r to extend to the left through point O and call the extension t. Make a

continued →

sketch and indicate with a curved arrow the angle with vertex O and sides s and t.

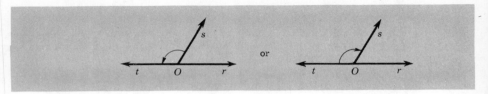

or

4 An angle is formed by two **(1)** _____ drawn from a fixed point called the **(2)**_____ of the angle.

(1) rays (half-lines) **(2)** vertex

5 We need to distinguish between the *initial* (starting) side and *terminal* (ending) side of the angle. In this sketch the angle shown by the curved arrow pointing in counterclockwise direction leads you to think of r as the **(1)** _____ side and s as the **(2)** _____ side.

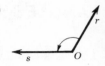

(1) initial (starting) **(2)** terminal (ending)

6 The amount of rotating necessary to move the initial side of an angle to its terminal side is the *measure* of the angle. (The units in which we measure this rotation will be discussed later.) Notice by the direction of the curved arrows in this sketch that there are two ways of rotating the initial side to the terminal side and that the two angles do not have the same

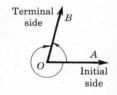

measure. Make a sketch with sides labeled as shown below and indicate with curved arrows the two possible rotations.

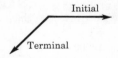

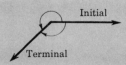

7 An angle is measured by the amount of _____ required to move the initial side of an angle to the terminal side.

rotation (turning)

8 The direction of the curved arrows indicates clockwise or counter-clockwise motion. Standard usage has accepted *counterclockwise motion* as giving the angle a *positive* measure or saying that the angle is "positive."

Which angle (α or β) is the positive angle?

α

Comment

In this program the following Greek letters will be used frequently to identify angles:

Alpha	α	pronounced al'fa
Beta	β	pronounced bā'ta
Gamma	γ	pronounced gam'a
Theta	θ	pronounced thā'ta

Practice making the symbols and pronouncing the letters until you are familiar with them. These symbols, and others, are listed for reference in Panel 19.

9 If rotation is *counterclockwise*, we say that the angle is "positive" or has a "positive measure." Conversely, if rotation is *clockwise* from initial side to terminal side, we say that the angle is "negative" or that the measure of the angle is *negative*. Identify as positive or negative the angles in the sketches below. In (2), (3), and (4), consider *OA* the initial side.

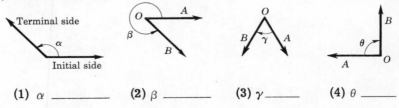

(1) α _____   **(2)** β _____   **(3)** γ _____   **(4)** θ _____

(1) positive   (2) positive   (3) negative   (4) negative

10 Make a drawing and indicate with a curved arrow the positive angle that has its vertex at the origin, its initial side along the positive x axis, and its terminal side along the negative y axis of a rectangular coordinate system such as the one shown here.

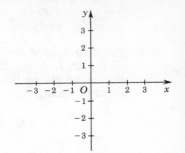

11 An angle is in *standard* position when its vertex is at the origin and its initial side is along the positive x axis of a coordinate system. Show a *positive acute* angle in *standard* position. Label the terminal side and show by a curved arrow the positive acute angle.

12 In this sketch if we use *OA* as the initial
side of the angle *AOA'* and consider the rotation through *O* counterclockwise from *OA*
to *OA'*, the angle is ____ (positive, negative).

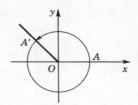

positive

13 When an angle is in standard position on a rectangular coordinate
system, where must the vertex of the angle be?

at the origin

14 The other requirement for placing an angle in *standard* position is
that the ____ (initial, terminal) side be along the positive *x* axis.

initial

15 Rotation in *clockwise* direction through a circular arc from initial
side to terminal side of an angle is said to generate a ____ (positive,
negative) angle.

negative

16 In this program both positive and negative angles, depending upon
the direction of rotation from initial side to terminal side, will be
discussed. We may also think of the initial side as moving through
more than one complete revolution before reaching the terminal
side.

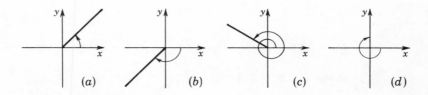

(1) Which angles are positive? (2) Which one shows more than one
revolution?

(1) *a, c* **(2)** *c*

▽17   (1) The angle shown is formed by two _____
_____ drawn from a fixed point to form the
sides of the angle.   (2) OA is the (a)_____ side.
OB is the (b)_____ side.   (3) The fixed point
O is the _____ of the angle.   (4) The angle is
measured by the amount of (a)_____
necessary to move from its (b)_____ side to its (c)_____ side.
(5) You should associate the word (a)_____ with clockwise motion and (b)_____ with counterclockwise motion.   (6) Sketch the
above angle in standard position on a coordinate system.

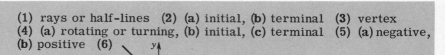

(1) rays or half-lines   (2) (a) initial, (b) terminal   (3) vertex
(4) (a) rotating or turning, (b) initial, (c) terminal   (5) (a) negative,
(b) positive   (6)

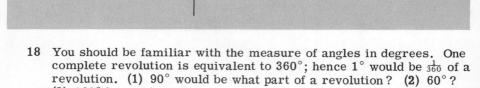

18   You should be familiar with the measure of angles in degrees. One
complete revolution is equivalent to 360°; hence 1° would be $\frac{1}{360}$ of a
revolution.   (1) 90° would be what part of a revolution?   (2) 60°?
(3) 180°?

(1) $\frac{90}{360} = \frac{1}{4}$ rev   (2) $\frac{60}{360} = \frac{1}{6}$ rev   (3) $\frac{180}{360} = \frac{1}{2}$ rev

19   Record the measure in degrees of each angle indicated by the revolutions shown in the sketches.

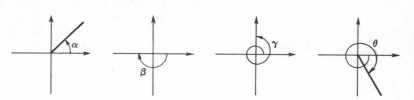

(1) $\alpha = \frac{1}{8}$ rev   (2) $\beta = -\frac{1}{2}$ rev   (3) $\gamma = \frac{5}{4}$ rev   (4) $\theta = -1\frac{1}{6}$ rev

(1) α = 45°   (2) β = -180°   (3) γ = 450°   (4) θ = -420°

20 Since there are different systems of recording the measure of angles, it is important when writing $\alpha = \frac{1}{8}$ rev or $\alpha = \frac{1}{8} \cdot 360° = 45°$ to use $°$ as the symbol for degree and "rev" as the abbreviation for revolution. If $\alpha = 45$ rev, the angle α would contain how many degrees?

$45 \cdot 360° = 16,200°$

21 In computational work we may require a further division of the degree. You will recall
        60 minutes = 1 degree, written 60' = 1°
        60 seconds = 1 minute, written 60" = 1'
One minute, therefore, is $\frac{1}{60}$ of a degree, and this in turn is $\frac{1}{60} \cdot \frac{1}{360}$ of a revolution. One second is what part of a revolution?

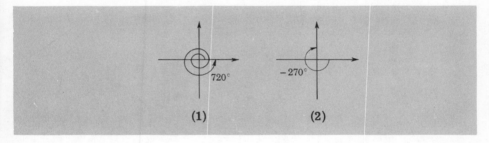

$\dfrac{1}{1,296,000}$ rev   *Solution:* $1" = \frac{1}{60} \cdot \frac{1}{60} \cdot \frac{1}{360}$ rev

$$= \dfrac{1}{60^2 \cdot 360} \text{ rev} = \dfrac{1}{1,296,000} \text{ rev}$$

22 Change the following measures of angles in revolutions to degree measure, and make a sketch of each using a curved arrow to indicate direction and revolution: (1) 2 rev, and (2) $-\frac{3}{4}$ rev.

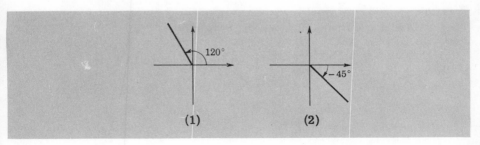

$720°$

$-270°$

(1)   (2)

23 Show as in frame 22 the angle and the number of degrees for (1) $\frac{1}{3}$ rev, and (2) -0.125 rev.

$120°$

$-45°$

(1)   (2)

▽24 Show as in frames 22 and 23 the angle and the number of degrees for
     (1) $\frac{3}{2}$ rev, and (2) $\frac{1}{6}$ rev.

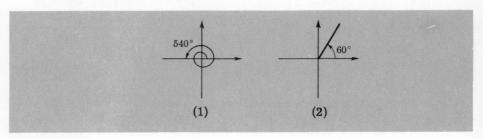

(1)   (2)

25   Show as in frames 22 to 24 the angle and the number of degrees for
     (1) -1 rev, and (2) 0.833 rev. *Note:* The symbol ≈ means "is ap-
     proximately equal to." Thus, 0.833 rev ≈ $\frac{5}{6}$ rev.

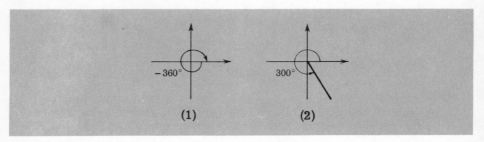

(1)   (2)

▽26 Make a sketch of the angle and state the measure in revolutions as
     in frame 25:   (1) -30°, and (2) -120°.

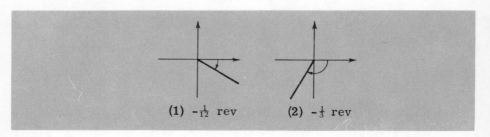

(1) $-\frac{1}{12}$ rev   (2) $-\frac{1}{3}$ rev

27   To change a reading such as 18°15' to revolutions, first change 15
     min to a fractional part of a degree; thus
          15 min = $\frac{15}{60}$° = 0.25° ($\frac{1}{4}$°)
     then 18°15' = 18.25° = 18.25/360 = 1,825/36,000 = 71/144 rev

continued →

(1) Change 67°30' to revolutions.   **(2)** Sketch the angle.

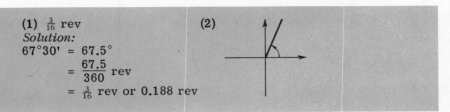

(1) $\frac{3}{16}$ rev   **(2)**
Solution:
67°30' = 67.5°

$= \dfrac{67.5}{360}$ rev

$= \frac{3}{16}$ rev or 0.188 rev

28 Change the following from degrees to revolutions and sketch the angle in standard position: **(1)** 120°48', and **(2)** 930°.

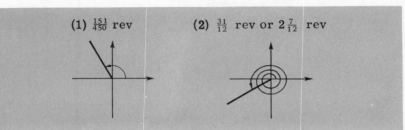

(1) $\frac{151}{450}$ rev   **(2)** $\frac{31}{12}$ rev or $2\frac{7}{12}$ rev

29 Change from degrees to revolutions as in frame 28 and make
sketches: **(1)** -150°, **(2)** -240°, and **(3)** 157°30'.

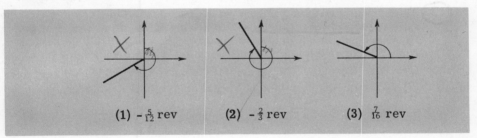

(1) $-\frac{5}{12}$ rev   **(2)** $-\frac{2}{3}$ rev   **(3)** $\frac{7}{16}$ rev

30 The x and y axes of a rectangular coordinate system divide the plane into four sections called
quadrants, numbered as in the sketch shown here.
The numbering of the quadrants is _____
(clockwise, counterclockwise) from I to IV.

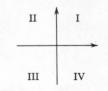

counterclockwise

31 When an angle is in standard position, the angle is an angle of the
quadrant in which its terminal side is located. Thus α is an angle

continued ➔

of the first quadrant and β is an angle of the fourth quadrant.

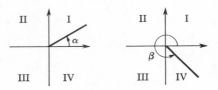

Show an angle of the second quadrant.

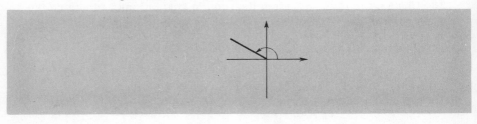

▽ 32   Identify the following as angles of quadrant I, II, III, or IV: **(1)** 60°, **(2)** -60°, **(3)** $\frac{2}{3}$ rev, **(4)** -480°, and **(5)** 0.8 rev.

(1) I   **(2)** IV   **(3)** III   **(4)** III   **(5)** IV

33 An angle in standard position whose *terminal* side lies on one of the axes is a *quadrantal* angle and is not identified as an angle of the first, second, third, or fourth quadrant. *Example:* 90° is a quadrantal angle. Which of the following are quadrantal angles?

(1) 180°, **(2)** -90°, **(3)** $\frac{5}{4}$ rev, **(4)** 240°, **(5)** 1 rev, **(6)** $-\frac{1}{3}$ rev, and **(7)** 135°30'.   Sketch the quadrantal angles as you answer.

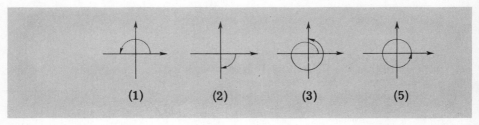

(1)   **(2)**   **(3)**   **(5)**

34   Two angles are *equal in magnitude* if the same amount of rotation is necessary to go from the initial to the terminal side of each angle.   Recall from geometry that the length of the sides of an angle does not determine the magnitude of the angle.   In which of the

continued →

sketches below is the angle labeled *AOA' not equal* in magnitude to angle *BOB'*?

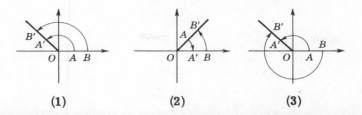

(1)   **(2)**   **(3)**

sketch 3

35 When we consider the *direction* of rotation as well
as the *amount* of rotation from initial to terminal
side of an angle, we use the term *directed* angle
and label the angle positive or negative. Look at
the angles in the sketch. Since the direction of rotation indicated by the curved arrow for α is
(1) _____ , the *directed* angle α =
(2) __°. The curved arrow on β indicates **(3)** _____
_____rotation; hence, *directed* angle β = **(4)** ___°.

(1) counterclockwise   **(2)** 60   **(3)** clockwise   **(4)** -60

36 Because the terminal side of each of these angles
(sketches *a* and *b*) lies on one of the axes, they
are called **(1)** _____ angles. As a directed
angle,

$$AOA' = \textbf{(2)} \underline{\quad}°$$
$$BOB' = \textbf{(3)} \underline{\quad}°$$

As an undirected angle,

$$AOA' = \textbf{(4)} \underline{\quad}°$$
$$BOB' = \textbf{(5)} \underline{\quad}°$$

(a)

(b)

(1) quadrantal   **(2)** 90   **(3)** -90   **(4)** 90   **(5)** 90

37 We *cannot always* say that two angles are equal if they are in
standard position and their terminal sides coincide. Study these
drawings and complete the statements following.

continued →

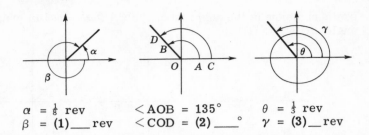

$\alpha = \frac{1}{8}$ rev $<$ AOB $= 135°$ $\theta = \frac{1}{3}$ rev
$\beta = $ **(1)**___ rev $<$ COD $=$ **(2)**___° $\gamma = $ **(3)**___rev

(1) $-\frac{7}{8}$ **(2)** 135 **(3)** $\frac{4}{3}$

38 _Coterminal_ is the word for two angles (in standard position) whose
terminal sides coincide. Which of the following would be coterminal
angles? (*a*) 90° and -270°, (*b*) $\frac{1}{4}$ rev and $\frac{5}{4}$ rev, (*c*) 120° and -120°,
(*d*) 120° and -240°, (*e*) 120° and $\frac{4}{3}$ rev, (*f*) 360° and 180°, and
(*g*) $\frac{5}{6}$ rev and 300°

a, b, d, e, g

39 Answer true or false for these statements: **(1)** If we add 360° (1
rev) to any angle α, we shall get an angle coterminal with α. **(2)** If
we add $k \cdot (360)°$ (where k is an integer) to any angle α, we have an
angle coterminal with α.

(1) true   **(2)** true

40 The angles α and β in sketch *a*
are **(1)** _____ angles, since
they are in standard position and
their terminal sides coincide.
The angle θ in sketch *b* is a(n)
(2) _____ angle, since it is
in standard position and its
terminal side coincides with one of the axes.

(1) coterminal   **(2)** quadrantal

41 List the coterminal angles of the following set:
$\{50°, 410°, -50°, [50° + 2(360°)], 40°, [50° + n(360°)]$ where n
is a negative integer}

$50°, 410°, [50° + 2(360°)], [50° + n(360°)]$

42 Write a statement telling what is meant by **(1)** coterminal angles and **(2)** a quadrantal angle.

(1) Coterminal angles are angles whose terminal sides coincide when the angles are in standard position.
(2) A quadrantal angle is an angle whose terminal side coincides with one of the axes when the angle is in standard position.

43 We have said that the measure of an angle is the amount of rotation necessary to carry the initial side of the angle to the terminal side. As units for this measure, we have discussed degrees and revolutions. When the vertex of an angle is at the center of a circle, an angle of one degree intercepts an arc that is equal in length to $\frac{1}{360}$ of the circumference. If the angle cuts off an arc equal in length to $\frac{1}{3}$ of the circumference, the angle expressed in revolutions is **(1)** _____ rev, and in degrees it is **(2)** _____ °.

(1) $\frac{1}{3}$ **(2)** 120

44 For use in the calculus and in many branches of scientific work, another unit of angular measure, a *radian*, is employed almost exclusively. When the sides of a central angle intercept an arc on the circle equal in length to the radius of the circle, we say that the measure of the angle is 1 *radian*. If α in this sketch measures 1 radian, what can you say about the length of arc S?

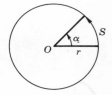

$S = r$ or the arc S is equal to the radius r

45 In *radian* measure the radius of the circle serves as the unit of measure. If the length of the arc cut off by the central angle is exactly the same as the length of the radius, then the measure of that central angle is one **(1)** _____ . If the length of the arc cut off by the central angle is twice as long as the radius, then the measure of the central angle is **(2)** _____ .

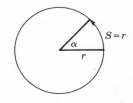

(1) radian **(2)** 2 radians

46 If S = 6 in. and r = 2 in., then
angle α = **(1)**__ radians. If S =
3 in. and r = 1 in., then angle
α = **(2)**__ radians.

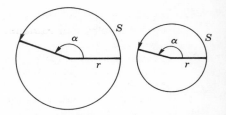

(1) 3   (2) 3

47 In sketch a, α intercepts an arc equal in length to the radius r.
(1) What is the measure of α in radians? In sketch b, β intercepts
an arc equal in length to $2\frac{1}{2}r$. **(2)** Express the measure of β in radians. In sketch c, θ = **(3)**__ radians.

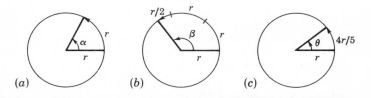

(a)   (b)   (c)

(1) 1 radian   (2) $2\frac{1}{2}$ radians   (3) $\frac{4}{5}$

48 A *radian* is the measure of a central angle which intercepts an arc
on the circle equal in length to the radius of the circle. An angle of
1 radian then has an intercepted arc whose length is r. (Simplify
each ratio.)

If S = $2r$, then θ = $\dfrac{2r}{r}$ = 2 radians

If S = $3\frac{1}{2}r$, then θ = $\dfrac{3.5r}{r}$ = **(1)** _____

If S = $0.4r$, then θ = **(2)**_____ = **(3)** _____
If S = πr, then θ = **(4)**___= **(5)** _____
If S = $2\pi r$, then θ = **(6)**_____ = **(7)** _____

(1) $3\frac{1}{2}$ or 3.5 radians   **(2)** $\dfrac{0.4r}{r}$ **(3)** 0.4 radian   **(4)** $\dfrac{\pi r}{r}$

(5) π radians   **(6)** $\dfrac{2\pi r}{r}$ **(7)** 2π radians

49 Radian measure is important. To find the measure of an angle in radians, use the formula
$\theta = S/r$, where θ is the central angle, S is the
length of the arc cut off by the sides of the angle,
and r is the length of the radius. Often angle
measure is given in terms of π, although we may
speak of 1 radian, 2 radians, etc. **(1)** $s = 3\pi$
and $r = 4$, find θ. **(2)** $\theta = \pi/2$ and $r = 12$,
find S. **(3)** $S = 2r$, find θ.

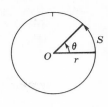

(1) $\theta = \dfrac{3\pi}{4}$ radians   *Solution:* $\theta = \dfrac{S}{r} = \dfrac{3\pi}{4}$

(2) $s = 6\pi$ radians   *Solution:* $\theta = \dfrac{S}{r}$; therefore, $\dfrac{\pi}{2} = \dfrac{S}{12}$, $S = 6\pi$

(3) $\theta = 2$ radians   *Solution:* $\theta = \dfrac{S}{r}$; therefore, $\theta = \dfrac{2r}{r}$, $\theta = 2$

50 Since the circumference of any circle is 2π
times its radius $(C = 2\pi r)$, a length of 1
radius can be measured off along the circumference 2π times, i.e., $2\pi r/r = 2\pi$. This
means that the entire circumference subtends a central angle of ___ radians.

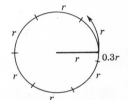

2π

51 From frame 50 you should be able to deduce the following facts:
2π radians = **(1)** ___° = **(2)** ___ rev.

(1) 360 **(2)** 1

52 If 2π radians = 360° = 1 rev, then
π radians = $\dfrac{360°}{2}$ = $\frac{1}{2}$ rev

$\dfrac{\pi}{2}$ radians = **(1)** ___° = **(2)** ___ rev

1 radian = **(3)** ___° = **(4)** ___ rev

(1) 90 **(2)** $\frac{1}{4}$ **(3)** $\dfrac{180}{\pi}$ **(4)** $\dfrac{1}{2\pi}$

▽53 The radian measure of an angle is the
ratio S/r, where S represents the
(1) _____
_____ and r represents the
(2) _____ . Thus far in this
program we have discussed three ways
of stating the measure of an angle.
(3) Name them.

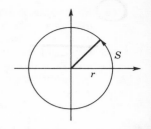

(1) length of the arc intercepted by the central angle
(2) radius of the circle (3) degrees, revolutions, radians

54 The length of the arc S in the figure is
$\pi/3$ in., and the radius is 2 in. Find θ in
radians.

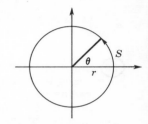

$\theta = \dfrac{\pi}{6}$ radians   *Solution:* θ in radians $= \dfrac{\text{arc}}{\text{radius}} = \dfrac{\pi/3}{2} = \dfrac{\pi}{6}$

55 A central angle cuts off an arc $S = 9.42$ in. on a circle whose radius
is 6 in. How many radians are in the angle ?

1.57 radians   *Solution:* $\dfrac{\text{arc}}{\text{radius}} = \dfrac{9.42}{6} = 1.57$

56 In frame 50 we found that an angle of 1 rev $= 2\pi r/r = 2\pi$ radians.
This gives us a way to change easily from one measure to another.
Remember that 1 rev $=$ (1) ____° $=$ (2) ___ radians.

(1) 360 (2) 2π

57 When the measure is given in radians, we can convert to degrees, if
necessary, since we have the fact that 2π radians $= 360°$. Suppose
θ measured in radians is $\pi/4$, and we want the degree measure.
Solution: The ratio of θ in radians to 2π will be equivalent to the

continued →

ratio of θ in degrees to 360°. Hence,

$$\frac{\pi/4}{2} = \frac{\theta}{360}$$

Solve for θ.

$\theta = 45°$

Solution: $\dfrac{\pi/4}{2\pi} = \dfrac{\theta}{360}, \quad \dfrac{\pi/4}{2\pi} = \dfrac{\pi}{4} \div \dfrac{2\pi}{1} = \dfrac{\pi}{4} \cdot \dfrac{1}{2\pi} = \dfrac{1}{8},$

$\dfrac{1}{8} = \dfrac{\theta}{360}, \quad \theta = 45°$

58 If we look again at the statement 2π radians = 360°, we can see (dividing both members by 2π) that 1 radian = $360°/2\pi = 180°/\pi$. To change any number of radians to *degrees*, multiply the number of degrees in 1 radian ($180°/\pi$) by the given number of radians. By this method $\pi/4$ radians = ___°. Your answer should agree with the one in frame 57.

45 *Solution:* $\dfrac{\pi}{4}$ radians $= \dfrac{\pi}{4} \cdot \dfrac{180°}{\pi} = 45°$

59 1 rev = 2π radians = 360°
π radians = 180° (dividing by 2)
1 radian $= \dfrac{180°}{\pi}$ (dividing by π)

How many degrees are in $\pi/3$ radians?

60° *Solution:* $\dfrac{\pi}{3}$ radians $= \dfrac{\pi}{3} \cdot \dfrac{180}{\pi} = 60°$

∇**60** $\dfrac{\pi}{6}$ radians $= (1)$ ___°

$\dfrac{\pi}{5}$ radians $= (2)$ ___°

$\dfrac{7\pi}{4}$ radians $= (3)$ ___°

(1) 30 (2) 36 (3) 315

61 Fill in the blanks.
1 rev = (1) ___ radians = (2) ___°

continued →

π radians = (3)____°
1 radian = (4)____°

(1) 2π (2) 360   (3) 180   (4) $\dfrac{180}{\pi}$

62 To find the approximate number of degrees in 1 radian, you may use the fact that

$$1 \text{ radian} = \frac{180°}{\pi}$$

$$\approx \frac{180°}{3.1416} \quad \pi \approx 3.1416$$

$$\approx \underline{\hspace{2cm}} \quad \text{carry out the division, writing your your answer correct to the nearest tenth}$$

57.3°

63 2 radians = $2 \cdot 180°/\pi = 360°/\pi \approx$ (1) ____°, but 2π radians = $2\pi \cdot 180/\pi =$ (2) ____°.

(1) 114.6   (2) 360

64 Radian measure is usually stated as a multiple of π, but as you noticed in frame 63, it may not be. You also noticed that there is considerable difference in the size of an angle of 2 radians and an angle of 2π radians. Compare an angle of 3 radians and an angle of 3π radians by changing each to degrees.

$$3 \text{ radians} = 3 \cdot \frac{180}{\pi} = \frac{540}{\pi} \approx 171.9°$$

$$3\pi \text{ radians} = 3\pi \cdot \frac{180}{\pi} = 540°$$

65 Change the following radian measures to degree measure: (1) π, (2) $\pi/2$, (3) $\pi/4$, and (4) $\pi/8$.

(1) 180°   (2) 90°   (3) 45°   (4) 22.5°

66 Change the following radian measures to degree measure: (1) $\pi/3$, (2) $2\pi/3$, (3) $4\pi/3$, (4) $5\pi/3$.

(1) 60°   (2) 120°   (3) 240°   (4) 300°

67 Change the following radian measures to degree measure: (1) $2\pi/3$, (2) 5π, (3) $-5/6\pi$, (4) $11\pi/5$, and (5) 4π.

> (1) 120° (2) 900° (3) –150° (4) 396° (5) 720°

68 To find a method to change in the reverse order from *degrees to radians*, start with the fundamental relationship 360° = ___ radians. Copy this equation. Give your answer in terms of π.

> 360° = 2π radians

69 360° = 2π radians. If you divide both members of this equation by 360, you find that 1° = ___ radians.

> $\dfrac{2\pi}{360}$ or $\dfrac{\pi}{180}$

70 In frame 69 you found that 1° = $\pi/180$ radians. Using this fact, you can change any measure in degrees to radian measure; thus

$$30° = 30 \cdot \frac{\pi}{180} \text{ radians} = \underline{\hspace{2cm}} \text{ radians.}$$

(Write your answer in simplified form in terms of π.)

> $\dfrac{30\pi}{180} = \dfrac{\pi}{6}$

71 Find the radian measure equivalent to 45°.

> $\dfrac{\pi}{4}$ *Solution:* $45° = 45 \cdot \dfrac{\pi}{180} = \dfrac{\pi}{4}$ radians
>
> You could reason that given $90° = \dfrac{\pi}{2}$ radians
>
> $\dfrac{1}{2} \cdot 90° = \dfrac{1}{2} \cdot \dfrac{\pi}{2}$ radians, $45° = \dfrac{\pi}{4}$ radians

72 (1) Change 60° to radian measure. (2) Change 210° to radian measure. (3) Change 135° to radian measure.

> (1) $60° = 60 \cdot \dfrac{\pi}{180} = \dfrac{\pi}{3}$ radians
>
> (2) $210° = \dfrac{7\pi}{6}$ radians   (3) $135° = \dfrac{3\pi}{4}$ radians

73 (1) Change 360° to radian measure.   (2) Change 300° to radian measure.   (3) Change 270° to radian measure.   (4) Change 240° to radian measure.

(1) $360° = 2\pi$ radians **(2)** $300° = \dfrac{300}{1} \cdot \dfrac{\pi}{180} = \dfrac{5\pi}{3}$ radians

(3) $270° = \dfrac{270}{1} \cdot \dfrac{\pi}{180} = \dfrac{3\pi}{2}$ radians

(4) $240° = \dfrac{240}{1} \cdot \dfrac{\pi}{180} = \dfrac{4\pi}{3}$ radians

74 Write your answers in terms of π. $1° =$ **(1)** ___ radians, $90° =$ **(2)** _____ radians, and $180° =$ **(3)** _____ radians.

(1) $\dfrac{\pi}{180}$ **(2)** $\dfrac{\pi}{2}$ **(3)** π

▽75 $260° =$ **(1)** ___ radians, $150° =$ **(2)** ___ radians, $9\pi/10 =$ **(3)** ___°, and $13\pi/12 =$ **(4)** ___°.

(1) $\dfrac{13\pi}{9}$ **(2)** $\dfrac{5\pi}{6}$ **(3)** 162   **(4)** 195

76 The word "radian" is often omitted when the angle measure is given in radians. For example,

$\alpha = \dfrac{\pi}{4}$ means $\alpha = \dfrac{\pi}{4}$ **(1)** _____

You recognize the unit easily when the reading is given as a multiple of π. However, if we write $\alpha = 2$, with no unit attached, you must remember that this means $\alpha = 2$ **(2)** _____   (Use degrees, radians, or revolutions for your answers.)

(1) radians   **(2)** radians

77 If $\alpha = \tfrac{1}{2}$, then $\alpha \approx$ **(1)** ___°. If $\alpha = \pi/2$, then $\alpha =$ **(2)** ___°.

(1) 28.7   **(2)** 90

78 When the radius r is used as a chord as shown in sketch a, the angle at the center of the circle is exactly 60°. When the radius is "wrapped" around the circle as in sketches b and c, the central angle is 1 radian which is slightly _____(more or less) than 60°.

continued →

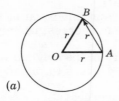 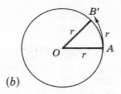 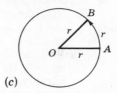

(a)   (b)   (c)

less

79 Express in radian measure in multiples of π: (1) 150° and
(2) 22°30'.

(1) $\dfrac{5\pi}{6}$ (2) $\dfrac{\pi}{8}$

80 Change to radian measure as in frame 79: (1) –315°, (2) 900°, and
(3) 78°18'.

(1) $\dfrac{-7\pi}{4}$ (2) 5π (3) $\dfrac{87\pi}{200}$

81 (1) Change $\pi/10$ radians to degrees.   (2) Change $13\pi/4$ radians to
degrees.

(1) 18°   (2) 585°

82 You need to be able to transfer easily from radians to degrees and
from degrees to radians since both units are used extensively in
mathematics.

2π radians = (1) ____°
π radians = (2) ____°
$\dfrac{\pi}{2}$ radians = (3) ____°
$\dfrac{\pi}{4}$ radians = (4) ____°

(1) 360   (2) 180   (3) 90   (4) 45

83 -3π = (1) ____°, $\dfrac{3\pi}{2}$ = (2) ____°.

(1) –540   (2) 270

84 If you keep in mind that 2π radians = $360°$:

    (1) You can find, by dividing both members of this equation by 2π, the transfer unit for changing radians to degrees, namely, 1 radian = ___°.

    (2) You can find, by dividing both members of the original equation by 360, the transfer unit for changing degrees to radians, namely, ___ radians = $1°$.

    (3) Show how to change $7\pi/10$ radians to degrees.

    (1) $\dfrac{180}{\pi}$ **(2)** $\dfrac{\pi}{180}$ **(3)** $\dfrac{7\pi}{10} \cdot \dfrac{180}{\pi}°$ = $126°$

85 4π radians = **(1)** ___°, and 4 radians $\approx$ **(2)** ___°.

    (1) 720 **(2)** 229.2

86 In theoretical work the mathematician prefers the radian as a unit of measure. In practical applications the units may be degrees, revolutions, or radians. In this program you are required to work with all three.

    $\frac{1}{2}$ rev = **(1)** ___ radians
    $\frac{1}{2}$ rev = **(2)** ___°
    5 rev = **(3)** ___ radians
    5 rev = **(4)** ___°
      $5°$ = **(5)** ___ radians

    (1) π **(2)** 180 **(3)** 10π **(4)** 1,800 **(5)** $\dfrac{\pi}{36}$

87 Draw in standard position the following angles: **(1)** $-160°$ and **(2)** $630°$.

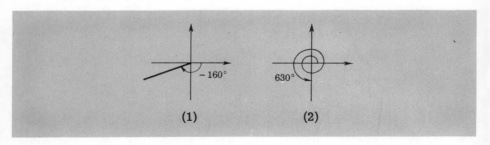

       (1)   **(2)**

88 Draw in standard position the following angles: (1) $1\frac{1}{2}$ rev and (2) -0.25 rev. State each angle in radian measure.

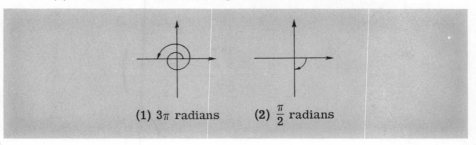

(1) 3π radians   (2) $\frac{\pi}{2}$ radians

89 Draw in standard position the following angles: (1) $\pi/15$ and (2) $7\pi/3$. Give the number of degrees in each angle.

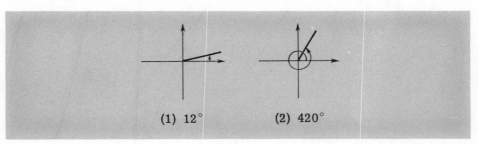

(1) 12°   (2) 420°

90 There are certain special angles which occur so frequently in mathematical discussions that you should have their measures in either unit well in mind. First, the quadrantal angles which, you remember, are those with terminal side on one of the axes. Name four of them in degrees and in radians.

$$90° = \frac{\pi}{2} \text{ radians} \qquad 180° = \pi \text{ radians}$$
$$270° = \frac{3\pi}{2} \text{ radians} \qquad 360° = 2\pi \text{ radians}$$

91 Make a sketch of each of the following angles: (1) π, (2) 270°, (3) $3\pi/2$, (4) 90°, (5) $\pi/2$, and (6) $\frac{1}{4}$ rev.

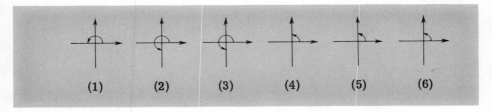

(1)   (2)   (3)   (4)   (5)   (6)

92   List and sketch the quadrantal angles in negative form (that is, -π/2 radians = -90°): -π radians = (1)_____ , -3π/2 radians = (2)_____ , and -2π radians = (3)_____ .

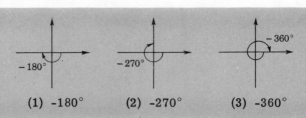

(1) -180°   (2) -270°   (3) -360°

93   On one set of coordinate axes show the terminal sides of the four angles 45°, 135°, 225°, and 315°.

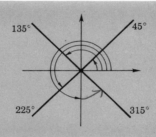

94   Change to radians: (1) 45°, (2) 135°, (3) 225°, and (4) 315°.

(1) $\frac{\pi}{4}$ (2) $\frac{3\pi}{4}$ (3) $\frac{5\pi}{4}$ (4) $\frac{7\pi}{4}$

95   State in radians and degrees the angles which equal one-half of each of the following: (1) π/4, (2) 3π/4, (3) 5π/4, and (4) 7π/4.

(1) $\frac{\pi}{8}$ = 22.5° (2) $\frac{3\pi}{8}$ = 67.5° (3) $\frac{5\pi}{8}$ = 112.5° (4) $\frac{7\pi}{8}$ = 157.5°

96   Other special angles which you should recognize in either unit are (1) 30°, (2) 150°, (3) 210°, and (4) 330°. Write these in radians.

(1) $\frac{\pi}{6}$ (2) $\frac{5\pi}{6}$ (3) $\frac{7\pi}{6}$ (4) $\frac{11\pi}{6}$

97 Write the number of degrees which corresponds to each of the following radians: **(1)** $\pi/3$, **(2)** $2\pi/3$, **(3)** $4\pi/3$, and **(4)** $5\pi/3$.

(1) $60°$ **(2)** $120°$ **(3)** $240°$ **(4)** $300°$

98 Radian measure of an angle has been defined as α in radians = **(1)** ___ / _____ . **(2)** What is the length of the arc that is cut off by an angle $\alpha = \pi/3$ radians in a circle of radius 4 in.?

(1) $\dfrac{arc}{radius}$ or $\dfrac{S}{r}$ **(2)** $S = \dfrac{4\pi}{3}$ in. ≈ 4.2 in.

Solution: $\dfrac{\pi}{3} = \dfrac{S}{4}$, $S = \dfrac{4\pi}{3} \approx \dfrac{4(3.1416)}{3} \approx 4.2$

99 In a circle of radius 6 in. there is a central angle of $3\pi/4$. What is the length of the arc the angle subtends (the arc AB cut off by the given angle)?

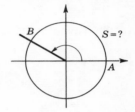

$\dfrac{9\pi}{2} \approx 14.1$ in.   Solution: $\dfrac{3\pi}{4} = \dfrac{S}{6}$, $S = \dfrac{9\pi}{2} \approx 14.1$ in.

100 What is the length of an arc S which has a central angle of $240°$ on a circle with radius 3 in.?

4π in. ≈ 12.6 in.   Note: In order to use the formula $S = \alpha r$, we must have α in radian measure.

▽**101** What is the radius of a circle such that an arc of 2π in. is cut off by a central angle of $\pi/4$ radians?

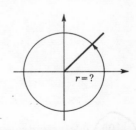

8 in.   Solution: $\alpha = \dfrac{S}{r}$, $\dfrac{\pi}{4} = \dfrac{2\pi}{r}$, $r = 8$

102 If we are given an angle α in radians, then the part of the circle bounded by the arc of length S and the two radii of length _r is called a sector of the circle._ From elementary geometry we know that the ratio of the area A of the sector is to the area of the entire circle πr^2 as the ratio of the central angle α of the sector is to a complete revolution; that is:

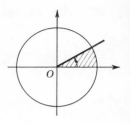

$$\frac{A}{\pi r^2} = \frac{\alpha}{2\pi} \quad \text{or} \quad A = \frac{\alpha r^2}{2}$$

Example: If $\alpha = \pi/3$ and $r = 2$, find the area of the sector.

$\dfrac{2\pi}{3}$ sq in.   _Solution:_ $\dfrac{\text{area of sector}}{\pi \cdot 2^2} = \dfrac{\pi/3}{2\pi}$

area $= \dfrac{(\pi/3) \cdot \pi \cdot 4}{2\pi} = \dfrac{4\pi}{6} = \dfrac{2\pi}{3}$

103   Given $\alpha = 150°$ and $r = 3$, find the area of the sector.

$\dfrac{15\pi}{4}$ sq in.   _Solution:_ $A = \dfrac{(5\pi/6) \cdot 9}{2} = \dfrac{15\pi}{4}$

TRIGONOMETRIC FUNCTIONS

104   You have seen how circular arcs are used to measure angles, that is, $\theta = S/r$. Shortly two new terms will be introduced and defined; they will enable you to use linear (straight-line) segments for angle measurement. Let θ be a positive _acute_ angle. Place the angle θ in standard position on a coordinate system and draw a circle about the origin using a convenient radius.

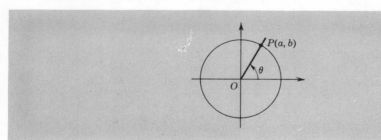

105 A circle drawn about the origin is called the _unit circle._ The radius could be 1 in., $\frac{1}{2}$ in., 3 in., etc.; whatever you use is considered a unit.

continued →

Make three more sketches so that you have a positive angle θ in standard position terminating in each of the four quadrants. Label the point where the terminal side cuts the circle $P(a, b)$. Keep these sketches for frame 111.

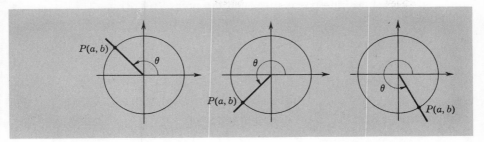

106 Notice that the point $P(a, b)$, which you labeled on the terminal side of each angle, is a point on the rectangular coordinate system whose first coordinate is **(1)**___ and whose second is **(2)**___.

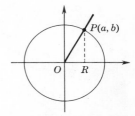

(1) a   **(2)** b

107 From your work with graphs you will recall that we refer to the *directed distance OR = a* as the *abscissa* of the point P and the *directed distance RP = b* as the *ordinate* of the point P. Direction to the right of the origin on the x axis is positive. Direction upward from the origin on the y axis is positive. Show that you can distinguish ordinate and abscissa correctly by locating a point having ordinate 5 and abscissa 2.

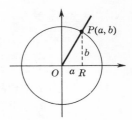

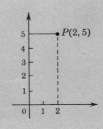

108   Remember that the ordered pair (a, b) which we use to identify a point $P(a, b)$ on the coordinate system has as the first coordinate a which is the abscissa and as the second coordinate b which is the ordinate of the point P. Draw an angle in standard position so that its terminal side passes through the point $P(4, 2)$.

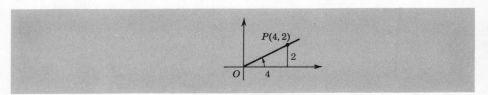

109   Note the first coordinate a of the point $P(a, b)$ is the *horizontal* coordinate (abscissa), the second coordinate b is the vertical coordinate (ordinate).   (1) Locate a point P whose abscissa is +3 and ordinate is -4.   (2) Locate a point Q whose vertical component is +2 and whose horizontal component is -1.

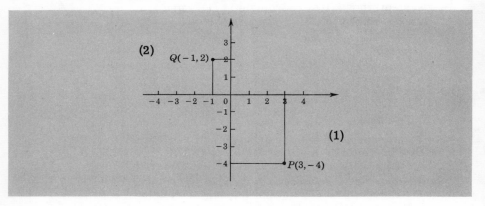

110   The ordinate and abscissa are directed distances. Therefore, a point on the terminal side of a *second-quadrant* angle will have the abscissa, the first coordinate (1)_____ , and the ordinate, second coordinate (2)_____ . (Use "positive" or "negative" for the blanks above.)

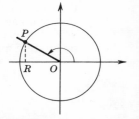

(1) negative (*OR* abscissa)   (2) positive (*RP* ordinate)

111   On your sketches for frame 105 where θ terminates in quadrants III and IV, identify segments (use *OR* or *RP*) representing abscissa

continued ➝

a and ordinate *b* of point *P*. Indicate in each case whether the distance is positive or negative.

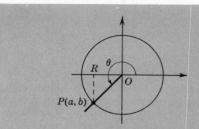

quadrant III   *a* = *OR* negative
       b = *RP* negative

quadrant IV   *a* = *OR* positive
       b = *RP* negative

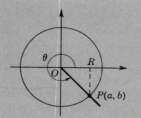

112 *P(a, b)* is a general way of indicating a point on a plane. The *a* may represent any real number, positive or negative, as may the *b*. If *a* = -3 and *b* = -2, then *P*(*a, b*) is *P*(-3, -2) and is a point in quadrant _____.

III

113 Consider an angle θ in standard position on a coordinate system and a unit circle drawn with its center at the origin. (See frame 105 for unit circle.) The terminal side of the angle will meet the circle in a point *P* whose coordinates are (*a, b*). For any angle θ, we define the sine and cosine functions as follows:

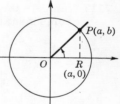

  sine θ = ordinate, *b*, of *P*
  cosine θ = abscissa, *a*, of *P*

In the sketch the directed distance _____ (*OP, OR, RP*) is the sine of θ.

RP = *b*

114 Sine of θ is usually abbreviated and written *sin* θ. It is one of the basic trigonometric functions. The sine is a *function* because it associates with each real number (a value of θ) exactly one other real number (a value for sin θ). (1) Which coordinate, *x* or *y*, represents sin θ in this sketch?

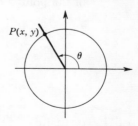

continued →

(2) Is it positive or negative? *Note:* The unit of measure for θ may be either radians or degrees.

---

(1) y (2) positive

---

115 The important thing for you to have well in mind now is the definition for sine of an angle; i.e., the *sine* of an angle θ is the *ordinate* of the point of intersection of the terminal side of θ with the unit circle when the angle is in standard position. If P has coordinates (a, b), then sin θ = ___

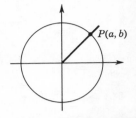

---

b

∇116 By definition sin θ is the _____ (first, second) coordinate of the ordered pair (a, b).

---

second

∇117 Sin θ is the _____ (horizontal, vertical) component of the ordered pair $P(a, b)$.

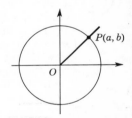

---

vertical

∇118 Sin θ is the _____ (ordinate, abscissa) of the point $P(a, b)$.

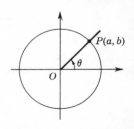

---

ordinate

119 When the angle θ is in standard position,
we define the <u>cosine of</u> θ (written "cos θ")
as the *abscissa* of the point of intersection
of the terminal side of θ with the unit circle.
In this sketch identify cos θ. Is it x or y?

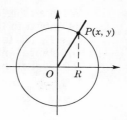

$\cos \theta = x$

∇**120** By definition the _____ (first, second) coordinate of P is cos θ.

first

121 Is the following statement true? Cos θ is the abscissa of the point
$P(x,\ y)$, if $P(x,\ y)$ is the point where the unit circle intersects the
terminal side of θ.

yes

122 (1) On a sketch similar to the one shown
here write "sin θ" and "cos θ" to identify
these functions with the proper segment.
If O is a unit circle, then the length of OP
is (2) ___ unit(s).

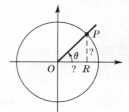

(1)

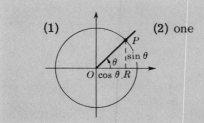

(2) one

123 When an angle terminates in quadrant II
     as shown in the sketch, **(1)** is sin θ posi-
     tive?   **(2)** Is cos θ positive?   **(3)** Does
     OR represent sin θ or cos θ?   **(4)** Does
     RP represent sin θ or cos θ?

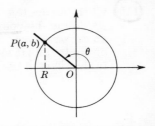

(1) yes   **(2)** no   **(3)** cos θ **(4)** sin θ

124 If an angle terminates in quadrant III, both its sine and cosine are
     _____ (positive, negative).

negative

125 If an angle θ terminates in quadrant IV,
     sin θ is **(1)**_____ (positive, negative)
     and cos θ is **(2)**_____ (positive,
     negative).

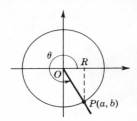

(1) negative   **(2)** positive

126 If sin θ = ordinate and cos θ = abscissa
     of point P in the sketch, can we correctly
     label point $P(a, b)$ as $P(\cos \theta, \sin \theta)$?

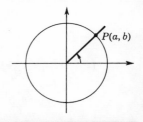

yes, a is the abscissa and b is the ordinate of point P

127 **(1)** In which quadrants is the ordinate of a point positive?   **(2)** This
     would tell us that the sine of an angle is positive if θ terminates in
     which quadrants?

(1) I, II   **(2)** I, II

128 (1) In which quadrants is the ordinate negative? (2) This would tell us that the sine of θ is negative if the angle terminates in which quadrants?

(1) III, IV   (2) III, IV

129

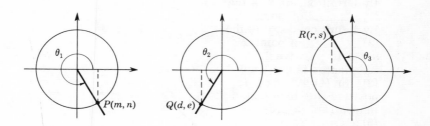

sin θ_1 = ordinate of point P = n, where n is negative.
sin θ_2 = (1) _____ , where (2) _____ .
sin θ_3 = (3) _____ , where (4) _____ .

(1) ordinate of Q = e (2) e is negative
(3) ordinate of R = s (4) s is positive

130

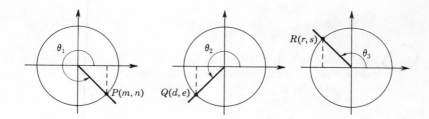

cos θ_1 = abscissa of point P = m, where m is positive.
cos θ_2 = (1) _____ , where (2) _____ .
cos θ_3 = (3) _____ , where (4) _____ .

(1) abscissa of Q = d (2) d is negative
(3) abscissa of R = r (4) r is negative

131   These sketches should
help you to see in which
quadrants the sine or
cosine is positive and to
identify the ordinate and
abscissa of a point in
each of the four quadrants.
By definition, sin θ is the
(1) _____ of point P.
By definition, cos θ is the
(2) _____ of point P.
sin θ is positive if θ
terminates in quadrant
(3)_or (4)_. cos θ is
positive if θ terminates
in quadrant (5)_or
(6)_ .

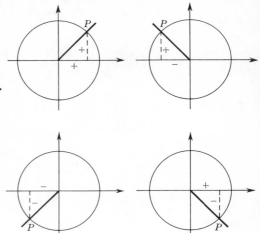

(1) ordinate   **(2)** abscissa   **(3)** I   **(4)** II   **(5)** I   **(6)** IV

132   Suppose we are given sin $\theta = \frac{3}{5}$. Let us see for what angle or angles this value holds. We said in frame 131 that if sin θ is
positive, the angle may terminate in either quadrant (1)_or (2)_.
Continued in frames 133 to 135.

(1) I   **(2)** II

(133) The sketches below show two angles: θ_1 which terminates in quadrant I, and θ_2 which terminates in quadrant II. P_1 and P_2, respectively, are the points where the terminal sides of θ_1 and θ_2 intersect a unit circle.

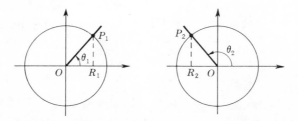

From frame 132 we know that the ordinate of P_1 is R_1P_1 = (1)_
and the ordinate of P_2 is R_2P_2 = (2) ____ . To find the abscissa of

continued →

P_1 and P_2, we apply the <u>distance formula from geometry:</u> $(OR)^2 + (RP)^2 = (OP)^2$. (3) Write this formula with numerical values supplied for RP and OP from either sketch.

(1) $\frac{3}{5}$ (2) $\frac{3}{5}$ (3) $(OR)^2 + (\frac{3}{5})^2 = 1^2$

134   Find the two numerical values for OR by completing the solution of the equation from frame 133: $(OR)^2 + (\frac{3}{5})^2 = 1$

$OR = \pm\frac{4}{5}$
Solution: $(OR)^2 + \frac{9}{25} = 1$, $(OR)^2 = \frac{16}{25}$, $\pm OR = \frac{4}{5}$, $OR = \pm\frac{4}{5}$

135   We have found two points through which the terminal side of an angle θ may pass if $\sin\theta = \frac{3}{5}$, namely, $P(\frac{4}{5}, \frac{3}{5})$ and $P(-\frac{4}{5}, \frac{3}{5})$. Make sketches showing the two angles: (1) $P(\frac{4}{5}, \frac{3}{5})$ and (2) $P(-\frac{4}{5}, \frac{3}{5})$.

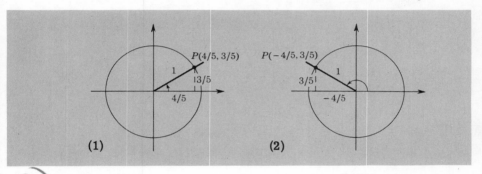

136   Frames 136 to 145 review the procedure for finding the distance between two points on a rectangular coordinate system.
Case I: If Q and P are on the same vertical line, the <u>undirected distance from Q to P,</u> written $d(Q, P)$, can be found by taking the difference of their ordinates:
<u>$d(Q, P) = y_1 - y_2$ or $y_2 - y_1$.</u>
Given $P(5, 8)$ and $Q(5, 3)$, $d(Q, P) = $ (1)___,
and given $P(-2, -4)$ and $Q(-2, 6)$, $d(Q, P) = $ (2)___. (Undirected distance means the distance between two points without regard to direction, i.e., P to Q or Q to P.)

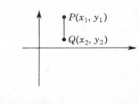

(1) 5   (2) 10

137   Sometimes we use the absolute-value sym-
bol | | thus, $d(Q, P) = |y_2 - y_1|$, to indi-
cate the numerical value of the expression
within the symbols without regard to sign.

$$d(Q, P) = |y_2 - y_1| = |3 - (-1)| =$$
$$|4| = 4$$
or $d(Q, P) = |y_1 - y_2| = |-1 - (3)| =$
$$|-4| = 4$$

Given points $R(-2, -5)$ and $S(-2, 3)$, make
a sketch and find $d(R, S)$. Write the steps
in the solution using absolute-value signs.

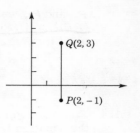

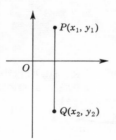

$$d(R, S) = |-5 - (3)| = |-8| = 8$$
or
$$d(R, S) = |3 - (-5)| = |3 + 5| = |8| = 8$$

138

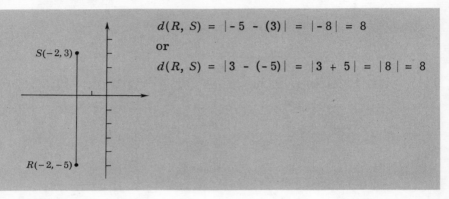

Given $P(3, 5)$ and $Q(3, -7)$,
then $d(P, Q) = (1)\underline{\quad}$.

Given $P(4, -2)$ and $Q(4, -9)$,
$d(P, Q) = (2)\underline{\quad}$.

(1) 12   (2) 7

139   If Q and P are on the same *horizontal* line, then the undirected
distance from Q to P is the difference of their *abscissas*,

$$d(Q, P) = |x_1 - x_2| \text{ or } |x_2 - x_1|$$

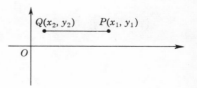

continued →

1. Given $Q(2, 3)$ and $P(7, 3)$, then $d(P, Q) =$ **(1)**___.
2. Given $Q(-5, -4)$ and $P(8, -4)$, then $d(Q, P) =$ **(2)**___.
In Example 2, directed distance $QP =$ **(3)**___.
In Example 2, directed distance $PQ =$ **(4)**___.

(1) 5 **(2)** 13 **(3)** 13 **(4)** -13

▽140

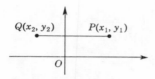   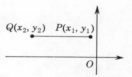

Given $Q(-4, 3)$ and $P(6, 3)$, then $d(Q, P) =$ **(1)**_____ or _____ $=$ **(2)**___ .

Given $Q(-9, 3)$ and $P(-1, 3)$, then $d(Q, P) =$ **(3)**_____ or _____ $=$ **(4)**___ .

(1) $x_2 - x_1$ or $x_1 - x_2$ **(2)** 10
(3) $x_2 - x_1$ or $x_1 - x_2$ **(4)** 8

141 If P and Q, with respect to each other, are on neither a horizontal nor a vertical line, we locate a point R thus: Through P draw a line parallel to the y axis. Through Q draw a line parallel to the x axis. From geometry we

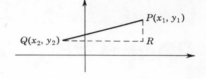

know that these two lines intersect at right angles; we shall call this point R. Also from geometry we know that in any right triangle the sum of the squares of the two sides enclosing the right angle is equal to the square of the hypotenuse. Hence, in right triangle PRQ we have:

$$[d(Q, P)]^2 = [d(Q, R)]^2 + [d(R, P)]^2$$
$$= (x_2 - x_1)^2 + (y_2 - y_1)^2 \text{ or}$$
$$[(x_1 - x_2)^2 + (y_1 - y_2)^2]$$
$$d(Q, P) = \sqrt{(x_1 - x_2)^2 + (y_1 - y_2)^2}$$

Problem: Given $Q(-4, 2)$ and $P(8, 6)$, find $d(Q, P)$.

$d(Q, P) = \sqrt{160}$ or $4\sqrt{10}$
Solution: $[d(Q, P)]^2 = (-4 - 8)^2 + (2 - 6)^2 = 160$
or $[8 - (-4)]^2 + (6 - 2)^2 = 160$
$d(Q, P) = \sqrt{160} = 4\sqrt{10}$

142   If one of the points P or Q coincides with the origin, then the distance from Q to P, labeled r in the drawing, is $r^2 = (x_1 - 0)^2 + (y_1 - 0)^2$ which simplifies to $r^2 = x_1^2 + y_1^2$. (1) Given $Q(0, 0)$ and $P(\frac{4}{5}, \frac{3}{5})$, find r. (2) Given $Q(0, 0)$ and $P(-\frac{4}{5}, \frac{3}{5})$, find r. *Note:* The distance from the origin is considered positive.

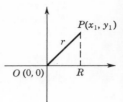

(1) $r = 1$ (2) $r = 1$
Solution: *Solution:*

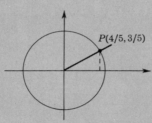

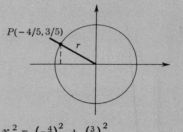

$$r^2 = \left(\tfrac{4}{5}\right)^2 + \left(\tfrac{3}{5}\right)^2$$
$$= \tfrac{16}{25} + \tfrac{9}{25} = \tfrac{25}{25} = 1$$
$$r = 1$$

$$r^2 = \left(-\tfrac{4}{5}\right)^2 + \left(\tfrac{3}{5}\right)^2$$
$$r = 1$$

▽143   Find $d(P, Q)$.

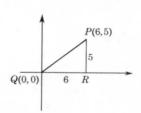

$r = \sqrt{61}$ *Solution:* $d(P, Q) = \sqrt{(6 - 0)^2 + (5 - 0)^2} = \sqrt{61}$

144   Find r in terms of x and y.

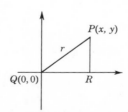

$r = \sqrt{x^2 + y^2}$

145 Given $Q(0, 0)$ and $P(-4, 3)$, **(1)** Make a sketch locating point P and **(2)** find $d(Q, P)$. **(3)** Should your answer be positive or negative?

(1)

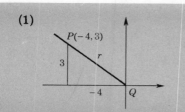

(2) $r = 5$
Solution:
$$d(Q, P) = r = \sqrt{(-4)^2 + (3)^2}$$
$$r = 5$$
(3) positive

---

146 Point P in the sketch can be written in terms of sin θ and cos θ:
$$P((1)\underline{\quad\quad}, \ (2)\underline{\quad\quad})$$

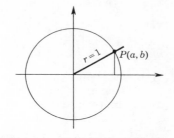

(1) cos θ **(2)** sin θ *Note:* When $r = 1$ unit, you may give these answers as cos $\theta/1$ and sin $\theta/1$

---

147 Given that cos $\theta = \frac{1}{2}$ and θ terminates in quadrant I, use the distance formula to find sin θ. Remember the circle is a unit circle and so $OP = 1$. Keep your work for frame 148.

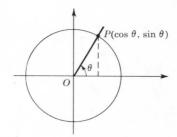

sin $\theta = \dfrac{\sqrt{3}}{2}$ *Solution:* $1^2 = (\frac{1}{2})^2 + y^2$, $y = \dfrac{\sqrt{3}}{2}$

148 There is another positive angle less than 360° whose cosine is $\frac{1}{2}$.
     This angle terminates in quadrant (1)___. (2) Sketch this angle and
     give the coordinates of the point where the terminal side intersects
     the unit circle.

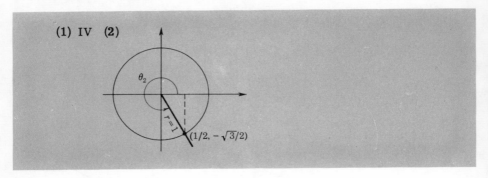

(1) IV (2)

$(1/2, -\sqrt{3}/2)$

149 The *sine* and *cosine* are the basic trigonometric functions. The
     sine of θ (sin θ) is the (1) _____ of the point of intersection of
     the terminal side of θ with the unit circle when the angle is in
     standard position.   The *cosine* of θ (cos θ) is the (2) _____ of
     the same point.   (Use "ordinate" or "abscissa" to fill the blanks
     above.)

(1) ordinate (2) abscissa

150 If you are given the sine of θ as
     a real number, you can use the
     distance formula to find the cosine
     of θ (two values, + and -). Given
     sin θ = $\sqrt{3}/2$, find two values for
     cos θ.

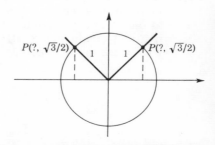

$P(?, \sqrt{3}/2)$ $P(?, \sqrt{3}/2)$

$$1^2 = x^2 + \left(\frac{\sqrt{3}}{2}\right)^2; \; x = \tfrac{1}{2}, \; -\tfrac{1}{2}$$

151 If you know $\cos \theta = -\frac{1}{2}$, you can use the distance formula to find the two values of $\sin \theta$, and you can construct the two angles θ_1 and θ_2 having $\cos \theta = -\frac{1}{2}$. Do this.

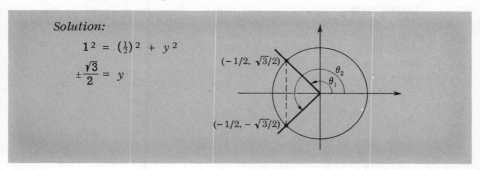

Solution:

$$1^2 = (\tfrac{1}{2})^2 + y^2$$

$$\pm \frac{\sqrt{3}}{2} = y$$

$(-1/2, \sqrt{3}/2)$

θ_2

θ_1

$(-1/2, -\sqrt{3}/2)$

152 If $Q(x, y)$ is *any* point on the terminal side of the angle θ and r is the *distance* of Q from the origin, can we say that
$$r^2 = x^2 + y^2?$$
Continued in frame 153.

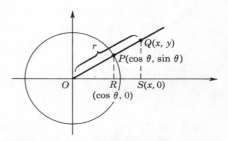

r

$Q(x, y)$

$P(\cos \theta, \sin \theta)$

O R $S(x, 0)$
      $(\cos \theta, 0)$

yes, in right triangle OSQ, $r^2 = x^2 + y^2$
(using the distance formula).

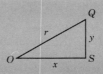

Q

r y

O —— x —— S

153 If $P(\cos \theta, \sin \theta)$ is the intersection of the terminal side of θ with the unit circle, we know from geometry that triangles ORP and OSQ are similar; hence, $OR/OP = $ (1)____ , and $RP/OP = $ (2)____ because corresponding sides of similar triangles are proportional. Keep this work for frames 154 and 155.

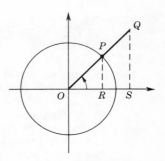

Q

P

O R S

(1) $\dfrac{OS}{OQ}$ (2) $\dfrac{SQ}{OQ}$

154 In the sketch as labeled here you can see that $OR = \cos\theta$, $OP = 1$, $OS = x$, $OQ = r$; therefore, $OR/OP = OS/OQ$ may be written ___/___ = ___/___. (Fill in the four parts of the proportion. Copy the equal sign as you answer.) Make a copy of this sketch for frame 155.

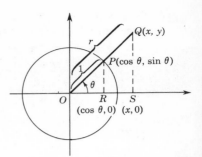

$$\frac{\cos\theta}{1} = \frac{x}{r} \quad \text{or} \quad \cos\theta = \frac{x}{r}$$

155 From the sketch in frame 154 decide what you can substitute for each of the following: $RP = \sin\theta$, $OP = (1)$__, $SQ = (2)$__, and $OQ = (3)$__. Therefore, $RP/OP = SQ/OQ$ may be written (4)___ /__ = __/__. (Include the equality sign in this answer.)

(1) 1   **(2)** y **(3)** r **(4)** $\dfrac{\sin\theta}{1} = \dfrac{y}{r}$ or $\sin\theta = \dfrac{y}{r}$

156 If the point $Q(x, y)$ coincides with P, then $r = 1$ and the statements $\sin\theta/1 = y/r$ and $\cos\theta/1 = x/r$, which we have just derived, reduce to **(1)**_____ and **(2)**_____, respectively. These were the original definitions for $\sin\theta$ and $\cos\theta$.

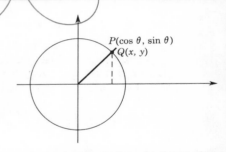

(1) $\sin\theta = y$ **(2)** $\cos\theta = x$

157 In fact, we could have given $\sin\theta = y/r$ and $\cos\theta = x/r$ as our definitions at the beginning and then have shown that they reduce to $\sin\theta = y$ (ordinate) and $\cos\theta = x$ (abscissa) when $r = 1$, the radius of the unit circle. If y, y_1, and y_2 are segments each drawn

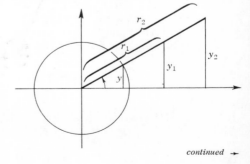

continued →

perpendicular to the x axis from points on the terminal side of θ and if sin $\theta = y/1$, then sin $\theta = y_1/r_1$ and sin $\theta = y_2/r_2$. Why?

The ratios of corresponding sides of similar triangles are equal. (Corresponding sides of similar triangles are proportional.)

158 Likewise from similar triangles in the sketch, cos θ = $x/1$ = **(1)** _____ = **(2)** _____ .

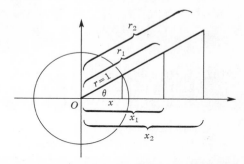

(1) $\dfrac{x_1}{r_1}$ **(2)** $\dfrac{x_2}{r_2}$

159 Look at these two statements:

$$\cos \theta = \frac{x}{r} \qquad \cos \theta = x$$

If you use cos $\theta = x$ to compute the cosine of θ, then r must be equal to **(1)** _____ . You should know both definitions; the first is necessary when r is not equal to **(2)** _____ .

(1) one   (2) one

160 **(1)** If $r = 1$, point A **(a)** _____ (lies, does not lie) on the unit circle. In this case cos θ = **(b)** _____ . (Use the simplest correct form for your answer.)
(2) If $r \neq 1$ ($\neq$ means "is not equal to"), point A **(a)** _____ (lies, does not lie) on the unit circle. In this case cos θ = **(b)** ____/____.
(3) cos θ = ____/____ is a more general statement and is true in either case.

(1) (a) lies, **(b)** x **(2) (a)** does not lie, **(b)** $\dfrac{x}{r}$ **(3)** $\dfrac{x}{r}$

161 If $x = 2$ and $y = 3$,
then r = (1) _____
cos θ = (2) _____
sin θ = (3) _____

(1) $\sqrt{13}$ (2) $\dfrac{2}{\sqrt{13}}$ (3) $\dfrac{3}{\sqrt{13}}$

162 1. If $y = 3$ and $r = 5$, sin θ = (1)___ .
2. If $y = \frac{3}{5}$ and $r = 2$, sin θ = (2)___ .
3. If $y = \frac{3}{5}$ and $r = 1$, sin θ = (3)___ .

(4) sin $\theta = y/r$ can be applied in which examples above ?
(5) sin $\theta = y$ can be applied in which examples ?

(1) $\frac{3}{5}$ (2) $\frac{3}{10}$ (3) $\frac{3}{5}$ (4) all (5) 3

163 sin θ = (1) _____
cos θ = (2) _____

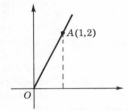

(1) $\dfrac{2}{\sqrt{5}}$ (2) $\dfrac{1}{\sqrt{5}}$

164 sin θ = (1) _____
cos θ = (2) _____

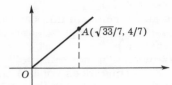

(1) $\frac{4}{7}$ (2) $\dfrac{\sqrt{33}}{7}$

165 You have shown that when (x, y) is any point on the terminal side of an acute angle in standard position, $\sin \theta = y/r$ and $\cos \theta = x/r$. **(1)** Would these statements hold if we used directed distances and had θ terminating in each of the four quadrants?
Example: Second quadrant:

$$\frac{-(OR)}{OP} = \frac{-(OS)}{OQ}$$

$$\frac{-\cos \theta}{1} = \frac{-x}{r}$$

therefore, $\dfrac{\cos \theta}{1} = \dfrac{x}{r}$

$$\frac{RP}{OP} = \frac{SQ}{OQ}$$

(2) $\dfrac{\sin \theta}{?} = \dfrac{?}{?}$

therefore, **(3)** $\sin \theta = \dfrac{?}{?}$

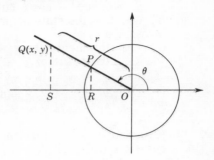

(1) yes **(2)** $\dfrac{\sin \theta}{1} = \dfrac{y}{r}$ **(3)** $\sin \theta = \dfrac{y}{r}$

166 $r =$ **(1)** _____
$\sin \theta =$ **(2)** _____

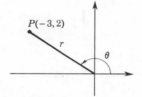

(1) $\sqrt{13}$ **(2)** $\dfrac{2}{\sqrt{13}}$

167 **(1)** Compare $\sin 30°$ with $\sin (-330°)$. **(2)** Compare $\sin 30°$ with $\sin 390°$. Study these sketches and think of your definition for $\sin \theta$.

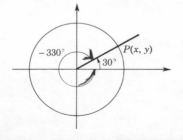
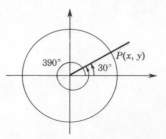

(1) $\sin 30° = \sin (-330°)$ **(2)** $\sin 30° = \sin 390°$

168 (1) Which of the following is (are) true:
     a. sin 120° = sin (-240°)
     b. cos 40° = cos 400°
     c. sin 120° = sin (-120°)
     d. cos 300° = cos (-60°)
(2) Which of the statements above, *a*, *b*, *c*, *d*, involve coterminal angles?
(3) The statements above which involve coterminal angles are all _____ (true, false).

(1) *a*, *b*, *d* (2) *a*, *b*, *d* (3) true

▽169 If θ_1 and θ_2 are coterminal angles, then sin θ_1 = (1)___ θ_2 and cos θ_1 = (2)___ θ_2.

(1) sin (2) cos

170 (1) Sketch an angle θ in standard position whose terminal side goes through the point $P(3, -4)$. (2) Compute the length of r. Keep your work for frame 171.

(1)

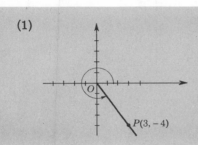

(2) $r = 5$
Solution:
$$r = \sqrt{3^2 + (-4)^2}$$
$$= \sqrt{25} = 5$$
Recall that the distance r is considered positive.

171 Compute (1) sin θ and (2) cos θ, for the problem in frame 170.

(1) sin $\theta = -\frac{4}{5}$ (2) cos $\theta = \frac{3}{5}$

172 Sketch θ in standard position and find sin θ and cos θ if the point $P(-4, 3)$ is on the terminal side of the angle θ.

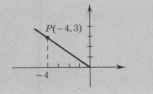

sin $\theta = \frac{3}{5}$

cos $\theta = -\frac{4}{5}$

▽173 $P(x, y)$ is any point on the terminal side of angle θ. Express r in terms of OR and RP.

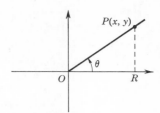

$$r = \sqrt{(OR)^2 + (RP)^2}$$

174   Select the correct word (abscissa, ordinate) for the blanks below.

$$\sin \theta = \frac{(1)\text{_____ of } P}{r} \quad \text{and} \quad \cos \theta = \frac{(2)\text{_____ of } P}{r}$$

when P is a point on the terminal side of θ.

(1) ordinate   (2) abscissa

175   If P is the point where the terminal side of θ cuts the unit circle, then $r = $ (1)_____ . The statements

$$\sin \theta = \frac{\text{ordinate of } P}{r}$$

and

$$\cos \theta = \frac{\text{abscissa of } P}{r}$$

can be written in the simpler form:

$$\sin \theta = (2)\text{_____}$$
$$\cos \theta = (3)\text{_____}$$

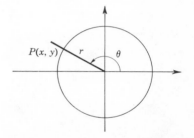

(1) 1   (2) $\dfrac{\text{ordinate of } P}{1}$ = ordinate of P

(3) $\dfrac{\text{abscissa of } P}{1}$ = abscissa of P

176   In succeeding frames you should be able to tell from the context whether $r = 1$ or whether r has some other value. *Examples:*
If $P(x, y)$ is a point on the *unit* circle, you know that $r = $ (1)____ . If $Q(-2, -1)$ is a point on the terminal side of an angle θ, you can see by applying the distance formula that $r = $ (2)_____ .

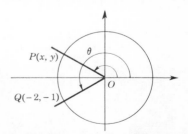

(1) 1   (2) $\sqrt{5}$

177 (1) Find **(a)** r_1 and **(b)** r_2. (2) Which point, P_1 or P_2, is on the unit circle? How do you know? (3) $\sin\theta_1$ = **(a)**___, $\sin\theta_2$ = **(b)**___, $\cos\theta_1$ = **(c)**___, and $\cos\theta_2$ = **(d)**___.

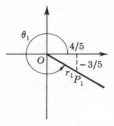 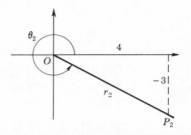

(1) **(a)** 1, **(b)** 5   (2) P_1, because $r_1 = 1$
(3) **(a)** $-\frac{3}{5}$, **(b)** $-\frac{3}{5}$, **(c)** $\frac{4}{5}$, **(d)** $\frac{4}{5}$

178 From this sketch give **(1)** $\sin\theta$ and **(2)** $\cos\theta$.

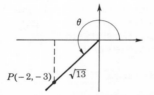

(1) $\sin\theta = \dfrac{-3}{\sqrt{13}} = \dfrac{-3\sqrt{13}}{13}$ **(2)** $\cos\theta = \dfrac{-2}{\sqrt{13}} = \dfrac{-2\sqrt{13}}{13}$

179 A certain angle θ terminates in quadrant III and has $\cos\theta = -2/\sqrt{5}$. Find $\sin\theta$. *Suggestion:* Use the distance formula to find y. Select the proper sign for y. Find $\sin\theta$.

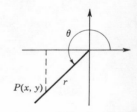

$\sin\theta = \dfrac{-1}{\sqrt{5}}$ *Solution:* $x = -2$, $r = \sqrt{5}$
$\sqrt{5} = \sqrt{(-2)^2 + y^2}$, $5 = 4 + y^2$, $\pm 1 = y$
$\sin\theta = \dfrac{y}{r} = \dfrac{-1}{\sqrt{5}}$

180 Why did we select -1 instead of +1 for y when we wrote sin θ = $-1/\sqrt{5}$ in frame 179?

This is a third-quadrant angle; the sine is negative. *Note:* In the third quadrant both the ordinate and abscissa are negative for any given point on the terminal side of an angle.

▽181 Given cos θ_1 = $-3/\sqrt{13}$ and cos θ_2 = $-3/\sqrt{13}$. Find (1) sin θ_1 and (2) sin θ_2.

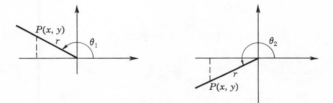

(1) sin θ_1 = $\dfrac{2}{\sqrt{13}}$ (2) sin θ_2 = $\dfrac{-2}{\sqrt{13}}$

Solution: x = -3, r = $\sqrt{13}$
$\quad x^2 + y^2 = r^2$, 9 + y^2 = 13, y = ±2
y = 2 if θ_1 terminates in quadrant II
y = -2 if θ terminates in quadrant III
therefore, sin θ_1 = $\dfrac{y}{r}$ = $\dfrac{2}{\sqrt{13}}$ and sin θ_2 = $\dfrac{y}{r}$ = $\dfrac{-2}{\sqrt{13}}$

182 $P(-a, b)$ is a point on the terminal side of an angle θ in standard position. (1) Make a sketch of this angle and (2) compute r, the distance of P from the origin. Assume that a and b are positive numbers.

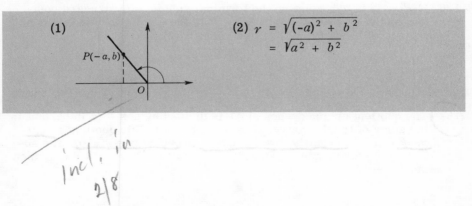

(1)

(2) r = $\sqrt{(-a)^2 + b^2}$
$\quad\quad$ = $\sqrt{a^2 + b^2}$

183   Find **(1)** sin θ and **(2)** cos θ for the problem in frame 182.

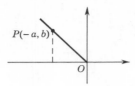

(1) sin θ = $\dfrac{b}{\sqrt{a^2 + b^2}}$ **(2)** cos θ = $\dfrac{-a}{\sqrt{a^2 + b^2}}$

▽184   Compute **(1)** sin θ and **(2)** cos θ if $P(+2, -3)$ is a point on the terminal side of θ. First make a sketch.

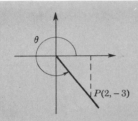

(1) sin θ = $\dfrac{-3}{\sqrt{13}}$

(2) cos θ = $\dfrac{2}{\sqrt{13}}$

185   If $P(a, b)$ is the point where the terminal side of angle θ intersects the unit circle when the angle is in standard position, our definitions for sin θ and cos θ are sin θ = **(1)** _____ and cos θ = **(2)** _____ .

(1) ordinate of point P **(2)** abscissa of point P

186   If $P(x, y)$ is *any* point on the terminal side of θ in standard position and if r is the distance from P to the origin, then in terms of x, y, and r, sin θ = **(1)**__ and cos θ = **(2)**__ .

(1) $\dfrac{y}{r}$ **(2)** $\dfrac{x}{r}$

187   The quotient obtained when sin θ is divided by cos θ is important in the study of trigonometry. The name given to this quotient is *tangent* θ, i.e., tangent θ = sin θ/cos θ, provided cos $\theta \neq 0$. The abbreviation for tangent is "tan." If sin θ = $\sqrt{3}/2$ and cos θ = $\frac{1}{2}$, then tan θ = __.

$\sqrt{3}$

188 Let $P(x, y)$ be any point on the terminal side of θ, $x \neq 0$. Find $\tan \theta$ in terms of x, y, and r by making the proper substitutions for $\sin \theta$ and $\cos \theta$ in the formula

$$\tan \theta = \frac{\sin \theta}{\cos \theta}$$

Simplify the result. *Note:* $x = 0$ is excluded since we cannot have a zero divisor. Consult an algebra textbook for an explanation regarding zero as a divisor.

$$\tan \theta = \frac{y/r}{x/r} = \frac{y}{x}, \; x \neq 0$$

189 (1) If $\sin \theta = 0$ and $\cos \theta = x$, find $\tan \theta$.
     (2) If $\sin \theta = y$ and $\cos \theta = 0$, find $\tan \theta$.

(1) 0   (2) $\tan \theta$ is not defined

▽190 If $\sin \theta = y/r$ and $\cos \theta = x/r$, $x \neq 0$, then $\tan \theta = $___. (Use x and y correctly to complete the statement.)

$$\frac{y}{x}$$

▽191 If $\sin \theta = \frac{3}{5}$ and $\cos \theta = \frac{4}{5}$, find $\tan \theta$.

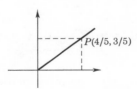

$P(4/5, 3/5)$

$\tan \theta = \frac{3}{4}$

▽192 Find $\tan \theta$ if $P(5, 8)$ is a point on the terminal side of θ.

$\tan \theta = \frac{8}{5}$

▽193 If $\tan \theta = \frac{1}{7}$ and θ is a first-quadrant angle, find (1) $\sin \theta$ and (2) $\cos \theta$. Recall $\tan \theta = y/x$. You now have a number for x and a number for y so that you should be able to find r and hence write $\sin \theta$ and $\cos \theta$.

---

(1) $\sin \theta = \dfrac{1}{\sqrt{50}}$ or $\dfrac{1}{5\sqrt{2}}$ (2) $\cos \theta = \dfrac{7}{\sqrt{50}}$ or $\dfrac{7}{5\sqrt{2}}$

---

194 Given $r = \sqrt{34}$, $x = 5$, and θ terminates in quadrant I. Find $\tan \theta$.

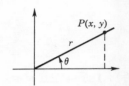

$\tan \theta = \frac{3}{5}$
Solution: $r^2 = x^2 + y^2$, $34 = 25 + y^2$, $\pm 3 = y$
$\tan \theta = \dfrac{y}{x} = \dfrac{3}{5}$ ($\tan \theta$ is positive in quadrant I)

---

195 Given θ terminates in the first quadrant and $\tan \theta = 3$.
  $\tan \theta = 3 = \frac{3}{1}$
therefore, $x =$ (1)___ and $y =$ (2)___
  $r =$ (3)_____
  $\sin \theta =$ (4)_____
  $\cos \theta =$ (5)_____

---

(1) 1 (2) 3 (3) $\sqrt{10}$ (4) $\dfrac{3}{\sqrt{10}}$ (5) $\dfrac{1}{\sqrt{10}}$

---

196 Given θ terminates in the third quadrant and $\tan \theta = 3$.
  $\tan \theta = 3 = \dfrac{-3}{-1}$
therefore, $x =$ (1)___, $y =$ (2)___
  $r =$ (3)_____
  $\sin \theta =$ (4)_____
  $\cos \theta =$ (5)_____

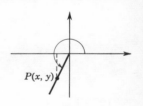

---

(1) –1 (2) –3 (3) $\sqrt{10}$ (4) $\dfrac{-3}{\sqrt{10}}$ (5) $\dfrac{-1}{\sqrt{10}}$

197 A very important trigonometric formula is obtained when we substitute cos θ and sin θ properly in the formula $x^2 + y^2 = r^2$. Observe that $r = 1$ when P is a point on the *unit* circle. Write the formula making the substitutions suggested above. This formula is sometimes referred to as a Pythagorean relation since it is based on the famous theorem of that name in geometry.

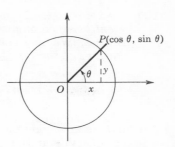

$$d(O, P)^2 = (\cos \theta)^2 + (\sin \theta)^2 = 1^2 \quad \text{or} \quad \cos^2 \theta + \sin^2 \theta = 1$$

198 Assume a *unit* circle with center O. If θ terminates in quadrant II and we want to find the length of OP in terms of the coordinates of point P, we may start again with $x^2 + y^2 = r^2$ and substitute (1)_____ for x and (2)_____ for y, and have the trigonometric formula (or identity) (3)_____

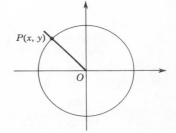

(1) cos θ   (2) sin θ
(3) $(\cos \theta)^2 + (\sin \theta)^2 = 1^2$ or $\cos^2 \theta + \sin^2 \theta = 1$
Note: Although cos θ represents a negative number in quadrant II, the statement is valid.

199 If θ is an angle terminating in quadrant III or IV and P is the point where the unit circle intersects the terminal side, we can also show that $(\cos \theta)^2 + (\sin \theta)^2 = $ (1)___.   (2) Make a sketch for the angle in quadrant IV and indicate the trigonometric coordinates of P.

(1) 1^2 or 1   (2)

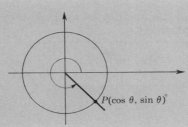

200   We refer to the formula $\cos^2 \theta + \sin^2 \theta = 1$ as a trigonometric
identity since no matter what angle θ may represent, the statement
is true. We may restate this in words thus: The sum of the
squares of the **(1)**_____ and **(2)**____ of any angle is equal to **(3)**__.

> **(1)** cosine   **(2)** sine   **(3)** 1

201   If P is any point on the terminal side
of θ (θ in standard position) and r is
the distance of P from O, prove that
$(\cos \theta)^2 + (\sin \theta)^2 = 1$. Here are
suggestions:
$$\cos \theta = \frac{x}{r} \quad x = r \cos \theta$$
(1) $\sin \theta =$ __/__
(2) $y =$ _____
(3) Now substitute these values of y
and x in the distance formula.

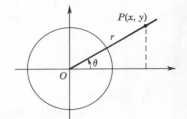

> **(1)** $\frac{y}{r}$ **(2)** $r \sin \theta$
> **(3)** $r^2 = (r \cos \theta)^2 + (r \sin \theta)^2 = r^2(\cos \theta)^2 + r^2(\sin \theta)^2$
>   Therefore, $(\cos \theta)^2 + (\sin \theta)^2 = 1$

202   The identity $(\cos \theta)^2 + (\sin \theta)^2 = 1$ is useful in simplifying trigonometric expressions. Suppose in a certain problem you have found
that
$$d(P, Q) = (\cos \theta)^2 - 2 \sin \theta \cos \theta + 1 + (\sin \theta)^2$$
By rearranging the terms, you could write this in the form:
$$d(P, Q) = (\cos \theta)^2 + (\sin \theta)^2 - 2 \sin \theta \cos \theta + 1$$
What simplification can you make by using the identity above?

> $d(P, Q) = 1 - 2 \sin \theta \cos \theta + 1$ or
> $d(P, Q) = 2 - 2 \sin \theta \cos \theta$

203   Useful forms of the identity $(\cos \theta)^2 + (\sin \theta)^2 = 1$ can be found in
the following manner:
1. Solve the above identity for **(1)** $(\cos \theta)^2$, then for **(2)** $\cos \theta$.
2. Solve the above identity for **(3)** $(\sin \theta)^2$, then for **(4)** $\sin \theta$.

> **(1)** $(\cos \theta)^2 = 1 - (\sin \theta)^2$ **(2)** $\cos \theta = \pm \sqrt{1 - (\sin \theta)^2}$
> **(3)** $(\sin \theta)^2 = (1 - \cos \theta)^2$ **(4)** $\sin \theta = \pm \sqrt{1 - (\cos \theta)^2}$

204 Use the information in frame 203 to show a simplification for:

(1) $(\cos \theta)^2 + 1 - (\sin \theta)^2$ and (2) $\sin \theta - \sqrt{1 - (\cos \theta)^2}$.

---

(1) Possible answers are $2(\cos \theta)^2$, $2 - 2(\sin \theta)^2$, $2[1 - (\sin \theta)^2]$

(2) $\sin \theta - \sin \theta = 0$

---

205 State the form of the distance formula used to find $d(P, Q)$ when the coordinates of P are (x_1, y_1) and the coordinates of Q are (x_2, y_2).

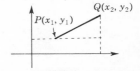

$$d(P, Q) = \sqrt{(x_2 - x_1)^2 + (y_2 - y_1)^2}$$

---

206 We shall now apply the distance formula to find the *length* d of the chord PQ which subtends a central angle θ in a circle of radius r. First, what coordinates has point Q in terms of θ and r?

$\sin \theta = \dfrac{y_2}{r}$

therefore, (1) _____ $= y_2$

$\cos \theta = \dfrac{x_2}{r}$

therefore, (2) _____ $= x_2$

Continued in frame 207.

---

(1) $r \sin \theta$ (2) $r \cos \theta$

---

207 Rewrite the statement $d = d(P, Q) =$ $\sqrt{(x_2 - x_1)^2 + (y_2 - y_1)^2}$ substituting the values shown in the drawing for x_1, y_1, x_2, and y_2. Continued in frame 208.

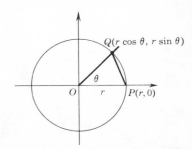

$$d = \sqrt{(r \cos \theta - r)^2 + (r \sin \theta - 0)^2}$$

208   Continue the problem of finding the
distance d from P to Q.

$$d = \sqrt{(r\cos\theta - r)^2 + (r\sin\theta - 0)^2}$$

(1) Write the indicated products
$d =$ _____

(2) Complete this statement
$d = r\sqrt{}$

Continued in frame 209.

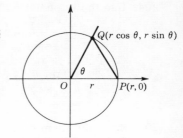

(1) $\sqrt{r^2(\cos\theta)^2 - 2r^2\cos\theta + r^2 + r^2(\sin\theta)^2}$

(2) $r\sqrt{(\cos\theta)^2 - 2\cos\theta + 1 + (\sin\theta)^2}$

209   Recall the trigonometric identity in frame 204 and continue the simplification of the formula for the length of the chord PQ.

$$d = r\sqrt{(\cos\theta)^2 + (\sin\theta)^2 - 2\cos\theta + 1}$$
$$= r\sqrt{1 - 2\cos\theta + 1} = r\sqrt{2 - 2\cos\theta}$$

210   The formula $d = r\sqrt{2 - 2\cos\theta}$ which you have derived may be
used to find the length d of the chord subtended by a central angle θ
in a circle of radius r.
Example: $\cos\theta = -\frac{1}{2}$ and $r = 5$. Find the length of the chord PQ.

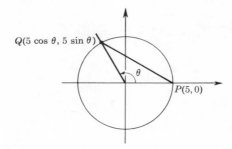

$$d = 5\sqrt{2 - 2\left(-\tfrac{1}{2}\right)} = 5\sqrt{2 + 1} = 5\sqrt{3}$$

▽211   Derive the formula $d = r\sqrt{2 - 2\cos\theta}$
        where d = length of the chord PQ,
        r = radius of the circle, and θ is
        the central angle which subtends
        chord PQ. Start with:
        $$d = d(P, Q)$$
        $$= \sqrt{(x_2 - x_1)^2 + (y_2 - y_1)^2}$$

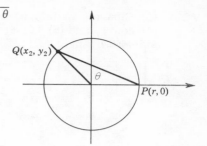

$$d = \sqrt{(r\cos\theta - r)^2 + (r\sin\theta - 0)^2}$$
$$= \sqrt{r^2(\cos\theta)^2 - 2r^2\cos\theta + r^2 + r^2(\sin\theta)^2}$$
$$= r\sqrt{(\cos\theta)^2 + (\sin\theta)^2 - 2\cos\theta + 1}$$
$$= r\sqrt{1 - 2\cos\theta + 1} = r\sqrt{2 - 2\cos\theta}$$

▽212   If θ is in standard position and
        $Q(a, b)$ is the point where the termi-
        nal side of θ intersects the unit
        circle, then
            $\sin\theta$ = (1) ____
            $\cos\theta$ = (2) ____
            $\tan\theta$ = (3) ____

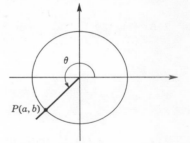

(1) b (2) a (3) $\dfrac{b}{a}$

▽213   If θ is in standard position and $P(x, y)$ is a
        point on the terminal side of θ whose dis-
        tance from O is r, then,
            $\sin\theta$ = (1) ____
            $\cos\theta$ = (2) ____
            $\tan\theta$ = (3) ____

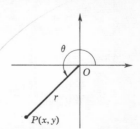

(1) $\dfrac{y}{r}$ (2) $\dfrac{x}{r}$ (3) $\dfrac{y}{x}$

▽ 214 (1) Show the angle θ in standard position, find (2) r, (3) sin θ, (4) cos θ, and (5) tan θ; given $P(5, -12)$ a point on the terminal side of the angle θ.

(1)

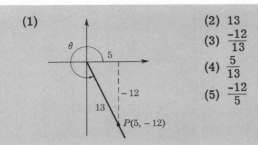

(2) 13

(3) $\dfrac{-12}{13}$

(4) $\dfrac{5}{13}$

(5) $\dfrac{-12}{5}$

215 An angle of 1 radian is the central angle whose intercepted arc is equal in length to _____ .

the radius of the circle

216 (1) 360° = (a) __ rev = (b) __ radians
     (2) 180° = (a) __ rev = (b) __ radians
     (3) 90° = (a) __ rev = (b) __ radians

(1) (a) 1, (b) 2π (2) (a) $\frac{1}{2}$, (b) π (3) (a) $\frac{1}{4}$, (b) $\dfrac{\pi}{2}$

217   1° = (1) __ radians
      30° = (2) __ radians
      45° = (3) __ radians
     240° = (4) __ radians

(1) $\dfrac{\pi}{180}$ (2) $\dfrac{\pi}{6}$ (3) $\dfrac{\pi}{4}$ (4) $\dfrac{4\pi}{3}$

218   1° = (1) _____ radians
      70° = (2) _____ radians
     400° = (3) _____ radians
    -520° = (4) _____ radians

(1) $\dfrac{\pi}{180}$ (2) $\dfrac{7\pi}{18}$ (3) $\dfrac{20\pi}{9}$ (4) $\dfrac{-26\pi}{9}$

219 π radians = (1)____°   1 radian = (2)____°   (Write this answer in terms of π.)

$\frac{\pi}{2}$ radians = (3)____° $\frac{3\pi}{2}$ radians = (4)____°

(1) 180 (2) $\frac{180}{\pi}$ (3) 90 (4) 270

220 210° = (1)____ radians, $\pi/5$ radians = (2)____°

(1) $\frac{7\pi}{6}$ (2) 36

221 Given $\cos \theta = -\frac{4}{5}$ and $\tan \theta$ is positive. (1) Make a sketch of angle θ. (2) Find the value of $2 \tan \theta/(1 - \tan^2\theta)$.

(1)

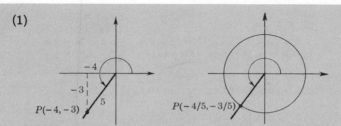

(2) $\dfrac{2 \tan \theta}{(1 - \tan^2 \theta)} = \dfrac{2 \cdot 3/4}{(1 - (3/4))} = \dfrac{3/2}{7/16} = \dfrac{24}{7}$

222 Angles in standard position whose terminal sides lie on one of the axes are called (1)_____ angles.

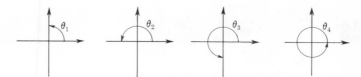

Report the measure of these angles in *degrees* and in *radians*.

(1) quadrantal (2) $\theta = 90° = \frac{\pi}{2}$ radians

(3) $\theta = 180° = \pi$ radians (4) $\theta = 270° = \frac{3\pi}{2}$ radians

(5) $\theta = 360° = 2\pi$ radians

223   Angles are (1)_____ if their terminal sides
      coincide when the angles are in standard position.
      If $\alpha = 120°$, $\beta = (2)$_____°.
      If $\alpha = 2\pi/3$ radians, $\beta = (3)$___ radians.

(1) coterminal   (2) –240   (3) $-\dfrac{4\pi}{3}$

▽224   (1) Are $\pi/4$ and $9\pi/4$ coterminal?
       (2) Are $\pi/4$ and $(\pi/4 + 2\pi)$ coterminal?
       (3) Are $\pi/4$ and $[\pi/4 + (n \cdot 2\pi)]$ coterminal? (n is any integer)
       (4) Are $\pi/4$ and $9\pi/4$ quadrantal angles?

(1) yes   (2) yes   (3) yes   (4) no

SPECIAL ANGLES AND THEIR FUNCTIONS

225   Applying facts from geometry, we can find
      the numerical values for sin θ, cos θ, and
      tan θ where θ is one of several special
      angles. The first angles we shall consider
      are the quadrantal angles. (1) If $\theta = 90°$,
      what are the coordinates of the point where
      the unit circle intersects the terminal side
      of θ? Therefore,
            sin 90° = (2)___
            cos 90° = (3)___

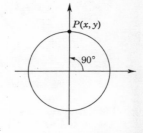

(1) $x = 0$, $y = 1$ (2) 1   (3) 0

226   Recall the definition tan $\theta = (1)$___ / ___.
      If $\theta = 90°$, what is the resulting statement
      when the numerical values are substituted,
      i.e., tan 90° = (2)__/__?   (3) Does this give
      us a numerical value for tan 90°? Explain.

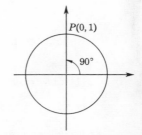

(1) $\dfrac{\sin\,\theta}{\cos\,\theta}$ (2) $\dfrac{1}{0}$ (3) no, division by 0 is impossible

227 If $P(0, 3)$ is a point on the terminal side of θ, then θ = (1)___°...
x = (2)___... y = (3)___... and r = (4)___.   (5) Make a sketch.
Use the following formula to compute sin θ, cos θ, and tan θ:

(6) sin $\theta = \dfrac{y}{r}$ = (a)___/___ = (b)___

(7) cos $\theta = \dfrac{x}{r}$ = (a)___/___ = (b)___

(8) tan $\theta = \dfrac{y}{x}$ = (a)___/___ = (b)___

(1) 90 (2) 0 (3) 3 (4) 3 (5)

(6) (a) $\frac{3}{3}$, (b) 1
(7) (a) $\frac{0}{3}$, (b) 0
(8) (a) $\frac{3}{0}$, (b) undefined

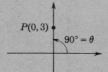

228 Find sin 0°, cos 0°, and tan 0°, using either one of
the methods described in the frames 226 and 227.
        sin 0° = (1)___
        cos 0° = (2)___
        tan 0° = (3)___

(1) 0   (2) 1   (3) 0

229 Find sin 180°, cos 180°, and tan 180°. Notice
that a point on the terminal side of θ is now
$P(-1, 0)$.
        sin 180° = (1)___
        cos 180° = (2)___
        tan 180° = (3)___

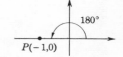

(1) 0   (2) -1   (3) 0

230 To find sin $(3\pi/2)$, cos $(3\pi/2)$, and tan $(3\pi/2)$, you first need to know
where the terminal side of the angle lies and how to represent a
point $P(a, b)$ on it. Make a sketch of the angle and show correct
number replacements for (a, b).

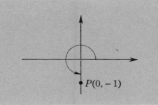

Note: You could have (0, -1/2),
(0, -7), etc. The second coordinate is -1 when P is a
point on the unit circle.

▽231   Complete these statements: sin $(3\pi/2)$ = (1)___, cos $(3\pi/2)$ = (2)___,
tan $(3\pi/2)$ = (3)_____ , and $3\pi/2$ = (4)___°.

(1) –1   (2) 0   (3) undefined   (4) 270

▽232   Complete the table shown in this frame.

Degrees	Radians	sin	cos	tan
0°				
90°				
180°				
270°				

Degrees	Radians	sin	cos	tan
0°	0	0	1	0
90°	$\pi/2$	1	0	undefined
180°	π	0	–1	0
270°	$3\pi/2$	–1	0	undefined

233   There are two quadrantal angles $0 \le \theta < 2\pi$
for which sin θ = 0 is true. Which are
they? Study this sketch if you are not sure.

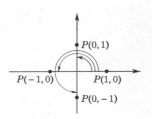

0° or 180°, both have sin θ = 0

234 However, if sin θ = 1, there is just one
quadrantal angle $0 \le \theta < 2\pi$ which would
qualify, namely, _____ .

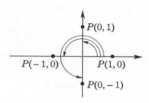

---

sin 90° = 1

---

235 The 45° angle is another *special* angle whose trigonometric functions are easy to obtain. Look at the
sketch to the right.

1. Since PQ is $\perp$ to OQ, angle OQP is 90°.
2. Angle QOP = 45° is given.
3. Therefore, angle OPQ = 45°, and triangle
   OQP is isosceles.
4. Therefore, $x = OQ = QP = y$.

Is $P(1, 1)$ a point on the terminal side of a 45° angle in standard
position?

---

yes   *Note:* $P(2, 2)$, $P(3, 3)$, $P(\frac{1}{2}, \frac{1}{2})$, etc., are also points on
            the terminal side of a 45° angle.

---

236 Find **(1)** r, then:
            sin 45° = **(2)** _____
            cos 45° = **(3)** _____
            tan 45° = **(4)** _____

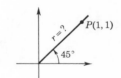

---

(1) $r = \sqrt{1^2 + 1^2} = \sqrt{2}$ **(2)** $\frac{1}{\sqrt{2}}$ **(3)** $\frac{1}{\sqrt{2}}$ **(4)** 1

---

237 Note that you could also write the trigonometric functions of 135° by observing that
$P(-1, 1)$ is a point on the terminal side of
an angle of 135° in standard position. Triangle OQP is again an isosceles right tri-
angle with $|OQ| = |QP|$. In quadrant II,
OQ is **(1)**_____and QP is **(2)**_____.
(Use "negative" or "positive" for blanks.)
$|OQ|$ is read **(3)** _____.

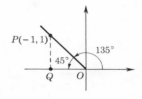

---

(1) negative   **(2)** positive
(3) absolute value of or length without regard to direction

238 Find (1) sin 135°, (2) cos 135°, and (3) tan 135°.

(1) sin 135° = $\frac{1}{\sqrt{2}}$ (2) cos 135° = $\frac{-1}{\sqrt{2}}$ (3) tan 135° = $\frac{1}{-1}$ = -1

239 Find (1) sin 225°, (2) cos 225°, and (3) tan 225°.

(1) sin 225° = $\frac{-1}{\sqrt{2}}$ (2) cos 225° = $\frac{-1}{\sqrt{2}}$ (3) tan 225° = $\frac{-1}{-1}$ = 1
Study frame 240 if your answers are incorrect. If they are correct, go on to frame 241.

240 Explanation for frame 239:
$$r = \sqrt{(-1)^2 + (-1)^2} = \sqrt{2}$$
$$\sin 225° = \frac{y}{r} = (1) \underline{\quad}$$
$$\cos 225° = \frac{x}{r} = (2) \underline{\quad}$$
$$\tan 225° = \frac{y}{x} = (3) \underline{\quad}$$

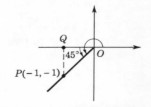

(1) $\frac{-1}{\sqrt{2}}$ (2) $\frac{-1}{\sqrt{2}}$ (3) 1

241 State in (1) radians and (2) degrees the angle terminating in quadrant IV whose terminal side goes through the point $P(1, -1)$.

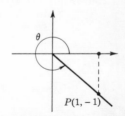

(1) $\frac{7\pi}{4}$ (2) 315°

▽**242** Find (1) sin 315°, (2) cos 315°, and (3) tan 315°.

(1) sin 315° = $\frac{-1}{\sqrt{2}}$ (2) cos 315° = $\frac{1}{\sqrt{2}}$ (3) tan 315° = $\frac{-1}{1}$ = -1

243 The three trigonometric functions for 30° and for 60° can be obtained by applying geometric facts you already know. (1) Sketch a
30° angle in standard position; label the vertex O. Drop a perpendicular line from any point P(x, y) on the terminal side of the angle
to the initial side. Call the point where the perpendicular meets the
initial side Q(x, 0). (2) Indicate the size of (a) ∠OQP, (b) ∠QOP,
and (c) ∠OPQ. This problem will be continued in frames 244 to 249.

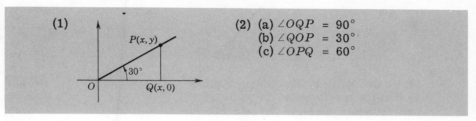

(1)

(2) (a) ∠OQP = 90°
    (b) ∠QOP = 30°
    (c) ∠OPQ = 60°

244 If the line PQ is extended through Q
so that d(QR) = d(PQ) and a line is
drawn through points O and R, what
geometric statement can you make
regarding triangles OQP and OQR?
Complete your sketch and keep your
copy.

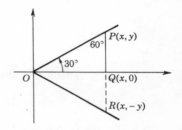

they are congruent

245 angle QOR = (1)___°, angle ROP = ____
(2)___°, angle ORQ = (3)___°; therefore, triangle OPR is (4)_____.
Hence, d(P, R) = d(O, P). (5) Compare the lengths of PQ and OP.

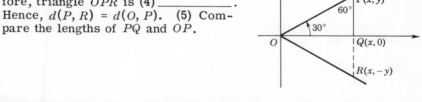

(1) 30   (2) 60   (3) 60   (4) equilateral or equiangular

(5) $|PQ| = |\tfrac{1}{2}OP|$

246 If we let the length of $QP = y = 1$,
then the length of $OP = r =$ _____ .

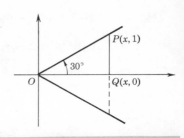

$2y = 2$ Recall that the length $QP = \frac{1}{2}OP$.

---

247 Write the formula that can be applied
to find the length of OQ (x in the
sketch shown here).

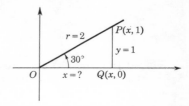

---

some form of the distance formula:
$$r^2 = x^2 + y^2, \quad x^2 = r^2 - y^2 \quad \text{or} \quad d^2 = (x_2 - x_2)^2 + (y_2 - y_2)^2$$

---

248 Compute the length of OQ. (Express
the answer in simple radical form.)

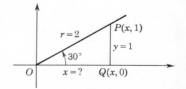

$x = \sqrt{3}$

---

249 Now find **(1)** $\sin 30°$, **(2)** $\cos 30°$, and
(3) $\tan 30°$.

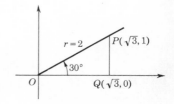

---

(1) $\sin 30° = \frac{1}{2}$ **(2)** $\cos 30° = \dfrac{\sqrt{3}}{2}$ **(3)** $\tan 30° = \dfrac{1}{\sqrt{3}}$

250   For a 60° angle in standard position, you can
see that $OQ = \frac{1}{2}OP$. Let $x = OQ = 1$; then
make a sketch similar to the one in this
frame and write the correct numbers where
the question marks appear.

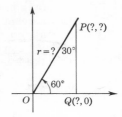

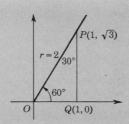

251   Find (1) sin 60°, (2) cos 60°, (3) tan 60°.

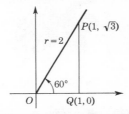

(1) $\sin 60° = \dfrac{\sqrt{3}}{2}$ (2) $\cos 60° = \frac{1}{2}$ (3) $\tan 60° = \dfrac{\sqrt{3}}{1} = \sqrt{3}$

252   In order to compute the values for
sin, cos, and tan of the special angles
30°, 45°, and 60°, you need to apply a
few geometric facts to obtain numerical
substitutions for x, y, and r. For a
30° angle, these are: $y = 1$, $r = $ (1)___,
and $x = $ (2)___ .

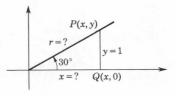

(1) 2   (2) $\sqrt{3}$

253 To help remember these numbers, recall
the theorem of geometry which states that
the side opposite a 30° angle of a right triangle is equal to *one-half* the hypotenuse.
With the triangle placed as shown here,
label x, y, and r numerically, starting
with $x = 1$, $r = $ (1)___, and $y = $ (2)___.

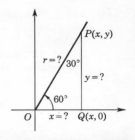

(1) 2   (2) $\sqrt{3}$

254 Let $\theta = \pi/6$ radians.   (1) Sketch this angle in standard position.
Indicate suitable numbers for x, y, and r, and find (2) sin ($\pi/6$),
(3) cos ($\pi/6$), and (4) tan ($\pi/6$).

(1)

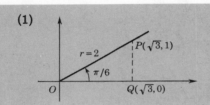

(2) $\sin \dfrac{\pi}{6} = \dfrac{1}{2}$

(3) $\cos \dfrac{\pi}{6} = \dfrac{\sqrt{3}}{2}$

(4) $\tan \dfrac{\pi}{6} = \dfrac{1}{\sqrt{3}}$

▽255 Let $\theta = \pi/3$ radians.   (1) Sketch this angle in standard position.
Indicate suitable numbers for x, y, and r; and find (2) sin ($\pi/3$),
(3) cos ($\pi/3$), and (4) tan ($\pi/3$).

(1)

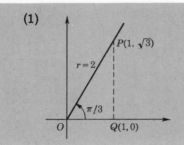

(2) $\sin \dfrac{\pi}{3} = \dfrac{\sqrt{3}}{2}$

(3) $\cos \dfrac{\pi}{3} = \dfrac{1}{2}$

(4) $\tan \dfrac{\pi}{3} = \sqrt{3}$

▽256 To find values for sin ($\pi/4$), cos ($\pi/4$), and tan ($\pi/4$), first sketch
an angle of $\pi/4$ radians in standard position. Then draw $PQ \perp OQ$.
In right triangle OQP, let $y = 1$; then $x =$ **(1)**____, $r =$ **(2)**____, and

$$\sin \frac{\pi}{4} = \textbf{(3)}\underline{\quad}$$

$$\cos \frac{\pi}{4} = \textbf{(4)}\underline{\quad}$$

$$\tan \frac{\pi}{4} = \textbf{(5)}\underline{\quad}$$

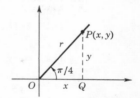

(1) 1   **(2)** $\sqrt{2}$ **(3)** $\frac{1}{\sqrt{2}}$ **(4)** $\frac{1}{\sqrt{2}}$ **(5)** 1

257 The work in frames 257 to 262 is optional. Another angle of special interest is $\pi/5$ (36° angle). You may recall that this angle can
be constructed using the usual geometric tools (straight edge and
compass), but since the steps are slightly complicated, it is not as
useful as other constructions of plane geometry. We introduce it
here since we are able to find exact values for the sine, cosine, and
tangent of $\pi/5$ as we have done for $\pi/3$, $\pi/4$, and $\pi/6$. First, we
need to review the construction by which we can divide a given segment OP into two parts such that $OP/OE = OE/EP$.

Make the construction if you recall how it is done; otherwise, follow
the steps given in the answer.

A possible solution is shown here.
1. Bisect OP, let M be the midpoint
    of OP.
2. Construct $CP \perp OP$ at P.
3. Let $AP = \frac{1}{2}OP$.
4. Draw OA.
5. With A as center and AP as
    radius, draw a circle cutting
    OA at B.
6. On OP find point E such that
    $OE = OB$.

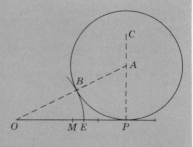

We now have point E such that $OP/OE = OE/EP$.
See frame 258 for a proof. Save your construction.

258 Prove that the construction in answer 257 locates a point E on OP
such that $OP/OE = OE/EP$.

1. Let OP = 1 unit.
2. By construction, $AP = \frac{1}{2}$ unit.
3. Since OPA is a right triangle,

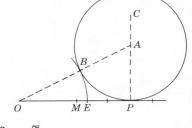

$$\overline{OA}^2 = \overline{OP}^2 + \overline{AP}^2$$
$$= 1 + (\tfrac{1}{2})^2 = \tfrac{5}{4}$$
$$OA = \frac{\sqrt{5}}{2}$$

4. $OE = OB = OA - AB$
$$= \frac{\sqrt{5}}{2} - \frac{1}{2} = \frac{\sqrt{5} - 1}{2}$$

5. $EP = 1 - OE = 1 - \dfrac{\sqrt{5} - 1}{2} = \dfrac{3 - \sqrt{5}}{2}$

Complete the proof thus:

6. Substitute these values for the ratios OP/OE and OE/EP and
thus show that $OP/OE = OE/EP$.

$$\frac{OP}{OE} = \frac{1}{(\sqrt{5} - 1)/2} = \frac{2}{\sqrt{5} - 1} = \frac{2(\sqrt{5} + 1)}{(\sqrt{5} - 1)(\sqrt{5} + 1)} = \frac{2\sqrt{5} + 2}{4}$$

$$\frac{OE}{EP} = \frac{(\sqrt{5} - 1)/2}{(3 - \sqrt{5})/2} = \frac{\sqrt{5} - 1}{3 - \sqrt{5}} = \frac{(\sqrt{5} - 1)(3 + \sqrt{5})}{(3 - \sqrt{5})(3 + \sqrt{5})} = \frac{2\sqrt{5} + 2}{4}$$

$$\frac{OP}{OE} = \frac{OE}{EP} \qquad \text{(This is what we wished to show.)}$$

259 With the information in frames 257 and 258, we are ready to construct a 36° angle and prove our construction correct. Construction:

1. Let OP be the radius of circle O.
   Find point E as before so that
   $OP/OE = OE/EP$

2. Find point A so that chord $AP = OE$.
   Draw OA.

3. In frame 260 we shall prove that angle AOP = 36°.

4. Add line AE to your drawing.

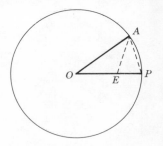

Your answer is a copy of this drawing. Keep your copy for later
work.

260 Given circle O with radius $OP = 1$
     unit, $AP = OE$, and $OP/OE = OE/EP$.
     Prove that angle $AOP = 36°$.

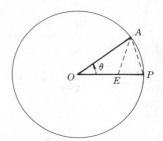

In triangles AOP and AEP *Supply reasons*

1. $AP = OE$, $\dfrac{OP}{OE} = \dfrac{OE}{EP}$ (1) _____

2. Therefore, $\dfrac{OP}{AP} = \dfrac{AP}{EP}$ (2) _____

3. $\angle P = \angle P$ (3) _____
4. Therefore, $\triangle AOP \sim \triangle AEP$ (4) _____
5. $OA = OP$ in $\triangle AOP$ (5) _____
6. Therefore, $AP = AE$ in   (6) _____
    $\triangle AEP$
7. $\angle OAP = \angle P = \angle AEP$ (7) _____
    $\angle AOE = \angle OAE = \theta$
8. $\angle AEP = \angle \theta + \angle EAO =$ (8) _____
    $2\angle\theta$
9. $\angle OAP + \angle P + \theta = 180°$ (9) _____
    or $5\angle\theta = 180°$
10. Therefore, $\theta = 36°$ (10) _____

---

(1) hypothesis (given)
(2) substitution, AP for OE
(3) identity ($\angle P$ is in both triangles)
(4) two triangles are similar if an angle of one equals an angle
     of another and the including sides are proportional
(5) radii of same circle are equal
(6) these sides correspond to the equal sides in $\triangle OAP$
(7) angles opposite equal sides in isosceles triangles are equal
(8) the exterior angle of a triangle is equal to the sum of the
     nonadjacent interior angles
(9) (a) the sum of the angles of a triangle is 180°
     (b) substitution
(10) division axiom

261   Remember that the original problem
      was to find the sine and cosine of 36°.
      We need the coordinates of point A, i.e.,
      the lengths OD and AD. Let AD be a $\perp$
      from A to OP. Find OD and AD, given
      in frame 258 that $OP = 1$, $OE =$

      $(\sqrt{5} - 1)/2$, $EP = (3 - \sqrt{5})/2$.

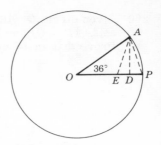

$$OD = 1 - \tfrac{1}{2}\overline{EP} = 1 - \frac{1}{2}\left(\frac{3 - \sqrt{5}}{2}\right)$$

$$= \frac{4 - 3 + \sqrt{5}}{4}$$

$$= \frac{1 + \sqrt{5}}{4}$$

$$\overline{AD}^2 = \overline{OA}^2 - \overline{OD}^2$$

$$= 1 - \left(\frac{1 + \sqrt{5}}{4}\right)^2$$

$$= \frac{16 - 1 - 2\sqrt{5} - 5}{16}$$

$$AD = \sqrt{\frac{5 - \sqrt{5}}{8}} \text{ or } \frac{\sqrt{10 - 2\sqrt{5}}}{4}$$

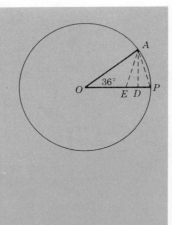

262   State in radical form the following: (1) $\sin 36°$,
      (2) $\cos 36°$, and (3) $\tan 36°$.

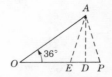

(1) $\sin 36° = \dfrac{\sqrt{10 - 2\sqrt{5}}}{4}$ (2) $\cos 36° = \dfrac{1 + \sqrt{5}}{4}$

(3) $\tan 36° = \dfrac{\sqrt{10 - 2\sqrt{5}}/4}{(1 + \sqrt{5})/4} = \dfrac{\sqrt{10 - 2\sqrt{5}}}{1 + \sqrt{5}}$

Comment

By adjusting for positive and negative ordinates and abscissas, we could
now find the sine, cosine, and tangent for a number of other angles such

as 120°, 135°, 144°, 150°, and 210°. In general the trigonometric functions are irrational. Other than the special angles discussed, we have, at this point, no simple way of calculating the values of the trigonometric functions. A table of reference is given in Panel 1 showing the values of the sine, cosine, and tangent for angles from 0 to 90° at intervals of 1°. These values are three-place approximations which were computed originally using infinite series. You will use Panel 1 for frames 263 to 268. The series to which we referred above are given here for the student who is interested: If x is any real number (x in radians), then

$$\sin x = x - \frac{x^3}{3!} + \frac{x^5}{5!} - \frac{x^7}{7!} + \cdots$$

$$\cos x = 1 - \frac{x^2}{2!} + \frac{x^4}{4!} - \frac{x^6}{6!} + \cdots$$

263 Use Panel 1 for practice in finding approximate values for trigonometric functions.
sin 33° ≈ _____.
Directions: Look in the left-hand column under degrees for 33, then under the column headed sine read the value corresponding to 33°.

0.545

264 Use Panel 1 to find cosine and tangent of 33°. Record your answer.
cos 33° ≈ (1)_____ and tan 33° ≈ (2)_____.

(1) 0.839 (2) 0.649

265 Use Panel 1 again. Find sin 58° ≈ (1)_____, cos 58° ≈ (2)_____, and tan 58° ≈ (3)_____.

(1) 0.848 (2) 0.530 (3) 1.600

266 Using Panel 1, find sin π/6 = (1)_____, cos π/4 = (2)_____, and tan 1.012 (radians) = (3)_____.
Note 1: Since Panel 1 shows angles in degrees and in decimal approximations of radians, it will be necessary to convert π/6 to degrees or to a decimal reading in radians.
Note 2: In another problem you found sin (π/6) and cos (π/4) without using Panel 1.

(1) 0.500 (2) 0.707 (3) 1.600

267   Panel 1 can also be used to find the *angle* when the trigonometric
      function is given or can be computed. Suppose sin $\theta \approx 0.191$. What
      is θ measured in degrees and in radians?

$\theta \approx 11° \approx 0.192$ radian

268   Find θ if **(1)** tan $\theta \approx 1.540$, **(2)** cos $\theta \approx 0.105$.

(1) $\theta \approx 57° \approx 0.995$ radian   **(2)** $\theta \approx 84° \approx 1.466$ radians

APPLICATIONS

269   You should be able to use the sine, cosine, or tangent to compute
      sides or angles of triangles when a limited amount of information is
      given. In the sketch you are given $OQ =$
      48 ft, angle $QOP = 35°$, and $PQ \perp OQ$.
      You can find QP by using the tangent
      function:

$$\tan = \frac{y}{x}$$

      thus, $\tan 35° = \dfrac{y}{48}$

      In Panel 1 find tan $35° \approx$ **(1)**_____. Substitute this value in the
      equation; then solve for y. $y \approx$ **(2)**_____.

(1) 0.700   **(2)** 34 ft   *Solution:* $0.700 \approx \dfrac{y}{48}$, $y \approx 33.6 \approx 34$

270   From a point 245 ft from the base of a building standing on level
      ground, the angle between a horizontal line and a line to the top of
      the building is 50°. Find the height of the building. First make a
      sketch showing that you understand the problem. The solution is
      continued in frame 271.

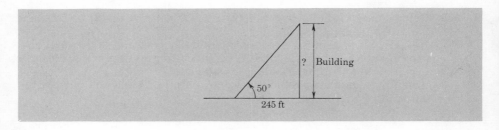

271 If the given angle 50° is placed in standard position and the distance 245 ft is used as the initial side of the angle, then the height of the building, which is what we are to find, will be the ordinate y of P. As in the problem in frame 269 we can use tan $\theta = y/x$, since $x \neq 0$, to find y. Find y.

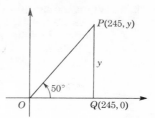

$y \approx 292$ ft   *Solution:* tan $50° \approx \dfrac{y}{245}$, $1.192 \approx = \dfrac{y}{245}$, $292 \approx y$

272 Here the problem is to find the width of a river. You are given the facts shown in the sketch. The tree located across the river serves as a guide. The angle at R is $\pi/3$, and R is 75 ft from the point directly across the river from the tree. (1) Make a sketch with the given angle in standard position, and (2) find the width of the river.

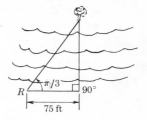

(1)

(2) $y \approx 130$ ft
Solution:

$$\tan \frac{\pi}{3} \approx \frac{y}{75}$$

$$1.732 \approx \frac{y}{75}$$

$$y \approx 130$$

273 Find the distance from O to P in the problem in frame 272.

$r = 150$ ft   Here is one solution: cos $\dfrac{\pi}{3} = \dfrac{75}{r}$, $0.500 = \dfrac{75}{r}$,

$$r = \frac{75}{0.500} = 150$$

274 When the angle of elevation of the
     sun is 30°, a flag pole casts a
     shadow 121 ft long. How tall is the
     flag pole?

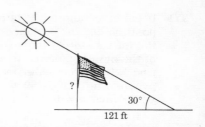

70 ft

275 An extension ladder 45 ft long is leaning against a
     building. The angle between the ladder and the
     ground is 70°. Will the ladder in this position
     reach a window sill 40 ft from the ground? Since
     we know r, for this problem we can use sin θ =
     y/r to find y.

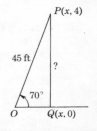

yes   *Solution:* sin 70° $\approx \dfrac{y}{45}$, $y \approx 0.940(45) \approx 42$

276 It is observed that a vertical pole 10.4 ft
     high standing on level ground casts a shadow
     6.5 ft long at a certain time of day. Deter-
     mine approximately the angle of elevation
     of the sun.

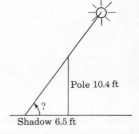

$\theta \approx 58°$ or 1.012 radians
Solution: tan $\theta = \dfrac{y}{x} = \dfrac{10.4}{6.5} \approx 1.600$
Using Panel 1, $\theta \approx 58°$ or 1.012 radians

277 We used the expression "angle of elevation" in frame 276. We de-
     scribe it as follows: From the observation point two lines are
     drawn, one to the elevated point or object P, the other a horizontal

continued →

line. The angle of elevation is the angle between these two lines.
Make a sketch to illustrate this statement: "From a point 100 ft
from the base of a tree standing on level ground, the angle of elevation of the top of the tree is 40°."

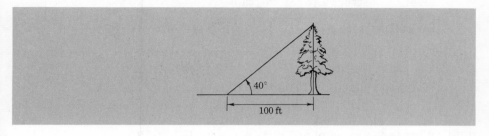

278 Find the height of the tree in frame 277 knowing that at a point 100
ft from the base of a tree the angle of elevation of the top of the tree
is 40°.

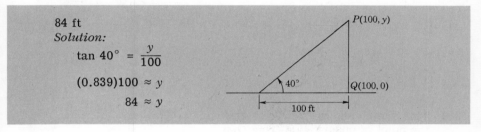

84 ft
Solution:

$$\tan 40° = \frac{y}{100}$$

$$(0.839)100 \approx y$$

$$84 \approx y$$

279 The phrase "angle of depression"
will be used thus: From the ele-
vated point of observation O, two
lines are drawn, one a horizontal
line, the other a line to the object
or point P. The angle between
these two lines is the *angle of depression*. Make a sketch to show
an angle of depression of 30° ob-

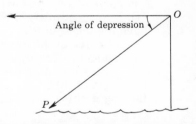

served when a boat at sea is sighted from a lighthouse tower known
to be 300 ft above sea level.

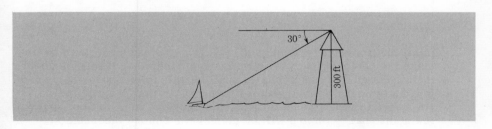

▽280   Find the distance of the boat
       from the base of the tower given
       the angle of depression is 30°
       and the tower is 300 ft above sea
       level. Construct a parallelogram
       $PQOQ'$. (Compare angle $Q'OP$
       with angle QPO.)

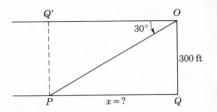

$x \approx 520$ ft

Solution: $\tan 30° = \dfrac{300}{x}$, $(0.577) \approx \dfrac{300}{x}$, $x \approx \dfrac{300}{0.577} \approx 520$

▽281   What is the name of angle **(1)** AO_1P ?   **(2)** PO_2B ?

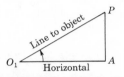
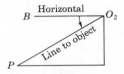

(1) AO_1P is the angle of elevation   **(2)** PO_2B is the angle of
depression

282   This sketch shows that if you shift
      the point of observation from O_1,
      where you have the angle of
      (1)_____ , to O_2, where you
      have the angle of **(2)**_____ ,
      the measure of the angle (size) has
      not changed. Hence, we sometimes
      say for a particular problem that
      the angle of **(3)**_____ equals
      the angle of **(4)**_____ .

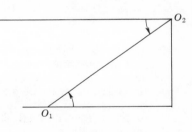

(1) elevation   **(2)** depression   **(3)** elevation   **(4)** depression

Comment

In all the preceding examples a *right triangle* was necessary to
make the computation. After we have studied other theorems about
the trigonometric functions, we shall be able to measure angles and
lengths by using a more general triangle. In this program we do
not spend a great amount of time on numerical computations, but a
few additional examples will be given before more theorems are

introduced. In a course where the emphasis is on numerical applications to the solution of triangles, definite procedures would be
outlined for accuracy of computation and measurement. In the examples here, state the answers in a form suitable to the data given
and the tables used.

REDUCTION FORMULAS

283   When θ is in standard position, the ordinate of the point of intersection of the terminal side with the unit circle is the (1)_____ of
the angle θ, and the abscissa of the point is the (2)_____ of the
angle θ. If cos $\theta \neq 0$, sin θ/cos θ = (3)_____ of the angle θ.

(1) sine   (2) cosine   (3) tangent

284   Two theorems easily established using the definitions in frame 283
and your knowledge of geometry are:
Theorem I: If $P(x, y)$ is any point on the terminal side of the
angle θ in standard position and $r = \sqrt{x^2 + y^2}$ is the distance of
P from the origin, then cos θ = (1)__/__ and sin θ = (2)__/__.
Theorem II: If $x \neq 0$, then tan θ = (3)__/__.
(Use x, y, r for the answers.)

(1) $\frac{x}{r}$ (2) $\frac{y}{r}$ (3) $\frac{y}{x}$

285   From Theorem I in frame 284 we have cos θ =
x/r and sin θ = y/r when $P(x, y)$ is *any* point
on the terminal side of the angle θ in standard
position and r is the distance of P from origin. Solving cos θ = x/r for x, we have x =
(1)_____. Solving sin θ = y/r for y, we
have y = (2)_____.

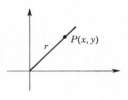

(1) r cos θ (2) r sin θ

286 When $P(x, y)$ is the point where the unit circle intersects the terminal side of θ (sketch a), we can use cos θ and sin θ for x and y, respectively, and the distance formula becomes the Pythagorean relation (1)_____. When P has the coordinates shown in sketch b, (2) show that the same identity holds.

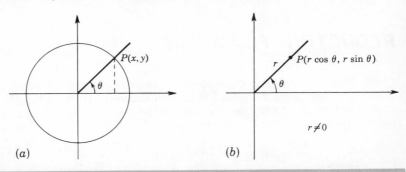

(a)   (b)

(1) $1 = (\cos\ \theta)^2 + (\sin\ \theta)^2$ (2) $r^2 = (r\ \cos\ \theta)^2 + (r\ \sin\ \theta)^2$
$= r^2(\cos\ \theta)^2 + r^2(\sin\ \theta)^2$
$1 = (\cos\ \theta)^2 + (\sin\ \theta)^2$

287 In review we mention also that
$d = r\ \sqrt{2 - 2\ \cos\ \theta}$ was shown to be the length of _____ when θ is a central angle in a circle of radius r.

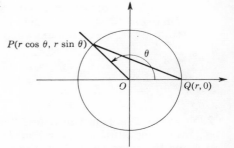

chord PQ (which is subtended by θ)

288 A *function* in mathematics is defined as a set of ordered pairs, no two pairs having the same first coordinate. *Example:* $\{(a, b), (c, d), (1, 2), ...\}$. Hence, we speak of the sine, cosine, and tangent as functions. The ordered pairs are respectively $(\theta, \sin\ \theta)$ for the sine function, (1) (_,____) for the cosine, (2) (_,____) for the tangent. (With *each* number θ, there is associated another number, sin θ; etc.)

(1) $(\theta, \cos\ \theta)$ (2) $(\theta, \tan\ \theta)$

289 *Example:* If θ = 15°, then (θ, sin θ) = (15°, 0.259). Write the ordered pairs (θ, sin θ) for the sine function for **(1)** θ = 18°, **(2)** 19°,
(3) 20°, and **(4)** 21°. Refer to Panel 1.

(1) (18°, 0.309)   **(2)** (19°, 0.326)
(3) (20°, 0.342)   **(4)** (21°, 0.358)

290 Write as ordered pairs the numerical values of the cosine function
for **(1)** θ = 60°, **(2)** 61°, **(3)** 62°, and **(4)** 63°.

(1) (60°, 0.500)   **(2)** (61°, 0.485)
(3) (62°, 0.470)   **(4)** (63°, 0.454)

291 Find the number of degrees in each angle indicated by the question
mark.

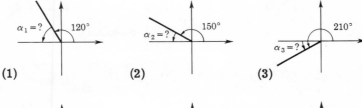

(1)   **(2)**   **(3)**

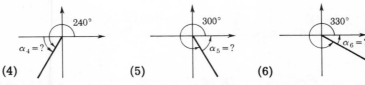

(4)   **(5)**   **(6)**

(1) α_1 = 60° **(2)** α_2 = 30° **(3)** α_3 = 30°
(4) α_4 = 60° **(5)** α_5 = 60° **(6)** α_6 = 30°

292 What are the measures of **(1)** α_1, **(2)** α_2, and **(3)** α_3 in radians?

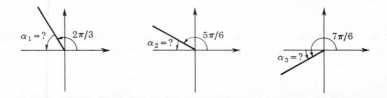

(1) $\alpha_1 = \dfrac{\pi}{3}$ **(2)** $\alpha_2 = \dfrac{\pi}{6}$ **(3)** $\alpha_3 = \dfrac{\pi}{6}$

293 Find **(1)** α_1, **(2)** α_2, and **(3)** α_3 in radians.

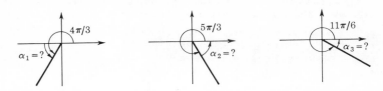

(1) $\alpha_1 = \dfrac{\pi}{3}$ **(2)** $\alpha_2 = \dfrac{\pi}{3}$ **(3)** $\alpha_3 = \dfrac{\pi}{6}$

▽**294** Find the angles indicated.

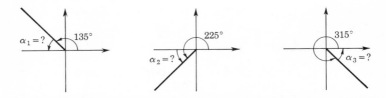

(1) $\alpha_1 = 45°$ **(2)** $\alpha_2 = 45°$ **(3)** $\alpha_3 = 45°$

295 State **(1)** α_1, **(2)** α_2, **(3)** α_3, and **(4)** α_4 in radians. *Note:* Each is indicated as a positive acute angle.

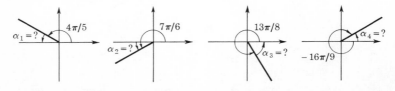

(1) $\alpha_1 = \dfrac{\pi}{5}$ **(2)** $\alpha_2 = \dfrac{\pi}{6}$ **(3)** $\alpha_3 = \dfrac{3\pi}{8}$ **(4)** $\alpha_4 = \dfrac{2\pi}{9}$

296 Make a sketch of the right triangle ABC having acute angles $\pi/3$ and $\pi/6$, and indicate the correct numerical relations of the three sides.

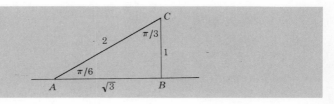

297 When working with angles that terminate in the second quadrant, remember that the ordinate y is positive and y is greater than 0, that the abscissa x is negative and x is less than 0, and that distance r is positive and r is greater than 0. Therefore, for θ a second-quadrant angle, sin θ (1)_____ 0, cos θ (2)_____ 0, and tan θ (3)_____ 0. (Use "is greater than" or "is less than" for each of the blanks.)

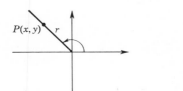   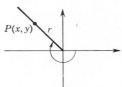

(1) is greater than   **(2)** is less than   **(3)** is less than

298 For an angle terminating in the third quadrant, ordinate y is (1)_____, abscissa x is (2)_____, and distance r is (3)_____; hence, sin θ is (4)_____, cos θ is (5)_____, and tan θ is (6)_____. (Use "positive" or "negative" for the blanks.)

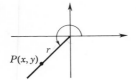   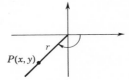

(1) negative   **(2)** negative   **(3)** positive
(4) negative   **(5)** negative   **(6)** positive

299 For an angle terminating in the fourth quadrant, ordinate y is (1)_____, abscissa x is (2)_____, and distance r is (3)_____; hence, sin θ is (4)_____, cos θ is (5)_____, tan θ is (6)_____.

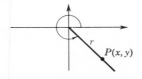   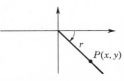

(1) negative   **(2)** positive   **(3)** positive
(4) negative   **(5)** positive   **(6)** negative

300 Indicate on drawings similar to the first one, the proper signs (+ or -) for the function listed above the sketch. In the first sketch, sin θ is positive in quadrants I and II, negative in quadrants III and IV.

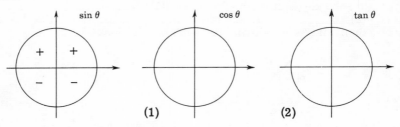

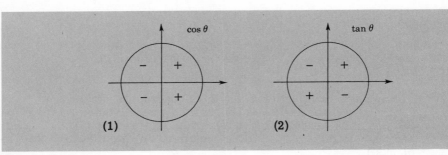

301 Without using the tables in Panel 1, find cos 135°.

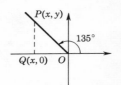

$$\cos 135° = \frac{-1}{\sqrt{2}}$$

Solution: Let $x = -1$. Then, $y = +1$ and $r = \sqrt{(-1)^2 + 1^2} = \sqrt{2}$.

$$\cos 135° = \frac{x}{r} = \frac{-1}{\sqrt{2}}$$

302   Compute sin (5π/6).

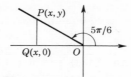

$$\sin \frac{5\pi}{6} = \frac{1}{2}$$

Solution:

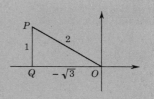

    angle $QOP = \dfrac{\pi}{6}$. The sides of right

triangle QOP have the relationship shown in the sketch.

Therefore, $\sin \dfrac{5\pi}{6} = \dfrac{y}{r} = \dfrac{1}{2}$

∇303   Compute tan (5π/4).

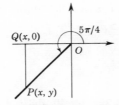

$$\tan \frac{5\pi}{4}$$

Solution: $x = -1,\ y = -1,\ \tan \dfrac{5\pi}{4} = \dfrac{y}{r} = \dfrac{-1}{-1} = 1$

∇304   Find (1) sin (5π/4) and (2) cos (5π/4).

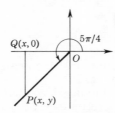

(1) $\sin \dfrac{5\pi}{4} = \dfrac{y}{r} = \dfrac{-1}{\sqrt{2}}$ **(2)** $\cos \dfrac{5\pi}{4} = \dfrac{x}{y} = \dfrac{-1}{\sqrt{2}}$

305 This problem will test your knowledge of the functions of the special angles we have been discussing.   Find in radical form the value of

$$\frac{\sin (2\pi/3) - \cos (4\pi/3) - \tan (5\pi/3)}{\cos (\pi/3) + \tan (3\pi/4) + \sin (7\pi/6)}$$

Be careful of signs as well as numerical values.

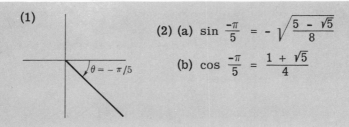

$$\frac{\sqrt{3}/2 + 1/2 + \sqrt{3}/1}{1/2 - 1 - 1/2} = \frac{(\sqrt{3} + 1 + 2\sqrt{3})/2}{-1}$$

$$= \frac{(1 + 3\sqrt{3})/2}{-1} = \frac{-1 - 3\sqrt{3}}{2}$$

306 Earlier we found the values for the functions of $\pi/5$ (36°) in radical form, i.e., $\sin (\pi/5) = \sqrt{(5 - \sqrt{5})/8}$ and $\cos (\pi/5) = (1 + \sqrt{5})/4$.   Find (1) $\sin (4\pi/5)$ and (2) $\cos (4\pi/5)$.   Make a copy of the value of $\sin (\pi/5)$ and $\cos (\pi/5)$ (in radical form) for use in frames 307 and 308.

(1) $\sin \dfrac{4\pi}{5} = \sqrt{\dfrac{5 - \sqrt{5}}{8}}$ (2) $\cos \dfrac{4\pi}{5} = -\dfrac{1 + \sqrt{5}}{4}$

307 (1) Make a sketch showing an angle $\theta = -\pi/5$.
     (2) Give in radical form (a) $\sin (-\pi/5)$ and (b) $\cos (-\pi/5)$.

(1)

$\theta = -\pi/5$

(2) (a) $\sin \dfrac{-\pi}{5} = -\sqrt{\dfrac{5 - \sqrt{5}}{8}}$

(b) $\cos \dfrac{-\pi}{5} = \dfrac{1 + \sqrt{5}}{4}$

▽308 (1) State in radians the positive angle (in standard position) which is coterminal with $-\pi/5$.
     (2) State in radians the negative angle (in standard position)
         (a) which is coterminal with $6\pi/5$. (b) Also state this answer in degrees.

(1) $\dfrac{9\pi}{5}$ (2) (a) $\dfrac{-4\pi}{5}$ radians,   (b) $-144°$

309 An escalator is built so that there is a rise of 1 ft with each 1.7 ft of travel on the escalator. What is its angle of elevation?

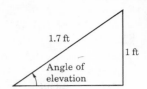

1.7 ft

1 ft

Angle of elevation

$\theta \approx 36°$ *Solution:* $\sin \theta = \dfrac{1}{1.7} \approx 0.588, \quad \theta \approx 36°$

310 If we say there is a rise of 3 ft in 100 ft, we mean 3 ft vertical rise in 100 ft along the horizontal. If a roadway has this grade, what is the angle of elevation of the roadway?

$\theta \approx 2°$
Solution:
$\tan \theta = \frac{3}{100} \approx 0.030$
$\theta \approx 2°$

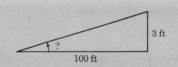

3 ft

?

100 ft

311 Suppose a driveway has an angle of elevation of approximately 2°. How high is the garage floor above the street level if the driveway measures 184 ft?

$h \approx 6.4$ ft
Solution:
$$\sin 2° = \frac{h}{184}$$
$$(0.035)(184) \approx h$$
$$6.4 \approx h$$

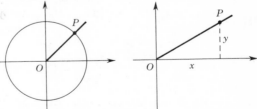

184 ft

? = h

2°

312 Up to this point, two interpretations for the sine and cosine of an angle have been given. Be sure that you understand and can use each of them.

I. If P is the point of intersection of the terminal side of an angle with the unit circle, then by *definition*
$$\sin \theta = (1)\text{_____}$$
$$\cos \theta = (2)\text{_____}$$

continued →

II. If P is *any* point on the terminal side of θ and r is the distance of P from O, then in terms of x, y, and r

$\sin \theta = (3)\_\_/\_\_$
$\cos \theta = (4)\_\_/\_\_$

---

(1) ordinate of P or $\dfrac{\text{ordinate of } P}{r} = \dfrac{\text{ordinate}}{1}$

(2) abscissa of P or $\dfrac{\text{abscissa of } P}{r} = \dfrac{\text{abscissa}}{1}$

(3) $\dfrac{y}{r}$ (4) $\dfrac{x}{r}$

---

313 If (-4, 5) is a point on the terminal side of an angle in standard position and you are asked to find the sine and cosine of this angle, how would you proceed?

1. Make a sketch.
2. Find r using

$$r = \sqrt{(-4)^2 + 5^2}$$
$$= \sqrt{41}$$

3. $\sin \theta = \dfrac{y}{r} = \dfrac{5}{\sqrt{41}}$

$\cos \theta = \dfrac{x}{r} = \dfrac{-4}{\sqrt{41}}$

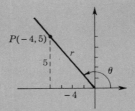

---

314 If you know that $\sin \theta = 3/\sqrt{13}$ and $\cos \theta = 2/\sqrt{13}$, you have two ways of interpreting this information.

I. If you note that $\sqrt{(3/\sqrt{13})^2 + (2/\sqrt{13})^2} = 1$ (check it), then you may consider

$P(2/\sqrt{13},\ 3/\sqrt{13})$ as the point where the *unit* circle intersects the terminal side of θ. In this case
the radius $OP = (1)\,$ _____
$OQ = (2)\,$ _____
$QP = (3)\,$ _____

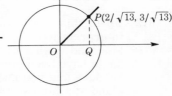

II. If you take the other interpretation, you may consider

$$\cos \theta = \dfrac{x}{r} = \dfrac{2}{\sqrt{13}}$$

$$\sin \theta = \dfrac{y}{r} = \dfrac{3}{\sqrt{13}}$$

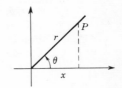

continued →

From this point of view,
r = (4)_____
x = (5)_____
y = (6)_____
This discussion will be continued in frame 315.

---

(1) 1   (2) $\frac{2}{\sqrt{13}}$ (3) $\frac{3}{\sqrt{13}}$ (4) $\sqrt{13}$ (5) 2   (6) 3

---

315   The information given and the question asked will determine which
of the descriptions for sin θ and cos θ will serve you better.
Remember 1. If P is the point of intersection of the terminal side
of θ with the unit circle (r = 1), then sin θ = (1)_____
and cos θ = (2)_____.
Remember 2. If P is *any* point on the terminal
side of θ and you are given cos θ = a/c, you
may assign a and c as measures of sides (3)_____
and (4)____, respectively, in triangle OQP, and
then find the remaining side of the triangle.
Find (5) sin θ and (6) tan θ if θ terminates in
quadrant I and cos θ = a/c.

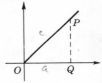

---

(1) ordinate of P or y (2) abscissa of P or x

(3) OQ (4) OP (5) sin θ = $\dfrac{\sqrt{c^2 - a^2}}{c}$ (6) tan θ = $\dfrac{\sqrt{c^2 - a^2}}{a}$

---

316   Given θ is in angle terminating in quadrant III and
sin θ = $-\frac{5}{8}$, find OQ.

OQ = $-\sqrt{39}$
            Using the fact that
$\sin \theta = \dfrac{y}{r}$
we know that y = -5 and r = 8. Using the
distance formula
$r = \sqrt{x^2 + y^2}$
we have
$8 = \sqrt{x^2 + (-5)^2}$
Therefore, $-\sqrt{39}$ = x
The negative answer is given since this is the directed distance OQ.

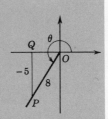

317 Given θ is an angle whose tangent is negative and $\cos \theta = \frac{4}{9}$, find $\sin \theta$ assuming that $\frac{4}{9}$ is the point of intersection of the *unit* circle with the terminal side of θ.

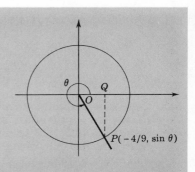

$$\sin \theta = -\frac{\sqrt{65}}{9}$$

Solution:

$$1 = \sqrt{\left(\tfrac{4}{9}\right)^2 + \sin^2 \theta}$$

$$1 - \tfrac{16}{81} = \sin^2 \theta$$

$$\pm \sqrt{\tfrac{65}{81}} = \sin \theta$$

$$\frac{-\sqrt{65}}{9} = \sin \theta$$

In quadrant IV, $\sin \theta$ is negative.

∇318 You are given the coordinates $(\frac{4}{5}, \frac{3}{5})$ of a point P on a unit circle. **(1)** Sketch the angle θ in standard position whose terminal side goes through this point. Show clearly on your drawing the segments whose lengths are $\frac{4}{5}$ and $\frac{3}{5}$. **(2)** What is the length of r? Now think of $\sin \theta = \frac{3}{5}$ and $\cos \theta = \frac{4}{5}$, where $\sin \theta$ and $\cos \theta$ are defined in terms of x, y, and r. **(3)** What are the lengths of x, y, and r? **(4)** Make a sketch in which this information is shown.

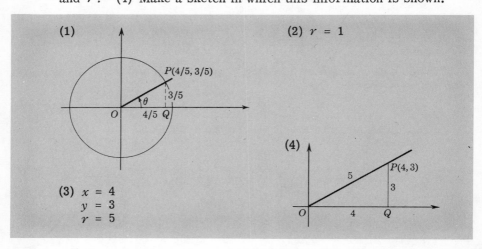

(1)

$P(4/5, 3/5)$

(2) $r = 1$

(3) $x = 4$
     $y = 3$
     $r = 5$

(4) $P(4, 3)$

319 The explanation following is another way of showing how both interpretations of $\sin \theta$ and $\cos \theta$ "tie" together. Suppose we are given

continued →

sin $\theta = \frac{3}{5}$ and cos $\theta = \frac{4}{5}$. We
shall first make a sketch of
the *unit* circle with $P(\frac{4}{5}, \frac{3}{5})$
the point where the terminal
side of θ intercepts the circle.

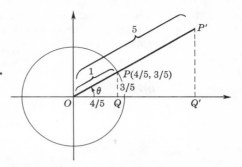

Check: $1 = \sqrt{(\frac{4}{5})^2 + (\frac{3}{5})^2}$

Then we shall extend OP so
that $OP' = 5r$ and draw a
perpendicular from P' to the
x axis. Note that triangles
OPQ and $OP'Q'$ are similar
(θ is an angle of each triangle and angle Q is equal to Q'). Find the
lengths of **(1)** OQ' and **(2)** $Q'P'$ using the fact that corresponding
sides of similar triangles are proportional.   **(3)** Do these results
agree with the values of x, y, and r of frame 318?

---

(1) $OQ' = 4$ **(2)** $P'Q' = 3$ **(3)** yes
Solution: $\dfrac{P'Q'}{PQ} = \dfrac{OP'}{OP}$, $\dfrac{P'Q'}{3/5} = \dfrac{5}{1}$, $P'Q' = 3$

$\dfrac{OQ'}{OQ} = \dfrac{OP'}{OP}$, $\dfrac{OQ'}{4/5} = \dfrac{5}{1}$, $OQ' = 4$

yes, $P'Q' = y = 3$, $OQ' = x = 4$

---

320 P is a point on the terminal side of θ. If $OP = 8$
units and $\theta = \pi/3$, find the coordinates of
point P.

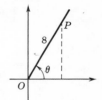

$x = 4$, $y = 4\sqrt{3}$
Solution:

$\sin \theta = \dfrac{\text{ordinate of } P}{r} = \dfrac{y}{r}$

$\sin \dfrac{\pi}{3} = \dfrac{y}{8}$, $\dfrac{\sqrt{3}}{2} = \dfrac{y}{8}$

$y = 4\sqrt{3}$

$\cos \theta = \dfrac{\text{abscissa of } P}{r} = \dfrac{x}{r}$

$\cos \dfrac{\pi}{3} = \dfrac{x}{8}$, $\dfrac{1}{2} = \dfrac{x}{8}$

$x = 4$

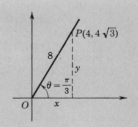

321   *PQ* is a chord subtending an angle of 120° in
      a circle whose radius is 8 in. Find the length
      of the chord *PQ*.

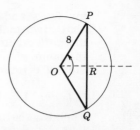

PQ = 8√3
One possible solution: If *OR* is perpendicular to *PQ*, then from
geometry we know that *PQ* is bisected and that angle *ROP* = ½
angle *QOP*.

$$\sin 60° = \frac{PR}{8}$$

PR = 4√3, *PQ* = 2(4√3) = 8√3

Another solution: Apply the formula $L = r\sqrt{2 - 2\cos\theta}$, where
L is the length of the chord subtending the central angle θ.

322   Find the radius of a circle in which a regular decagon is inscribed,
      each side of the decagon being 12 in. Study frame 323 carefully if
      you are not sure of the solution.

radius ≈ 19.4 in.

323   Let *RP* = 12 in. represent one side of the deca-
      gon inscribed in circle *O.* Construct *OQ* per-
      pendicular to *PR.* Angle *ROP* = $\frac{1}{10}$ (360°). An-
      gle *QOP* = 18°. Now find radius *r*, using sin θ =
      y/r. *Note:* The perpendicular *OQ* is necessary
      in this solution because the original definitions
      of sin θ and cos θ assumed a right angle at *Q.*
      Alternate solution: Apply the formula for *L*
      given in frame 321.

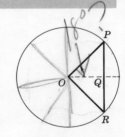

QP = 6 *Solution:* $\sin 18° = \frac{6}{r}$, $0.309 \approx \frac{6}{r}$,

$$r \approx \frac{6}{0.309} \approx 19.4$$

Alternate solution: $12 = r\sqrt{2 - 2\cos 36°}$, $r \approx 19.4$

324 How long is a chord that subtends an angle of 80° in a circle whose radius is 12 in. ? **(1)** Use the first solution of frame 323; then **(2)** check your work using the alternate solution.

---

(1) chord ≈ 15.4 in.

$$\sin 40° = \frac{PQ}{12}$$

$$PQ ≈ 7.7$$
$$PR ≈ 15.4$$

(2) $L = 12\sqrt{2 - 2\cos 80°}$

≈ 12 (1.285)

≈ 15.4

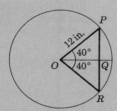
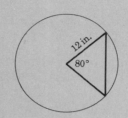

---

325 *Functions of coterminal angles:*
Given θ_1 and θ_2 as shown in the sketch. (Answer (1) and (2) using x, y, and r.)
(1) $\sin \theta_1$ = **(a)**___, $\sin \theta_2$ = **(b)**___.
(2) $\cos \theta_1$ = **(a)**___, $\cos \theta_2$ = **(b)**___.
In degrees $\theta_2 = \theta_1 +$ **(3)**___°
In radians $\theta_2 = \theta_1 +$ **(4)**___radians

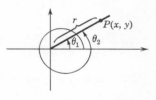

---

(1) (a) $\frac{y}{r}$, **(b)** $\frac{y}{r}$ **(2) (a)** $\frac{x}{r}$, **(b)** $\frac{x}{r}$ **(3)** 360 **(4)** 2π

---

326 By studying the definitions for $\sin \theta$ and $\cos \theta$, you see that these functions depend only on the position of the terminal side of the angle. Adding (subtracting) any number of complete revolutions to (from) θ does not change the final position of the terminal side of the angle. Hence,
In degrees $\sin \theta = \sin (\theta + 360°) = \sin (\theta + 2\cdot360°)$ = etc.
(1) In radians $\sin \theta = \sin (\theta +$ **(a)**___$) = \sin (\theta + 2\cdot$**(b)**___$)$ = etc.
(2) In degrees $\cos \theta = \cos (\theta +$ **(a)**___$) = \cos (\theta + 2\cdot$**(b)**___$)$ = etc.
(3) In radians $\cos \theta = \cos (\theta +$ **(a)**___$) = \cos (\theta + 2\cdot$**(b)**___$)$ = etc.

---

(1) (a) 2π, **(b)** 2π **(2) (a)** 360, **(b)** 360 **(3) (a)** 2π, **(b)** 2π

327 In general, if *k* is any integer, positive, zero, or negative, and θ any angle:

Degrees	Radians
sin θ = sin (θ + *k*·360°)	sin θ = sin (θ + *k*·2π)
cos θ = **(1)**	**(2)**

Write a complete statement for the last row of the table.

(1) cos θ = cos (θ + *k*·360°)   **(2)** cos θ = cos (θ + *k*·2π)

328 Given *k* = 2 and θ = 180°, **(1)** make a sketch of (θ + *k*·360°).
(2) Is 180° coterminal with (180° + 2·360°)?

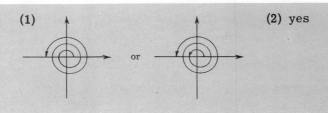

(1)   or   **(2)** yes

329 Given *k* = -1 and θ = 3π/4, **(1)** sketch $[\theta + (-1)·2\pi]$.
1. Working in radians $[3\pi/4 + (-1)·2\pi]$ = **(2)**____.
2. Working in degrees $[135° + (-1)·360°]$ = **(3)**_____.
(4) Is 3π/4 coterminal with 1 above?   **(5)** Is 135° coterminal with 2 above?

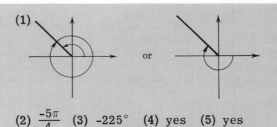

(1)   or

(2) $\frac{-5\pi}{4}$ **(3)** -225°   **(4)** yes   **(5)** yes

330 Simplify the following to a positive angle less than 360°: sin 540° = sin (1)____°, cos 1,000° = cos (2)____°, sin (-210°) = sin (3)____°, and cos (17π/8) = cos (4)____ radians.

(1) 180°   *Solution:*   Let sin 540° = sin (θ + k·360), where θ = 180° and k = 1, sin 540° = sin (180° + 360°); therefore, sin 540° = sin 180°.

(2) 280   (3) 150   (4) $\frac{\pi}{8}$

331 To find the value of sin (-θ) in terms of sin θ proceed as follows: The two angles θ and -θ are sketched on the same set of axes. A perpendicular is drawn from any point P on the terminal side of θ to the x axis and extended to the terminal side of -θ. Since θ and -θ are equal in absolute value, it can be shown 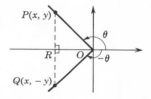 that triangles ROP and QOR are congruent. Hence, if P has coordinates (x, y) and Q has coordinates (x, -y), then sin θ = (1)____ and sin (-θ) = (2)____. (Give answers in terms of x, y, and r.)

(1) $\frac{y}{r}$ (2) $\frac{-y}{r}$

332 Perhaps a simpler and more general way of stating the idea in frame 331 is this: For any two angles θ and -θ, there is a point $Q(x, -y)$ on the terminal side of -θ which is the reflection, through the axis, of the point $P(x, y)$ on the terminal side of θ. Therefore, if sin θ = y/r, then sin (-θ) = ____.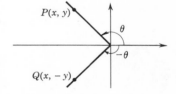

$\frac{-y}{r}$

333 Continuing from frame 332, if sin (-θ) = -y/r and sin θ = y/r, can we say that sin (-θ) = -sin θ?

yes

334 Express the following in terms of a positive angle: sin (-118°) =
(1)_____.   (2) Sketch the two angles on the same axis.

(1) -sin 118°   (2)
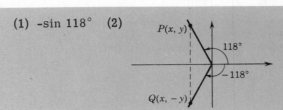

335 (1) Show -300° and 300° on the same axis. (2) Make a statement
regarding sin (-300°) with relation to sin 300°.

(1)   or
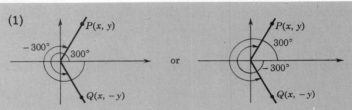

Either drawing is correct. Note that the sign of the *second* coordinate y of P is opposite that of Q (one +, the other -).
(2) sin (-300) = -sin 300°

336 (1) Make a sketch, and without tables compute (2) sin (-30°) and
(3) sin 30°.

(1)
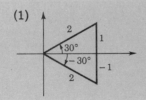

(2) sin (-30°) = $\frac{-1}{2}$

(3) sin 30° = $\frac{1}{2}$

337 (1) Is sin (-π) = -sin π?
(2) Make a sketch.
(3) What is the numerical value of sin π?

(1) yes   (2)
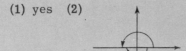
(3) sin π = 0

338 Here is a copy of the drawing we used to show that sin (-θ) = -sin θ. Let us see what can be said about cos (-θ). cos (-θ) = (1)___and cos θ = (2)___(answer in terms of x, y, and r). *Note:* The first co-ordinate x is the same for both points P and Q. (3) Can we say cos (-θ) = cos θ for this case?

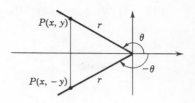

(1) $\dfrac{x}{r}$ (2) $\dfrac{x}{r}$ (3) yes

339 If we think of the point $Q(x, -y)$ on the terminal side of -θ as the reflection through the x axis of a point $P(x, y)$ on the terminal side of θ, then for any angles θ and -θ, cos θ = x/r and cos (-θ) = x/r; hence, cos (-θ) = cos θ. Do you agree that regardless of the position of the terminal side of θ, the abscissa of a point P will agree in sign as well as measure with its reflection point Q on -θ? Look at these sketches to help you decide.

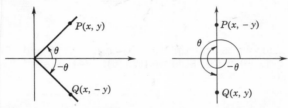

you should!

340 Prove that tan (-θ) = -tan θ (if tan θ exists).

by definition, tan (-θ) = $\dfrac{\sin (-θ)}{\cos (-θ)} = \dfrac{-\sin θ}{\cos θ} = -\tan θ$

341 (1) Without using Panel 1, find cos 30°. (2) What is cos (-30°)?

(1) $\cos 30° = \dfrac{\sqrt{3}}{2}$

(2) $\cos (-30°) = \dfrac{\sqrt{3}}{2}$

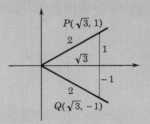

342 $7\pi/6$ radians = (1)____°. (2) Sketch this angle in standard position.

(1) 210   (2)

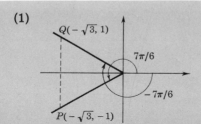

343 (1) Show by a drawing the two angles $7\pi/6$ and $-7\pi/6$. (2) Find sin $(-7\pi/6)$. (3) Find sin $(7\pi/6)$. (4) Is sin $(-7\pi/6)$ = $-$sin $(7\pi/6)$ = $\frac{1}{2}$?

(1)

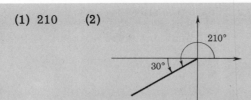

(2) $\sin \dfrac{-7\pi}{6} = \dfrac{1}{2}$

(3) $\sin \dfrac{7\pi}{6} = -\dfrac{1}{2}$

(4) yes

344 cos $(-7\pi/6)$ = (1)_____ and, cos $(7\pi/6)$ = (2)_____. Therefore, cos $(-7\pi/6)$ = (3)_____ .

(1) $\dfrac{-\sqrt{3}}{2}$ (2) $\dfrac{-\sqrt{3}}{2}$ (3) $\cos \dfrac{7\pi}{6}$

345 (1) Find tan $(7\pi/6)$. (2) Find tan $(-7\pi/6)$. (3) Is tan $(7\pi/6)$ = tan $(-7\pi/6)$? (4) If your answer is no, write a correct statement regarding tan $(7\pi/6)$ and tan $(-7\pi/6)$.

(1) tan $\dfrac{7\pi}{6} = \dfrac{-1}{-\sqrt{3}} = \dfrac{1}{\sqrt{3}}$ (2) tan $\dfrac{-7\pi}{6} = \dfrac{1}{-\sqrt{3}} = \dfrac{-1}{\sqrt{3}}$

(3) no   (4) tan $\dfrac{7\pi}{6}$ = -tan $\dfrac{-7\pi}{6}$

Comment

As an aid to remembering the signs in these statements:
   sin $(-\theta)$ = -sin θ
   cos $(-\theta)$ = cos θ
we mention that they are sometimes called the *odd* and *even* functions, respectively. For a discussion of odd and even functions see "Functional Trigonometry," Hillman and Alexanderson, – Allyn and Bacon, Boston, 1961.

346 Applying what we have just said, if
   sin 45° = $\dfrac{1}{\sqrt{2}}$, then sin $(-45°)$ = (1)_____
   cos 45° = $\dfrac{1}{\sqrt{2}}$, then cos $(-45°)$ = (2)_____
   sin 120° = $\dfrac{\sqrt{3}}{2}$, then sin $(-120°)$ = (3)_____
   cos 120° = $\dfrac{-1}{2}$, then cos $(-120°)$ = (4)_____
Check the numerical values without using a table such as Panel 1.

(1) $\dfrac{-1}{\sqrt{2}}$ (2) $\dfrac{1}{\sqrt{2}}$ (3) $\dfrac{-\sqrt{3}}{2}$ (4) $-\frac{1}{2}$

347 We also know that tan $(-\theta)$ = -tan θ. Therefore, if tan 45° = 1, then tan $(-45°)$ = (1)___. If tan 120° = $-\sqrt{3}/1$, then tan $(-120°)$ = (2)_____.

(1) -1   (2) $\dfrac{\sqrt{3}}{1}$

348 $\sin \dfrac{\pi}{2} =$ (1)___ $\sin \dfrac{-\pi}{2} =$ (2)___

   $\cos \dfrac{\pi}{2} =$ (3)___ $\cos \dfrac{-\pi}{2} =$ (4)___

---

(1) 1   **(2)** -1   **(3)** 0   **(4)** 0

---

349 We have stated that the trigonometric functions sine and cosine of all angles having the same terminal side (all coterminal angles) could be stated thus: $\sin \theta = \sin (\theta + k \cdot 360°)$ and $\cos \theta = \cos (\theta + k \cdot 360°)$ where k is an integer and θ an angle in degrees.
(1) Make a sketch for the case where $\theta = 240°$ and $k = 2$.
   $\sin 240° = \sin (240° + 2 \cdot 360°) =$ (2)_____
   $\cos 240° = \cos (240° + 2 \cdot 360°) =$ (3)_____

(1)

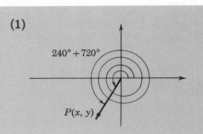

240° + 720°

$P(x, y)$

(2) $\sin 960° = \dfrac{-\sqrt{3}}{2}$

(3) $\cos 960° = \dfrac{-1}{2}$

▽**350** Make a sketch of the angle $(\theta + k \cdot 2\pi)$ where $\theta = \pi/3$ and $k = -1$.

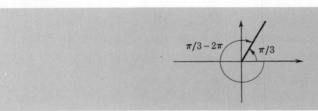

$\pi/3 - 2\pi$ $\pi/3$

351 In frame 350 the sketch should have indicated that $\sin (\pi/3) = \sin (-5\pi/3)$, and $\cos (\pi/3) = \cos (-5\pi/3)$, since $[\pi/3 + (-1)(2\pi)] = -5\pi/3$. Can you express any angle θ in terms of a *nonnegative, coterminal angle* α, less than 360°, in the form $\theta = (\alpha + k \cdot 360°)$, k an integer? yes or no

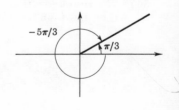

$-5\pi/3$ $\pi/3$

---

answer may be "yes" or "no" depending on student. (An explanation will be given in frames 352 and 353.)

352 Let k = an integer and α be an angle, $0° \le \alpha < 360°$ (read "α is an angle greater than or equal to $0°$ and less than $360°$"), coterminal with a given angle θ, then $\theta = (\alpha + k \cdot 360°)$.
Example: $\theta = 370°$, find α. Let $k = 1$, then $370° = (\alpha + 1 \cdot 360°)$. Therefore, $10° = \alpha$.
Given $\theta = 540°$, (1) find α. (2) Make a sketch.

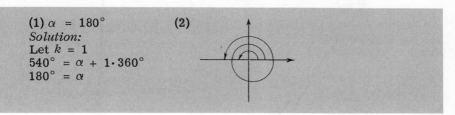

(1) $\alpha = 180°$ (2)
Solution:
Let $k = 1$
$540° = \alpha + 1 \cdot 360°$
$180° = \alpha$

353 $\theta = -350°$, find α such that $0° \le \alpha < 360°$ and α is coterminal with θ. (1) Make a sketch. Use the formula $\theta = (\alpha + k \cdot 360°)$, letting $k = -1$, and (2) solve for α.

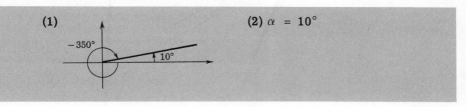

(1)   (2) $\alpha = 10°$

354 If θ is given in radians, then the formula $\theta = (\alpha + k \cdot 360°)$ becomes $\theta = (\alpha + k \cdot 2\pi)$. Find the positive angle α, in radians less than 2π, which is coterminal with θ if $\theta = 5\pi/2$.

$\alpha = \dfrac{\pi}{2}$ *Solution:* $\dfrac{5\pi}{2} = \alpha + 1 \cdot 2\pi$, $\alpha = \dfrac{5\pi}{2} - \dfrac{4\pi}{2} = \dfrac{\pi}{2}$

355 Suppose $\theta = \pi/6$. (1) What is α in the statement $\theta = (\alpha + k \cdot 2\pi)$? (2) What value has k? (3) Make a sketch.

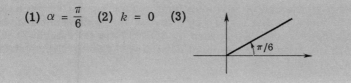

(1) $\alpha = \dfrac{\pi}{6}$ (2) $k = 0$ (3)

356 $\theta = 1,000°$, find α as in frame 355. *Suggestion:* In order to find values for k and α in the statement $\theta = (\alpha + k \cdot 360°)$, we divide $1,000°$ by $360°$. The result is 2 with a remainder of $280°$. This tells us that $1,000° = ($_____$ + 2 \cdot 360°)$.

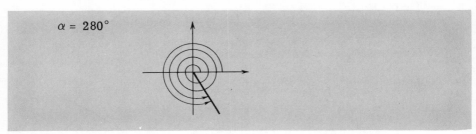

$\alpha = 280°$

357 $\theta = 10\pi/3$, find α as in frames 355 and 356. *Suggestion:* Since $(10\pi/3) - 2\pi = 4\pi/3$, we let $k = 1$ in the formula $\theta = (\alpha + k \cdot 2\pi)$.

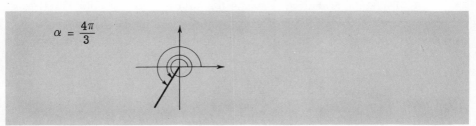

$\alpha = \dfrac{4\pi}{3}$

358 $\theta = -5\pi/3$, find α as in frames 355 to 357. *Suggestion:* Try $k = -1$.

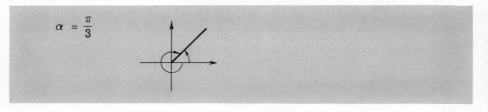

$\alpha = \dfrac{\pi}{3}$

359 Since by definition α is coterminal with θ in the statement $\theta = (\alpha + k \cdot 2\pi)$ or $\theta = (\alpha + k \cdot 360°)$, it follows that $\sin \theta = \sin \alpha$, $\cos \theta = \cos \alpha$, and $\tan \theta = \tan \alpha$. Therefore, the functions of an angle of any size can be given as functions of a positive angle less than $360°$ (or $0°$). Let $\theta = 1,750°$, then k is the quotient and α is the remainder when θ is divided by $360°$. Find (1) k and (2) α. (3) Write the answer in the form $\theta = (\alpha + k \cdot 360°)$. Hence, $1,750° = ($_____$ + $___$\cdot 360°)$

(1) $k = 4$ (2) $\alpha = 310°$ (3) $1,750° = (310° + 4 \cdot 360°)$

360 To indicate that α is between 0 and 2π we use the expression $0 < \alpha < 2\pi$. To indicate that α is in the interval from 0 to 2π, including 0, a bar is placed below the "less than" sign thus: $0 \leq \alpha < 2\pi$. How would you indicate that α is in the interval from 0 to 2π, including both 0 and 2π.

$0 \leq \alpha \leq 2\pi$

361 $a < b$ is read "a is less than b."
$a \leq b$ is read "a is less than or equal to b."
$a > b$ is read "a is greater than b."
$a \geq b$ is read (1) _____
$2 < x \leq 5$ is read (2) _____

(1) a is greater than or equal to b.
(2) 2 is less than x and x is less than or equal to 5. (x lies in the interval from 2 to 5, including 5.)

362 Find the *positive* angle α, $0° \leq \alpha < 360°$, coterminal with θ when $\theta = -1{,}750°$.
Solution: $-1{,}750° \div 360$, $k = -4$, $\alpha =$ (1) _____
$\qquad\qquad -1{,}750° \div 360$, $k = -5$, $\alpha =$ (2) _____
Therefore, $-1{,}750° = ($ (3) _____ $+$ (4) _____ $\cdot 360°)$.
(5) Make a sketch showing θ and α.

(1) $-310°$ (2) $50°$ (3) $50°$ (4) (-5)

(5)

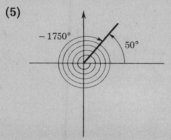

363 You should be able to change an angle θ of any size to the form $\theta = (\alpha + k \cdot 2\pi)$ or $\theta = (\alpha + k \cdot 360°)$, k an integer, $0° \leq \alpha < 360°$ or 2π. Reduce the following to the required form: (1) $\theta = 630°$, (2) $\theta = -98°$, (3) $\theta = -750°$, and (4) $\theta = 13\pi$.

(1) $630° = (270° + 1 \cdot 360°)$ (2) $-98° = [262° + (-1) \cdot 360°]$
(3) $-750° = [330° + (-3) \cdot 360°]$ (4) $13\pi = (\pi + 6 \cdot 2\pi)$

Comment

After we have found the angle α between 0 and 360° which has the same trigonometric functions as θ, we observe further that we can always find a nonnegative acute angle R between the *terminal side of the angle α and the x axis*. Study the sketches below. Notice the location of R in each quadrant and how we find its numerical value.

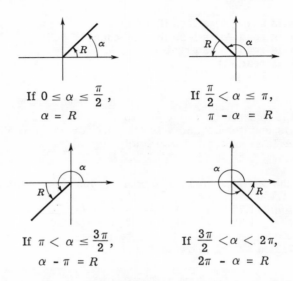

If $0 \leq \alpha \leq \dfrac{\pi}{2}$,

$\alpha = R$

If $\dfrac{\pi}{2} < \alpha \leq \pi$,

$\pi - \alpha = R$

If $\pi < \alpha \leq \dfrac{3\pi}{2}$,

$\alpha - \pi = R$

If $\dfrac{3\pi}{2} < \alpha < 2\pi$,

$2\pi - \alpha = R$

364 The sketches in the comment showed how to reduce an angle of any size to an angle between 0 and $\pi/2$ inclusive, which we labeled R. In the sketch in this frame, θ is an angle terminating in quadrant III. Indicate by a sketch of your own which angle is α and which is R in the following statements: $\theta = (\alpha + k \cdot 2\pi)$, $R = \alpha - \pi$.

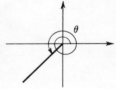

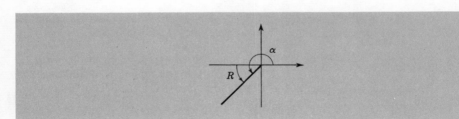

365 The angle -θ is shown in the sketch. Locate on a drawing of your own α and R as before. Remember that α and R are positive angles; 0 < α < 2π and 0 < R < π/2.

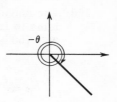

366 Indicate on a set of similar sketches the angle R such that R is a nonnegative *acute* angle.

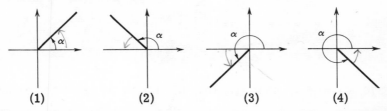

(1)   (2)   (3)   (4)

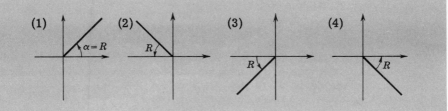

367 State which formula below will be proper for finding R in the following statements: (1) α is a second-quadrant angle. (2) α is a third-quadrant angle. (3) α is a fourth-quadrant angle.

    a. $\begin{cases} R = 360 - α \\ R = 2π - α \end{cases}$ *b.* $\begin{cases} R = α - 180 \\ R = α - π \end{cases}$ *c.* $\begin{cases} R = 180 - α \\ R = π - α \end{cases}$

(1) *c*   (2) *b*   (3) *a*

368   The nonnegative acute angle R which we found in each of the problems in frame 367 is sometimes called the *reference angle*. Let $\theta = 750°$, (1) make a sketch, (2) compute α, then (3) find R.

(1)

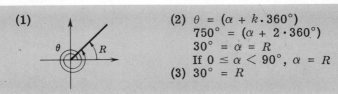

(2) $\theta = (\alpha + k \cdot 360°)$
   $750° = (\alpha + 2 \cdot 360°)$
   $30° = \alpha = R$
   If $0 \leq \alpha < 90°$, $\alpha = R$
(3) $30° = R$

▽369   Given $\theta = 480°$, (1) find R.   (2) Make a sketch showing α and R.

(1) $R = 60°$ *Solution:* $480° = (\alpha + 1 \cdot 360°)$, $120° = \alpha$,
   $R = 180° - \alpha = 60°$

(2)

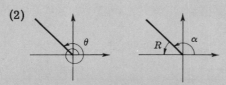

▽370   Given $\theta = -135°$, (1) find R.   (2) Make a sketch showing α and R.

(1) $R = 45°$ *Solution:* $-135° = [\alpha + (-1) \cdot 360°]$, $225° = \alpha$,
   $R = 225° - 180° = 45°$

(2)

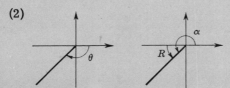

▽371   Given $\theta = 10\pi/9$, (1) make a sketch identifying α and R.   (2) Report the measure of R in radians.

(1)

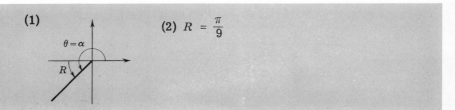

(2) $R = \dfrac{\pi}{9}$

372   We are ready now to show that in any quadrant:

$$|\sin \theta| = |\sin R|, \qquad |\cos \theta| = |\cos R| \qquad |\tan \theta| = |\tan R|$$

where θ is any angle and R is the reference angle as described previously. First, how do you read the signs $|\ \ |$?

"absolute value" or "numerical value without regard to sign"

373   Let θ be an angle terminating in quadrant II with reference angle R. Place angle R in standard position. If $P(-x, y)$ is a point on the terminal side of θ, then $Q(x, y)$ is a point on the terminal side of R. In either case, $r = \sqrt{x^2 + y^2}$; hence,

$$\sin \theta = \frac{y}{r} \quad \sin R = \frac{y}{r}$$

$$\cos \theta = \frac{-x}{r} \quad \cos R = \frac{x}{r}$$

$$\tan \theta = \frac{y}{-x} \quad \tan R = \frac{y}{x}$$

Thus, for an angle terminating in quadrant II, we can say $|\sin \theta| = |\sin R|$, $|\cos \theta| = |(1)\underline{\hspace{1cm}}|$, and $|\tan \theta| = |(2)\underline{\hspace{1cm}}|$.

(1) $\cos R$ **(2)** $\tan R$

374   Let $\theta = 5\pi/9$, find the reference angle R and fill in the blanks.

$$\sin \frac{5\pi}{9} = \sin (1) \underline{\hspace{2cm}}$$

$$\cos \frac{5\pi}{9} = \cos (2) \underline{\hspace{2cm}}$$

$$\tan \frac{5\pi}{9} = \tan (3) \underline{\hspace{2cm}}$$

(1) $\dfrac{4\pi}{9}$ **(2)** $\dfrac{4\pi}{9}$ **(3)** $\dfrac{4\pi}{9}$

375   If θ is an angle terminating in quadrant III, we can show that the sine, cosine, and tangent of θ equal, respectively, sine, cosine,

continued →

and tangent of R *except for the signs.*   (1) Sketch θ and show the reference angle R.   (2) Then make a sketch placing R in standard position.

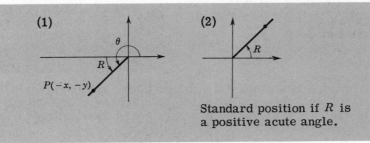

Standard position if R is a positive acute angle.

376   If $P(-x, -y)$ is a point on the terminal side of θ, what are the co-ordinates of the corresponding point Q when R of the problem in frame 375 is in standard position?

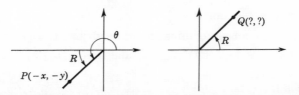

$Q(x, y)$

377   Complete these statements:

(1) $\sin \theta = \dfrac{-y}{r}$, $\sin R =$ _____

(2) $\cos \theta =$ (a)___, $\cos R =$ (b)___

(3) $\tan \theta =$ (a)___, $\tan R =$ (b)___

(Give each answer in terms of x, y, and r.)

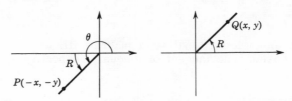

(1) $\dfrac{y}{r}$ (2) (a) $\dfrac{-x}{r}$, (b) $\dfrac{x}{r}$ (3) (a) $\dfrac{y}{x}$, (b) $\dfrac{y}{x}$

378 (1) Find cos $(13\pi/9)$.   (2) Find tan $(13\pi/9)$.

(1) $\cos \dfrac{13\pi}{9} = -0.174$ (2) $\tan \dfrac{13\pi}{9} = 5.671$

379 Complete the following: $\sin (7\pi/12) = $ (1)_____, $\cos (7\pi/12) = $ (2)_____, and $\tan (7\pi/12) = $ (3)_____.

(1) 0.966   (2) -0.259   (3) -3.732

380 Complete the following: $\sin (22\pi/3) = $ (1)_____, $\cos (22\pi/3) = $ (2)_____, and $\tan (22\pi/3) = $ (3)_____.

(1) $-0.866 = \dfrac{-\sqrt{3}}{2}$ (2) $-0.500 = -\tfrac{1}{2}$ (3) $1.732 = \sqrt{3}$

381 If an angle θ terminates in quadrant IV, we find by reasoning as before that $|\sin \theta| = |\sin R|$, etc. If $\theta = 5\pi/3$, the reference angle is (1)____.   (2) Which of the functions of θ will be negative?

(1) $\dfrac{\pi}{3}$ (2) sine and tangent

▽382 If $\sin \theta$ is positive and $\cos \theta$ is negative, then θ is an angle terminating in which quadrant?

quadrant II

▽383 If $\tan \theta$ is positive and $\sin \theta$ is positive, then θ is an angle terminating in quadrant (1)__. If $\tan \theta$ is positive and $\sin \theta$ is negative, then θ is an angle terminating in quadrant (2)__.

(1) I   (2) III

384 If $\sin \theta = -\tfrac{1}{2}$ and $\cos \theta = \sqrt{3}/2$, then θ terminates in quadrant (1)___.   (2) Find the measure of θ in degrees and radians, $0 \le \theta \le 360°$. Do not refer to Panel 1; this is one of the special angles.

(1) IV   (2) $\theta = 330° = \dfrac{11\pi}{6}$

385   (1) If sin θ = $1/\sqrt{2}$ and tan θ = -1, then θ terminates in which quadrant?   (2) Find, without referring to Panel 1, the angle θ less than 2π which satisfies the condition stated above.

(1) quadrant II   (2) θ = 135° = $\dfrac{3\pi}{4}$

386   By this time you should be able to report the numerical values of the three trigonometric functions of an angle of any size and attach the proper sign, positive or negative. There are several angles, in fact, whose functions you should be able to give without consulting a table. The quadrantal angles are examples.   (1) List, in degrees, the quadrantal angles from 0 to 360°.   (2) Give the sine of each angle in your list.

(1) 0°, 90°, 180°, 270°   (2) 0, 1, 0, -1

387   Other special angles whose functions you can compute by applications of geometry are _____.
(Give at least six, measured in degrees and in radians.)

30°, 45°, 60°, 120°, 135°, 150°, etc.
$\dfrac{\pi}{6}, \dfrac{\pi}{4}, \dfrac{\pi}{3}, \dfrac{2\pi}{3}, \dfrac{3\pi}{4}, \dfrac{5\pi}{6},$ etc.
Other examples are: 36°, 144°, 216°, 324°. $\dfrac{\pi}{5}, \dfrac{4\pi}{5}, \dfrac{6\pi}{5}, \dfrac{9\pi}{5}$

388   (1) If $\pi < \theta < 3\pi/2$, then θ terminates in which quadrant?   (2) Is sin $\theta > 0$? That is, is sin θ positive?   (3) Is cos $\theta > 0$?   (4) Is tan $\theta > 0$?   Notice that π and $3\pi/2$ are not included in the answer to frame 387.

(1) III   (2) no   (3) no   (4) yes

389   If $3\pi/2 < \theta < 2\pi$, then θ is an angle terminating in quadrant (1)____.
sin θ (2)__0 (use <, >, or =), cos θ (3)__0, and tan θ (4)__0.

(1) IV   (2) <   (3) >   (4) <

390 If $0 < \theta < \pi/2$, then θ is an angle terminating in quadrant **(1)**___.
(2) Is it true that $\sin \theta > 0$, $\cos \theta > 0$, and $\tan \theta > 0$? If your
answer is no, list the statement for which it is not true.

(1) I   **(2)** yes

391 Using the definition "sin θ equals
ordinate of the point of intersection
of the terminal side of θ with the
unit circle," you can see from the
drawing the changes in $\sin \theta$ as θ
increases from 0 to $\pi/2$. $\sin 0° =$
0, $\sin AOA' = A'A$,
   $\sin BOB' =$ **(1)**_____
   $\sin COC' =$ **(2)**_____
   $\sin \dfrac{\pi}{2}$ = **(3)**_____

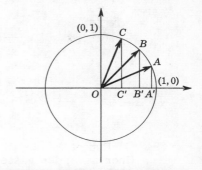

(1) $B'B$ **(2)** $C'C$ **(3)** 1

392 There is an increase from 0 to 1
in $\sin \theta$ as θ increases from 0
to $\pi/2$. The sketch shows that
$\sin \theta$ decreases from **(1)**___to
(2)___as θ increases from $\pi/2$
to π. Give numerical answers.

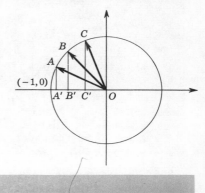

(1) 1   **(2)** 0

393 In a similar manner show three angles terminating in quadrant III
and indicate the segments representing $\sin \theta$. $\sin \theta$ **(1)**_____

continued →

(increases, decreases) from 0 to (2)____(-1, 1) as θ increases from π to $3\pi/2$.

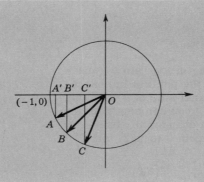

(1) decreases
(2) -1

394 (1) Repeat the sketch for the fourth quadrant. sin θ (2)_____
(increases, decreases) from (3)___ to (4)___as θ increases from $3\pi/2$ to 2π.

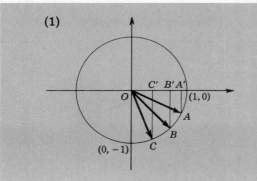

(1)

(2) increases

(3) -1

(4) 0

395 To see changes in cos θ as θ is increased from 0 to 2π, you must
watch the abscissa of the point of
intersection of the terminal side of
θ with the unit circle.

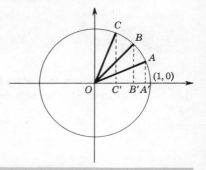

cos 0   = (1) _____
cos AOA' = (2) _____
cos BOB' = (3) _____
cos COC' = (4) _____
cos $\dfrac{\pi}{2}$ = (5) _____

(1) 1   (2) OA' (3) OB' (4) OC' (5) 0

396 Give numerical answers to the following: $\cos (\pi/2) = (1)\underline{\quad}$, $\cos (3\pi/4) = (2)\underline{\quad\quad}$, and $\cos \pi = (3)\underline{\quad}$.   (4) The value of the cosine changes in what way as the angle increases from $\pi/2$ to π?

---

(1) 0   **(2)** $\frac{-1}{\sqrt{2}}$ **(3)** -1

(4) cosine decreases from 0 to -1 as the angle increases from $\pi/2$ to π.

---

397 (1) Make a sketch of three angles terminating in quadrant III and label the segment on the x axis which is equivalent to the cosine of each angle. (2) How does the numerical value of the cosine change as the angle increases from π to $3\pi/2$?

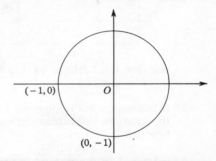

(1)

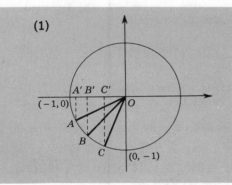

(2) cosine increases from -1 to 0.

---

398 Consider the quadrantal angles $3\pi/2$ and 2π and three angles terminating in quadrant IV:

$\cos \dfrac{3\pi}{2}$ = (1)_____

$\cos COC'$ = (2)_____

$\cos BOB'$ = (3)_____

$\cos AOA'$ = (4)_____

$\cos 2\pi$ = (5)_____

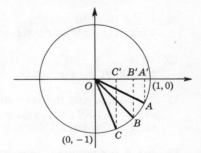

---

(1) 0   **(2)** OC' **(3)** OB' **(4)** OA' **(5)** 1

SELF-TEST 2

1   Tell in what quadrant the terminal side of θ lies if (a) cos θ is negative and tan θ is positive, (b) sin θ is positive and cos θ is negative, and (c) tan θ is negative and sin θ is negative.

2   (a) Fill in the following table:

θ	$\pi/4$	$\pi/2$	$3\pi/4$	π	$5\pi/4$	$3\pi/2$	$7\pi/4$	2π
cos θ								

(b) Use the table to sketch the graph of y = cos θ over the interval $0 \le \theta \le 2\pi$.

3   (a) What is the maximum value of sin θ if θ represents any angle?
(b) What is the minimum value?   (c) What is the period of the sine function?

4   (a) What is the period for the function y = tan θ?   (b) Discuss maximum and minimum values for this function.

5   Given triangle ABC having a = 14, b = 9, and angle γ = $\pi/3$, find side c.

6   Find the smallest angle of a triangle whose sides measure 7, 10, and 15 in., respectively. Use Panel 1.

7   Given triangle ABC having α = $\pi/4$, c = 9, and β = $\pi/6$, find (a) γ and (b) side a.

8   Given the triangle ABC with α = 35°, β = 48°, and a = 14, find (a) side b, and (b) the area of the triangle.

9   If the measurements α = 30°, a = 8, and b = 12 are given, how many triangles are determined?

10 Given α = 100°, a = 16, and b = 10, sketch the triangle(s) which may have these measurements.

11 Two sides and the included angle of a parallelogram are 12 cm, 20 cm, and 100°, respectively. (a) Find the length of the longer diagonal of the parallelogram. (b) Find the area of the parallelogram.

12 (a) A fundamental identity of trigonometry states that for any angle θ, $\sin^2 \theta + \cos^2 \theta$ = _____. (b) Use the identity of part a to find cos θ if sin θ = $-\frac{5}{7}$ and $3\pi/2 < \theta < 2\pi$.

13 Find the indicated products: (a) $(6 - \sqrt{3})(6 + \sqrt{3})$, (b) $(\sin x + \cos x)^2$, (c) $3b(1 - \sin x)^2$, and (d) $(\sqrt{1 - \sin \alpha})(\sqrt{1 + \sin \alpha})$.

14 Factor (a) $1 - \sin^2 \theta$, (b) $\sin x \cos^2 x - \sin^3 x$, and (c) $r \cos \theta + ri \sin \theta$.

15 Simplify (a) $\dfrac{r \cos \theta + r \sin \theta}{\cos^2 \theta + 2 \sin \theta \cos \theta + \sin^2 \theta}$ and (b) $\dfrac{1}{\sqrt{a} - \sqrt{b}}$

16 Add $\dfrac{\sin \theta}{1 - \sin^2 \theta} + \dfrac{1}{1 + \sin \theta}$.

17 Use the formula for the cosine of the difference of two angles to find $\cos 15°$. (Do not consult Panel 1 or 8.)

18 For any angle α prove that $\sin (\alpha - \pi/2) = -\cos \alpha$.

19 Given $\cos \alpha = -\frac{4}{5}$, α terminates in quadrant II, and $\sin \beta = \frac{12}{13}$, β terminates in quadrant I, find $\cos (\alpha - \beta)$.

20 Derive a formula for $\sin 2\alpha$.

21 If $\sin \theta = \frac{3}{5}$ and θ is a first-quadrant angle, find (a) $\sin 2\theta$, (b) $\cos 2\theta$, and (c) $\tan 2\theta$.

22 If $\sin \theta = \frac{3}{5}$ and θ is a first-quadrant angle, find (a) $\sin (\theta/2)$, (b) $\cos (\theta/2)$, and (c) $\tan (\theta/2)$.

23 Using $\sin (7\pi/6)$ and $\cos (7\pi/6)$, find (a) $\sin (7\pi/12)$ and (b) $\cos (7\pi/12)$. (Your answers may be left in simplified radical form.)

24 Given $\theta = 3\pi/4$, find

    (a) $\sin \theta$ = _____   (d) $\cot \theta$ = _____

    (b) $\cos \theta$ = _____   (e) $\sec \theta$ = _____

    (c) ~~cot~~ $\tan \theta$ = _____   (f) $\csc \theta$ = _____

GRAPHS OF THE TRIGONOMETRIC FUNCTIONS

Comment

To graph the sine function, we proceed as is customary in graphing by making a table of pairs $(\theta, \sin\theta)$ for selected values of θ. Then we locate the corresponding points on a rectangular coordinate system. On the horizontal axis we represent the numbers corresponding to $\sin\theta$. The set of axes below indicate the values of θ between 0 and $\pi/2$ which have been selected.

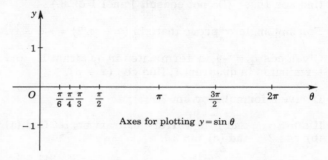

Axes for plotting $y = \sin\theta$

399 If $\theta = 0$, $\sin\theta =$ **(1)** _____

$\theta = \dfrac{\pi}{6}$, $\sin\theta =$ **(2)** _____

$\theta = \dfrac{\pi}{4}$, $\sin\theta =$ **(3)** _____

Answer without the aid of a table. Express the answer in radical form.

$\theta = \dfrac{\pi}{3}$, $\sin\theta =$ **(4)** _____

$\theta = \dfrac{\pi}{2}$, $\sin\theta =$ **(5)** _____

(1) 0   **(2)** $\frac{1}{2}$ **(3)** $\frac{1}{\sqrt{2}}$ **(4)** $\frac{\sqrt{3}}{2}$ **(5)** 1

400 In the table below express each value of sin θ as a decimal correct to two decimal places.

θ	0	$\pi/6$	$\pi/4$	$\pi/3$	$\pi/2$
$\sin \theta$	0	$1/2$	$1/\sqrt{2}$	$\sqrt{3}/2$	1
$\sin \theta$					

$$\sqrt{2} = 1.414 \qquad \sqrt{3} = 1.732$$

θ	0	$\pi/6$	$\pi/4$	$\pi/3$	$\pi/2$
$\sin \theta$	0	$1/2$	$1/\sqrt{2}$	$\sqrt{3}/2$	1
$\sin \theta$	0	0.5	0.71	0.87	1

401 On axes labeled as shown here, plot the points for the graph of $y = \sin \theta$ as given in frame 400. *Note:* Since $\pi \approx 3.14$, a suitable scale for the horizontal axis is $\pi = 3$ units (i.e., $\pi/3 = 1$ unit). Use this scale on all graphs unless otherwise directed.

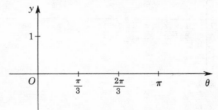

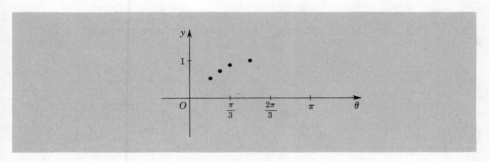

402 Remembering that the sine, cosine, and tangent of an angle terminating in any quadrant can be obtained from its reference angle R, $0 \le R \le \pi/2$, by attaching the proper sign, complete the following table.

continued →

	Quadrant I					Quadrant II			
θ	0	$\pi/6$	$\pi/4$	$\pi/3$	$\pi/2$	$2\pi/3$	$3\pi/4$	$5\pi/6$	π
$\sin\theta$									
θ	π	$7\pi/6$	$5\pi/4$	$4\pi/3$	$3\pi/2$	$5\pi/3$	$7\pi/4$	$11\pi/6$	2π
$\sin\theta$									
	Quadrant III					Quadrant IV			

see Panel 2 for the answer

403   Refer to frame 402. Plot all the points and draw a smooth line
     through them on a coordinate system similar to the one shown here.
     Leave space so that the graph may be extended both to the left and
     right.

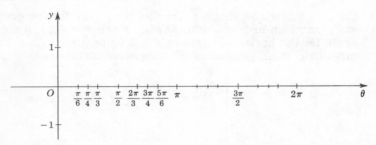

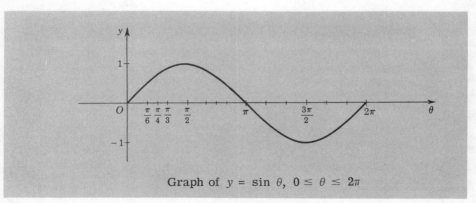

Graph of $y = \sin\theta$, $0 \le \theta \le 2\pi$

404 Using the fact that $\sin \theta = \sin (\theta + k \cdot 2\pi)$ where θ is any angle and k is an integer, describe the graph of $y = \sin \theta$ for θ in the interval $2\pi \leq \theta \leq 4\pi$.

this graph has the same "pattern" as the graph for the interval $0 \leq \theta \leq 2\pi$. See Panel 3.

405 Since the values of $\sin \theta$ are repeated in succession after the interval $0 \leq \theta < 2\pi$, we say that the sine function is *periodic* and that the period is 2π. We noted that the graph of $y = \sin \theta$ from 2π to 4π is an exact copy of the graph from 0 to 2π. Can we make a similar statement of the interval from -2π to 0?

yes

406 It is important that you have a mental picture of the graph of $y = \sin \pi$. In the interval $0 \leq \theta \leq 2\pi$, what is **(1)** the largest value of $\sin \theta$? **(2)** The smallest?

(1) 1 **(2)** –1

407 If $\sin \theta = 1$, then $\theta = $ **(1)**____. If $\sin \theta = -1$, then $\theta = $ **(2)**____.

(1) $\frac{\pi}{2}$ **(2)** $\frac{3\pi}{2}$

408 In the interval $-2\pi \leq \theta < 4\pi$ list all the values of θ for which **(1)** $\sin \theta = 1$ and **(2)** $\sin \theta = -1$.

(1) $\frac{-3\pi}{2}$, $\frac{\pi}{2}$, $\frac{5\pi}{2}$ **(2)** $\frac{-\pi}{2}$, $\frac{3\pi}{2}$, $\frac{7\pi}{2}$

409 The graph of $y = \sin \theta$ is a continuous line. We may indicate the range of values of $\sin \theta$ in either of two ways:
(1)___ $\leq \sin \theta \leq$___ or **(2)** $|\sin \theta| \leq$___. (Copy **(1)** and **(2)** completely as you answer.)

(1) $-1 \leq \sin \theta \leq 1$ **(2)** $|\sin \theta| \leq 1$

410 In the interval $0 \leq \theta < 2\pi$, if $\sin \theta = 0$, then $\theta =$ **(1)**___ or $\theta =$ **(2)**___.

(1) 0   **(2)** π

411 In the interval $0 \leq \theta < 4\pi$, if $\sin \theta = 0$, then $\theta =$ **(1)**___, **(2)**___, **(3)**___, **(4)**___.

(1) 0   **(2)** π **(3)** 2π **(4)** 3π

412 Complete the table below.

θ	$0 + 2\pi$	$\pi/6 + 2\pi$	$\pi/3 + 2\pi$	$\pi/2 + 2\pi$	$2\pi/3 + 2\pi$
$\sin \theta$					

θ	$5\pi/6 + 2\pi$	$\pi + 2\pi$	$7\pi/6 + 2\pi$	$4\pi/3 + 2\pi$
$\sin \theta$				

θ	$3\pi/2 + 2\pi$	$5\pi/3 + 2\pi$	$11\pi/6 + 2\pi$	$2\pi + 2\pi$
$\sin \theta$				

θ	$0 + 2\pi$	$\pi/6 + 2\pi$	$\pi/3 + 2\pi$	$\pi/2 + 2\pi$	$2\pi/3 + 2\pi$
$\sin \theta$	0	1/2	$\sqrt{3}/2$	1	$\sqrt{3}/2$

θ	$5\pi/6 + 2\pi$	$\pi + 2\pi$	$7\pi/6 + 2\pi$	$4\pi/3 + 2\pi$
$\sin \theta$	1/2	0	-1/2	$-\sqrt{3}/2$

θ	$3\pi/2 + 2\pi$	$5\pi/3 + 2\pi$	$11\pi/6 + 2\pi$	$2\pi + 2\pi$
$\sin \theta$	-1	$-\sqrt{3}/2$	-1/2	0

or

continued →

θ	$0 + 2\pi$	$\pi/6 + 2\pi$	$\pi/3 + 2\pi$	$\pi/2 + 2\pi$	$2\pi/3 + 2\pi$
$\sin\theta$	0	0.50	0.87	1	0.50

θ	$5\pi/6 + 2\pi$	$\pi + 2\pi$	$7\pi/6 + 2$	$4\pi/3 + 2\pi$
$\sin\theta$	0.50	0	-0.50	-0.87

θ	$3\pi/2 + 2\pi$	$5\pi/3 + 2\pi$	$11\pi/6 + 2\pi$	$2\pi + 2\pi$
$\sin\theta$	-1	-0.87	-0.50	0

413 On a set of axes labeled as shown below, plot points at intervals of $\pi/6$ radians. Then sketch the graph of $y = \sin\theta$ over the interval $0 \le \theta \le 4\pi$.

Graph of $y = \sin\theta$, $0 \le \theta \le 4\pi$

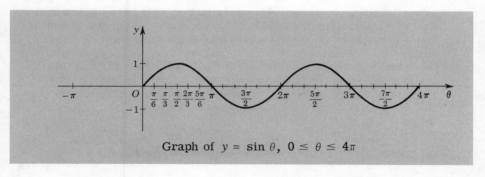

Graph of $y = \sin\theta$, $0 \le \theta \le 4\pi$

414 The graph of $y = \sin\theta$ for $-2\pi \le \theta \le 0$ is a left-hand extension of the graph you have been making. Remember that $\sin\theta = \sin(\alpha + k\cdot2\pi)$; this time $k = -1$. Extend your graph to show $y = \sin\theta$ for $-2\pi \le \theta < 0$. Here is a partial table to guide you.

continued →

θ	$0 - 2\pi$	$\pi/6 - 2\pi$	$\pi/3 - 2\pi$	$\pi/2 - 2\pi$
$\sin \theta$	0	1/2	3/2	1

θ	$2\pi/3 - 2\pi$	. . .	$11\pi/6 - 2\pi$	$2\pi - 2\pi$
$\sin \theta$	3/2	. . .	-1/2	0

see Panel 3 for the answer.

▽415   The graph of $y = \sin \theta$ indicates that (1) $\sin \theta$ is positive if θ is an angle of quadrant (a)___ or (b)___.   (2) $\sin \theta$ is negative if θ terminates in quadrant (a)___ or (b)___.   In the interval from 0 to 2π: (3) $\sin \theta$ increases from 0 to 1 as θ increases from (a)___ to (b)___. (4) $\sin \theta$ decreases from 1 to -1 as θ increases from (a)___ to (b)___;   (5) $\sin \theta$ increases from -1 to 0 as θ increases from (a)___ to (b)___.

(1) (a) I, (b) II   (2) (a) III, (b) IV   (3) (a) 0, (b) $\frac{\pi}{2}$

(4) (a) $\frac{\pi}{2}$, (b) $\frac{3\pi}{2}$ (5) (a) $\frac{3\pi}{2}$, (b) 2π

416   To sketch the graph of $y = \sin \theta$, we chose multiples of π as points along the horizontal axis. We could just as well have chosen decimal approximations for θ (0.1, 0.12, etc.) and obtained a value for $\sin \theta$ for each of the approximations from a table such as Panel 1. Hence, we say that θ may be any real number, i.e., the *domain* of the function $y = \sin \theta$ is the set of *real numbers*.   (1) Corresponding to these numbers for θ are the real-number values of $\sin \theta$ ranging from (a)___ to (b)___ inclusive.   (2) Therefore, we say that the *range* of $y = \sin \theta$ is the set of *real numbers* (a)___ $\leq y \leq$ (b)___.

(1) (a) -1, (b) 1   (2) (a) -1, (b) 1

417   The graph of $y = \cos \theta$ is constructed in a manner similar to that for $y = \sin \theta$. Complete the following table for values of $\cos \theta$ in the interval $0 \leq \theta \leq 2\pi$. (Do not consult Panel 1.)

continued →

θ	0	$\pi/6$	$\pi/3$	$\pi/2$	$2\pi/3$	$5\pi/6$	π
$\cos\theta$							

θ	$7\pi/6$	$4\pi/3$	$3\pi/2$	$5\pi/3$	$11\pi/6$	2π
$\cos\theta$						

θ	0	$\pi/6$	$\pi/3$	$\pi/2$	$2\pi/3$	$5\pi/6$	π
$\cos\theta$	1	$\sqrt{3}/2$	$1/2$	0	$-1/2$	$-\sqrt{3}/2$	-1

θ	$7\pi/6$	$4\pi/3$	$3\pi/2$	$5\pi/3$	$11\pi/6$	2π
$\cos\theta$	$-\sqrt{3}/2$	$-1/2$	0	$1/2$	$\sqrt{3}/2$	1

418 Construct a graph of the cosine function using the table of values
prepared in frame 417.   (Arrange the graph so that you can extend
it to the right or left in a later frame.)

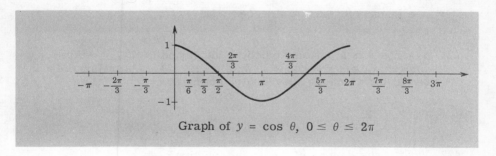

Graph of $y = \cos\theta$, $0 \leq \theta \leq 2\pi$

419 Complete the following table for values of $\cos\theta$ in the interval
$-2\pi \leq \theta \leq 0$.

continued →

θ	-2π	$-11\pi/6$	$-5\pi/3$	$-3\pi/2$	$-4\pi/3$	$-7\pi/6$	$-\pi$
$\cos \theta$							

θ	$-5\pi/6$	$-2\pi/3$	$-\pi/2$	$-\pi/3$	$-\pi/6$	0
$\cos \theta$						

θ	-2π	$-11\pi/6$	$-5\pi/3$	$-3\pi/2$	$-4\pi/3$	$-7\pi/6$	$-\pi$
$\cos \theta$	1	$\sqrt{3}/2$	$1/2$	0	$-1/2$	$-\sqrt{3}/2$	-1

θ	$-5\pi/6$	$-2\pi/3$	$-\pi/2$	$-\pi/3$	$-\pi/6$	0
$\cos \theta$	$-\sqrt{3}/2$	$-1/2$	0	$1/2$	$\sqrt{3}/2$	1

420 (1) Extend the graph of $y = \cos \theta$ in frame 418 over the interval $-2\pi \leq \theta < 0$ using the table prepared in frame 419. (2) Extend the graph of $y = \cos \theta$ over the interval $2\pi < \theta \leq 4\pi$.

see Panel 5 for the answer.

421 $y = \cos \theta$ is a periodic function; the period is (1)___, since for any integer k, $\cos \theta = \cos (\theta + k \cdot (2)$___$)$. (3)___ is the smallest interval for which the above statement holds.

(1) 2π (2) 2π (3) 2π

422 What is the *domain* of the cosine function?

all real numbers (to *each* real number θ, there corresponds a value of $\cos \theta$.)

423 Note that the range of y is from
(1)__ to (2)___. When $\theta = 0$,
$\cos \theta =$ (3)__. When $\theta = \pi$,
$\cos \theta =$ (4)___. When $\theta = 2\pi$,
$\cos \theta =$ (5)__. When $\theta = 3\pi$,
$\cos \theta =$ (6)___ ; etc. $|\cos \theta|$ is
never greater than 1 because, by
definition, $\cos \theta$ is the abscissa of
the point of intersection of the terminal side of the angle with the
unit circle.

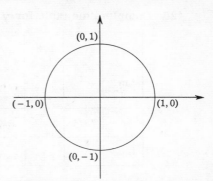

(1) 1   (2) -1   (3) 1   (4) -1   (5) 1   (6) -1

424 In the interval $-2\pi \le \theta \le 2\pi$, $\cos \theta = 0$ when $\theta =$ ___,___, ___, ___.

$$\frac{-3\pi}{2}, \ \frac{-\pi}{2}, \ \frac{\pi}{2}, \ \frac{3\pi}{2}$$

▽**425** Another observation which could be made is the great similarity between the two graphs $y = \sin \theta$ and $y = \cos \theta$. If the *sine curve*
were shifted (1)____ units to the left, it would coincide with the *cosine curve*. (2) Identify the graph shown here as $y = \sin \theta$ or
$y = \cos \theta$.

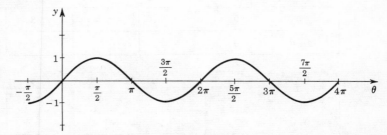

(1) $\frac{\pi}{2}$ (2) $y = \sin \theta$

426   Complete the table for $y = \tan \theta$.

θ	0	$\pi/6$	$\pi/4$	$\pi/3$	$\pi/2$	$2\pi/3$	$3\pi/4$	$5\pi/6$	π
$\tan \theta$									

θ	$7\pi/6$	$5\pi/4$	$4\pi/3$	$3\pi/2$	$5\pi/3$	$7\pi/4$	$11\pi/6$	2π
$\tan \theta$								

θ	0	$\pi/6$	$\pi/4$	$\pi/3$	$\pi/2$	$2\pi/3$	$3\pi/4$	$5\pi/6$	π
$\tan \theta$	0	$1/\sqrt{3}$	1	$\sqrt{3}$	unde-fined	$-\sqrt{3}$	-1	$-1/\sqrt{3}$	0

θ	$7\pi/6$	$5\pi/4$	$4\pi/3$	$3\pi/2$	$5\pi/3$	$7\pi/4$	$11\pi/6$	2π
$\tan$	$1/\sqrt{3}$	1	$\sqrt{3}$	unde-fined	$-\sqrt{3}$	-1	$-1/\sqrt{3}$	0

427   The values in this table are also used in plotting the graph of $y = \tan \theta$.   Complete the table.

θ	0	$-\pi/6$	$-\pi/4$	$-\pi/3$	$-\pi/2$
$\tan \theta$	0				

θ	0	$-\pi/6$	$-\pi/4$	$-\pi/3$	$-\pi/2$
$\tan \theta$	0	$-1/\sqrt{3}$	-1	$-\sqrt{3}$	undefined

428   Using the tables in frames 426 and 427, sketch the graph of $y = \tan \theta$, $-\pi/2 < \theta < 2\pi$, on a set of axes similar to the one shown here.

continued →

Note: Look at Panel 1 to see changes in tan θ as θ increases from $\pi/3$ to $\pi/2$ (as θ approaches $\pi/2$); i.e., look at tan 70°, tan 80°, and tan 85°.

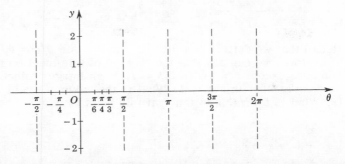

see Panel 7 for the answer.

429 To understand the changes in the values of tan θ as θ increases from 0 to $\pi/2$, recall the definition tan θ = (1)_____.   Then when θ = 0, sin θ = 0 and cos θ = 1; hence, tan 0 = (2)___. As θ increases from θ to $\pi/2$, sin θ (3)_____ (increases, decreases) and cos θ (4)_____ (increases, decreases); therefore, tan θ (5)_____ (increases, decreases).

(1) $\dfrac{\sin\,\theta}{\cos\,\theta}$ (2) 0   (3) increases   (4) decreases   (5) increases

430 As θ gets close to $\pi/2$, sin θ approaches 1 and cos θ approaches 0. Hence, tan θ gets increasingly larger. By taking θ close enough to $\pi/2$, we can make tan θ larger than any number we choose. The graph of tan θ showed that tan θ was increasing rapidly as θ came near to $\pi/2$. Describe the graph at the point where θ = $\pi/2$.

the graph is discontinuous. The graph does not intersect the vertical line drawn at the point where θ = $\pi/2$.

431 A study of the graph of y = tan θ shows that this function is periodic; the period, however, is (1)___ instead of 2π, since the graph repeats itself every (2)___. (Answer in radians.)

(1) π (2) π

432   Values of θ where tan θ is undefined are___, ___, ___, etc.

$-\dfrac{\pi}{2}, \dfrac{\pi}{2}, \dfrac{3\pi}{2}$ in any order (also $\dfrac{5\pi}{2}, \dfrac{7\pi}{2}$, etc.)

433   Recall that we defined tan θ thus: tan θ = sin θ/cos θ, cos $\theta \neq 0$. Therefore, we can say that the *domain* of this function is all real numbers except $\theta = (\pi/2) \cdot (2k + 1)$, k an integer, since cos $(\pi/2)$ = 0, cos $(3\pi/2)$ = 0, etc.   (1) What is the value of θ when k = -1? (2) What is the value of tan θ at this point?

(1) $\dfrac{-\pi}{2}$ (2) tan θ is undefined

434   Examining Panel 1 and your graph, you can see that tan θ has values *ranging* over the real-number system. By taking θ near to $\pi/2$, the value of tan θ becomes increasingly large in absolute value. Keep in mind, however, that we are *not* assigning a value to tan $(\pi/2)$. We say instead that tan θ is _____ at $\theta = \pi/2$.

undefined or no value

435   *Note:* Occasionally in tables of trigonometric functions the symbol ∞ (infinity) is used and the expression tan $(\pi/2)$ = ∞ appears. Students should know that ∞ is not a number. This symbol as used above means simply that $|\text{tan } \theta|$ can be made arbitrarily large by taking θ close enough to $\pi/2$ and that tan θ is not defined for θ = $\pi/2$. Examine the graph of y = tan θ in Panel 7 for the interval $-\pi/2$ to $\pi/2$. You will see that on the right from 0 to $\pi/2$ the graph (1)_____ (increases, decreases) indefinitely, whereas on the left from 0 to $-\pi/2$ the graph (2)_____ indefinitely. At θ = $\pi/2$ and θ = $-\pi/2$, tan θ is undefined.

(1) increases   (2) decreases

436 Identify the graphs shown here.

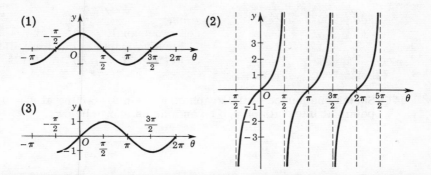

(1) $y = \cos \theta$ (2) $y = \tan \theta$ (3) $y = \sin \theta$

Comment

The property of periodicity of the trigonometric functions makes them useful in the study of problems where motion is of a recurrent nature. In physics, engineering, and other sciences, their applications are of great importance. A wheel turning on its axis, the rise and fall of the tides, and sound waves are but a few examples of recurring, or periodic, motions. A more complete study of the periodicity of the sine and cosine functions will appear later in this program. No answer required.

437 Using the formula $\theta = (\alpha + k \cdot 360°)$, k an integer, find α such that $0 \le \alpha < 360°$, given $\theta = 440°$. *Note:* A sketch of the angle in standard position is often helpful.

$\alpha = 80°$ *Solution:* $440° = \alpha + 1 \cdot 360°$, $80° = \alpha$

438 As in frame 437, find α given $\theta = -107°$.

$\alpha = 253°$ *Solution:* $-107° = \alpha + (-1) \, 360°$, $253° = \alpha$

439 Find α in radians, $0 \le \alpha < 2\pi$, given $\theta = 29\pi/10$.

$\alpha = \dfrac{9\pi}{10}$ *Solution:* $\theta = \alpha + k \cdot 2\pi$, $\dfrac{29\pi}{10} = \alpha + 1 \cdot 2\pi$, $\dfrac{9\pi}{10} = \alpha$

440 From Panel 1 find the approximate value of cos (-100°).

cos (-100°) = -0.174   *Solution:*
                      reference angle = 80°
                      -100° terminates in quadrant III
                      cos (-100°) = cos 80° = -0.174

441 Sketch one period of the graph of $y = \sin \theta$ starting at $\theta = 0$. Plot points at intervals of $\pi/6$ on an axis as shown below.

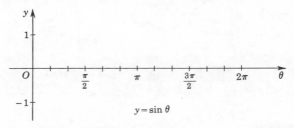

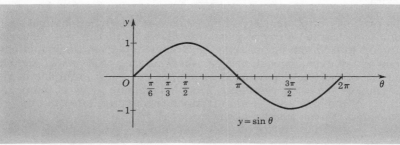

442 Sketch in a similar manner one period of $y = \cos \theta$ starting at $\theta = 0$.

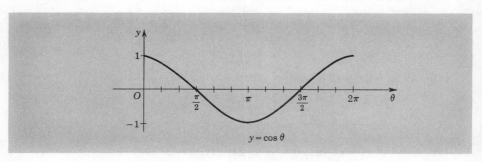

443 Sketch in a similar manner one period of $y = \tan \theta$ starting at $\theta = -\pi/2$.

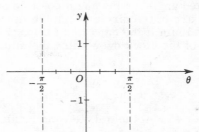

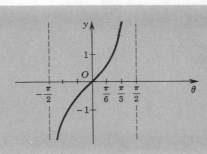

444 *Radian measure.* Find angle θ in radians if
     S = arc length in inches
     r = radius in inches
Then $\theta = $ _____

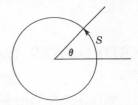

$$\theta = \frac{S}{r} \text{ or } \theta \text{ in radians} = \frac{\text{arc}}{\text{radius}}$$

445 A central angle intercepts an arc whose length is $9\pi/5$ on a circle whose radius is 3. (1) How many radians are in the central angle? If a central angle is $\pi/3$ radians and the arc it intercepts is 2π, (2) find the radius of the circle.

(1) $\theta = \dfrac{3\pi}{5}$ *Solution:* θ in radians $= \dfrac{\text{arc}}{\text{radius}} = \dfrac{9\pi/5}{3} = \dfrac{3\pi}{5}$

(2) $r = 6$ *Solution:* $\theta = \dfrac{\text{arc}}{\text{radius}}, \ \dfrac{\pi}{3} = \dfrac{2\pi}{r}, \ r = 6$

446 (1) (a) What is the radian measure of the angle through which the minute hand of a clock revolves in 45 min? (b) If you consider this as a directed angle, is the angle positive or negative? (2) How long is the arc of the circle which the tip of a minute hand has traversed in 45 min if the hand is 2 in. long? (3) What is the area of the sector of the clock over which the minute hand has passed in 45 min?

(1) (a) $\frac{-3\pi}{2}$, (b) negative

Solution: In 45 min the minute hand rotates through three-quarters of a revolution

$$\text{rev} = \frac{3}{4} \cdot \frac{2\pi}{1} = \frac{3\pi}{2} \text{ radians}$$

(2) 3π in.

Solution: $S = \alpha \cdot r = \frac{3\pi}{2} \cdot \frac{2}{1} = 3\pi$ in.

(3) 3π sq in.

Solution 1: $a = \frac{\alpha r^2}{2} = \frac{3\pi/2 \cdot 2^2}{2} = 3\pi$

or

Solution 2: Since the minute hand turns through three-quarters of a revolution, the area of the sector is three-fourths of the area of the circle or $\frac{3}{4}\pi r^2$.

SOLUTION OF TRIANGLES

447 The solutions of problems which you have encountered thus far in this program have depended upon right triangles. We are now ready to introduce the formulas that will enable you to make computations in a general triangle. First, we shall state the *law of cosines* as a theorem and then construct a proof.
Theorem: Given triangle ABC with lengths of sides designated as a, b, and c and angle measures as α, β, and γ respectively, then:

Case I. $c^2 = a^2 + b^2 - 2ab \cos \gamma$
Case II. $b^2 = a^2 + c^2 - 2ac \cos \beta$
Case III. $a^2 = b^2 + c^2 - 2bc \cos \alpha$

continued →

Make a copy of the triangle below, placing angle γ in standard position and using a as the initial side; also, copy the above three statements for use in the following frames.

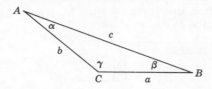

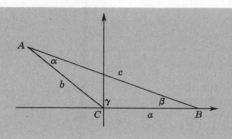

Note: In standard notation, the side opposite vertex C is c; the side opposite vertex B is b; etc.

448 Next we label the three vertices of the triangle with the information available. Point C would have coordinates **(1)** (__, __), and point B would have coordinates **(2)** (__, __).

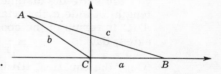

(1) $(0, 0)$ **(2)** $(a, 0)$

449 Look at sketch I. Recall that given any angle θ in standard position with $P(x, y)$ a point on the terminal side of θ whose distance from 0 is designated by r, we have $\sin \theta = y/r$, and $\cos \theta = x/r$. Therefore, $y =$ **(1)**_____ and $x =$ **(2)**_____.   Look at sketch II, point $A(x, y)$ can be labeled as **(3)** $A($_____, _____$)$.   *Note:* The notation $P(x, y)$ is general, Either x or y or both may represent negative quantities.

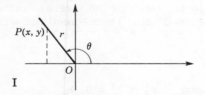

I

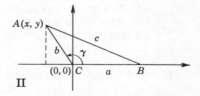

II

(1) $r \sin \theta$ **(2)** $r \cos \theta$ **(3)** $(b \cos \theta, b \sin \theta)$

450 For the next part of the proof we need the formula for the dis-
     tance between two points on a coordinate system. Let $P_1(x_1, y_1)$
     and $P_2(x_2, y_2)$ be any two
     points, then the formula for
     the distance P_1P_2 is $d^2 =$
     (1)_____.
     For this sketch
     $$x_1 = (2)\_\_, \quad x_2 = (3)\_\_\_\_\_$$
     $$y_1 = (4)\_\_, \quad y_2 = (5)\_\_\_\_\_$$

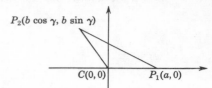

> **(1)** $(x_2 - x_1)^2 + (y_2 - y_1)^2$ **(2)** a **(3)** $b \cos \gamma$
>
> **(4)** 0   **(5)** $b \sin \gamma$

451 You now have coordinates for the
     two points A and B, so that using
     the distance formula

$$d^2 = (x_2 - x_1)^2 + (y_2 - y_1)^2$$

     you can state the distance (or
     length) of side c for triangle
     ABC in terms of the coordi-
     nates, that is
$$c^2 = (_____)^2 + (_____)^2$$
     (Copy the equation, fill in the blanks, and do the multiplication.)

> $$c^2 = (b \cos \gamma - a)^2 + (b \sin \gamma - 0)^2$$
> $$= b^2 (\cos \gamma)^2 - 2ab \cos \gamma + a^2 + b^2 (\sin \gamma)^2$$

Comment

From now on $(\cos \gamma)^2$, $(\sin \gamma)^2$, etc., will be written without parentheses in the form $\cos^2 \gamma$, $\sin^2 \gamma$, etc. In general $(\cos \theta)^n$ will be
written $\cos^n \theta$. The exception to this notation will occur when $n =$
-1; this exception is caused by the fact that the inverse functions
for the cosine and sine functions (Part IV) are sometimes written
as $\cos^{-1} \theta$ and $\sin^{-1} \theta$.

452 The terms of the equation
$$c^2 = b^2 \cos^2 \gamma - 2ab \cos \gamma + a^2 + b^2 \sin^2 \gamma$$
     may be rearranged as follows:
$$c^2 = b^2 [_____] + a^2 - 2ab \cos \gamma$$

> $\cos^2 \gamma + \sin^2 \gamma$

453 For any angle γ we know that $\cos^2 \gamma + \sin^2 \gamma =$ ___.

> 1

454 Completing the simplification, if we substitute $1 = \cos^2 \gamma + \sin^2 \gamma$ in
> $c^2 = b^2 (\cos^2 \gamma + \sin^2 \gamma) + a^2 - 2ab \cos \gamma$

we have $c^2 =$ _____. This is Case I of the law of cosines.

> $c^2 = a^2 + b^2 - 2ab \cos \gamma$

455 Suppose γ had been the angle $\pi/2$, **(1)** make a drawing of the triangle ABC with γ in standard position. Label the vertices of the triangle carefully. *Note:* Vertex B will have coordinates **(2)** (__, __) as before. Vertex A can be labeled more simply than before, namely, **(3)** (__, __).

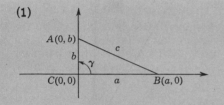

(1)

(2) $(a, 0)$

(3) $(0, b)$

456 Using the distance formula and the coordinates from frame 455 as recorded here in the sketch, find c^2.

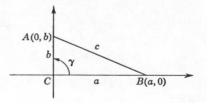

> $c^2 = (a - 0)^2 + (0 - b)^2$ or $c^2 = a^2 + b^2$

457 To what does $c^2 = a^2 + b^2 - 2ab \cos \gamma$ reduce if the numerical value of $\cos (\pi/2)$ is used?

> $c^2 = a^2 + b^2$ *Solution:* $c^2 = a^2 + b^2 - 2ab (0) = a^2 + b^2$

458 The material in frames 456 and 457 does *not* constitute a proof of the Pythagorean theorem:
$$c^2 = a^2 + b^2 \text{ for any right triangle } ABC$$
even though the development of the law of cosines was based on the use of this theorem. However, we can show that if $c^2 = a^2 + b^2$, then triangle ABC is a right triangle. Study the following:

1. If $c^2 = a^2 + b^2$, then
   $c^2 - a^2 - b^2 = 0$
2. $c^2 = a^2 + b^2 - 2ab \cos \gamma$
3. $c^2 - a^2 - b^2 = 2ab \cos \gamma$

4. $0 = -2ab \cos \gamma$

5. $0 = \cos \gamma$
6. If γ is an angle of triangle ABC, then $0 < \gamma < \pi$.
(2) What angle in this range has $\cos \gamma = 0$?

1. adding $-a^2 - b^2$ to both members
2. law of cosines
3. adding $-a^2 - b^2$ to both members of Step 2
4. since $c^2 - a^2 - b^2 = 0$ in Step 1
5. dividing by $-2ab$
6. (1) Why?

---

(1) sum of three angles of a plane triangle is π **(2)** $\frac{\pi}{2}$

---

459 Let β be an acute angle of the general triangle ABC; place the triangle on a set of coordinate axes so that β is in standard position with BC along the positive x axis. Make a sketch and label the vertices as you think proper for developing the law of cosines for $b^2 = a^2 + c^2 - 2ac \cos \beta$.

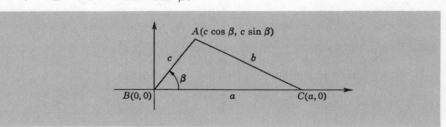

460 Here is the figure from frame 459. Show how to derive the law of cosines for b^2, starting with the distance formula
$$b^2 = (x_2 - x_1)^2 + (y_2 - y_1)^2$$

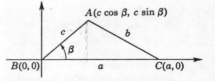

$$b^2 = (c \cos \beta - a)^2 + (c \sin \beta - 0)^2$$
$$= c^2 \cos^2 \beta - 2ac \cos \beta + a^2 + c^2 \sin^2 \beta$$
$$= c^2(\cos^2 \beta + \sin^2 \beta) + a^2 - 2ac \cos \beta$$
$$= c^2 + a^2 - 2ac \cos \beta \quad \text{since } \cos^2 \beta + \sin^2 \beta = 1$$

461 Make a figure labeling the vertices carefully to show that $a^2 = b^2 + c^2 - 2bc \cos \alpha$ in a general triangle ABC. Let α be either an acute or obtuse angle. Keep a correct copy for frame 462.

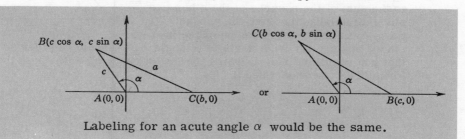

Labeling for an acute angle α would be the same.

462 Complete the work to show that $a^2 = b^2 + c^2 - 2bc \cos \alpha$ starting with the distance formula for a^2.

$$a^2 = (\cos \alpha - b)^2 + (c \sin \alpha - 0)^2$$
$$= c^2 \cos^2 \alpha - 2bc \cos \alpha + b^2 + c^2 \sin^2 \alpha$$
$$= c^2 (\cos^2 \alpha + \sin^2 \alpha) + b^2 - 2bc \cos \alpha$$
$$= c^2 + b^2 - 2bc \cos \alpha$$

463 Problem: Given triangle ABC, with length of sides designated by a, b, and c and angle measures by α, β, and γ, and given $\gamma = 40°$, $a = 12$, and $b = 7$, find c.

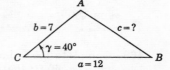

$c \approx 8$ *Solution:* $c^2 = 12^2 + 7^2 - 2(12)(7) \cos 40°$
$$\approx 193 - 168(0.766)$$
$$\approx 64.3$$
$$c \approx 8$$

▽**464** Notice that the law of cosines was used in frame 463 thus: Given two sides and the included angle, find the third side of the triangle. (1) Can we apply the law of cosines in the following problem? In triangle ABC, $\alpha = 60°$, $c = 60$ ft, and $b = 40$ ft, find the third side. (2) If you gave an affirmative answer, write the law of cosines you should use to solve the problem.

(1) yes   **(2)** $a^2 = b^2 + c^2 - 2bc \cos \alpha$

465 As an aid to remembering the law of co-sines, we can state it in words thus: The square of one side of a triangle is equal to the sum of the squares of the other two sides diminished by twice the product of these two sides and the cosine of the included angle.   (1) What parts of triangle ABC should be given so that you could find side b, using the law of cosines?   (2) State the formula as you should use it.

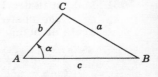

(1) a, c, B (2) $b^2 = a^2 + b^2 - 2ab \cos \beta$

466 Find a, given $\alpha = 60°$, $b = 40$ ft, and $c = 60$ ft in triangle ABC.

$a \approx 53$ ft   *Solution:* $a^2 = b^2 + c^2 - 2bc \cos \alpha$
$= 40^2 + 60^2 - 2(40)(60) \cos 60°$
$= 1,600 + 3,600 - 2,400 \qquad a \approx 53$

467 To find side a of triangle ABC, given $\alpha = 100°$, $b = 40$ ft, and $c = 60$ ft, by means of the law of cosines requires the numerical value for cos 100°.   Find cos 100°.

$\cos 100° = -0.174$ *Solution:* $\cos 100° = -\cos 80° = -0.174$

468 Complete the solution of the problem given $\alpha = 100°$, $b = 40$ ft, and $c = 60$ ft; that is, find side a for the triangle ABC.

$a \approx 78$ ft   *Solution:* $a \approx 1,600 + 3,600 - 4,800 \ (-0.174)$
$\approx 5,200 + 835 \approx 6,035 \qquad a \approx 78$

469 We pointed out that the law of cosines was useful in finding the third side of a triangle given two sides and the included angle. A triangle is determined when its three sides are known. Would the law of cosines serve to find the measure of the angles of a triangle if the three sides were given?

yes

470 As a review, state the three forms of the law of cosines: $a^2 = $
(1)_____, and $b^2 = $ (2)_____, and
$c^2 = $ (3)_____.

(1) $b^2 + c^2 - 2bc \cos \alpha$ (2) $a^2 + c^2 - 2ac \cos \beta$
(3) $a^2 + b^2 - 2ab \cos \gamma$

471 Given $b^2 = a^2 + c^2 - 2ac \cos \beta$, write the formula for $\cos \beta$ in
terms of a, b, and c.

$\cos \beta = \dfrac{a^2 + c^2 - b^2}{2ac}$ *Solution:* $b^2 = a^2 + c^2 - 2ac \cos \beta$
$2ac \cos \beta = a^2 + c^2 - b^2$

$$\cos \beta = \dfrac{a^2 + c^2 - b^2}{2ac}$$

472 The three sides of a triangle ABC have lengths $a = 12$, $b = 7$, and
$c = 8$; find β.

$\beta \approx 34° \approx 0.593$ radian

Solution: $\cos \beta = \dfrac{12^2 + 8^2 - 7^2}{2(12(8)} = \dfrac{159}{192} \approx 0.828$

$\beta \approx 34° \approx 0.593$ radian

473 (1) State the formula you should use to find α in the problem in
frame 472 in which $a = 12$, $b = 7$, and $c = 8$. $\cos \alpha = $
(2)_____.

(1) $a^2 = b^2 + c^2 - 2bc \cos \alpha$ (2) $\dfrac{b^2 + c^2 - a^2}{2bc}$

474 If $a = 12$, $b = 7$, and $c = 8$, what is the value of $\cos \alpha \approx$ _____,
correct to three decimal places ?

–0.277

475 Given cos $\alpha \approx -0.277$. What is the approximate measure of α **(1)** in degrees and **(2)** in radians? Remember that when cos α is negative and α is an angle of a plane triangle, then $\pi/2 < \alpha < \pi$.

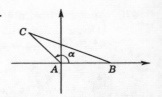

(1) $\alpha = 106°$ **(2)** 1.850 radians
Solution:
    If cos $\alpha \approx 0.277$, then
        $\alpha \approx 74°$ or 1.292 radians

    If cos $\alpha \approx -0.277$, then
        $\alpha \approx 180° - 74 \approx 106°$
            $\approx \pi - 1.292$
            $\approx 3.142 - 1.292$
            ≈ 1.850 radians

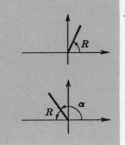

476 The two adjacent sides AD and AB of a parallelogram are 4.0 and 6.0 in., and the angle α formed by them is 60°. **(1)** Find the shorter diagonal of the parallelogram. **(2)** Make a sketch which shows the information given (note that the law of cosines applies), and **(3)** complete the solution.

(1) $a \approx 5.3$ in.   **(2)**

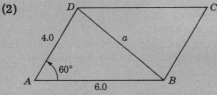

(3) $a^2 = (4.0)^2 + (6.0)^2 - 2(4.0)(6.0) \cos 60°$
        $= 28$
    $a \approx 5.3$ in.

477 **(1)** How many degrees are in angle B of parallelogram $ABCD$? **(2)** What is cos 60°? **(3)** What is cos β?

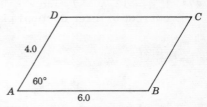

(1) 120°   **(2)** cos 60° = 0.5   **(3)** cos β = -0.5

478 Using the same information as given in frame 477, find the longer diagonal of the parallelogram.

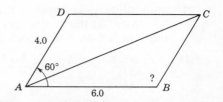

$b \approx 8.7$ in.

Solution: Let $AC = b$.

$$b^2 = (4.0)^2 + (6.0)^2 - 2(4.0)(6.0) \cos 120°$$
$$= 16 + 36 - (24)(-0.5) = 76 \qquad b \approx 8.7$$

479 One of the angles formed by the diagonals of a parallelogram at their point of intersection is $\pi/4$. The diagonals are 8.0 and 10.0 in. Find the length of the shorter sides of the parallelogram.

$s_1 \approx 3.6$ in.

Solution:

$$s_1^2 = (4.0)^2 + (5.0)^2 -$$
$$2(4.0)(5.0) \cos \frac{\pi}{4}$$
$$\approx 16.0 + 25.0 - 40.0(0.707)$$
$$\approx 12.72 \qquad s_1 \approx 3.6$$

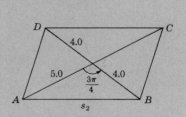

480 Find the length of the longer sides of the parallelogram in frame 479.

$s_2 \approx 8.3$ in.

Solution:

$$s_2^2 = (5.0)^2 + (4.0)^2 -$$
$$\approx 2(5.0)(4.0) \cos \frac{3\pi}{4}$$
$$\approx 69.28$$
$$s_2 \approx 8.3$$

To find $\cos (3\pi/4)$, we sketched the angle in standard position as shown and noted the reference angle.

481   Find the largest angle of the triangle whose sides measure 15, 10, 7.   *Note:* If the cosine of an angle (of a triangle) is negative, the angle is *not* an acute angle.

$\alpha = 123°$
Solution:

$$a^2 = b^2 + c^2 - 2bc \cos \alpha$$

$$\cos \alpha = \frac{b^2 + c^2 - a^2}{2bc}$$

$$= \frac{-76}{140} \approx -0.543$$

$$\alpha = 123°$$

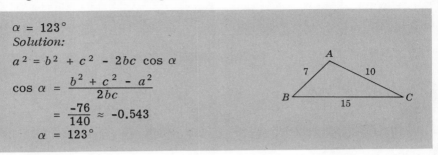

482   Another formula for solving a general triangle is known as the *law of of sines*. It is stated here as a theorem with a proof following. *Theorem:*   Given triangle ABC with length of sides designated as a, b, c respectively and angle measures α, β, and γ respectively, then:

$$\frac{\sin \alpha}{a} = \frac{\sin \beta}{b} = \frac{\sin \gamma}{c}.$$

Proof: Place triangle ABC so that γ is in standard position and CB is the initial side.   Label the vertices with proper coordinates. γ may be either acute or obtuse.

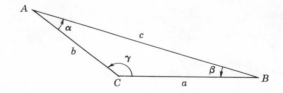

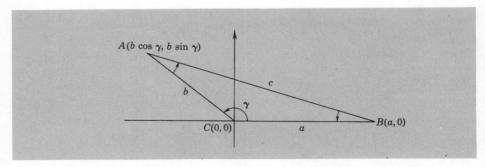

483 The altitude h of triangle ABC, using CB (with length a) as the base, is the ordinate of point A, which is _____.

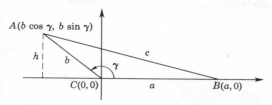

$b \sin \gamma$

484 In terms of base and altitude, the area of a triangle equals one-half the product of its base and altitude. Therefore, the area of triangle ABC, using CB as base, = _____.

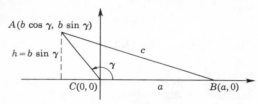

$\frac{1}{2}ab \sin \gamma$

485 For the same triangle ABC, having angle A in standard position and using length c as base, (1) state the area of triangle ABC. (2) What are the coordinates of point C?

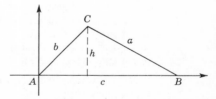

(1) $\frac{1}{2}cb \sin \alpha$ **(2)** $(b \cos \alpha, b \sin \alpha)$

486 Note the new position of triangle
ABC; that is, B is in standard
position and side a is the initial
side. State the area of triangle
ABC.

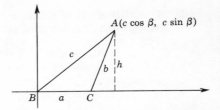

$\frac{1}{2}ac \sin \beta$

487 In frames 484 to 486 we have given the area of ABC in three ways:
area $ABC = \frac{1}{2}ab \sin \gamma$, area $ABC = \frac{1}{2}cb \sin \alpha$, area $ABC = \frac{1}{2}ac \sin \beta$. Therefore, $\frac{1}{2} ab \sin \gamma = $ _____ = _____
(write the complete equation as you answer).

$\frac{1}{2}ab \sin \gamma = \frac{1}{2} cb \sin \alpha = \frac{1}{2}ac \sin \beta$

488 Multiplying by $2/abc$, the statement in the answer of frame 487 becomes the law of sines stated earlier. Write it.

$$\frac{\sin \gamma}{c} = \frac{\sin \alpha}{a} = \frac{\sin \beta}{b}$$

489 Using the law of sines, the law of cosines, and your knowledge of
geometry, you can now solve (find unknown parts of) a general triangle (or a polygon which can be cut into triangles) given a minimum amount of information. You are given two angles and the included side of triangle ABC*: $\alpha = \pi/3$, $c = 16$, and $\beta = \pi/4$. We
proceed as follows to find sides a and b and angle γ: **(1)** Make a
sketch indicated the known parts and **(2)** compute γ.

Note: A triangle is determined if two angles and the included side
are known.

(1)

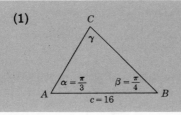

(2) $\alpha + \beta + \gamma = \pi$, $\gamma = \dfrac{5\pi}{12}$

490 Given $\alpha = \pi/3$, $c = 16$, and $\beta = \pi/4$, we found that $\gamma = 5\pi/12$.
Now, having the law of sines which states
$$\frac{\sin\alpha}{a} = \frac{\sin\beta}{b} = \frac{\sin\gamma}{c}$$
we can compute side a using $(\sin\alpha)/a = (\sin\gamma)/c$. Do this
computation.

$$\frac{\sin\alpha}{a} = \frac{\sin\gamma}{c}, \ a = \frac{c\sin\alpha}{\sin\gamma} = \frac{16\sin(\pi/3)}{\sin(5\pi/12)} \approx 14$$

491 Given $c = 16$, $\beta = \pi/4$, $\gamma = 5\pi/12$, and the law of sines $(\sin\alpha)/a = (\sin\beta)/b = (\sin\gamma)/c$, find b.

$b \approx 12$ *Solution:* $\dfrac{\sin\beta}{b} = \dfrac{\sin\gamma}{c}, \ b = \dfrac{c\sin\beta}{\sin\gamma} \approx 12$

492 Find the height h, as shown in the
sketch, of the triangle ABC knowing
that $\alpha = \pi/3$, $\beta = \pi/4$, $c = 16$,
$b = 12$, and $a = 14$.

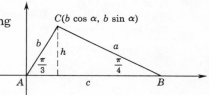

$h \approx 10.4$ *Solution:* $h = b\sin\alpha = 12\cdot\dfrac{\sqrt{3}}{2} \approx 10.4$

493 (1) Find the area of triangle ABC given base $c = 14$ and height $h = 10.4$.   (2) When b, c, and α are given, the area of triangle ABC
may be found directly by means of the formula:
area = _____.

(1) area $\approx$ 83 square units

Solution: area $= \frac{1}{2}$ base $\cdot h \approx \frac{1}{2}\cdot 16\cdot 10.4 \approx 83$
(2) $\frac{1}{2}bc\sin\alpha$

494 Find the area using $A = \frac{1}{2}ab\sin\gamma$ when the dimensions are the
same as in frame 492, namely, $\alpha = \pi/3$, $\beta = \pi/4$, $c = 16$, $\gamma = 5\pi/12$, $b = 12$, and $a = 14$.   *Note:* This answer will not agree exactly with the results in frame 493 because b and c are approxi-
mate readings.

area $\approx$ 81 square units   *Solution:* area $\approx \frac{1}{2}(14\cdot 12)\sin\dfrac{5\pi}{12} \approx 81$

495 To help you remember the area formula that you have been using, notice that the area equals one-half the product of any two sides and the sine of the included angle. Write the three forms for the area in terms of two sides and the included angle.

area = $\frac{1}{2}ab$ sin γ area = $\frac{1}{2}bc$ sin α area = $\frac{1}{2}ac$ sin β

▽**496** Given a = 15, b = 20, and β = 70°, can you find the area directly by applying one of the formulas in frame 495? Explain.

no, the given angle is not the angle included between sides a and b. (It will be shown later that when we are given two sides and an angle opposite one of the given sides, there may be no, one, or two triangles determined.)

497 It is a fact that exactly one triangle ABC can be constructed in which a = 15, b = 20, and β = 70°. Make use of whatever formulas are necessary to find the area of triangle ABC.

area ≈ 136 square units
Solution: First, find α.

$$\frac{\sin \alpha}{a} = \frac{\sin \beta}{b}, \quad \sin \alpha = \frac{15 \sin 70°}{20} \approx 0.705, \ \alpha \approx 45°$$

Second, find γ.

$$\gamma \approx 180° - (70° + 45°) \approx 65°$$

Third, find the area.

$$\text{area} = \frac{1}{2}ab \ \sin \gamma \approx \frac{1}{2} \cdot 15 \cdot 20 \ \sin 65° \approx 136 \text{ square units}$$

498 Notice in the law of sines that in any triangle, the *sines* of the angles are proportional to the opposite sides, i.e., sin α/a = sin β/b = sin γ/c. Given α = 90°, γ = 50°, and b = 24, find **(1)** β and **(2)** a of triangle ABC.

(1) β = 40°   *Solution:* β = 180 - $(\alpha + \gamma)$ = 40°

(2) a ≈ 37   *Solution:* $\dfrac{\sin \alpha}{a} = \dfrac{\sin \beta}{b}$, $a = \dfrac{b \sin \alpha}{\sin \beta} \approx 37$

499 Given β = 120°, γ = 35°, and a = 15, find b, c, and α of triangle ABC. Before solving this problem, answer the following questions

continued →

concerning β.   (1) If β is in standard position, in which quadrant does the terminal side of β lie?   (2) Is sin 120° positive or negative?

(1) II   (2) positive

500 Solve the problem proposed in frame 499: given β = 120°, γ = 35°, and a = 15, find (1) α, (2) c, and (3) b.

(1) $\alpha = 180° - (\beta + \gamma) = 25°$ (2) $c = \dfrac{a \sin \gamma}{\sin \alpha} \approx 20$

(3) $b = \dfrac{a \sin \beta}{\sin \alpha} \approx 31$

501 Now find the area of triangle ABC given β = 120°, γ = 35°, and a = 15.

If you use area $= \frac{1}{2} ab \sin \gamma$, then area $\approx$ 133 square units.
If you use area $= \frac{1}{2} ac \sin \beta$, then area $\approx$ 130 square units.
If you use area $= \frac{1}{2} bc \sin \alpha$, then area $\approx$ 131 square units.

502 We have indicated that the law of sines can be used to solve a tri-angle given two angles and the included side. Since the third angle of a triangle is determined when two angles are given, we expand the statement above to say that we can solve the triangle given two angles and *any* side.   (1) If the information given is "two sides and the included angle," is there one and only one triangle indicated?   (2) Is this enough information for a solution?   (3) If so, which side, or angle, should you find first?

(1) yes   (2) yes, if the given angle is less than 180°
(3) side opposite the given angle, using law of cosines

503 Given two sides and the included an-gle, a, b, γ, a triangle is determined, and the law of cosines

$$c^2 = a^2 + b^2 - 2ab \cos \gamma$$

can be used for obtaining side c. What is the next step in finding the missing parts?

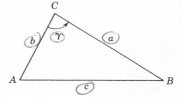

use the law of sines for finding α and β
$$\frac{\sin \alpha}{a} = \frac{\sin \gamma}{c} \qquad \frac{\sin \beta}{b} = \frac{\sin \gamma}{c}$$

▽504   Another familiar statement of geometry is that three sides determine a triangle. If a, b, and c are given, how can you find a specified angle, for example, α?

use $\cos \alpha = \dfrac{b^2 + c^2 - a^2}{2bc}$

which is a form of the law of cosines $a^2 = b^2 + c^2 - 2bc \cos \alpha$

505   If the dimensions given are $a = 4$, $b = 6$, and $c = 12$, you are
aware that a triangle does not exist having these three lengths as
sides. What impossible answer results when you try to apply the
law of cosines to find γ?

$\cos \gamma = \dfrac{a^2 + b^2 - c^2}{2ac} = \dfrac{52 - 144}{48} = \dfrac{-92}{48}$

This is impossible!   Cosine of an angle falls between –1 and
1, i.e., $-1 \le \cos \alpha \le 1$.

506   We now look at the possibility of
solving a triangle when measurements for two sides and the angle
opposite one of them are given.
Suppose $a = 18$, $b = 12$, and $\alpha =$
$51°$. Do you see how β can be
found? (1) State the formula as
you would use it, and (2) find β.

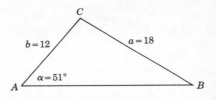

(1) $\dfrac{\sin \beta}{b} = \dfrac{\sin \alpha}{a}$ or $\sin \beta = \dfrac{b \sin \alpha}{a}$ (2) $\beta \approx 31°$

507   In the solution for β, given $a = 18$, $b = 12$, and $\alpha = 51°$, you had
$\sin \beta \approx 0.518$, $\beta \approx 31°$. Since the sine of an angle is positive in
quadrants I and II, could $\beta = 180 - 31° = 149°$? Explain.

no, $\alpha + \beta = 51° + 149° > 180°$.

508 We were forced to discard the possibility of two measurements for α;
hence, we have $\alpha = 51°$, $\beta \approx 31°$,
$a = 18$, and $b = 12$. **(1)** find γ, the
third angle of the triangle. **(2)** Find
side c.

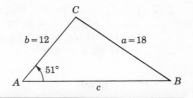

(1) $\gamma = 98°$ (2) $c \approx 23$
Note: $\sin \gamma = \sin 98° = \sin (180 - 98) = \sin 82°$

509 If a triangle has measurements $\alpha = 26°$, $a = 8$, and $b = 12$, should $a = 8$ units be drawn as CB_2 in the sketch shown here, i.e., are there two triangles which meet the requirements given above? Give your opinion.

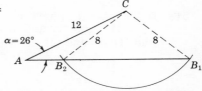

there are two triangles AB_2C and AB_1C.

510 Find the angle β_1 of frame 509.
β_2 will be discussed in frame 511.

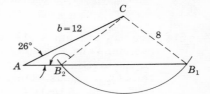

$$\frac{\sin \beta}{b} = \frac{\sin \alpha}{a}, \quad \sin \beta = \frac{b \sin \alpha}{a} \quad \beta \approx 0.657, \quad \beta_1 \approx 41°$$

511 In frame 510 you found $\sin \beta_1 \approx 0.657$ and reported $\beta_1 \approx 41°$. How many degrees are in β_2, the other angle whose $\sin \approx 0.657$?

$\beta_2 = 139°$

512 (1) Can we have a triangle in which $\alpha = 26°$, $\beta_2 = 139°$, $a = 8$, and $b = 12$? If so, find (2) the third angle γ_2 and (3) the third side c for this triangle.

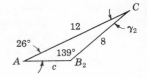

(1) yes   (2) $\gamma_2 = 15°$ Solution: $\gamma_2 = 180 - (\alpha + \beta_2) = 15°$

(3) $c \approx 5$ Solution: $\dfrac{\sin \gamma_2}{c} = \dfrac{\sin \alpha}{a}$, $= \dfrac{a \sin \gamma}{\sin \alpha} \approx 4.7 \approx 5$

513 In the triangle where $\alpha = 26°$, $\beta_1 = 41°$, $a = 8$, and $b = 12$, find (1) γ_1 and (2) c.

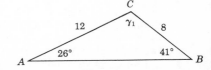

(1) $\gamma_1 = 113°$ Solution: $\gamma_1 = 180 - (\alpha + \beta_1) = 113°$

(2) $c \approx 17$

Solution: $\dfrac{\sin \gamma_1}{c} = \dfrac{\sin \alpha}{a}$ or $c = \dfrac{a \sin \gamma_1}{\sin \alpha} \approx \dfrac{8(0.921)}{0.438} \approx 17$

514 You saw in frames 512 and 513 that with the given data consisting of two sides and an angle opposite one of them, there could be two triangles meeting the conditions AB_1C and AB_2C. However, you may recall a previous example where only one triangle met the given conditions. Is there a theorem from geometry which states that if two triangles have, respectively, two sides and an angle opposite one of the sides equal, the triangles are congruent?

no

515 Let α be an acute angle and let the measurements for b and a be as shown.

continued ➔

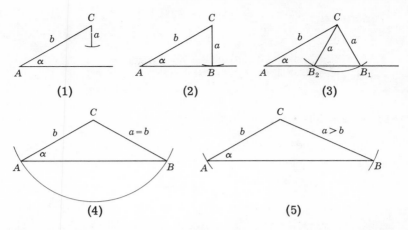

(1)   (2)   (3)

(4)   (5)

These sketches show five possibilities for $\alpha < 90°$, with side a varied as shown. Study them. Notice that for sketch 1, no triangle is formed. Let $\alpha = 30°$, $a = 8$, and $b = 24$, and try to compute β using the law of sines. What is wrong?

$$\frac{\sin \beta}{b} = \frac{\sin \alpha}{a}, \quad \sin \beta = \frac{b \sin \alpha}{a} = 1.5!$$

Recall, for any angle x, $-1 \le \sin x \le 1$.

516 Let $\alpha = 30°$, $a = 12$, and $b = 24$.
(1) Find β.   (2) How many triangles do you have?

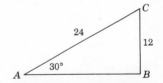

(1) $\beta = 90°$ **(2)** one triangle, the triangle is a right triangle.

517 If $\alpha = 30°$, $a = 16$, and $b = 24$, find β. The sketch indicates that you can expect two measurements for β. What are the measurements for β?

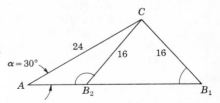

$\beta \approx 49°$, $\beta \approx 131°$

continued →

Solution:
   sin β = 0.750
   $\beta_1 \approx 49°$, $\beta_2 \approx 131°$
Note: In both cases $\alpha + \beta < 180°$
so that a triangle is possible.

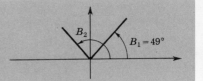

518 If $\alpha = 30°$, $a = 24$, and
$b = 24$, find β. This is
an easy one!

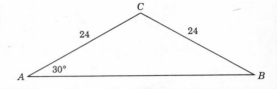

$\beta = 30°$
Solution: sin β = 0.5, $\beta = 30°$ The triangle is isosceles,
$a = b$; therefore, $\beta = \alpha$.

519 If $\alpha = 30°$, $a = 32$, and $b = 24$, (1) find β. Check to see why we
cannot use both angles whose sine you have computed, the one terminating in quadrant II as well as the one in quadrant I. (2) Write
your reason.

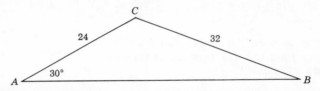

(1) $\beta \approx 22°$
(2) If $\beta = 180° - 22° = 158°$, then $\alpha + \beta > 180°$; hence,
     one triangle only.

520 If $\alpha = 90°$ or $\alpha > 90°$, i.e., a right angle or an obtuse angle, and
a and b are given, it would appear that no triangle is possible if
$a < b$, and only one triangle if $a > b$. *Numerical example:* Use
the law of sines to compute β and comment on the result if $\alpha =$
$90°$, $b = 24$, and $a = 12$.

 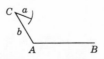

If $\alpha = 90°$, sin $\beta = \dfrac{24 \sin 90°}{12} = 2$ (impossible)

521 Another numerical example: $\alpha = 150°$, $b = 24$, and $a = 12$ (α is obtuse, $a < b$). Apply the law of sines to **(1)** find β and **(2)** explain why you cannot use the apparent answer you get for β.

(1) $\beta = 90°$

Solution: If $\alpha = 150°$, $\sin\beta = \dfrac{24 \sin 150°}{12} = \dfrac{24 \cdot (0.5)}{12} = 1$,

$\beta = 90°$

(2) $\alpha = 150°$, $\beta = 90°$, no triangle possible

522 Recalling a statement of geometry, we could dispose very quickly of the case where $\alpha > 90°$ and $a < b$ by saying that the number of possible triangles is _____ (none, one, two) since "the side opposite a right angle or an obtuse angle of a triangle must be the greatest side of the triangle."

523 When $\alpha \leq 90°$ and $a > b$, you know that the condition named in frame 522 is satisfied, namely, $a > b$. One triangle is possible but not more than one since "in a plane triangle there can not be more than one right angle or one obtuse angle." $\alpha = 120°$, $a = 9$, and $b = 6$. Find β.

$\beta \approx 35°$
Solution: $\sin\beta \approx 0.577$, $\beta \approx 35°$ or $145°$
We discard the $145°$ angle; triangle ABC cannot have two obtuse angles.

524 We shall summarize what has been discussed regarding the number of triangles, given two sides and an angle opposite one of the sides. If $\alpha < 90°$, **(1)** make a sketch and **(2)** give the number of solutions with side a less than side b, and side a also less than the altitude h.

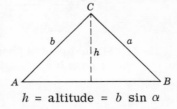

$h = $ altitude $= b \sin \alpha$

(1)

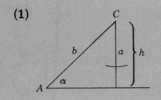

(2) no triangle

525 **(1)** Show the sketch $\alpha < 90°$, $a < b$, and $a = h$.   **(2)** State the number of solutions.

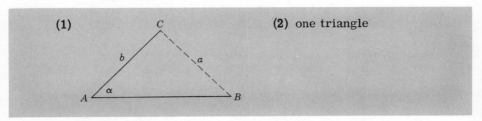

(1)   **(2)** one triangle

526 **(1)** Make a sketch showing $\alpha < 90°$ and $a = b$.   **(2)** State the number of possible triangles.

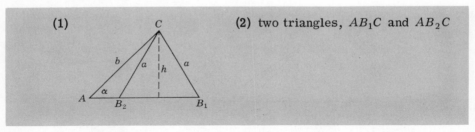

(1)   **(2)** one triangle

527 **(1)** Make a sketch showing $\alpha < 90°$, $a < b$, and $a > h$.   **(2)** State the number of possible triangles.

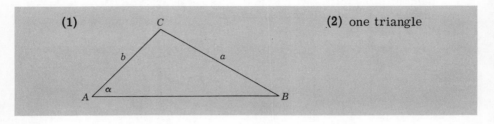

(1)   **(2)** two triangles, AB_1C and AB_2C

528 **(1)** Make a sketch showing $\alpha < 90°$ and $a > b$.   **(2)** State the number of possible triangles.

(1)   **(2)** one triangle

529 Given $90° \leq \alpha < 180°$ and $a < b$, **(1)** how many triangles are possible? Given $90° \leq \alpha < 180°$ and $a > b$, **(2)** how many triangles are possible?

(1) none   **(2)** one

530 We have discussed "the ambiguous case." Two triangles resulted when $\alpha < 90°$, $a < b$, and $a > h$. Let us review the procedure for finding h. Since CD is perpendicular to AB in triangle ADC, you know that $\sin \alpha = h/b$. Solve for h.

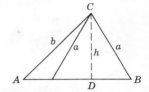

$h = b \sin \alpha$

531 If the information given is $\beta = 27°$, $b = 31$, and $c = 37$, **(1)** is there a possibility of two triangles? **(2)** Make a sketch (watch the lettering). Check the following points. There will *not* be two triangles *unless*: the given angle is **(3)**_____ (acute, obtuse), the side opposite the given angle is **(4)**_____ (less than, greater than) the other given side, the side opposite the given angle is **(5)**_____ (less than, greater than) the altitude $c \sin \beta$.

(1) yes   **(2)**

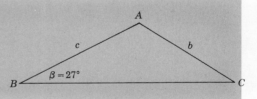

(3) acute   **(4)** less than
(5) greater than

532 Compute the altitude for the problem in frame 531 to assure yourself that $b > h$. Keep a record of your work for later frames.

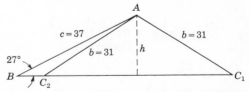

$h = 37 \sin 27° \approx 16.8$
Notice $b > h$ and $b < c$; therefore, we have two solutions.

533   We want to point out that careful thinking as you work may show the unusual aspects of a problem. Since the information "two sides and an angle opposite one of them" may lead to no, one, or two triangles, this case needs to be worked with care. Suppose you had applied the law of sines to the problem in frame 531, given $\beta = 27°$, $b = 31$, $c = 37$. Remembering that there are two angles less than 180° with positive sine, you should check both possibilities. Use the law of sines and find the two measurements for angle γ.

$\gamma = 33°$, $\gamma = 147°$

534   We have discussed two ways of determining the number of possible triangles when the given angle is acute and the side opposite that angle is less than the other given side. Either method may be used. Remember to investigate when this type of information is given. Continuing the problem $\beta = 27°$, $b = 31$, and $c = 37$, we have found $\gamma_1 = 33°$, or $\gamma_2 = 147°$. What are the two corresponding measurements for α?

$\alpha_1 = 120$, $\alpha_2 = 6°$

535   Complete the solution of triangle ABC_1 by finding side a_1 using the law of sines.

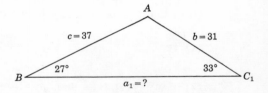

$a_1 \approx 59$, by using $a = \dfrac{b \sin \alpha}{\sin \beta}$ or $a = \dfrac{c \sin \alpha}{\sin \gamma}$

536   As a review for the law of cosines, complete the solution of triangle ABC_2 by finding side a_2 using the law of cosines.

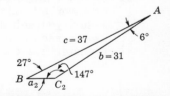

$a_2 \approx 7$, by using $a_2{}^2 = b^2 + c^2 - 2bc \cos \alpha_2$

537 Find the areas of the two triangles.

(1)

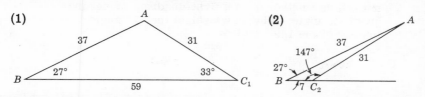

(2)

(1) area$_1$ $\approx$ 496   *Solution:*   area = $\frac{1}{2}ac \sin \beta$
$\approx \frac{1}{2} \cdot 59 \cdot 37 \sin 27° \approx 496$

(2) area$_2$ $\approx$ 59   *Solution:*   area = $\frac{1}{2}ac \sin \beta$
$\approx \frac{1}{2} \cdot 7 \cdot 37 \sin 27° \approx 59$

538 Given $\gamma = 30°$, $b = 5$, and $c = 2$, find β.

no triangle exists   *Explanation:* Since $\sin \beta = \dfrac{b \sin \gamma}{c}$

$\sin \beta = \dfrac{5 \sin 30°}{2} = 1.25$ (impossible)

539 Given $b = 60$, $c = 32$, and $\alpha = 72°$. Is this the ambiguous case ?

no

540 Continuing the problem from frame 539, given $b = 60$, $c = 32$, and $\alpha = 72°$, find a. ≈ 17

$a \approx 58.7 \approx 59$

541 Given $b = 60$, $c = 32$, and $\alpha = 72°$, you found $a \approx 59$. You can find γ by using the law of cosines or the law of sines. Since the amount of numerical work is less if the law of sines is used, problems of this sort are usually completed by means of the law of sines. Compute γ.

$\gamma \approx 31°$ See frame 542 for discussion of γ.

542 Earlier we mentioned that finding sin $\gamma \approx 0.516$ does
not tell us whether γ is a first-quadrant or second-
quadrant angle. Why do we select the 31° angle
instead of the 149° angle ?

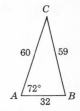

Since side $c < a$, then $\gamma < \alpha$, and so we must use $\gamma = 31°$

543 To find β, you might use $\beta = 180° - (\alpha + \gamma)$. Let us reserve this
formula as a check on our work and compute β using the law of
sines. Check as suggested above.

sin $\beta \approx 0.9675 \approx 0.968$, $\beta \approx 75.5° \approx 76°$
Note: We cannot use (180 - 76°) for β, when $\alpha = 72°$ and
$\gamma = 31°$.
Check: $\beta = 180° - (72° + 31°) \approx 77°$

Comment

You should acquire some skill in solving triangles (finding the sides
or angles not given). This program does not emphasize the numerical aspects of trigonometry; hence, the examples will be as simple
as possible, but we shall give you typical problems. A slide rule,
a desk calculator, or logarithms may be used in computations if you
are familiar with any one of them. You will be applying the law of
cosines, the law of sines, and the definitions of the sine and cosine
of an angle, along with your previous knowledge of geometry. As
you solve the problem, check mentally to see that you are getting
sensible answers.

544 State the formula you should use to
find side a given b, c, and α.

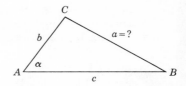

$a^2 = b^2 + c^2 - 2bc \cos \alpha$

545 (1) Write the formula for finding b given a, c, and β. (2) Make a sketch showing the positions of a, c, and β in a triangle.

(1) $b^2 = c^2 + a^2 - 2ac \cos \beta$

(2)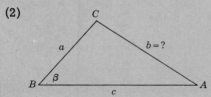

This is just one position of the triangle; you may use any side as base.

546 Suppose a, b, and c are all known. State the formula you should use to find γ.

$$\cos \gamma = \frac{b^2 + a^2 - c^2}{2ab} \quad \text{or} \quad c^2 = a^2 + b^2 - 2ab \cos \gamma$$

547 The law of sines may be given in one statement for all three sides and angles. State it.

$$\frac{\sin \alpha}{a} = \frac{\sin \beta}{b} = \frac{\sin \gamma}{c}$$

548 In a triangle $\beta = 60°$, $\gamma = 45°$, and $b = 12$. (1) Make a sketch of the given triangle. (2) Is this the ambiguous case? (3) State a formula for finding side c.

(1)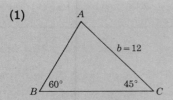

(2) no

(3) $\dfrac{\sin \gamma}{c} = \dfrac{\sin \beta}{b}$

549 Find (1) α, (2) c, and (3) a of the problem in frame 548.

(1) $\alpha = 75°$ (2) $c \approx 9.8$ or 10 (3) $a \approx 13.4$ or 13

550 Given $a = 10$, $c = 15$, and $\beta = 53°$. (1) Make the sketch and
(2) outline your method of solution.

(1)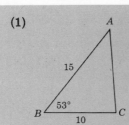

(2) Use law of cosines to find b.
$$b^2 = a^2 + c^2 - 2ac \cos \beta.$$

Use law of sines for α or γ.
Check with $\alpha + \beta + \gamma = 180$.

551 Find (1) b, (2) α, and (3) γ of the problem in frame 550.
Note: The degree of accuracy of this work will not give exactly
180° when you check using $\alpha + \beta + \gamma$.

(1) $b \approx 12$ (2) $\alpha \approx 42°$ (3) $\gamma \approx 86°$
Note: γ could not be $180 - 86° = 104°$ when $\beta = 53°$ and
$\alpha = 42°$.

552 Given $\beta = 65°$, $\gamma = 35°$, and $c = 20.0$. Complete the solution for
parts α, a, and b of triangle ABC.

$\alpha = 80°$

$\dfrac{\sin \beta}{b} = \dfrac{\sin \gamma}{c}$

$b \approx 32$

$\dfrac{\sin \alpha}{a} = \dfrac{\sin \gamma}{c}$

$a \approx 34$

553 $\gamma = 120°$, $\beta = 25°$, and $c = 100$. Find the missing parts of triangle ABC.

$\alpha = 35°$
$b \approx 49$
$a \approx 66$

554 In order to find the distances
AB and CB to a landmark
across a swamp from two
points A and C, the following
measurements were made:
angle A = 40°, angle C = 62°,
and AC = 80 yards. Compute
the distances.

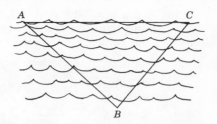

$a \approx 53$ yards, $c \approx 72$ yards
This answer was computed using the law of sines

555 If two adjacent sides of a parallelogram are 18 in. and 27 in., respectively, and they form an angle of 60° at one vertex of the parallelogram, how long is the shorter diagonal?

$BD \approx 24$ in.

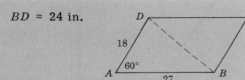

556 Find the area of the parallelogram of
the problem in frame 555. *Suggestion:*
Compute the altitude from D to AB and
use the formula A = base times altitude.
Or compute twice the area of triangle
ABD.

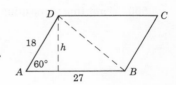

area $\square$ ≈ 421
Solution: $\sin 60° = \dfrac{h}{18}$; therefore, h = 18 sin 60°
area $\square$ = base $\cdot$ height = 27 $\cdot$ 18 sin 60° ≈ 421

557 Can there be a triangle such that β = 60°, b = 18, and c = 27? If
your answer is yes, compute angle γ.

no
Explanation:
    No triangle exists.
    Note: $\sin \gamma = \dfrac{c \sin \beta}{b}$, $\dfrac{27 \sin 60°}{18}$
        $\sin \gamma > 1$

558 Given $\gamma = 30°$, $a = 5.0$, and $c = 2.5$, find α of triangle ABC. If more than one triangle is possible with γ, a, and c as given, find both values for α.

$\alpha = 90°$
Solution:

$$\sin \alpha = \frac{a \sin \gamma}{c}$$
$$= 1$$
$$\alpha = 90°$$

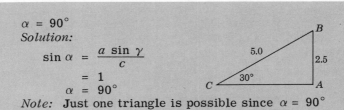

Note: Just one triangle is possible since $\alpha = 90°$

559 Given the following parts for triangle ABC: $\gamma = 42°$, $c = 6.0$, and $a = 8.0$. Find α. If there are two solutions, give both values for α.

$\alpha \approx 63°$ or $117°$
Solution:
$$\sin \alpha = 0.892$$
$$\alpha \approx 63° \text{ or } 117°$$

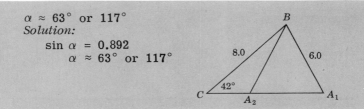

560 Find the remaining parts of triangle CA_1B.

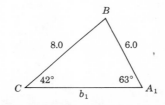

$\beta_1 \approx 75°$, $b_1 \approx 8.7$

561 Find the remaining parts of triangle CA_2B.

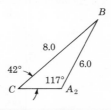

$\beta_2 \approx 21°$, $b_2 \approx 3.2$

562 $\beta = 20°$, $\alpha = 50°$, and $c = 900$.   Solve the triangle.

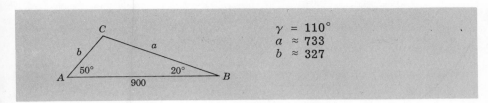

$\gamma = 110°$
$a \approx 733$
$b \approx 327$

▽**563** $a = 8$, $b = 10$, and $c = 12$.   Find the smallest angle of the triangle.

$\alpha = 41°$ *Solution:* $a^2 = b^2 + c^2 - 2bc \cos \alpha$

$$\cos \alpha = \frac{b^2 + c^2 - a^2}{2bc} = 0.75 \qquad \alpha \approx 41°$$

Note: The smallest angle of the triangle is the angle opposite the smallest side.

564 Which of the following represent parts of triangles that have two solutions?
1. $a = 21$, $c = 21$, $\alpha = 35°$ $a = b$
2. $b = 13$, $c = 20$, $\gamma = 53°$ $a > b$
3. $\alpha = 110°$, $a = 40$, $b = 25$ $a > b$
4. $a = 8$, $b = 12$, $\alpha = 34°$ $a < b$ ✓
5. $b = 12$, $c = 15$, $\gamma = 90°$ $a > b$

4. see the sketch below. Note that $h < 8$.

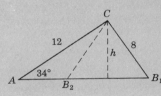

565 Some of the special angles we have studied have been recorded in radians in the following sketch. Give the corresponding measures in degrees, starting with 0 radians.

continued ➝

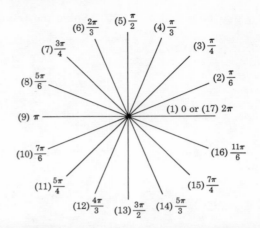

(1) $0 = 0$	**(2)** $\frac{\pi}{6} = 30°$	**(3)** $\frac{\pi}{4} = 45°$	**(4)** $\frac{\pi}{3} = 60°$
(5) $\frac{\pi}{2} = 90°$	**(6)** $\frac{2\pi}{3} = 120°$	**(7)** $\frac{3\pi}{4} = 135°$	**(8)** $\frac{5\pi}{6} = 150°$
(9) $\pi = 180°$	**(10)** $\frac{7\pi}{6} = 210°$	**(11)** $\frac{5\pi}{4} = 225°$	**(12)** $\frac{4\pi}{3} = 240°$
(13) $\frac{3\pi}{2} = 270°$	**(14)** $\frac{5\pi}{3} = 300°$	**(15)** $\frac{7\pi}{4} = 315°$	**(16)** $\frac{11\pi}{6} = 330°$
(17) $2\pi = 360°$			

566 Frame 565 did not include the 36° angle and its multiples, i.e., 72°, 108°, 144°, ..., 360°. State the above angles in radians starting with 36°.

$36° = \frac{\pi}{5}$, $72° = \frac{2\pi}{5}$, $108° = \frac{3\pi}{5}$, $144° = \frac{4\pi}{5}$, ..., $360° = 2\pi$

567 Review of signs of the functions. In quadrant I, sin θ, cos θ, and tan θ are all positive. **(1)** In quadrant II which is positive? **(2)** In quadrant III which is positive? **(3)** In quadrant IV which is positive?

(1) sin θ **(2)** tan θ **(3)** cos θ

568 A very useful and important statement which we call a trigonometric identity is obtained by applying the definitions of sin θ, cos θ, and the distance formula when θ is any angle in standard position and P is the point where the unit circle intersects the terminal side. Use proper substitutions in the statement below to report the identity.

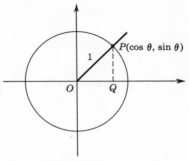

$$d(O, P)^2 = d(O, Q)^2 + d(P, Q)^2$$

Recall that $d(O, P)$ means the undirected distance from O to P.

$$1 = (\sin\ \theta)^2 + (\cos\ \theta)^2 \quad \text{or} \quad 1 = \sin^2\theta + \cos^2\theta$$

---

569 The statement $\sin^2\theta + \cos^2\theta = 1$ holds for any angle θ, hence, the name "identity." Suppose θ terminates in quadrant II, III, or IV; the statement says that $\sin^2\theta + \cos^2\theta = $ **(1)**___. *Example:* $\theta = 7\pi/6$, $\sin\theta = $ **(2)**___ and $\cos\theta = $ **(3)**___. **(4)** Find $[\sin (7\pi/6)]^2 + [\cos (7\pi/6)]^2$. *Note:* We call an equation involving trigonometric functions an *identity* if the two members of the equation are equal for all values of the angles for which both members of the equation are defined.

---

(1) 1   **(2)** $-\frac{1}{2}$ **(3)** $\frac{-\sqrt{3}}{2}$ **(4)** 1

---

570 Without referring to Panel 1, fill in a table like this with correct numerical values.

degrees	radians	sine	cosine	tangent
0				
90				
180				
270				

continued →

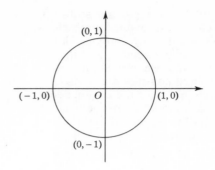

degrees	radians	sine	cosine	tangent
0	0	0	1	0
90	$\pi/2$	1	0	undefined
180	π	0	-1	0
270	$3\pi/2$	-1	0	undefined

571 If x is any angle, state the numerical value of $\sin^2 2x + \cos^2 2x$.

1   Recall that $\sin^2 \theta + \cos^2 \theta = 1$ is an identity.
In this problem, $\theta = 2x$

572 To determine the sine, cosine, and
tangent of 30° and 60° without the use
of Panel 1, first assign the proper
numerical values to the three sides of
a 30°, 60° right triangle. What are y,
r, and x?

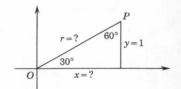

$y = 1$, $r = 2$, $x = \sqrt{3}$
Recall that the side opposite the 30° angle is equal to one-half
the hypotenuse in a 30°, 60° right triangle.

573 Complete the following statements: sin 30° = (1)_____, cos 30° = (2)_____, tan 30° = (3)____, sin 60° = (4)____, cos 60° = (5)____, and tan 60° = (6)_____.

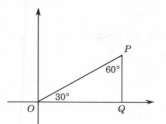 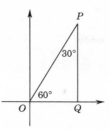

(1) $\frac{1}{2}$ (2) $\frac{\sqrt{3}}{2}$ (3) $\frac{1}{\sqrt{3}}$ (4) $\frac{\sqrt{3}}{2}$ (5) $\frac{1}{2}$ (6) $\frac{\sqrt{3}}{1}$

574 To determine the sine, cosine, and tangent of 45° without using Panel 1, you should assign what numerical values to the sides of the 45° right triangle?

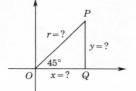

$x = 1, \; y = 1, \; r = \sqrt{2}$

575 What are (1) sin 45°, (2) cos 45°, and (3) tan 45°?

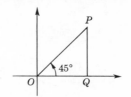

(1) $\sin 45° = \frac{1}{\sqrt{2}}$ (2) $\cos 45° = \frac{1}{\sqrt{2}}$ (3) $\tan 45° = 1$

576 State the formula for expressing a negative angle, or an angle greater than 2π, in terms of α where $0 \le \alpha < 2\pi$. This is equivalent to saying "what is the formula for finding the angle in the

continued →

interval 0 to 2π which is coterminal with any given angle?" If you cannot give the formula, explain in words how you would find α.

$\theta = (\alpha + k \cdot 2\pi)$, given k is an integer
or
Add or subtract a multiple of 2π to θ which will leave a positive remainder in the interval $0 \leq R < 2\pi$. This remainder is α.

577 Sketch the following angles and state the positive angle α less than $360°$ (or 2π) coterminal with the given angle: (1) $-500°$, (2) $7\pi/2$, and (3) -4π.

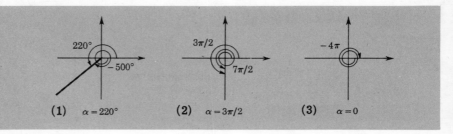

(1) $\alpha = 220°$ **(2)** $\alpha = 3\pi/2$ **(3)** $\alpha = 0$

578 If θ and α are any two coterminal angles, what important statements can you make regarding the trigonometric functions of θ and α?

$\sin \theta = \sin \alpha$, $\cos \theta = \cos \alpha$, $\tan \theta = \tan \alpha$
or
Trigonometric functions of θ and α are identical.

579 Since we know that any angle θ in radians can be expressed as $(\alpha + k \cdot 2\pi)$, where α is in the interval $0 \leq \alpha < 2\pi$, and k is an integer, we have the reduction formulas:
$$\sin \theta = \sin (\alpha + k \cdot 2\pi) = \sin \alpha$$
$$\cos \theta = (1)\underline{\hspace{3cm}}$$
$$\tan \theta = (2)\underline{\hspace{3cm}}$$

(1) $\cos (\alpha + k \cdot 2\pi) = \cos \alpha$ **(2)** $\tan (\alpha + k \cdot 2\pi) = \tan \alpha$

580 Sketch the following angles and state each function listed in terms of an angle α, $0 \le \alpha < 2\pi$: **(1)** $\sin 3\pi$, **(2)** $\tan (-20\pi/9)$, and **(3)** $\cos 820°$.

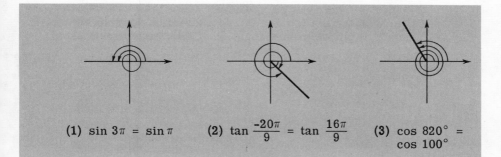

(1) $\sin 3\pi = \sin \pi$ **(2)** $\tan \dfrac{-20\pi}{9} = \tan \dfrac{16\pi}{9}$ **(3)** $\cos 820° = \cos 100°$

581 With each angle α in the interval $0 \le \alpha < 2\pi$ is associated a reference angle R. R is the positive acute angle formed by the terminal side of α and the x axis. Sketch and identify the reference angle R for each of the following: **(1)** $\alpha = 220°$, **(2)** $\alpha = 7\pi/8$, and **(3)** $\alpha = 11\pi/6$.

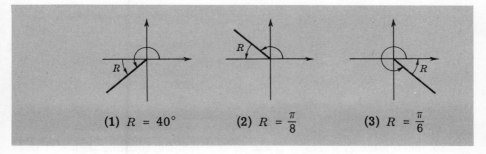

(1) $R = 40°$ **(2)** $R = \dfrac{\pi}{8}$ **(3)** $R = \dfrac{\pi}{6}$

582 In general, when α is a positive angle, $\alpha < 2\pi$:
     If α terminates in quadrant II, $R_2 = \pi - \alpha$
     If α terminates in quadrant III, $R_3 =$ **(1)**_____
     If α terminates in quadrant IV, $R_4 =$ **(2)**_____
Make sketches of **(3)** R_3 and **(4)** R_4.

(1) $\alpha - \pi$ **(2)** $2\pi - \alpha$

(3)   **(4)**

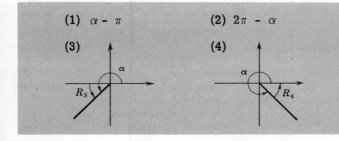

583 Given α a positive angle, $\pi/2 < \alpha \le \pi$, then α is a second-quadrant angle, and

$$\sin \alpha = \sin (\pi - \alpha) = \sin R$$
$$\cos \alpha = -\cos (\pi - \alpha) = -\cos R$$
$$\tan \alpha = -\tan (\pi - \alpha) = -\tan R$$

Make a similar list for α a third-quadrant angle, showing how to reduce α to the reference angle R. Check carefully on signs.

$\left(\pi < \alpha \le \dfrac{3\pi}{2}\right)$, α positive, then α is a third-quadrant angle

$$\sin \alpha = -\sin (\alpha - \pi) = -\sin R$$
$$\cos \alpha = -\cos (\alpha - \pi) = -\cos R$$
$$\tan \alpha = \tan (\alpha - \pi) = \tan R$$

584 Express the following accurately in terms of a reference angle R, which is a positive acute angle, and give the numerical value of the function without referring to a table (check signs):

(1) $\sin \dfrac{5\pi}{3}$ = (a)_____ = (b)_____

(2) $\cos \dfrac{7\pi}{4}$ = (a)_____ = (b)_____

(3) $\tan \dfrac{11\pi}{6}$ = (a)_____ = (b)_____

(1) (a) $-\sin \dfrac{\pi}{3}$,   (b) $\dfrac{-\sqrt{3}}{2}$ (2) (a) $\cos \dfrac{\pi}{4}$,   (b) $\dfrac{1}{\sqrt{2}}$

(3) (a) $-\tan \dfrac{\pi}{6}$,   (b) $\dfrac{-1}{\sqrt{3}}$

585 Sketch the graph of $y = \sin \alpha$, $0 \le \alpha < 2\pi$, locating points at intervals of $\pi/6$. Do not refer to any panel.

see Panel 3 for the answer.

586 The graph you constructed in frame 585 represents one period of the sine function. What does this statement mean?

The graph is of one cycle of $\sin \alpha$. Adding or subtracting any number of complete revolutions does not change the position of the terminal side of α. As α increases from 0 to 2π, the $\sin \alpha$ is represented by the different values shown on the graph; this interval, 0 to 2π, is the smallest in which all the values can be shown. As α increases through another 2π radians, the values of $\sin \alpha$ repeat in the same order.

587 Sketch the graph of $y = \cos \alpha$, $0 \le \alpha < 2\pi$, locating points at intervals of $\pi/6$. Do not refer to any panel.

see Panel 5 for the answer.

588 (1) Did your graph in frame 587 represent one period of the cosine function? (2) What was the greatest value of cos α? (3) the smallest?

(1) yes (2) cos $0° = 1$ (3) cos $180° = -1$

589 The maximum numerical (absolute) value of sin α or cos α is called the *amplitude* of the function. As you have seen from your tables (or graphs), the amplitude of sin α is (1)__ and the amplitude of cos α is (2)__. Write the correct number for each blank.

(1) 1 (2) 1
This is the vertical distance from the x axis to the highest (or lowest) point of the graph.

590 Complete the table below and sketch the graph.

α	$-\pi/2$	$-\pi/3$	$-\pi/4$	$-\pi/6$	0	$\pi/6$	$\pi/4$	$\pi/3$	$\pi/2$
tan α	unde-fined	$-\sqrt{3}$							

see Panels 6 and 7 for the answer. Check from $\alpha = -\pi/2$ to $\alpha = \pi/2$

591 Examining Panels 6 and 7 and recalling previous discussions, (1) state the number of degrees or radians in one period of tan α. (2) What are the values of α for which tan α is undefined in the interval $-\pi \le \alpha < \pi$? (3) At these points is your graph continuous or discontinuous? *Note:* A continuous function over a given interval has a value at every point of the interval.

(1) π radians or $180°$ (2) $\frac{-\pi}{2}, \frac{\pi}{2}$ (3) discontinuous

592   Are there any points of discontinuity on the graph of (1) $y = \sin \alpha$?
(2) $y = \cos \alpha$? If so, state the values of α at which they occur.
One period for either $\sin \alpha$ or $\cos \alpha$ is (3)___ radians; hence, an
examination of such an interval would reveal whether or not the
graph is continuous. *Note:* A more complete study of the graphs
of the trigonometric functions will be made later in this program.

(1) no   (2) no   (3) 2π

593   θ is a third-quadrant angle, and $\sin \theta = -\frac{1}{2}$.   (1) Make a sketch.
Find (2) $\cos \theta$ and (3) $\tan \theta$.

(1)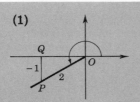

(2) $\cos \theta = \dfrac{-\sqrt{3}}{2}$

(3) $\tan \theta = \dfrac{1}{\sqrt{3}}$

or

(1)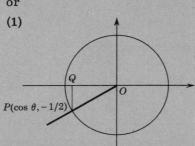

(2) $\cos \theta = \dfrac{-\sqrt{3}}{2}$

Solution:
$$1 = \cos^2 \theta + (-\tfrac{1}{2})^2$$
$$\frac{\sqrt{3}}{2} = \pm\cos \theta$$
For quadrant III
$$\cos \theta = \frac{-\sqrt{3}}{2}$$

(3) $\tan \theta = \dfrac{1}{\sqrt{3}}$

Solution:
$$\tan = \frac{-1/2}{-\sqrt{3}/3} = \frac{1}{\sqrt{3}}$$

594   $\cos \theta = -1/\sqrt{2}$.   (1) Find the two values of θ, $0 \le \theta < 2\pi$, for which
this is true.   (2) Make a sketch.

(1) $\theta = 135°, 225°$ (2)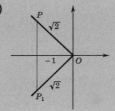

595 Without using Panel 1, find the value of cos (-5π/3) · cos (13π/6).
Notice that you are asked to find the *product* of the two cosines
given above.

$$\frac{1}{2} \cdot \frac{\sqrt{3}}{2} = \frac{\sqrt{3}}{4}$$

596 Without referring to Panel 1, find the acute angle θ such that
(1) sin θ = $\sqrt{2}/2$ and (2) tan θ = $\sqrt{3}$.

(1) $\theta = \dfrac{\pi}{4} = 45°$ **(2)** $\theta = \dfrac{\pi}{3} = 60°$

Solution: Make a sketch and recall the special angles for
which you have expressed functions in radical form.

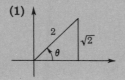 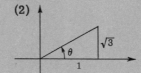

▽597 From point A, a boy drives 12 miles due west on a highway to point
B. He then changes routes and travels 5 miles on a road bearing
directly northwest and stops at point C. Measured in a straight
line, how far is he from his starting point? (Directly northwest
means 45° west of north.)

$b \approx 16$ miles
Solution:
$$\begin{aligned}
b^2 &= a^2 + c^2 - 2ac \cos B \\
&\approx 12^2 + 5^2 - 2 \cdot 12 \cdot 5 \cdot (-0.707) \\
&\approx 254 \\
b &\approx 16
\end{aligned}$$

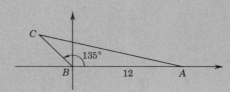

598   Three sides of a triangle are 7, 12, and 13. Find the smallest angle of the triangle.

$\alpha \approx 32°$
Solution:

$$\cos \alpha = \frac{b^2 + c^2 - a^2}{2bc}$$

$$\approx 0.846$$
$$\alpha \approx 32°$$

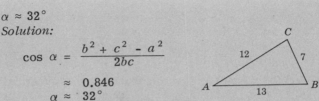

Note: α is an acute angle if cos α is positive.

599   If two angles α and β of triangle ABC are 30° and 45°, respectively, and side b is 18 in., find **(1)** the third angle and **(2)** side a without using tables.

(1) $\gamma = 105°$ **(2)** $a \approx 12.7$ *Solution:* $\dfrac{a}{\sin \alpha} = \dfrac{b}{\sin \beta}$

$$a = \frac{18 \cdot 1/2}{1/\sqrt{2}} \approx 12.7$$

▽**600**   Compute the numerical value of the following without referring to tables:
$4(\cos 180°) + (5(\sin 90°) - 8(\sin 210°) + 10(\cos 660°)$

$4(-1) + (5(1) - 8(-\frac{1}{2}) + 10(\frac{1}{2}) = 10$

601   Given $a = 21$, $b = 18$, and $\beta = 50°$, how many triangles are possible?

two triangles,

$\alpha \approx 63°$ or   117°

602 Prove that in triangle ABC,

$$\frac{\sin \alpha - \sin \beta}{\sin \alpha + \sin \beta} = \frac{a - b}{a + b}$$

One possibility is to solve $a/\sin \alpha = b/\sin \beta$ for $\sin \alpha$ and use this as a substitution in the left member. Try it.

Here is the solution:
Substituting $\sin \alpha = a \sin \beta/b$ in the left member, we get

$$\frac{a \sin \beta/b - \sin \beta/1}{a \sin \beta/b + \sin \beta/1} = \frac{(a \sin \beta - b \sin \beta)/b}{(a \sin \beta + b \sin \beta)/b}$$

$$= \frac{(a - b) \sin \beta}{(a + b) \sin \beta} = \frac{a - b}{a + b}$$

Therefore, $\dfrac{\sin \alpha - \sin \beta}{\sin \alpha + \sin \beta} = \dfrac{a - b}{a + b}$

603 You saw in frame 602 that you could work from the left member of $\dfrac{\sin \alpha - \sin \beta}{\sin \alpha + \sin \beta} = \dfrac{a - b}{a + b}$ and show that it is equivalent to the right member. Now start with the right member and show that it is equivalent to the left. Use the law of sines again and make a substitution.

One solution is given, there are others.
Substituting $a = b \sin \alpha/\sin \beta$ in the right member, we get

$$\frac{b \sin \alpha/\sin \beta - b/1}{b \sin \alpha/\sin \beta + b/1} = \frac{(b \sin \alpha - b \sin \beta)/\sin \beta}{(b \sin \alpha + b \sin \beta)/\sin \beta}$$

$$= \frac{b(\sin \alpha - \sin \beta)}{b(\sin \alpha + \sin \beta)} = \frac{\sin \alpha - \sin \beta}{\sin \alpha + \sin \beta}$$

Therefore, $\dfrac{a - b}{a + b} = \dfrac{\sin \alpha - \sin \beta}{\sin \alpha + \sin \beta}$

604 Use the distance formula

$$d = \sqrt{(x_2 - x_1)^2 + (y_2 - y_1)^2}$$ to find

the length of the chord PQ which subtends the central angle θ in the circle whose radius is r.

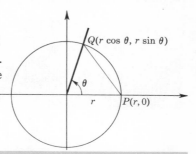

$d = r\sqrt{2 - 2 \cos \theta}$

continued →

Solution:
$$d = \sqrt{(r \cos \theta - r)^2 + (r \sin \theta)^2}$$
$$= \sqrt{r^2 \cos^2 \theta - 2r^2 \cos \theta + r^2 + r^2 \sin^2 \theta}$$
$$= r\sqrt{\cos^2 \theta + \sin^2 \theta + 1 - 2 \cos \theta}$$
$$= r\sqrt{1 + 1 - 2 \cos \theta} = r\sqrt{2 - 2 \cos \theta}$$

In the third step recall that $\cos^2 \theta + \sin^2 \theta = 1$

REVIEW OF ALGEBRA

Comment

Proving theorems, deriving new formulas, solving equations, etc., in the study of trigonometry require accuracy and skill in performing ordinary algebraic operations. In frames 605 to 621 illustrative review examples are given. Study them. Then complete the problem in which you will find trigonometric applications.

605 Type 1: Special products and factoring.
    Example: $(a - b)(a + b) = a^2 - b^2$
    Problems: $(x - y)(x + y) =$ **(1)** _____
                  $(7 - m)(7 + m) =$ **(2)** _____
                  $(\sin \theta - \cos \theta)(\sin \theta + \cos \theta) =$ **(3)** _____

(1) $x^2 - y^2$ **(2)** $49 - m^2$ **(3)** $\sin^2 \theta - \cos^2 \theta$

606 Type 1. *Example:* $a^2 - b^2 = (a - b)(a + b)$
    Problems: $4 - x^2 =$ **(1)** (_____)(_____)
              $9^2 - 25y^2 =$ **(2)** (_____)(_____)
              $\cos^2 x - \sin^2 x =$ **(3)** (_____)(_____)
              $\cos^2 x - 1 =$ **(4)** (_____)(_____)

(1) $(2 - x)(2 + x)$ **(2)** $(3x - 5y)(3x + 5y)$
(3) $(\cos x - \sin x)(\cos x + \sin x)$ **(4)** $(\cos x - 1)(\cos x + 1)$

607   Type 1: Finding products and factoring.

$(3 - \sqrt{2})(3 + \sqrt{2}) = $ (1)_____

$(1 - 3 \tan \theta)(1 + 3 \tan \theta) = $ (2)_____

(3) (_____)(_____) $= 1 - \sin^2 \theta$

(4) (_____)(_____) $= \cos^2 \beta - \sin^2 \alpha$

(1) $9 - \sqrt{4} = 9 - 2 = 7$ **(2)** $1 - 9 \tan^2 \theta$
(3) $(1 - \sin \theta)(1 + \sin \theta)$ **(4)** $(\cos \beta - \sin \alpha)(\cos \beta + \sin \alpha)$

608   Type 2: Squaring a binomial.

Examples: 1. $(a - b)^2 = a^2 - 2ab + b^2$ *Solution:*
   2. $(a + b)^2 = a^2 + 2ab + b^2$

$$\begin{array}{r} a - b \\ a - b \\ \hline ab + b^2 \\ a^2 - ab \\ \hline a^2 - 2ab + b^2 \end{array}$$

Problems: $(x + y)^2 = $ (1)_____
$(3x - 2y)^2 = $ (2)_____
$(\sin x + \cos x)^2 = $ (3)_____
$(1 - \tan x)^2 = $ (4)_____

(1) $x^2 + 2xy + y^2$ **(2)** $9x^2 - 12xy + 4y^2$
(3) $\sin^2 x + 2 \sin x \cos x + \cos^2 x$ **(4)** $1 - 2 \tan x + \tan^2 x$
Note: In (3) if we rearrange the terms thus $(\sin^2 x + \cos^2 x) +$
$2 \sin x \cos x$, and recall that $\sin^2 x + \cos^2 x = 1$, we can write
this as $1 + 2 \sin x \cos x$.

609   Type 2: Factoring.

Examples: 1. $a^2 - 2ab + b^2 = (a - b)(a - b) = (a - b)^2$

   2. $a^2 + 2ab + b^2 = (a + b)(a + b) = (a + b)^2$

Problems: $x^2 + 6xy + 9y^2 = $ (1)_____

$36m^2 - 60ms + 25s^2 = $ (2)_____

$\sin^2 \alpha + 2 \sin \alpha + 1 = $ (3)_____

$\tan^2 x - 2 \tan x \tan y + \tan^2 y = $ (4)_____

(1) $(x + 3y)^2$ **(2)** $(6m - 5s)^2$
(3) $(\sin \alpha + 1)^2$ **(4)** $(\tan x - \tan y)^2$

610 Type 3: Operating with a common monomial factor.
    Examples: 1. $a(x - y) = ax - ay$
                2. $a(x - y)^2 = a(x^2 - 2xy + y^2) = ax^2 - 2axy + ay^2$

    Problems: $4(x^2 - 3x) = (1)$_____
               $r(\cos \theta + i \sin \theta) = (2)$_____
               $3x(\sin \alpha - \cos \beta)(\sin \alpha + \cos \beta) = (3)$_____

(1) $4x^2 - 12x$ **(2)** $r \cos \theta + ri \sin \theta$
(3) $3x \sin^2 \alpha - 3x \cos^2 \beta$

611 Type 3 (continued).
    Examples: 1. $ax + ay = a(x + y)$
                2. $8ax^2 - 24axy + 18ay^2 = 2a(2x - 3y)^2$

    Problems: $5 \sin x - 5 \cos y = (1)$_____

             $\dfrac{\sqrt{2}}{2} \cos x + i \dfrac{\sqrt{2}}{2} \sin x = (2)$_____

             $\sin x \cos^2 x - \sin^3 x = (3)$_____

             $\cos x \sin^2 x + \cos^3 x = (4)$_____
                                 (Simplify this answer)

(1) $5(\sin x - \cos y)$ **(2)** $\dfrac{\sqrt{2}}{2}(\cos x + i \sin x)$

(3) $\sin x(\cos^2 x - \sin^2 x)$ or
    $\sin x(\cos x - \sin x)(\cos x + \sin x)$

(4) $\cos x(\sin^2 x + \cos^2 x) = \cos x$
Note: Since $\sin^2 x + \cos^2 x = 1$, we can simplify thus:
$\cos x (1) = \cos x$.

612 Simplifying fractions: Multiplying (or dividing) both numerator and denominator of a fraction by the same nonzero quantity does not change the value of the fraction.

    Examples: 1. $\dfrac{a^2}{ab} = \dfrac{a^2/a}{ab/a} = \dfrac{a}{b}$

               2. $\dfrac{x^2 - y^2}{x^2 + 2xy + y^2} = \dfrac{(x - y)\overset{1}{\cancel{(x + y)}}}{(x + y)\underset{1}{\cancel{(x + y)}}} = \dfrac{x - y}{x + y}$

continued →

Examples: $\dfrac{\sin^2 \alpha}{\sin \alpha \cos \alpha}$ = (1)_____

$\dfrac{\sin^2 \alpha + 2 \sin \alpha \cos \alpha + \cos^2 \alpha}{\sin^2 \alpha - \cos^2 \alpha}$ = (2)_____

(1) $\dfrac{\sin^2 \alpha}{\sin \alpha \cos \alpha} = \dfrac{\sin \alpha}{\cos \alpha}$

(2) $\dfrac{\sin^2 \alpha + 2 \sin \alpha \cos \alpha + \cos^2 \alpha}{\sin^2 \alpha - \cos^2 \alpha}$

$= \dfrac{(\sin \alpha + \cos \alpha) \overset{1}{\cancel{(\sin \alpha + \cos \alpha)}}}{(\sin \alpha - \cos \alpha) \underset{1}{\cancel{(\sin \alpha + \cos \alpha)}}} = \dfrac{\sin \alpha + \cos \alpha}{\sin \alpha - \cos \alpha}$

613 Simplify the fractions

$\dfrac{3x - 9y}{x^2 - 6xy + 9y^2}$ = (1)_____

$\dfrac{\sin \alpha \cos \beta - \cos^2 \beta}{\sin^2 \alpha - \sin \alpha \cos \beta}$ = (2)_____

(1) $\dfrac{3\overset{1}{\cancel{(x - 3y)}}}{(x - 3y) \underset{1}{\cancel{(x - 3y)}}} = \dfrac{3}{x - 3y}$

(2) $\dfrac{\cos \beta \overset{1}{\cancel{(\sin \alpha - \cos \beta)}}}{\sin \alpha \underset{1}{\cancel{(\sin \alpha - \cos \beta)}}} = \dfrac{\cos \beta}{\sin \alpha}$

614 Notice below the advantage of writing $y - x$ in the equivalent form $-1(x - y)$.

Example: $\dfrac{y - x}{x - y} = \dfrac{-1\overset{1}{\cancel{(x - y)}}}{\underset{1}{\cancel{x - y}}} = -1$

Problems: $\dfrac{\cos \alpha - \sin \alpha}{r \sin \alpha - r \cos \alpha}$ = (1)_____

$\dfrac{1 - \sin^2 x}{\sin x - 1}$ = (2)_____

(1) $\dfrac{-1\overset{1}{\cancel{(\sin \alpha - \cos \alpha)}}}{r \underset{1}{\cancel{(\sin \alpha - \cos \alpha)}}} = \dfrac{-1}{r}$

continued →

(2) $\dfrac{\overset{1}{\cancel{(1 - \sin x)}}(1 + \sin x)}{-1\underset{1}{\cancel{(1 - \sin x)}}} = \dfrac{1 + \sin x}{-1}$

$$= -1 - \sin x \quad \text{or} \quad -1(1 + \sin x)$$

615 Simplifying fractions containing radical terms (simplifying the denominator).

Examples: 1. $\dfrac{1}{\sqrt{a}} = \dfrac{1 \cdot \sqrt{a}}{\sqrt{a} \cdot \sqrt{a}} = \dfrac{\sqrt{a}}{\sqrt{a}^2} = \dfrac{\sqrt{a}}{a}$

2. $\dfrac{\sqrt{a} - b}{\sqrt{a} + b} = \dfrac{(\sqrt{a} - b) \cdot (\sqrt{a} - b)}{(\sqrt{a} + b) \cdot (\sqrt{a} - b)}$

$$= \dfrac{a - 2b\sqrt{a} + b^2}{\sqrt{a}^2 - b^2} = \dfrac{a - 2b\sqrt{a} + b^2}{a - b^2}$$

Problems: $\dfrac{1}{\sqrt{3}}$ = (1)_____

$\dfrac{a + \sqrt{b}}{a - \sqrt{b}}$ = (2)_____

Note: Be sure that your choice of multiplier will produce a denominator free of radicals.

(1) $\dfrac{1 \cdot 3}{\sqrt{3} \cdot \sqrt{3}} = \dfrac{\sqrt{3}}{\sqrt{9}} = \dfrac{\sqrt{3}}{3}$

(2) $\dfrac{(a + \sqrt{b}) \cdot (a + \sqrt{b})}{(a - \sqrt{b}) \cdot (a + \sqrt{b})} = \dfrac{a^2 + 2a\sqrt{b} + b}{a^2 - b}$

616 *Problems:* Simplify the denominators.

$\dfrac{1}{\sqrt{a} + \sqrt{b}}$ = (1)_____

$\dfrac{b - \sqrt{b}}{\sqrt{b}}$ = (2)_____

$\dfrac{\sqrt{3}}{\sqrt{3} - a}$ = (3)_____

(1) $\dfrac{1 \cdot (\sqrt{a} - \sqrt{b})}{(\sqrt{a} + \sqrt{b}) \cdot (\sqrt{a} - \sqrt{b})} = \dfrac{\sqrt{a} - \sqrt{b}}{a - b}$

continued →

(2) $\dfrac{(b - \sqrt{b}) \cdot \sqrt{b}}{\sqrt{b} \cdot \sqrt{b}} = \dfrac{b\sqrt{b} - b}{b} = \dfrac{\overset{1}{\cancel{b}}(\sqrt{b} - 1)}{\underset{1}{\cancel{b}}} = \sqrt{b} - 1$

(3) $\dfrac{\sqrt{3} \cdot (\sqrt{3} + a)}{(\sqrt{3} - a) \cdot (\sqrt{3} + a)} = \dfrac{3 + a\sqrt{3}}{3 - a^2}$

617 Notice the difference in the denominators of the examples below.

Examples: 1. $\dfrac{a}{\sqrt{a - b}} = \dfrac{a \cdot \sqrt{a - b}}{\sqrt{a - b} \cdot \sqrt{a - b}} = \dfrac{a\sqrt{a - b}}{\sqrt{(a - b)^2}} = \dfrac{a\sqrt{a - b}}{a - b}$

2. $\dfrac{a}{\sqrt{a} - \sqrt{b}} = \dfrac{a \cdot (\sqrt{a} + \sqrt{b})}{(\sqrt{a} - \sqrt{b}) \cdot (\sqrt{a} + \sqrt{b})} = \dfrac{a\sqrt{a} + a\sqrt{b}}{a - b}$

Problems: Simplify the denominators.

$\dfrac{1}{\sqrt{1 - \cos \theta}} =$ (1)_____

$\dfrac{\sqrt{1 + \cos \theta}}{\sqrt{1 - \cos \theta}} =$ (2)_____

(1) $\dfrac{1 \cdot \sqrt{1 - \cos \theta}}{\sqrt{1 - \cos \theta} \cdot \sqrt{1 - \cos \theta}} = \dfrac{\sqrt{1 - \cos \theta}}{1 - \cos \theta}$

(2) $\dfrac{\sqrt{1 + \cos \theta} \cdot \sqrt{1 - \cos \theta}}{\sqrt{1 - \cos \theta} \cdot \sqrt{1 - \cos \theta}} = \dfrac{\sqrt{1 - \cos \theta}}{\sqrt{(1 - \cos \theta)^2}} = \dfrac{\sqrt{1 - \cos^2 \theta}}{1 - \cos \theta}$

Note: We might write $\sin^2 \theta + \cos^2 \theta = 1$ in the form
$\sin^2 \theta = 1 - \cos^2 \theta$. Therefore, the last statement above may
be written

$\dfrac{\sqrt{\sin^2 \theta}}{1 - \cos \theta} = \dfrac{\sin \theta}{1 - \cos \theta}$

618 Occasionally we find that eliminating the radical terms from the numerator of a fraction is an advantage.

Problem: $\dfrac{\sqrt{1 - \cos x}}{\sqrt{1 + \cos x}}$

Simplify by first multiplying both numerator and denominator by
$\sqrt{1 - \cos x}$.

$\dfrac{\sqrt{1 - \cos x} \cdot \sqrt{1 - \cos x}}{\sqrt{1 + \cos x} \cdot \sqrt{1 - \cos x}} = \dfrac{\sqrt{(1 - \cos x)^2}}{\sqrt{1 - \cos^2 x}} = \dfrac{1 - \cos x}{\sin x}$

619 Simplify the fraction $\sqrt{1 - \cos\ x}/\sqrt{1 + \cos\ x}$ in frame 618 by using $\sqrt{1 + \cos\ x}$ as the multiplier of both numerator and denominator.

$$\frac{\sqrt{1 - \cos\ x}}{\sqrt{1 + \cos\ x}} = \frac{\sqrt{1 - \cos\ x}\cdot\sqrt{1 + \cos\ x}}{\sqrt{1 + \cos\ x}\cdot\sqrt{1 + \cos\ x}} = \frac{\sqrt{1 - \cos^2\ x}}{\sqrt{(1 + \cos x)^2}} = \frac{\sin\ x}{1 + \cos\ x}$$

Note: The purpose for which the simplification is made would determine which form is better for a particular problem.

620 Addition or subtraction of fractions requires a common denominator.

Example: $\dfrac{a}{x} + \dfrac{b}{y} = \dfrac{a\cdot y + b\cdot x}{x\cdot y} = \dfrac{ay + bx}{xy}$

Problems: $\dfrac{3}{2x} - \dfrac{5}{3y} = $ **(1)**_____

$\dfrac{1}{\sin^2\alpha} + \dfrac{1}{\cos^2\alpha} = $ **(2)**_____

(1) $\dfrac{9y - 10x}{6xy}$ **(2)** $\dfrac{\cos^2\alpha + \sin^2\alpha}{\sin^2\alpha\ \cos^2\alpha}$

Note: In **(2)** the fraction can be further simplified to

$$\frac{1}{\sin^2\alpha\ \cos^2\alpha}$$

▽621 Fractions (*continued*). Study this example showing addition of fractions.

$$\frac{x + y}{2x - 2y} - \frac{3x^2 - 2y^2}{x^2 - y^2} = \frac{x + y}{2(x - y)} - \frac{3x^2 - 2y^2}{(x - y)(x + y)}$$

$$= \frac{(x + y)(x + y) - 2(3x^2 - 2y^2)}{2(x - y)(x + y)}$$

$$= \frac{x^2 + 2xy + y^2 - 6x^2 + 4y^2}{2(x - y)(x + y)}$$

$$= \frac{5x^2 + 2xy + 5y^2}{2(x - y)(x + y)} \quad \text{or} \quad \frac{-5x^2 + 2xy + 5y^2}{2x^2 - 2y^2}$$

continued →

Solve the problem: $\dfrac{\sin x}{1 - \cos^2 x} - \dfrac{\sin x}{1 + \cos x} = $ _____

$$\frac{\sin x}{(1 - \cos x)(1 + \cos x)} - \frac{\sin x}{1 + \cos x}$$

$$= \frac{\sin x - \sin x (1 - \cos x)}{(1 - \cos x)(1 + \cos x)} = \frac{\sin x - \sin x + \sin x \cos x}{(1 - \cos x)(1 + \cos x)}$$

$$= \frac{\sin x \cos x}{1 - \cos^2 x} \qquad \text{We may reduce this term since}$$
$$\qquad\qquad\qquad\qquad 1 - \cos^2 x = \sin^2 x$$

$$= \frac{\sin x \cos x}{\sin^2 x} = \frac{\cos x}{\sin x}$$

BASIC TRIGONOMETRIC FORMULAS

Comment

Addition Formulas.   We are ready now to state and prove important theorems which express sines and cosines of the sum (or difference) of two angles in terms of the individual angle functions.

622 Given any two angles α and β
    Theorem I. $\cos(\alpha - \beta) = \cos \alpha \cos \beta + \sin \alpha \sin \beta$
    Theorem II. $\sin(\alpha - \beta) = \sin \alpha \cos \beta - \cos \alpha \sin \beta$
First be sure you read the theorems correctly. (1) Could the left
member of Theorem I be written $\cos \alpha - \cos \beta$? Let $\alpha = 60°$ and
$\beta = 45°$, use Panel 1 to (2) compare the two statements
$\cos(60° - 45°)$ and $\cos 60° - \cos 45°$.

(1) no   (2) $\cos(60° - 45°) = \cos 15° \approx 0.966$
              $\cos 60° - \cos 45° \approx 0.500 - 0.707 \approx -0.207$
              $0.966 \neq -0.207$

623 Verify Theorem I, $\cos(\alpha - \beta) = \cos \alpha \cos \beta + \sin \alpha \sin \beta$, for
the particular case when $\alpha = 60°$ and $\beta = 45°$. This means to
show by substitution of numerical values that
    $\cos(60° - 45°) = \cos 60° \cos 45° + \sin 60° \sin 45°$

continued →

Use the simple radical values for the functions on the right member. Recall from frame 622 that cos (60° - 45°) = cos 15° ≈ 0.966.

$$\cos(60° - 45°) = \cos 60° \cos 45° + \sin 60° \sin 45°$$
$$0.966 = \frac{1}{2} \cdot \frac{1}{\sqrt{2}} + \frac{\sqrt{3}}{2} \cdot \frac{1}{\sqrt{2}} = \frac{1 + \sqrt{3}}{2\sqrt{2}} \approx 0.966$$

624 Let $\alpha = 90°$ and $\beta = 60°$. Verify numerically the following:
(1) $\cos(\alpha - \beta) = \cos \alpha \cos \beta + \sin \alpha \sin \beta$
(2) $\cos(\alpha - \beta) \neq \cos \alpha - \cos \beta$

(1) $\cos(90° - 60°) = \cos 90° \cos 60° + \sin 90° \sin 60°$

$$\cos 30° = 0 \cdot \frac{1}{2} + 1 \cdot \frac{\sqrt{3}}{2}, \ \frac{\sqrt{3}}{2} = \frac{\sqrt{3}}{2}$$

(2) $\cos(90° - 60°) \neq \cos 90° - \cos 60°$

$$\cos 30° \neq 0 - \cos 60°, \ \frac{\sqrt{3}}{2} \neq -\frac{1}{2}$$

625 The theorem $\cos(\alpha - \beta) = \cos \alpha \cos \beta + \sin \alpha \sin \beta$ states that the cosine of $(\alpha - \beta)$ can be obtained in a special way using sines and cosines of α and β. Make a sketch of α and β on the same set of axes, letting α terminate in quadrant III and β terminate in quadrant II, and indicate the angle $(\alpha - \beta)$ in your sketch.
Notes: Keep a copy of this sketch; you will add to it later. The choice of quadrants in which α and β terminate is arbitrary.

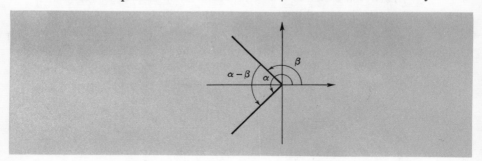

626 Some observations are in order before we make the proof. Recall that the sine or cosine of an angle greater than 2π or less than 0 may be expressed as sine or cosine, respectively, of a coterminal angle in the interval 0 to 2π thus: Let A and B represent any two angles.
$$\cos A = \cos(\alpha + k_1 \cdot 2\pi) = \cos \alpha, \ 0 \leq \alpha < 2\pi, \ k_1 \text{ an integer}$$
$$\cos B = \cos(\beta + k_2 \cdot 2\pi) = \cos \beta, \ 0 \leq \beta < 2\pi, \ k_2 \text{ an integer}$$

continued →

We can state the angle which represents the difference of A and B
thus
$$A - B = (\alpha + k_1 \cdot 2\pi) - (\beta + k_2 \cdot 2\pi) = (\alpha - \beta) + (k_1 - k_2) \cdot 2\pi$$
Therefore, $\cos (A - B) = \cos [(\alpha - \beta) + (k_1 - k_2)2] = \cos (\alpha - \beta)$
A similar conclusion can be made for the $\sin (A - B)$. State it.

$$\sin (A - B) = \sin (\alpha - \beta)$$

627 Recall also that for any angle θ we have shown that $\cos \theta =$
$\cos (-\theta)$; hence, we do not need to require that α be larger than β
in the formula for $\cos (\alpha - \beta)$. In other words $\cos (\alpha - \beta) =$
$\cos [-(\alpha - \beta)] = \cos (\underline{\hspace{2cm}})$. (For the blank insert the
simplified form for $-(\alpha - \beta)$ and then look at your sketch or make a
new one to see the application.)

$$-\alpha + \beta = \beta - \alpha$$

628 We should remind you at this point that:
$\cos \theta = \cos (-\theta)$ but $\sin \theta \neq \sin (-\theta)$.
Study this sketch and answer the
following: **(1)** $\cos \theta =$ **(a)**_____,
$\cos (-\theta) =$ **(b)**_____; hence, $\cos \theta =$
$\cos (-\theta)$. **(2)** $\sin \theta =$ **(a)**_____,
$\sin (-\theta) =$ **(b)**_____; hence, $\sin \theta \neq$
$\sin (-\theta)$ but $\sin \theta = -\sin (-\theta)$. (Answer
in terms of $\pm x$, $\pm y$, and r.)

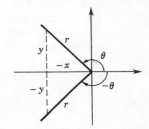

(1) (a) $\frac{-x}{r}$, **(b)** $\frac{-x}{r}$ **(2) (a)** $\frac{y}{r}$, **(b)** $\frac{-y}{r}$

629 Summary. First, the sine and cosine of angle θ, $\theta > 2\pi$ or $\theta < 0$,
may be expressed as sine and cosine, respectively, of coterminal
angles in the interval 0 to 2π. Second, for any angle θ, $\cos \theta =$
$\cos (-\theta)$. Hence, there are two observations:
1. We do not need to require that α be larger than β in the formula
   for $\cos (\alpha - \beta)$.
2. The theorem we are about to establish is true for any angles α
   and β and will therefore be referred to as an *identity*.

continued ➤

On the sketch you started in frame 625 draw a unit circle and let
$P(\cos \alpha, \sin \alpha)$ and $Q(\cos \beta, \sin \beta)$ be the points of intersection of
the terminal sides of α and β, respectively, with the circle.

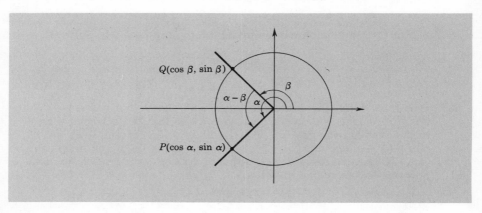

630 In frames 630 to 634 is the proof for Theorem I, $\cos (\alpha - \beta) =$
$\cos \alpha \cos \beta - \sin \alpha \sin \beta$. Step I: Use the distance formula and
the coordinates as you have them on your sketch to get a statement
for $d(P, Q)^2$ in terms of sines and cosines of α and β. You will be
asked to simplify the statement in frame 631.

Formula: Distance between two points $P(x_1 y_1)$ and $Q(x_2 y_2)$
$$d(P, Q)^2 = (x_1 - x_2)^2 + (y_1 - y_2)^2$$
$$= (\cos \alpha - \cos \beta)^2 + (\sin \alpha - \sin \beta)^2$$

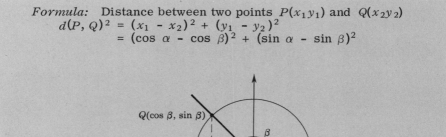

631 Simplify the right member of the statement
$$d(P, Q)^2 = (\cos \alpha - \cos \beta)^2 + (\sin \alpha - \sin \beta)^2$$

$$
\begin{aligned}
d(P, Q)^2 &= \cos^2 \alpha - 2 \cos \alpha \cos \beta + \cos^2 \beta + \sin^2 \alpha \\
&\qquad\qquad\qquad\qquad\qquad - 2 \sin \alpha \sin \beta + \sin^2 \beta \\
&= (\cos^2 \alpha + \sin^2 \alpha) + (\cos^2 \beta + \sin^2 \beta) \\
&\qquad\qquad\qquad\qquad - 2 \cos \alpha \cos \beta - 2 \sin \alpha \sin \beta \\
&= 1 + 1 - 2(\cos \alpha \cos \beta + \sin \alpha \sin \beta) \\
&= 2 - 2(\cos \alpha \cos \beta + \sin \alpha \sin \beta)
\end{aligned}
$$

Recall for Step 2 above that $\cos^2 \theta + \sin^2 \theta = 1$ for all θ.

632 Another statement for $d(P, Q)^2$ can be obtained by thinking of a triangle OPQ and applying the law of cosines with $(\alpha - \beta)$ the angle opposite side PQ. Fill in the statement for the law of cosines and simplify
$$d(P, Q)^2 = \underline{\hspace{3cm}}$$
Note: OQ and OP are radii of the unit circle; therefore, $OQ = OP = 1$

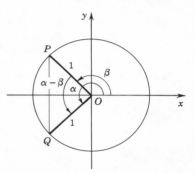

$$
\begin{aligned}
d(P, Q)^2 &= \overline{OQ}^2 + \overline{OP}^2 - 2 \cdot \overline{OQ} \cdot \overline{OP} \cdot \cos (\alpha - \beta) \\
&= 1^2 + 1^2 - 2 \cdot 1 \cdot 1 \cdot \cos (\alpha - \beta) = 2 - 2 \cos (\alpha - \beta)
\end{aligned}
$$

633 You have from frames 631 and 632 two statements for $d(P, Q)^2$:
$$d(P, Q)^2 = 2 - 2 (\cos \alpha \cos \beta + \sin \alpha \sin \beta)$$
$$d(P, Q)^2 = 2 - 2 \cos (\alpha - \beta)$$

Combine these two statements and solve for $\cos (\alpha - \beta)$.

$$2 - 2 \cos (\alpha - \beta) = 2 - 2 (\cos \alpha \cos \beta + \sin \alpha \sin \beta)$$
$$\cos (\alpha - \beta) = \cos \alpha \cos \beta + \sin \alpha \sin \beta$$

634 You have just completed the proof for the identity
$$\cos (\alpha - \beta) = \cos \alpha \cos \beta + \sin \alpha \sin \beta$$

continued →

Suppose $\alpha - \beta = \gamma$, then $\beta - \alpha = -\gamma$. You know that $\cos \gamma = \cos (-\gamma)$. Therefore, $\cos (\alpha - \beta) = \cos (\beta - \alpha) = $ _____.
(Complete the statement.)

$\cos \alpha \cos \beta + \sin \alpha \sin \beta$

635   Frame 634 reviews the fact that regardless of which is larger, α or β, we have the formula: $\cos (\alpha - \beta) = $ _____.
(Complete the formula.)

$\cos \alpha \cos \beta + \sin \alpha \sin \beta$

636   Furthermore, we need to note that regardless of the fact that α, β, or $(\alpha - \beta)$ may not be an angle in the interval 0 to 2π, by proper use of the reduction formula we can establish the truth of the theorem for $\cos (\alpha - \beta)$. *Example:* Let $\alpha = 13\pi/6$ and $\beta = 10\pi/3$. Find the value of $\cos (\alpha - \beta)$ using Theorem I.

$$\cos (\alpha - \beta) = \frac{-\sqrt{3}}{2}$$

Solution: $\cos \left(\dfrac{13\pi}{6} - \dfrac{10\pi}{3} \right) = \cos \dfrac{13\pi}{6} \cos \dfrac{10\pi}{3} + \sin \dfrac{13\pi}{6} \sin \dfrac{10\pi}{3}$

$$= \frac{\sqrt{3}}{2} \cdot \left(-\frac{1}{2} \right) + \frac{1}{2} \left(-\frac{\sqrt{3}}{2} \right) = -\frac{\sqrt{3}}{2}$$

Note: $\cos \left(\dfrac{13\pi}{6} - \dfrac{10\pi}{3} \right) = \cos \left(-\dfrac{7\pi}{6} \right) = \cos \dfrac{7\pi}{6} = \dfrac{-\sqrt{3}}{2}$

637   From Theorem I we can deduce the following theorem which we shall label *Theorem Ia*: $\cos (\alpha + \beta) = \cos \alpha \cos \beta - \sin \alpha \sin \beta$. Let α and $-\beta$ be the two given angles. Substitute these values in Theorem I.

$\cos [\alpha - (-\beta)] = \cos \alpha \cos (-\beta) + \sin \alpha \sin (-\beta)$

638   Simplify $\cos [\alpha - (-\beta)] = \cos \alpha \cos (-\beta) + \sin \alpha \sin (-\beta)$

Theorem I*a*: $\cos (\alpha + \beta) = \cos \alpha \cos \beta + \sin \alpha (-\sin \beta)$
$= \cos \alpha \cos \beta - \sin \alpha \sin \beta$
Note: $\cos (-\theta) = \cos \theta$, $\sin (-\theta) = -\sin \theta$.

639 Let α terminate in quadrant II and β terminate in quadrant I. Reconstruct the proof for our original statement

$$\cos (\alpha - \beta) = \cos \alpha \cos \beta + \sin \alpha \sin \beta$$

following these steps:
(1) Make a sketch and label appropriately the points of intersection, P and Q, of the terminal sides of α and β with the unit circle.
(2) Apply the distance formula to find $d(P, Q)^2$.
(3) Apply the law of cosines to find $d(P, Q)^2$.

(1)

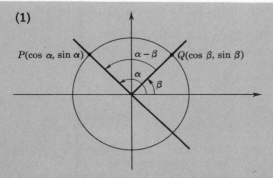

(2) $d(P, Q)^2 = (\cos \alpha - \cos \beta)^2 + (\sin \alpha - \sin \beta)^2$

$= \cos^2 \alpha + \sin^2 \alpha + \cos^2 \beta + \sin^2 \beta$
$\qquad\qquad\qquad -2 \cos \alpha \cos \beta - 2 \sin \alpha \sin \beta$

$= 2 - 2 (\cos \alpha \cos \beta + \sin \alpha \sin \beta)$

(3) $d(P, Q)^2 = 1^2 + 1^2 - 2 \cdot 1 \cdot 1 \cdot \cos (\alpha - \beta) = 2 - 2 \cos (\alpha - \beta)$

Equating Steps 2 and 3 yields

$$2 - 2 \cos (\alpha - \beta) = 2 - 2 (\cos \alpha \cos \beta + \sin \alpha \sin \beta)$$
$$\cos (\alpha - \beta) = \cos \alpha \cos \beta + \sin \alpha \sin \beta$$

640 Let $\alpha = 90°$ and $\beta = 30°$. Show that
$$\cos (\alpha - \beta) \neq \cos \alpha - \cos \beta.$$

$$\cos (90° - 30°) = \cos 60° = \frac{1}{2}$$

$$\cos 90° - \cos 30° = 0 - \frac{\sqrt{3}}{2} = \frac{-\sqrt{3}}{2} \qquad \frac{1}{2} \neq \frac{-\sqrt{3}}{2}$$

641 Let $\alpha = 90°$ and $\beta = 30°$. Show that
$$\cos (90° - 30°) = \cos 90° \cos 30° + \sin 90° \sin 30°$$

$$\cos (90° - 30°) = \cos 60° = \frac{1}{2}$$

$$\cos 90° \cos 30° + \sin 90° \sin 30° = 0 \cdot \frac{\sqrt{3}}{2} + 1 \cdot \frac{1}{2} = \frac{1}{2} \qquad \frac{1}{2} = \frac{1}{2}$$

642 Which of the following statements are true for any two angles α and β?
1. $\cos (\alpha - \beta) = \cos \alpha \cos \beta + \sin \alpha \sin \beta$
2. $\cos (\alpha - \beta) = \cos \alpha - \cos \beta$
3. $\cos (\alpha - \beta) = \cos \alpha + \cos \beta$
4. $\cos (\alpha + \beta) = \cos \alpha \cos \beta - \sin \alpha \sin \beta$

1 and 4

▽**643** *Theorem* II. Given any two angles α and β, $\sin (\alpha - \beta) = \sin \alpha \cos \beta - \cos \alpha \sin \beta$. This theorem gives us a way to express the sine of the difference of two angles α and β in terms of the individual functions of α and β. From your experience with the theorem for $\cos (\alpha - \beta)$, **(1)** do you think that $\sin (\alpha - \beta)$ could be read $\sin \alpha - \sin \beta$; i.e., **(2)** is $\sin (\alpha - \beta) = \sin \alpha - \sin \beta$ true? **(3)** Check with a numerical example to verify your answer. Let $\alpha = 45°$ and $\beta = 30°$.

(1) no   **(2)** no   **(3)** $\sin (45° - 30°) \neq \sin 45° - \sin 30°$

$$\sin 15° \neq \frac{\sqrt{2}}{2} - \frac{1}{2} \qquad 0.259 \neq 0.207$$

644 The following proof will require careful study. You are to supply the reasons as you read, recalling Theorem I and the numerical values of special angles as they appear.

Theorem II. Given any two angles α and β, $\sin (\alpha - \beta) = \sin \alpha \cos \beta - \cos \alpha \sin \beta$.

Statements   *Reasons*

①. Let $\beta = \dfrac{\pi}{2}$ 1. α and β are any
                                                              angles

Theorem I

2. $\cos \left(\alpha - \dfrac{\pi}{2}\right)$ 2. _____

$= \cos \alpha \cos \dfrac{\pi}{2} + \sin \alpha \sin \dfrac{\pi}{2}$

3. $= \cos \alpha \cdot 0 + \sin \alpha \cdot 1$ 3. _____

continued →

Statements (continued)   *Reasons* (continued)

4. Therefore, $\cos\left(\alpha - \frac{\pi}{2}\right) = \sin\,\alpha$ 4. simplifying Step 3

5. $\sin\,\theta = \cos\left(\theta - \frac{\pi}{2}\right)$ 5. rewriting Step 4 in terms of a general angle
   Label this Corollary 1

6. Now let $\theta = \alpha - \frac{\pi}{2}$ 6. θ represents any angle

7. Therefore, $\sin\left(\alpha - \frac{\pi}{2}\right)$ 7. _____

   $= \cos\left(\alpha - \frac{\pi}{2} - \frac{\pi}{2}\right)$

   $= \cos\,(\alpha - \pi)$

8. $\sin\left(\alpha - \frac{\pi}{2}\right)$ 8. _____

   $= \cos\,\alpha\,\cos\,\pi + \sin\,\alpha\,\sin\,\pi$

9. $= \cos\,\alpha(-1) + \sin\,\alpha\cdot 0$ 9. _____

10. Therefore, $\sin\left(\alpha - \frac{\pi}{2}\right) = -\cos\,\alpha$ 10. simplifying Step 9
    Label this Corollary 2

11. Finally letting $\theta = \alpha - \beta$ in   11. θ represents any angle
    Corollary 1, we have

    $\sin\,(\alpha - \beta) = \cos\left[(\alpha - \beta) - \frac{\pi}{2}\right]$

    $= \cos\left[\left(\alpha - \frac{\pi}{2}\right) - \beta\right]$

12. $\sin\,(\alpha - \beta)$ 12. _____

    $= \cos\left(\alpha - \frac{\pi}{2}\right)\cos\,\beta$

    $+ \sin\left(\alpha - \frac{\pi}{2}\right)\sin\,\beta$

13. $= \sin\,\alpha\,\cos\,\beta$ 13. applying Steps 5 and 10,
    $+ (-\cos\,\alpha)\,\sin\,\beta$ i.e., Corollaries 1 and 2

14. Therefore, $\sin\,(\alpha - \beta)$ 14. simplifying Step 13.
    $= \sin\,\alpha\,\cos\,\beta - \cos\,\alpha\,\sin\,\beta$

2. Theorem 1
3. $\cos\,\frac{\pi}{2} = 0$, $\sin\,\frac{\pi}{2} = 1$
7. Corollary 1 or substituting in Step 5 and simplifying
8. Theorem 1
9. $\cos\,\pi = -1$, $\sin\,\pi = 0$
12. Theorem 1

645 In frames 645 to 652 we shall reconstruct the proof of Theorem II, which you have just seen. The proof of Theorem II, sin $(\alpha - \beta) =$ sin α cos β - cos α sin β, depends on Theorem I and two corollaries of Theorem I which we shall derive as we go along. Find to what cos $(\alpha - \beta) =$ cos α cos β + sin α sin β reduces if $\beta = \pi/2$.

$$\cos\left(\alpha - \frac{\pi}{2}\right) = \cos\alpha\cos\frac{\pi}{2} + \sin\alpha\sin\frac{\pi}{2}$$
$$= \cos\alpha\cdot 0 + \sin\alpha\cdot 1 = \sin\alpha$$

646 In frame 645 we saw that cos $(\alpha - \pi/2) =$ sin α. Since we are going to use this as a general statement, let us use θ as our angle and write what we have just developed thus:
Corollary 1. For any angle θ, sin $\theta =$ cos $(\theta - \pi/2)$.
(1) Make a copy of Corollary 1 for use in the proof of Theorem II.
(2) Also write Theorem I as a reference.

(1) for any angle θ, sin $\theta =$ cos $\left(\theta - \dfrac{\pi}{2}\right)$

(2) cos $(\alpha - \beta) =$ cos α cos β + sin α sin β

647 In frame 646 we said that Corollary 1 is true for any angle θ. Suppose $\theta = (\alpha - \pi/2)$, **(1)** what is the result when this is substituted in Corollary 1? Simplify your answer by applying Theorem I. (We shall label this result Corollary 2.)

$$\sin\left(\alpha - \frac{\pi}{2}\right) = \cos\left[\left(\alpha - \frac{\pi}{2}\right) - \frac{\pi}{2}\right] = \cos\left[\alpha - \left(\frac{\pi}{2} + \frac{\pi}{2}\right)\right]$$
$$= \cos(\alpha - \pi)$$
$$= \cos\alpha\cos\pi + \sin\alpha\sin\pi$$
$$= \cos\alpha\,(-1) + \sin\alpha\cdot 0 = -\cos\alpha$$

648 Corollary 2, sin $(\alpha - \pi/2) = -\cos\alpha$.
(1) Copy Corollary 2 for later reference.
(2) For what values of α is Corollary 2 a true statement? **(3)** For what values of θ is Corollary 1 a true statement?

(1) sin $\left(\alpha - \dfrac{\pi}{2}\right) = -\cos\alpha$ **(2)** all values of α
(3) all values of θ

$\frac{\pi}{2}$ in Theorem 1 — get Corollary 1
$\left(\alpha - \frac{\pi}{2}\right)$ in Corollary 1 — get Corollary 2
$(\alpha - \beta)$ in Corollary 1 & subst. values of Corol. 1 & 2 —
get Theorem

649 Go back to Corollary 1. If we now let $\theta = (\alpha - \beta)$, then Corollary 1
reads

$$\sin(\alpha - \beta) = \cos\left[(\alpha - \beta) - \frac{\pi}{2}\right] = \cos\left[\left(\alpha - \frac{\pi}{2}\right) - \beta\right]$$

$$= \cos\left(\alpha - \frac{\pi}{2}\right)\cos\beta + \sin\left(\alpha - \frac{\pi}{2}\right)\sin\beta$$

by Theorem I

Now look at Corollaries 1 and 2.   (1) What can we substitute for
$\cos(\alpha - \pi/2)$?   (2) For $\sin(\alpha - \pi/2)$?

(1) $\sin\alpha$ **(2)** $-\cos\alpha$

650 From frame 649 we have:

1. $\cos\left(\alpha - \frac{\pi}{2}\right) = \sin\alpha$

2. $\sin\left(\alpha - \frac{\pi}{2}\right) = -\cos\alpha$

3. $\sin(\alpha - \beta) = \cos\left(\alpha - \frac{\pi}{2}\right)\cos\beta + \sin\left(\alpha - \frac{\pi}{2}\right)\sin\beta$

When statements 1 and 2 are substituted into the right member of
statement 3, the result is Theorem II, which we want to establish.
Write it.

$\sin(\alpha - \beta) = \sin\alpha\cos\beta - \cos\alpha\sin\beta$

651 In frames 645 to 650 by applying our knowledge of $\sin(\pi/2)$, $\cos$
$(\pi/2)$, $\sin\pi$, $\cos\pi$, and Theorem I, we were able to derive Theorem
II, namely:
    $\sin(\alpha - \beta) = \sin\alpha\cos\beta - \cos\alpha\sin\beta$.
This required considerable work. It is relatively easy now to de-
rive Theorem II , namely:
    $\sin(\alpha + \beta) = \sin\alpha\cos\beta + \cos\alpha\sin\beta$
Let $\beta = -\beta$ in Theorem II above and derive Theorem IIa as stated.

$\sin[\alpha - (-\beta)] = \sin\alpha\cos(-\beta) - \cos\alpha\sin(-\beta)$
$= \sin\alpha\cos\beta - \cos\alpha(-\sin\beta)$
Therefore, $\sin(\alpha + \beta) = \sin\alpha\cos\beta + \cos\alpha\sin\beta$

652   Let us repeat the work in frame 651. For sin $(\alpha + \beta)$ we need
merely to let $\beta = -\beta$ in our formula
$$\sin (\alpha - \beta) = \sin \alpha \cos \beta - \cos \alpha \sin \beta$$
and get
$$\sin [\alpha - (-\beta)] = (1)\underline{\hspace{4cm}}$$
$$(2)\underline{\hspace{2cm}} = (3)\underline{\hspace{4cm}}$$

(1) $\sin \alpha \cos (-\beta) - \cos \alpha \sin (-\beta)$
(2) $\sin (\alpha + \beta) = (3) \sin \alpha \cos \beta + \cos \alpha \sin \beta$

▽653   You should have noticed that to establish the formulas for cos
$(\alpha + \beta)$, sin $(\alpha - \beta)$, and sin $(\alpha + \beta)$, we made frequent use of the
following facts:
1. For any angle θ, cos $(-\theta) = \cos \theta$, but sin $(-\theta) = (1)\underline{\hspace{2cm}}$.
2. For any two angles α and β, cos $(\alpha - \beta) = (2)\underline{\hspace{3cm}}$.
3. $\sin \dfrac{\pi}{2} = (3)\underline{\hspace{1cm}}$, $\cos \dfrac{\pi}{2} = (4)\underline{\hspace{1cm}}$, $\sin \pi = (5)\underline{\hspace{1cm}}$, and
   $\cos \pi = (6)\underline{\hspace{1cm}}$.

(1) $-\sin \theta$ (2) $\cos \alpha \cos \beta + \sin \alpha \sin \beta$
(3) 1   (4) 0   (5) 0   (6) −1

654   Without referring to your written work from the preceding frames,
write a proof for Theorem II as stated below.
Theorem II: Given any two angles α and β,
$$\sin (\alpha - \beta) = \sin \alpha \cos \beta - \cos \alpha \sin \beta$$

Here is the outline for a proof of Theorem II
1. Letting $\beta = \pi/2$ in Theorem I and simplifying, we get
   $\cos (\alpha - \pi/2) = \sin \alpha$
2. Generalizing, we write Corollary 1: $\sin \theta = \cos (\theta - \pi/2)$
3. Now letting $\theta = \alpha - \pi/2$ in Corollary 1, we have sin
   $(\alpha - \pi/2) = \cos [(\alpha - \pi/2) - \pi/2] = \cos (\alpha - \pi)$
4. Applying Theorem I to the right member of Step 3 and simplifying, we get Corollary 2: $\sin (\alpha - \pi/2) = -\cos \alpha$
5. Going back to Corollary 1 and letting $\theta = \alpha - \beta$, we get sin
   $(\alpha - \beta) = \cos [(\alpha - \beta) - \pi/2] = \cos [(\alpha - \pi/2) - \beta]$.
6. When Theorem I is applied to Step 5, we get $\sin (\alpha - \beta) = \cos$
   $(\alpha - \pi/2) \cos \beta + \sin (\alpha - \pi/2) \sin \beta$
7. Using Corollaries 1 and 2, we finally can write $\sin (\alpha - \beta) =$
   $\sin \alpha \cos \beta - \cos \alpha \sin \beta$.

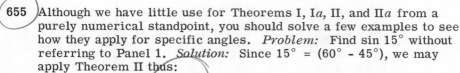

655 Although we have little use for Theorems I, Ia, II, and IIa from a purely numerical standpoint, you should solve a few examples to see how they apply for specific angles. *Problem:* Find sin 15° without referring to Panel 1. *Solution:* Since 15° = (60° - 45°), we may apply Theorem II thus:

sin 15° = sin (60° - 45°) = sin 60° cos 45° - cos 60° sin 45°

Complete the numerical solution using simple radical or fractional forms for the functions required.

$$\sin 15° = \left(\frac{\sqrt{3}}{2} \cdot \frac{1}{\sqrt{2}}\right) - \left(\frac{1}{2} \cdot \frac{1}{\sqrt{2}}\right) = \frac{\sqrt{3}}{2\sqrt{2}} - \frac{1}{2\sqrt{2}} = \frac{\sqrt{3} - 1}{2\sqrt{2}}$$

$$= \frac{\sqrt{6} - \sqrt{2}}{4} \approx 0.259$$

Check Panel 1 to see that this agrees with sin 15°.

656 Follow the plan used in frame 655 to find cos 15°.

$$\cos 15° = \cos (60° - 45°) = \cos 60° \cos 45° + \sin 60° \sin 45°$$

$$= \left(\frac{1}{2} \cdot \frac{1}{\sqrt{2}}\right) + \left(\frac{3}{\sqrt{2}} \cdot \frac{1}{\sqrt{2}}\right) = \frac{1 + \sqrt{3}}{2\sqrt{2}} = \frac{\sqrt{2} + \sqrt{6}}{4} \approx 0.966$$

Check Panel 1

657 Below are stated Theorems I, Ia, II, IIa. Use the proper theorem and functions of special angles to find cos 75°.

cos (α - β) = cos α cos β + sin α sin β
cos (α + β) + cos α cos β - sin α sin β
sin (α - β) = sin α cos β - cos α sin β
sin (α + β) = sin α cos β + cos α sin β

Note: You should be able to quote these formulas.

$$\cos 75° = \cos (45° + 30°) = \cos 45° \cos 30° - \sin 45° \sin 30°$$

$$= \left(\frac{1}{\sqrt{2}} \cdot \frac{\sqrt{3}}{2}\right) - \left(\frac{1}{\sqrt{2}} \cdot \frac{1}{2}\right) = \frac{\sqrt{3} - 1}{2\sqrt{2}} = \frac{\sqrt{6} - \sqrt{2}}{4} \approx 0.259$$

658 Find in simplest fractional or radical form sin 165°. Use one of the four theorems that we have established.

Let 165° = 120° + 45°, then
sin (165°) = sin (120° + 45°)
= sin 120° cos 45° + cos 120° sin 45°

$$= \left(\frac{\sqrt{3}}{2} \cdot \frac{\sqrt{2}}{2}\right) + \left(-\frac{1}{2} \cdot \frac{\sqrt{2}}{2}\right) = \frac{\sqrt{6} - \sqrt{2}}{4} \approx 0.259$$

659 You must be careful in your interpretation of the formula for sin $(\alpha + \beta)$. In frame 658 we found that since $165° = 120° + 45°$, we could write sin $165°$ = sin $120°$ cos $45°$ + cos $120°$ sin $45°$ and get the numerical value for sin $165° \approx 0.259$. Could we solve this problem by assuming that sin $165°$ = sin $(120° + 45°)$ = sin $120°$ + sin $45°$?

no   *Solution:* $\sin 120° = \dfrac{\sqrt{3}}{2}$, $\sin 45° = \dfrac{\sqrt{2}}{2}$

$$\sin 120° + \sin 45° = \frac{\sqrt{3}}{2} + \frac{\sqrt{2}}{2}$$

$$= \frac{\sqrt{3} + \sqrt{2}}{2} \approx 3.146$$

660 By thinking of $495°$ as the sum of $225°$ and $270°$, find cos $495°$.

$\cos 495° \approx -0.707$
Solution: $\cos 495°$ = cos $(225° + 270°)$
         = cos $225°$ cos $270°$ - sin $225°$ sin $270°$

$$= \left(\frac{-1}{\sqrt{2}} \cdot 0\right) - \left(\frac{-1}{\sqrt{2}} \cdot (-1)\right) = \frac{-1}{\sqrt{2}} = \frac{-\sqrt{2}}{2} \approx -0.707$$

Note: This process is complicated and you cannot always find combinations of angles for which you have simple radical forms to substitute.

661 (1) Find cos $495°$ by means of the *reduction formula* used earlier in this program.   (2) Make a sketch to see in which quadrant the angle terminates.

(1) cos $495°$ = cos $135°$ (2)
        = -cos $45°$

$$= \frac{-1}{\sqrt{2}} = \frac{-\sqrt{2}}{2} \approx -0.707$$

662 Without referring to Panel 1, find side a of triangle ABC given $b = 14$, $c = 17$, and $\alpha = 105°$.

$a \approx 24.7 \approx 25$

continued →

Solution: Apply the law of cosines $a^2 = b^2 + c^2 - 2bc \cos$

$$
\begin{aligned}
a^2 &= 14^2 + 17^2 - 2(14 \cdot 17) \cos 105° \\
&= 196 + 289 - 476 \cos (60° + 45°) \\
&= 485 - 476(\cos 60° \cos 45° - \sin 60° \sin 45°) \\
&= 485 - 476\left(\frac{1}{2} \cdot \frac{1}{\sqrt{2}} - \frac{\sqrt{3}}{2} \cdot \frac{1}{\sqrt{2}}\right) \\
a &\approx \sqrt{485 - 476(-0.259)} \approx 24.7 \approx 25
\end{aligned}
$$

∇663 Use the proper theorem (I, Ia, II, or IIa) and the correct numerical values for the quadrantal angles to verify the following statement: $\sin (\pi - \theta) = \sin \theta$.

$$
\begin{aligned}
\sin (\pi - \theta) &= \sin \pi \cos \theta - \cos \pi \sin \theta = 0 \cdot \cos \theta - (-1) \sin \theta \\
&= \sin \theta
\end{aligned}
$$

664 Work as in frame 663 to show that $\sin (\pi + \theta) = -\sin \theta$.

$$
\begin{aligned}
\sin (\pi + \theta) &= \sin \pi \cos \theta + \cos \pi \sin \theta = 0 \cdot \cos \theta + (-1) \sin \theta \\
&= -\sin \theta
\end{aligned}
$$

665 Note that the two statements $\sin (\pi - \theta) = \sin \theta$ and $\sin (\pi + \theta) = -\sin \theta$ are true for all values of θ. If θ is an acute angle, we know from previous work that $(\pi - \theta)$ is an angle terminating in quadrant II and that $\sin (\pi - \theta) = \sin \theta$. However, the proofs in the previous frames did not specify any particular values of θ; hence, the statements are true in general.

Example: If $\theta = 2\pi/3$, $\pi - \theta = \pi/3$, and $\pi + \theta = 5\pi/3$, then

$$\sin \frac{2\pi}{3} = (1)\underline{\hspace{1cm}}$$

$$\sin (\pi - \theta) = \sin \frac{\pi}{3} = (2)\underline{\hspace{1cm}}$$

$$\sin (\pi + \theta) = \sin \frac{5\pi}{3} = (3)\underline{\hspace{1cm}}$$

Hence, if $\theta = 2\pi/3$, $\sin (\pi - \theta) = \sin \theta$ and $\sin (\pi + \theta) = -\sin \theta$.

(1) $\frac{\sqrt{3}}{2}$ (2) $\frac{\sqrt{3}}{2}$ (3) $\frac{-\sqrt{3}}{2}$

666   If $\theta = 5\pi/4$, verify as in frame 665 that $\sin (\pi - \theta) = \sin \theta$ and $\sin (\pi + \theta) = -\sin \theta$.

If $\theta = 5\pi/4$, $\pi - \theta = -\pi/4$, and $\pi + \theta = 9\pi/4$, then

$$\sin \frac{5\pi}{4} = \frac{-1}{\sqrt{2}}$$

$$\sin (\pi - \theta) = \sin \frac{-\pi}{4} = \frac{-1}{\sqrt{2}}$$

$$\sin (\pi + \theta) = \sin \frac{9\pi}{4} = \frac{1}{\sqrt{2}}$$

Hence, if $\theta = 5\pi/4$, $\sin (\pi - \theta) = \sin \theta$ and $\sin (\pi + \theta) = -\sin \theta$.

667   As further practice with Theorems I, Ia, II, and IIa, find the simplified form for each of the following: $\cos (\pi - \theta) = $ (1)_____ and $\cos (\pi + \theta) = $ (2)_____.

(1) $-\cos \theta$
Solution: $\cos (\pi - \theta) = \cos \pi \cos \theta + \sin \pi \sin \theta$
$\qquad\qquad\quad = (-1) \cos \theta + 0 \cdot \sin \theta = -\cos \theta$
(2) $-\cos \theta$
Solution: $\cos (\pi + \theta) = \cos \pi \cos \theta - \sin \pi \sin \theta$
$\qquad\qquad\quad = (-1) \cos \theta - 0 \cdot \sin \theta = -\cos \theta$

668   Simplify as before $\sin (2\pi - \theta) = $ (1)_____ and $\cos (2\pi - \theta) = $ (2)_____.

(1) $-\sin \theta$
Solution: $\sin (2\pi - \theta) = \sin 2\pi \cos \theta - \cos 2\pi \sin \theta$
$\qquad\qquad\qquad = 0 \cdot \cos \theta - 1 \cdot \sin \theta = -\sin \theta$
(2) $\cos \theta$
Solution: $\cos (2\pi - \theta) = \cos 2\pi \cos \theta + \sin 2\pi \sin \theta$
$\qquad\qquad\qquad = 1 \cos \theta + 0 \cdot \sin \theta = \cos \theta$

669   Simplify as before $\sin (270° - \theta) = $ (1)_____ and $\cos (270° - \theta) = $ (2)_____.

(1) $-\cos \theta$
Solution: $\sin (270° - \theta) = \sin 270° \cos \theta - \cos 270° \sin \theta$
$\qquad\qquad\qquad\quad = -1 \cdot \cos \theta - 0 \cdot \sin \theta = -\cos \theta$
(2) $-\sin \theta$
Solution: $\cos (270° - \theta) = \cos 270° \cos \theta + \sin 270° \sin \theta$
$\qquad\qquad\qquad\quad = 0 \cdot \cos \theta + (-1) \sin \theta = -\sin \theta$

670 Given sin α = -5/13, α terminates in quadrant III, and cos β = $\frac{4}{5}$, β terminates in quadrant I. Find sin $(\alpha + \beta)$. *Note:* In order to use Theorem I, you must have values for cos α and sin β. If you make a sketch of each angle in standard position, you should be able to get the required data. Try it!

1. In right triangle OPQ
   $$13^2 = (-5)^2 + x^2$$
   $$\pm 12 = x$$
   Since α terminates in quadrant III,
   $x = -12$; therefore, cos α = $\frac{-12}{13}$

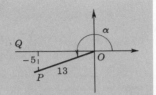

2. In a similar manner we find
   sin β = $\frac{3}{5}$.

3. sin $(\alpha + \beta)$ = sin α cos β + cos α sin β
   $$= \left(\frac{-5}{13}\right)\left(\frac{4}{5}\right) + \left(\frac{-12}{13}\right)\left(\frac{3}{5}\right)$$
   $$= \left(\frac{-20}{65}\right) + \left(\frac{-36}{65}\right)$$
   $$= \frac{-56}{65}$$

671 Given cos α = $\frac{3}{5}$, α terminates in quadrant IV, and sin β = -12/13, β terminates in quadrant III. Find cos $(\alpha - \beta)$

cos $(\alpha - \beta)$ = $\frac{33}{65}$

Solution: cos $(\alpha - \beta)$ = cos α cos β + sin α sin β
$$= \left(\frac{3}{5}\right)\left(\frac{-5}{13}\right) + \left(\frac{-4}{5}\right)\left(\frac{-12}{13}\right) = \frac{-15}{65} + \frac{48}{65} = \frac{33}{65}$$

672 Four identities are listed below. You should be able to prove each of them.
1. sin 2α = 2 sin α cos α
2. cos 2α = $\cos^2 \alpha - \sin^2 \alpha$
3. cos 2α = 1 - 2 $\sin^2 \alpha$
4. cos 2α = 2 $\cos^2 \alpha$ - 1
Proof for identity 1. *Suggestion:* Start with Theorem IIa, i.e., sin $(\alpha + \beta)$ = sin α cos β + cos α sin β. Since α and β are any angles, let $\beta = \alpha$, then sin $(\alpha + \alpha)$ = (1)_____.
Complete and simplify this statement, i.e., sin 2α = (2)_____.

(1) sin α cos α + cos α sin α (2) 2 sin α cos α

673   Recall Theorem Ia. Write a proof for identity 2 in frame 672, namely, $\cos 2\alpha = \cos^2 \alpha - \sin^2 \alpha$

> Let $\beta = \alpha$, then
> $$\cos (\alpha + \alpha) = \cos \alpha \cos \alpha - \sin \alpha \sin \alpha$$
> $$\cos 2\alpha = \cos^2 \alpha - \sin^2 \alpha$$

674   You know that $\sin^2 \alpha + \cos^2 \alpha = 1$ is an identity. Make use of this fact and the identity in frame 672, namely, $\cos 2\alpha = \cos^2 \alpha - \sin^2 \alpha$, to prove identity 3, $\cos 2\alpha = 1 - 2 \sin^2 \alpha$.

> 1. $\sin^2 \alpha + \cos^2 \alpha = 1$ identity
> 2. If we solve for $\cos^2 \alpha$, we have   adding ($-\sin^2 \alpha$)
> $\cos^2 \alpha = 1 - \sin^2 \alpha$
> 3. $\cos 2\alpha = \cos^2 \alpha - \sin^2 \alpha$ identity 2
> 4. $\cos 2\alpha = 1 - \sin^2 \alpha - \sin^2 \alpha$ substituting
> $1 - \sin^2 \alpha$ for $\cos^2 \alpha$
> 5. Therefore, $\cos 2\alpha = 1 - 2 \sin^2 \alpha$

675   Write a proof for identity 4 in frame 672, namely, $\cos 2\alpha = 2 \cos^2 \alpha - 1$, using ideas given in frame 674.

> 1. $\sin^2 \alpha + \cos^2 \alpha = 1$ identity
> 2. $\sin^2 \alpha = 1 - \cos^2 \alpha$ adding ($-\cos^2 \alpha$)
> 3. $\cos 2\alpha = \cos^2 \alpha - \sin^2 \alpha$ identity 2
> 4. $\cos 2\alpha = \cos^2 \alpha - (1 - \cos^2 \alpha)$ substituting
> 5. Therefore, $\cos 2\alpha = 2 \cos^2 \alpha - 1$

676   The identities 1, 2, 3, and 4 in frame 672 which you have proved are called the *double-angle formulas*. These double-angle formulas hold for any angle. Thus:
1. $\sin 4\theta = 2 \sin 2\theta \cos 2\theta$
2. $\cos 4\theta = \cos^2 2\theta - \sin^2 2\theta$
3. $\cos 4\theta = 1 - 2 \sin^2 2\theta$
4. $\cos 4\theta = 2 \cos^2 2\theta - 1$

Complete the following:
      $\sin 5\theta = (1)$ $2 \sin \frac{5}{2}\theta \cos \frac{5}{2}\theta$
      $\cos 5\theta = (2)$ _____
      $\cos 5\theta = (3)$ _____
      $\cos 5\theta = (4)$ _____

> (1) $2 \sin \dfrac{5\theta}{2} \cos \dfrac{5\theta}{2}$ (2) $\cos^2 \dfrac{5\theta}{2} \sin^2 \dfrac{5\theta}{2}$
>
> (3) $1 - 2 \sin^2 \dfrac{5\theta}{2}$ (4) $2 \cos^2 \dfrac{5\theta}{2} - 1$

677 Complete the following using form 1, 2, 3, or 4, as directed, from the double-angle formulas:

Double-angle
formula number

$\sin \theta$ = (1)_____   1

$\cos \dfrac{14\alpha}{3}$ = (2)_____   2

$\cos 12\beta$ = (3)_____   3

$\sin \dfrac{3\pi}{2}$ = (4)_____   1

$\cos 372°$ = (5)_____   4

$\sin 2$ = (6)_____   1

$\cos 1.3$ = (7)_____   2

---

(1) $2 \sin \dfrac{\theta}{2} \cos \dfrac{\theta}{2}$ (2) $\cos^2 \dfrac{7\alpha}{3} - \sin^2 \dfrac{7\alpha}{3}$

(3) $1 - 2 \sin^2 6\beta$ (4) $2 \sin \dfrac{3\pi}{4} \cos \dfrac{3\pi}{4}$

(5) $2 \cos^2 186° - 1$ or $\cos 12° = 2 \cos^2 6° - 1$

(6) $2 \sin 1 \cos 1$ (7) $\cos^2 0.65 - \sin^2 0.65$

---

678 Let us consider negative angles. Recall that $\sin (-\theta) = -\sin \theta$. Therefore, $\sin (-2\beta) = -\sin 2\beta = -2 \sin \beta \cos \beta$. Recall also that $\cos (-\theta) = $ (1)_____. Hence, from identity 2 we have $\cos (-2\beta) = $ (2)_____.

---

(1) $\cos \theta$ (2) $\cos^2 \beta - \sin^2 \beta$

---

679 Find the numerical value for $\sin 2\alpha$ if $\sin \alpha = -12/13$ and α terminates in quadrant III.

Solution:
$$13^2 = (-12)^2 + x^2$$
$$25 = x^2$$
$$\pm 5 = x$$
For quadrant III, $x = -5$.

Hence, $\cos \alpha = -\dfrac{5}{13}$

$$\sin 2\alpha = 2\left(\dfrac{-12}{13}\right)\left(\dfrac{-5}{13}\right) = \dfrac{120}{169}$$

680   Find the numerical value for $\cos 2\alpha$ if $\sin \alpha = -12/13$ and α terminates in quadrant III.

$$\cos 2\alpha = \frac{-119}{169}$$

Note: Any one of the three formulas 2, 3, or 4 could be used. Since $\sin \alpha$ is given, we used formula 3 thus:

$$\cos 2\alpha = 1 - 2\left(\frac{-12}{13}\right)^2 = \frac{-119}{169}$$

681   If $\alpha = -\pi/4$, then substituting in the double-angle formulas, we have:

sin _____ = _____
cos _____ = _____

Copy the entire equations as you answer. Show that these statements are true.

$$\sin \frac{-\pi}{2} = -\sin \frac{\pi}{2} = -2 \sin \frac{\pi}{4} \cos \frac{\pi}{4}$$

$$\cos \frac{-\pi}{2} = \cos \frac{\pi}{2} = \cos^2 \frac{\pi}{4} - \sin^2 \frac{\pi}{4}$$

Verification:

$$\sin \frac{-\pi}{2} = -1, \quad -2 \sin \frac{\pi}{4} \cos \frac{\pi}{4} = -2\left(\frac{1}{\sqrt{2}} \cdot \frac{1}{\sqrt{2}}\right) = -1$$

$$\cos \frac{-\pi}{2} = 0, \quad \cos^2 \frac{\pi}{4} - \sin^2 \frac{\pi}{4} = \left(\frac{1}{\sqrt{2}}\right)^2 - \left(\frac{1}{\sqrt{2}}\right)^2 = 0$$

682   Is the following statement true: $\sin 2\theta = 2 \sin \theta$? If it is true, prove it. If it is not true, cite an example where it does not hold.

no   Let $\alpha = 30°$, $\sin 2\alpha = \sin 60° = \dfrac{\sqrt{3}}{2}$

$$2 \sin \alpha = 2 \sin 30° = 2 \cdot \frac{1}{2} = 1, \quad \frac{\sqrt{3}}{2} \neq 1.$$

683   List examples in which (1) $\sin 2\theta$ is equal to twice the sine of θ and (2) $\cos 2\theta$ is equal to twice the cosine of θ.

(1) Let $\theta = 0$, then $\sin 2 \cdot 0 = 2 \sin 0$ **(2)** There are none.
        $\theta = \pi$, then $\sin 2 \cdot \pi = 2 \sin \pi$

684   Find cos $(2\pi/3)$ by applying one of the identities for cos 2α.

$$\cos \frac{2\pi}{3} = \left(\frac{1}{2}\right)^2 - \left(\frac{\sqrt{3}}{2}\right)^2 = \frac{1}{4} - \frac{3}{4} = -\frac{1}{2}$$

685   Theorem III.

The identity tan $(\alpha + \beta) = \dfrac{\tan \alpha + \tan \beta}{1 - \tan \alpha \tan \beta}$ can readily be proved [if tan $(\alpha + \beta)$ exists] by using Theorems Ia and IIa and the definition for tangent of an angle.

Proof:

1. tan $(\alpha + \beta) = \dfrac{\sin (\alpha + \beta)}{\cos (\alpha + \beta)}$, cos $(\alpha + \beta) \neq 0$ (1) give reason

2. tan $(\alpha + \beta) = \dfrac{\sin \alpha \cos \beta + \cos \alpha \sin \beta}{\cos \alpha \cos \beta - \sin \alpha \sin \beta}$ (2) give reason

3. tan $(\alpha + \beta) = \dfrac{\dfrac{\sin \alpha \cos \beta}{\cos \alpha \cos \beta} + \dfrac{\cos \alpha \sin \beta}{\cos \alpha \cos \beta}}{\dfrac{\cos \alpha \cos \beta}{\cos \alpha \cos \beta} - \dfrac{\sin \alpha \sin \beta}{\cos \alpha \cos \beta}}$ 3. both numerator and denominator of the fraction are divided by cos α cos β

cos $\alpha \neq 0$, cos $\beta \neq 0$

4. tan $(\alpha + \beta) = $ (3)_____   4. simplifying each term

(1) definition of tangent
(2) substituting from Theorems IIa and Ia

(3) tan $(\alpha + \beta) = \dfrac{\sin \alpha/\cos \alpha + \sin \beta/\cos \beta}{1 - (\sin \alpha \sin \beta/\cos \alpha \cos \beta)}$

$= \dfrac{\tan \alpha + \tan \beta}{1 - \tan \alpha \tan \beta}$

Note: Be sure that you understand the plan of this proof. You will apply the idea in frame 686.

686   Theorem IIIa.

Write a proof.   tan $(\alpha - \beta) = \dfrac{\tan \alpha - \tan \beta}{1 + \tan \alpha \tan \beta}$.

1. tan $(\alpha - \beta) = \dfrac{\sin (\alpha - \beta)}{\cos (\alpha - \beta)}$, cos $(\alpha - \beta) \neq 0$ 1. definition

2. tan $(\alpha - \beta) = \dfrac{\sin \alpha \cos \beta - \cos \alpha \sin \beta}{\cos \alpha \cos \beta + \sin \alpha \sin \beta}$ 2. Theorems II and I

continued →

3. $\tan(\alpha - \beta) = \dfrac{\dfrac{\sin\alpha\cos\beta}{\cos\alpha\cos\beta} - \dfrac{\cos\alpha\sin\beta}{\cos\alpha\cos\beta}}{\dfrac{\cos\alpha\cos\beta}{\cos\alpha\cos\beta} + \dfrac{\sin\alpha\sin\beta}{\cos\alpha\cos\beta}}$ 3. dividing by $\cos\alpha\cos\beta$

$\cos\alpha \neq 0,\ \cos\beta \neq 0$

4. $\tan(\alpha - \beta) = \dfrac{\tan\alpha - \tan\beta}{1 + \tan\alpha\tan\beta}$ 4. simplifying

See frame 687 for another suggested proof.

687 An easier way to derive Theorem IIIa is simply to replace β by $-\beta$ in the theorem and use the fact, proved earlier, that $\tan(-\beta) =$ $-\tan\beta$. Starting with $\tan(\alpha + \beta) = (\tan\alpha + \tan\beta)/(1 - \tan\alpha\tan\beta)$ derive the formula for $\tan(\alpha - \beta)$.

$\tan[\alpha + (-\beta)] = \dfrac{\tan\alpha + \tan(-\beta)}{1 - \tan\alpha\ \tan(-\beta)} = \dfrac{\tan\alpha - \tan\beta}{1 - \tan\alpha\ (-\tan\beta)}$

$= \dfrac{\tan\alpha - \tan\beta}{1 + \tan\alpha\tan\beta}$

688 Use Theorem III, $\tan(\alpha + \beta) = (\tan\alpha + \tan\beta)/(1 - \tan\alpha\tan\beta)$ to show that for any angle θ, $\tan(\pi + \theta) = \tan\theta$.

$\tan(\pi + \theta) = \dfrac{\tan\pi + \tan\theta}{1 - \tan\pi\ \tan\theta} = \dfrac{0 + \tan\theta}{1 - 0\cdot\tan\theta} = \tan\theta$

689 Using Theorem IIIa, can you prove that $\tan(\pi - \theta) = -\tan\theta$? If your answer is yes, show the steps of your proof.

yes $\tan(\pi - \theta) = \dfrac{\tan\pi - \tan\theta}{1 + \tan\pi\ \tan\theta} = \dfrac{0 - \tan\theta}{1 + 0\cdot\tan\theta} = -\tan\theta$

690 We can also find an identity for $\tan 2\alpha$ using a method similar to that for obtaining $\sin 2\alpha$ and $\cos 2\alpha$. If we let $\beta = \alpha$ in Theorem III, then $\tan(\alpha + \alpha) = $ (1)_____.   (2) Simplify your answer.

(1) $\dfrac{\tan\alpha + \tan\alpha}{1 - \tan\alpha\tan\alpha}$ (2) $\tan 2\alpha = \dfrac{2\tan\alpha}{1 - \tan^2\alpha}$

691 Note that the theorems we have proved are called identities. This means that they "work" for all permissible angles. The names of the angles and their units of measure are immaterial. Show that you can find the numerical value for tan $(\pi/12)$ by means of Theorem IIIa with $\alpha = \pi/4$ and $\beta = \pi/6$.

$$\tan \frac{\pi}{12} \approx 0.268$$

Solution: $\tan \dfrac{\pi}{12} = \tan\left(\dfrac{\pi}{4} - \dfrac{\pi}{6}\right) = \dfrac{\tan (\pi/4) - \tan (\pi/6)}{1 + \tan (\pi/4) \tan (\pi/6)}$

$$= \frac{1 - 1/\sqrt{3}}{1 + 1 \cdot 1/\sqrt{3}} = \frac{\sqrt{3} - 1}{\sqrt{3} + 1}$$

$$= 2 - \sqrt{3} \approx 0.268$$

692 Find cos 22°30' in radical form. *Suggestion:* You know that 45° = 2(22°30') and that cos $2\alpha = 2 \cos^2 \alpha - 1$. Let $\alpha = 22°30'$, then $2\alpha = 45°$.

$\cos 22°30' = \frac{1}{2}\sqrt{\sqrt{2} + 2}$
Solution:
$\cos 45° = 2 \cos^2 \alpha - 1$

$\dfrac{1}{\sqrt{2}} = 2 \cos^2 \alpha - 1$ substituting $\dfrac{1}{\sqrt{2}}$ for cos 45°

$\dfrac{1}{2}\left(\dfrac{1 + \sqrt{2}}{\sqrt{2}}\right) = \dfrac{1}{2}\left(\dfrac{\sqrt{2} + 2}{2}\right) = \cos^2 \alpha$

           simplifying

$\dfrac{1}{2}\sqrt{\sqrt{2} + 2} = \cos \alpha$

Note: Use the positive answer since 22°30' is a first-quadrant angle.

693 Find cos 11°15' in radical form, using the information in frame 692.

$$\cos 22°30' = \frac{1}{2} \cdot \sqrt{\sqrt{2} + 2}$$

$\cos 11°15' = \frac{1}{2}\sqrt{2 + \sqrt{\sqrt{2} + 2}}$
Solution: Let $\alpha = 11°15'$, then $2\alpha = 22°30'$.

$\cos 22°30' = 2 \cos^2 11°15' - 1$

$\frac{1}{2}\left(1 + \frac{1}{2}\sqrt{\sqrt{2} + 2}\right) = \cos^2 11°15'$

$\cos^2 11°15' = \dfrac{2 + \sqrt{\sqrt{2} + 2}}{4}$ $\cos 11°15' = \frac{1}{2}\sqrt{2 + \sqrt{\sqrt{2} + 2}}$

694   *Half-angle formulas.*   The previous frames suggest that we can derive formulas for $\sin \frac{1}{2}\theta$, $\cos \frac{1}{2}\theta$, and $\tan \frac{1}{2}\theta$ in terms of functions of θ.   Starting with the double-angle formula

$$\cos 2\alpha = 2 \cos^2 \alpha - 1$$

we can get a formula for $\cos \frac{1}{2}\alpha$ in terms of $\cos \alpha$ thus:
Step 1. Solve the formula given above for cos α
Step 2. See frame 695.

$$\cos \ \alpha = \pm \sqrt{\frac{1 + \cos 2\alpha}{2}}$$

Note: In applying the above formula, you must select the proper sign preceding the radical. The sign is determined by the quadrant in which the terminal side of α lies.

695   The half-angle formula is useful in the form shown in frame 694. Note that α is half of 2α. However, the formula is usually written as shown below.
Step 2. If we let $\theta = 2\alpha$ and $\frac{1}{2}\theta = \alpha$, the formula $\cos \alpha = \pm \sqrt{(1 + \cos 2\alpha)/2}$ becomes

$$\left(\cos \tfrac{1}{2}\theta = \pm \sqrt{\frac{1 + \cos \ \theta}{2}} \ \right)$$

The numerical problem which you solved in frame 692 "Find cos 22°30'" could now be done more easily using this formula. Try it!

$$\cos 22°30' = \pm \sqrt{\frac{1 + \cos 45°}{2}} = \sqrt{\frac{1 + 1/\sqrt{2}}{2}}$$

$$= \sqrt{\frac{\sqrt{2} + 1}{2\sqrt{2}}} = \tfrac{1}{2}\sqrt{2 + \sqrt{2}}$$

Note the choice of sign above.

696   Start with the double-angle formula $\cos 2\alpha = 1 - 2 \sin^2 \alpha$ and derive a formula for $\sin \frac{1}{2}\alpha$ in terms of $\cos \alpha$.

$$\cos 2\alpha = 1 - 2 \sin^2 \alpha, \ \sin^2 \ \alpha = \frac{1 - \cos 2\alpha}{2}$$

$$\sin \ \alpha = \pm \sqrt{\frac{1 - \cos 2\alpha}{2}}$$

Now let $\theta = 2\alpha$ and $\frac{1}{2}\theta = \alpha$

$$\left(\sin \tfrac{1}{2}\theta = \pm \sqrt{\frac{1 - \cos \ \theta}{2}} \ \right)$$

Note: The choice of sign in a numerical example depends on the quadrant in which the terminal side of $\frac{1}{2}\theta$ lies.

697 Find $\sin 11°15'$ using the half-angle formula and the fact that $\cos 22°30' = \frac{1}{2}\sqrt{2 + \sqrt{2}}$

$$\sin 11°15' = +\sqrt{\frac{1 - \cos 22°30'}{2}} = \sqrt{\frac{1 - \frac{1}{2}\sqrt{2 + \sqrt{2}}}{2}}$$

$$= \frac{1}{2}\sqrt{2 - \sqrt{2 + \sqrt{2}}}$$

Note: For a positive acute angle the sign is positive.

▽**698** Again we remark that the formulas $\sin \frac{1}{2}\theta = \pm\sqrt{(1 - \cos \theta)/2}$ and $\cos \frac{1}{2}\theta = \pm\sqrt{(1 + \cos \theta)/2}$ are identities and hence are true for all permissible values of θ.

Examples: $\sin \pi = \pm\sqrt{\dfrac{1 - \cos 2\pi}{2}}$ $\cos 125° = \pm\sqrt{\dfrac{1 + \cos 250°}{2}}$

Complete the following, copying the entire equations as you answer.

(1) $\sin \underline{\quad} = \pm\sqrt{\dfrac{1 - \cos 4A}{2}}$ **(2)** $\cos \dfrac{\pi}{3} = \pm \sqrt{}$

(3) $\sin 5° = \pm \sqrt{}$ **(4)** $\underline{\quad} = \pm\sqrt{\dfrac{1 - \cos 3\theta}{2}}$

(1) $\sin 2A = \pm\sqrt{\dfrac{1 - \cos 4A}{2}}$ **(2)** $\cos \dfrac{\pi}{3} = \pm\sqrt{\dfrac{1 + \cos (2\pi/3)}{2}}$

(3) $\sin 5° = \pm\sqrt{\dfrac{1 - \cos 10°}{2}}$ **(4)** $\sin \dfrac{3\theta}{2} = \pm\sqrt{\dfrac{1 - \cos 3\theta}{2}}$

699 For the $\tan \frac{1}{2}\theta$ we may recall that for any angle α, $\tan \alpha = \sin \alpha/\cos \alpha$; hence, $\tan \frac{1}{2}\theta = \sin \frac{1}{2}\alpha/\cos \frac{1}{2}\theta = \underline{\qquad\qquad}$. Find a formula for <u>$\tan \frac{1}{2}\theta$</u> in terms of $\sin \theta$ and $\cos \theta$.

$$= \pm\frac{\sqrt{(1 - \cos \theta)/2}}{\sqrt{(1 + \cos \theta)/2}} = \pm\sqrt{\frac{1 - \cos \theta}{1 + \cos \theta}}$$

700 There are alternate forms for $\tan \frac{1}{2}\theta$ which are derived from $\tan \frac{1}{2}\theta = \sin \frac{1}{2}\theta/\cos \frac{1}{2}\theta$. First multiply both numerator and denominator of the right member by $\sin \frac{1}{2}\theta$ and then simplify thus:

continued →

1. $\tan \frac{1}{2}\theta = \dfrac{\sin \frac{1}{2}\theta}{\cos \frac{1}{2}\theta} \cdot \dfrac{\sin \frac{1}{2}\theta}{\sin \frac{1}{2}\theta}$

2. $\qquad = \dfrac{\sin^2 \frac{1}{2}\theta}{\cos \frac{1}{2}\theta \cdot \sin \frac{1}{2}\theta}$

3. $\qquad = \dfrac{(1 - \cos\,\theta)/2}{\cos \frac{1}{2}\theta \cdot \sin \frac{1}{2}\theta}$ 　　　explain this step

4. $\qquad = \dfrac{1 - \cos\,\theta}{2\cos \frac{1}{2}\theta \cdot \sin \frac{1}{2}\theta}$

5. $\qquad = \dfrac{1 - \cos\,\theta}{\sin\,\theta}$ 　　　explain this step

Thus we have the identity

$$\tan \tfrac{1}{2}\theta = \frac{1 - \cos\,\theta}{\sin\,\theta}.$$

3. We have the half-angle identity

$$\sin \tfrac{1}{2}\theta = \sqrt{\frac{1 - \cos\,\theta}{2}}$$

Therefore $\sin^2 \frac{1}{2}\theta = \dfrac{1 - \cos\theta}{2}$

5. We have the double-angle identity
   $\sin 2\alpha = 2 \sin\alpha \, \cos\alpha$.
   Replacing 2α by θ and α by $\frac{1}{2}\theta$, we have
   $\sin\,\theta = 2 \sin \frac{1}{2}\theta \cos \frac{1}{2}\theta$.

Note: Another form for $\tan \frac{1}{2}\theta$ is obtained by using $\cos \frac{1}{2}\theta$ as the multiplier in Step 1, i.e., $\tan \frac{1}{2}\theta = \sin\,\theta / (1 + \cos\,\theta)$.

701 The next formulas we shall derive are called *product-to-sum* formulas. Recall your identities for $\sin(\alpha + \beta)$ and $\sin(\alpha - \beta)$ and prove that $\sin(\alpha + \beta) + \sin(\alpha - \beta) = 2 \sin\alpha \, \cos\alpha$.

Simplify the left member thus:
$\sin\alpha \cos\beta + \cos\alpha \sin\beta + \sin\alpha \cos\beta - \cos\alpha \sin\beta = 2 \sin\alpha \, \cos\beta$

702 Prove that $\sin(\alpha + \beta) - \sin(\alpha - \beta) = 2\cos\alpha\sin\beta$.

Simplify the left member thus:
$\sin\alpha\cos\beta + \cos\alpha\sin\beta - (\sin\alpha\cos\beta - \cos\alpha\sin\beta) = 2\cos\alpha\sin\beta$

703 Prove that $\cos(\alpha + \beta) + \cos(\alpha - \beta) = 2\cos\alpha\cos\beta$.

Simplify the left member thus:
$\cos\alpha\cos\beta - \sin\alpha\sin\beta + \cos\alpha\cos\beta + \sin\alpha\sin\beta = 2\cos\alpha\cos\beta$

704 Prove that $\cos(\alpha + \beta) - \cos(\alpha - \beta) = -2\sin\alpha\sin\beta$.

Simplify the left member thus:
$\cos\alpha\cos\beta - \sin\alpha\sin\beta - (\cos\alpha\cos\beta + \sin\alpha\sin\beta) = -2\sin\alpha\sin\beta$

705 Complete the four addition formulas below.
(1) $\sin(\alpha + \beta) =$ _____
(2) $\sin(\alpha - \beta) =$ _____
(3) $\cos(\alpha + \beta) =$ _____
(4) $\cos(\alpha - \beta) =$ _____
Keep this list for reference as you review the product formulas.
You will not be expected to memorize the product formulas, but you
should be able to derive them easily from the addition formulas.

(1) $\sin(\alpha + \beta) = \sin\alpha\cos\beta + \cos\alpha\sin\beta$
(2) $\sin(\alpha - \beta) = \sin\alpha\cos\beta - \cos\alpha\sin\beta$
(3) $\cos(\alpha + \beta) = \cos\alpha\cos\beta - \sin\alpha\sin\beta$
(4) $\cos(\alpha - \beta) = \cos\alpha\cos\beta + \sin\alpha\sin\beta$

706 Refer to your list from frame 705. By the algebraic addition of two
of these you have the formula for the product $2\sin\alpha\cos\beta$. Write
the formula.

add (1) and (2): $2\sin\alpha\cos\beta = \sin(\alpha + \beta) + \sin(\alpha - \beta)$

707 Refer to your list from frame 705 again. Complete the formula for
$2\cos\alpha\sin\beta$.

subtract (2) from (1): $2\cos\alpha\sin\beta = \sin(\alpha + \beta) - \sin(\alpha - \beta)$

708   Refer to your list again. Complete the formula for $2 \cos \alpha \cos \beta$.

add **(3)** and **(4)**: $2 \cos \alpha \cos \beta = \cos (\alpha + \beta) + \cos (\alpha - \beta)$

709   Refer to your list again. Complete the formula for $-2 \sin \alpha \sin \beta$.

subtract **(4)** from **(3)**: $-2 \sin \alpha \sin \beta = \cos (\alpha + \beta) - \cos (\alpha - \beta)$

710 Here are the four _product formulas_ which you have established.

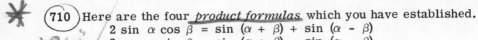

$$2 \sin \alpha \cos \beta = \sin (\alpha + \beta) + \sin (\alpha - \beta)$$
$$2 \cos \alpha \sin \beta = \sin (\alpha + \beta) - \sin (\alpha - \beta)$$
$$2 \cos \alpha \cos \beta = \cos (\alpha + \beta) + \cos (\alpha - \beta)$$
$$-2 \sin \alpha \sin \beta = \cos (\alpha + \beta) - \cos (\alpha - \beta)$$

Although there is nothing wrong with them as they stand, the _products-to-sums_ formulas are usually written without the factor 2 on the left. Copy the entire equations as you answer. Thus:

(1) $\sin \alpha \cos \beta =$ _____

(2) $\cos \alpha \sin \beta =$ _____

(3) $\cos \alpha \cos \beta =$ _____

(4) $\sin \alpha \sin \beta =$ _____

(1) $\sin \alpha \cos \beta = \frac{1}{2}[\sin (\alpha + \beta) + \sin (\alpha - \beta)]$

(2) $\cos \alpha \sin \beta = \frac{1}{2}[\sin (\alpha + \beta) - \sin (\alpha - \beta)]$

(3) $\cos \alpha \cos \beta = \frac{1}{2}[\cos (\alpha + \beta) + \cos (\alpha - \beta)]$

(4) $\sin \alpha \sin \beta = \frac{1}{2}[\cos (\alpha + \beta) - \cos (\alpha - \beta)]$

711   It is desirable and sometimes necessary to have a formula for $\sin \theta + \sin \phi$ as well as a formula for $\sin \alpha \sin \beta$. This can be obtained by a simple substitution: We have shown that

1. $\sin (\alpha + \beta) + \sin (\alpha - \beta) = 2 \sin \alpha \cos \beta$

2. $\sin (\alpha + \beta) - \sin (\alpha - \beta) = 2 \cos \alpha \sin \beta$

If we let $\alpha + \beta = \theta$

and $\underline{\alpha - \beta = \phi}$

$2\alpha \qquad = \theta + \phi$ by addition

$2\beta = \theta - \phi$ by subtraction

Then $\alpha = \frac{1}{2}(\theta + \phi)$ and $\beta = \frac{1}{2}(\theta - \phi)$. Write statements 1 and 2 when these substitutions have been made.

1. $\sin \theta + \sin \phi = 2 \sin \frac{1}{2}(\theta + \phi) \cos \frac{1}{2}(\theta - \phi)$

2. $\sin \theta - \sin \phi = 2 \cos \frac{1}{2}(\theta + \phi) \sin \frac{1}{2}(\theta - \phi)$

712   1. $\sin \theta + \sin \phi = 2 \sin \frac{1}{2}(\theta + \phi) \cos \frac{1}{2}(\theta - \phi)$

2. $\sin \theta - \sin \phi = 2 \cos \frac{1}{2}(\theta + \phi) \sin \frac{1}{2}(\theta - \phi)$

The above two formula give us a way to change from sums (or differences) to products. Study them. State the resulting formula when similar substitutions are made in:

(1) $\cos (\alpha + \beta) + \cos (\alpha - \beta) = 2 \cos \alpha \cos \beta$

(2) $\cos (\alpha + \beta) - \cos (\alpha - \beta) = -2 \sin \alpha \sin \beta$

> (1) $\cos \theta + \cos \phi = 2 \cos \frac{1}{2}(\theta + \phi) \cos \frac{1}{2}(\theta - \phi)$
>
> (2) $\cos \theta - \cos \phi = -2 \sin \frac{1}{2}(\theta + \phi) \sin \frac{1}{2}(\theta - \phi)$

713   Suppose now that equation 1 in frame **712** is divided by equation 2. Thus:

$$\frac{\sin \theta + \sin \phi}{\sin \theta - \sin \phi} = \frac{2 \sin \frac{1}{2}(\theta + \phi) \cos \frac{1}{2}(\theta - \phi)}{2 \cos \frac{1}{2}(\theta + \phi) \sin \frac{1}{2}(\theta - \phi)}$$

Since $\tan \alpha = \sin \alpha / \cos \alpha$, $\cos \alpha \neq 0$, then the right member can be expressed in terms of tangents as shown here. Copy the entire equation as you answer.

$$\frac{\sin \theta + \sin \phi}{\sin \theta - \sin \phi} = \tan \tfrac{1}{2}(\underline{\quad}) \cdot \frac{1}{\tan \tfrac{1}{2}(\underline{\quad})} = \frac{\tan \tfrac{1}{2}(\underline{\quad})}{\tan \tfrac{1}{2}(\underline{\quad})}$$

Note: We assumed above that $\sin \theta - \sin \phi \neq 0$

> $$\frac{\sin \theta + \sin \phi}{\sin \theta - \sin \phi} = \tan \tfrac{1}{2}(\theta + \phi) \cdot \frac{1}{\tan \tfrac{1}{2}(\theta - \phi)} = \frac{\tan \tfrac{1}{2}(\theta + \phi)}{\tan \tfrac{1}{2}(\theta - \phi)}$$
>
> *Note:* You have completed the proof for the statement
>
> $$\frac{\sin \theta + \sin \phi}{\sin \theta - \sin \phi} = \frac{\tan \tfrac{1}{2}(\theta + \phi)}{\tan \tfrac{1}{2}(\theta - \phi)}$$

714   As a review of the work in frame **713**, write a proof for the following: Given

1. $\sin \theta - \sin \phi = 2 \cos \frac{1}{2}(\theta + \phi) \sin \frac{1}{2}(\theta - \phi)$

2. $\sin \theta + \sin \phi = 2 \sin \frac{1}{2}(\theta + \phi) \cos \frac{1}{2}(\theta - \phi)$

Show that

$$\frac{\sin \theta - \sin \phi}{\sin \theta + \sin \phi} = \frac{\tan \frac{1}{2}(\theta - \phi)}{\tan \frac{1}{2}(\theta + \phi)}$$

> *Proof:*
>
> 1. $\sin \theta - \sin \phi = 2 \cos \frac{1}{2}(\theta + \phi) \sin \frac{1}{2}(\theta - \phi)$ given
>
> 2. $\sin \theta + \sin \phi = 2 \sin \frac{1}{2}(\theta + \phi) \cos \frac{1}{2}(\theta - \phi)$ given

continued →

3. $\dfrac{\sin\theta - \sin\phi}{\sin\theta + \sin\phi} = \dfrac{2\cos\frac{1}{2}(\theta + \phi)\,\sin\frac{1}{2}(\theta - \phi)}{2\sin\frac{1}{2}(\theta + \phi)\,\cos\frac{1}{2}(\theta - \phi)}$ dividing equation 1 by 2

4. $\qquad\qquad = \dfrac{1}{\tan\frac{1}{2}(\theta + \phi)} \cdot \tan\frac{1}{2}(\theta - \phi)$ definition of tangent

5. $\qquad\qquad = \dfrac{\tan\frac{1}{2}(\theta - \phi)}{\tan\frac{1}{2}(\theta + \phi)}$ simplifying

715 Recall that in frames 602 and 603 you proved that in triangle

$$\frac{\sin\alpha - \sin\beta}{\sin\alpha + \sin\beta} = \frac{a - b}{a + b}$$

We are also asserting from frame 714 that for two angles α and β

$$\frac{\sin\alpha - \sin\beta}{\sin\alpha + \sin\beta} = \frac{\tan\,(\alpha - \beta)}{\tan\,(\alpha + \beta)}$$

Combining these two equations whose left members are identical, we can state the law of tangents for triangle ABC in terms of sides a and b and angles α and β thus:

$$\underline{\hspace{3cm}} = \underline{\hspace{4cm}}$$

$$\frac{a - b}{a + b} = \frac{\tan\,(\alpha - \beta)}{\tan\,(\alpha + \beta)}$$

Comment

The law of tangents, one form of which you derived in frame 715

$$\frac{a - b}{a + b} = \frac{\tan\,(\alpha - \beta)}{\tan\,(\alpha + \beta)}$$

is useful in solving triangles in which two sides and the included angle are given. Since we are not specifically interested in this type of problem now, we shall not ask you to solve numerical examples. The advantage which this formula has over the law of cosines is that computations can be made by logarithms. As has been pointed out, this program does not emphasize solutions of triangles.

716   Prove that $\sin(\alpha + \beta) \cdot \sin(\alpha - \beta) = \sin^2 \alpha - \sin^2 \beta$. Refer to Panel 8 for identities or formulas you may use as replacements in the left member.

Working from the left member

$\sin(\alpha + \beta)\sin(\alpha - \beta)$ Panel 8II(1), (2)

$= (\sin \alpha \cos \beta + \cos \alpha \sin \beta)(\sin \alpha \cos \beta - \cos \alpha \sin \beta)$

$= \sin^2 \alpha \cos^2 \beta - \cos^2 \alpha \sin^2 \beta$ multiplying and collecting terms

$= \sin^2 \alpha(1 - \sin^2 \beta) - \sin^2 \beta(1 - \sin^2 \alpha)$ Panel 8I(1)

$= \sin^2 \alpha - \sin^2 \alpha \sin^2 \beta - \sin^2 \beta + \sin^2 \alpha \sin^2 \beta$ simplifying

$= \sin^2 \alpha - \sin^2 \beta$ simplifying

Therefore, $\sin(\alpha + \beta)\sin(\alpha - \beta) = \sin^2 \alpha - \sin^2 \beta$

Comment

also do csc $A = \dfrac{2}{\sqrt{3}}$
sin

You could derive or prove many additional identities with the background you now have. Frames 717 to 720 are examples.

▽**717**   Show that $\cos(\alpha + \beta)\cos(\alpha - \beta) = \cos^2 \alpha - \sin^2 \beta$. Refer to Panel 8 if necessary.

Working from the left member

$\cos(\alpha + \beta)\cos(\alpha - \beta)$ Panel 8II(3), (4)

$= (\cos \alpha \cos \beta - \sin \alpha \sin \beta)(\cos \alpha \cos \beta + \sin \alpha \sin \beta)$

$= \cos^2 \alpha \cos^2 \beta - \sin^2 \alpha \sin^2 \beta$ multiplying

$= \cos^2 \alpha(1 - \sin^2 \beta) - (1 - \cos^2 \alpha)\sin^2 \beta$ Panel 8I(1)

$= \cos^2 \alpha - \sin^2 \beta \cos^2 \alpha - \sin^2 \beta + \sin^2 \beta \cos^2 \alpha$ simplifying

$= \cos^2 \alpha - \sin^2 \beta$ simplifying

Therefore, $\cos(\alpha + \beta)\cos(\alpha - \beta) = \cos^2 \alpha - \sin^2 \beta$

718 Express sin 3α in terms of sin α and cos α. *Suggestions:* Use the formula for the sum of two angles, then the double-angle formula. Start with sin 3α = sin $(2\alpha + \alpha)$.

Let sin 3α = sin $(2\alpha + \alpha)$

$\qquad$ = sin 2α cos α + cos 2α sin α $\qquad$ Panel 8II(1)

$\qquad$ = 2 sin α cos α cos α $\qquad\qquad\qquad$ Panel 8III(1), (2)
$\qquad$ $\;$ + (cos^2 α - sin^2 α) sin α

$\qquad$ = 2 sin α cos^2 α $\qquad\qquad\qquad\quad$ simplifying
$\qquad$ $\;\;$ + sin α cos^2 α - sin^3 α

$\qquad$ = 3 sin α cos^2 α - sin^3 α $\qquad\quad$ simplifying

$\qquad$ = sin α(3 cos^2 α - sin^2 α) $\qquad\;\;$ simplifying

Therefore, sin 3α = sin α(3 cos^2 α - sin^2 α)
Note: Using another form from Panel 8III(2), you may report your answer as
$\qquad$ sin 3α = sin α(3 - 4 sin^2 α)
or $\quad$ sin 3α = sin α(4 cos^2 α - 1).

719 Express cos 3α in terms of sin α and cos α.

Let cos 3α = cos $(2\alpha + \alpha)$

$\qquad$ = cos 2α cos α - sin 2α sin α $\qquad$ Panel 8II(3)

$\qquad$ = (cos^2 α - sin^2 α) cos α $\qquad\qquad$ Panel 8III(1), (2)
$\qquad$ $\;$ - (2 sin α cos α) sin α

$\qquad$ = cos^3 α - sin^2 α cos α $\qquad\qquad$ simplifying
$\qquad$ $\;$ - 2 sin^2 α cos α

$\qquad$ = cos^3 α - 3 sin^2 α cos α $\qquad\;\;$ simplifying

$\qquad$ = cos α(cos^2 α - 3 sin^2 α) $\qquad\;$ simplifying

Therefore, cos 3α = cos α(cos^2 α - 3 sin^2 α)
or using other forms of III(2) in line 3 above, you might write either

$\qquad$ cos 3α = 2 cos^3 α - cos α - 2 sin^2 α cos α

$\qquad$ cos 3α = cos α - 4 sin^2 α cos α

720 There are three additional trigonometric functions less commonly used which we shall define at this time.

1. secant θ, $\qquad$ sec θ = $\dfrac{1}{\cos \theta}$, $\qquad$ if cos $\theta \neq 0$

continued →

2. cosecant θ, $\csc \theta = \dfrac{1}{\sin \theta}$, if $\sin \theta \neq 0$

3. cotangent θ, $\cot \theta = \dfrac{\cos \theta}{\sin \theta}$ if $\sin \theta \neq 0$

Using x, y, and r as shown in the sketch

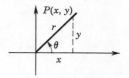

$$\sec \theta = \dfrac{1}{x/r} = \dfrac{r}{x}$$
$$\csc \theta = \textbf{(1)} \underline{\hspace{2cm}}$$
$$\cot \theta = \textbf{(2)} \underline{\hspace{2cm}}$$

(1) $\dfrac{1}{y/r} = \dfrac{r}{y}$ **(2)** $\dfrac{x/r}{y/r} = \dfrac{x}{y}$

721 Here is the definition for the cotangent of θ.

$$\cot \theta = \dfrac{\cos \theta}{\sin \theta} \qquad \text{when } \sin \theta \neq 0$$

Prove that whenever $\tan \theta$ and $\cot \theta$ are defined, $\cot \theta = 1/\tan \theta$.

One method is shown below:

$\cot \quad = \dfrac{\cos \theta}{\sin \theta}$ by definition

$\quad = \dfrac{\cos \theta/\cos \theta}{\sin \theta/\cos \theta}$ multiply both numerator and denominator of the right member by $\cos \theta$

$\quad = \dfrac{1}{\tan \theta}$ simplify and apply the definition of tangent

Therefore, $\cos \quad = \dfrac{1}{\tan \theta}$

722 We remark that by definition the secant of θ equals the reciprocal of the cosine of θ, i.e., $\sec \theta = 1/\cos \theta$.

In the sketch $\cos \theta = x/r$

Therefore, $\sec \theta = \dfrac{1}{x/r} = \dfrac{r}{x}$

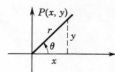

If $\cos \theta = \frac{5}{8}$, **(1)** find $\sec \theta$.

If $\cos \theta = -\frac{2}{3}$, **(2)** find $\sec \theta$.

If $\cos \theta = 0.500$, **(3)** find $\sec \theta$.

Note: The reciprocal of a number b is $1/b$.

(1) $\sec \theta = \frac{8}{5}$ **(2)** $\sec \theta = -\frac{3}{2}$ **(3)** $\sec \theta = \dfrac{1}{0.500} = 2$

723 (1) Given sec $\theta = \frac{5}{4}$, find cos θ. (2) In which quadrants may the terminal side of θ lie? (3) Sketch the two angles.

(1) cos $\theta = \frac{4}{5}$ (2) quadrants I, IV

(3)

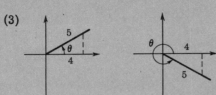

724 Since by definition cosecant $\theta = 1/\sin \theta$, that is, csc $\theta = 1/\sin \theta$, we say that the cosecant θ and sine θ are reciprocal functions. In this sketch sin $\theta = y/r$

Therefore, csc $\theta = \dfrac{1}{y/r} = \dfrac{r}{y}$

If sin $\theta = \frac{5}{7}$, (1) find csc θ.

If sin $\theta = -\frac{1}{3}$, (2) find csc θ

If sin $\theta = 0.75$, (3) find csc θ.

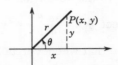

(1) cos $\theta = \frac{7}{5}$ (2) csc $\theta = -\frac{3}{1} = -3$ (3) $\dfrac{1}{0.750} = \dfrac{4}{3} \approx 1.333$

725 (1) Given csc $\theta = 2/\sqrt{3}$, find sin θ. (2) If csc $\theta = 2/\sqrt{3}$, θ is an angle terminating in quadrant (a)____ or (b)____.   Sketch the two angles θ such that csc $\theta = 2/\sqrt{3}$.

(1) sin $\theta = \dfrac{\sqrt{3}}{2}$ (2) (a) I, (b) II

(3)

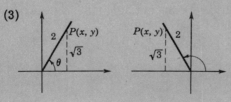

csc θ has the same sign as sin θ.

726 **(1)** Define csc θ.

(2) In terms of x, y, and r, csc θ = _____ .

(3) Therefore, $|\text{csc } \theta| \geq$ _____ .

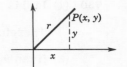

(1) csc $= \dfrac{1}{\sin \theta}$ **(2)** $\dfrac{r}{y}$ **(3)** 1

Remember: In a right triangle the hypotenuse is the longest side.

727 **(1)** Define sec θ.

(2) Using the letters x, y, and r, and your definition, show that sec θ = r/x.

(3) Could the absolute value of r/x be less than 1?

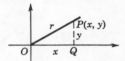

(1) sec $\theta = \dfrac{1}{\cos \theta}$ **(2)** sec $\theta = \dfrac{1}{x/r} = \dfrac{1}{1} \cdot \dfrac{r}{x} = \dfrac{r}{x}$

(3) no, OPQ is a right triangle and r is the hypotenuse.

728 Since sin $0° = 0$, what can you conclude about csc $0°$? Recall your definition for csc θ.

csc θ is undefined, since division by zero is undefined.

729 sec θ is undefined when θ has which of these values:

$$1. \ 0 \qquad 2. \ \frac{\pi}{2} \qquad 3. \ \pi \qquad 4. \ \frac{3\pi}{2}$$

2 and 4

Note: sec $\theta = \dfrac{1}{\cos \theta}$

Therefore, sec $\dfrac{\pi}{2} = \dfrac{1}{\cos (\pi/2)} = \dfrac{1}{0}$ and sec $\dfrac{3\pi}{2} = \dfrac{1}{\cos (3\pi/2)} = \dfrac{1}{0}$

730 (1) In this sketch tan $\theta = y/x$.

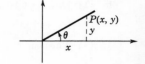

Therefore, $\cot \theta = \dfrac{1}{y/x} = $ _____ .

(2) If $\tan \theta = 1/\sqrt{3}$, $\cot \theta = $ _____ .

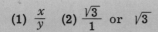

(1) $\dfrac{x}{y}$ (2) $\dfrac{\sqrt{3}}{1}$ or $\sqrt{3}$

731 (1) $\cot \theta = -\frac{2}{3}$, find $\tan \theta$. (2) Make sketches showing the two quadrants in which θ may terminate if $\cot \theta = -\frac{2}{3}$.

(1) $\tan \theta = -\frac{3}{2}$

(2)

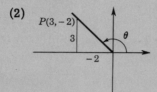
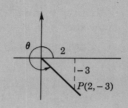

732 You should note that if $\tan \theta = 0$, $\cot \theta$ is undefined. In the interval $0 \le \theta < 2\pi$ there are two values of θ for which $\cot \theta$ is undefined. What are these two?

0 and π

733 Given $\sin \theta = 7/\sqrt{74}$ and θ is an angle of quadrant II. Find the numerical value in radical form for each of the following: $\cos \theta = $ (1) _____ , $\tan \theta = $ (2) _____ , $\cot \theta = $ (3) _____ , $\sec \theta = $ (4) _____ , and $\csc \theta = $ (5) _____ . *Suggestions:* Make a sketch, watch the signs carefully.

(1) $\dfrac{-5}{\sqrt{74}}$ (2) $\dfrac{-7}{5}$ (3) $\dfrac{-5}{7}$

(4) $\dfrac{-\sqrt{74}}{5}$ (5) $\dfrac{\sqrt{74}}{7}$

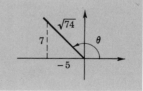

734 Using your previous knowledge of the numerical values of sin 0,
     cos 0, and tan 0, fill in the blanks (unless the function is undefined)
     for all six functions of an angle θ = 0 radians, i.e., sin 0 =
     (1) _____ , cos 0 = (2) _____ , tan 0 = (3) _____ , cot 0 =
     (4) _____ , sec 0 = (5) _____ , and csc 0 = (6) _____ .

(1) 0   (2) 1   (3) 0   (4) undefined   (5) 1   (6) undefined

▽735 Find the numerical values (if they exist) for the six functions of
     $\pi/2$, i.e., sin $(\pi/2)$ = (1) _____ , cos $(\pi/2)$ = (2) _____ ,
     tan $(\pi/2)$ = (3) _____ , cot $(\pi/2)$ = (4) _____ , sec $(\pi/2)$ =
     (5) _____ , and csc $(\pi/2)$ = (6) _____ .

(1) 1   (2) 0   (3) undefined   (4) 0   (5) undefined   (6) 1

▽736 Find the numerical values (if they exist) for the six functions of π,
     i.e., sin π = (1) _____ , cos π = (2) _____ , tan π =
     (3) _____ , cot π = (4) _____ , sec π = (5) _____ , and
     csc π = (6) _____ .

(1) 0   (2) -1   (3) 0   (4) undefined   (5) -1   (6) undefined

▽737 Find the numerical values (if they exist) for the six functions of
     $3\pi/2$, i.e., sin $(3\pi/2)$ = (1) _____ , cos $(3\pi/2)$ = (2) _____ ,
     tan $(3\pi/2)$ = (3) _____ , cot $(3\pi/2)$ = (4) _____ ,
     sec $(3\pi/2)$ = (5) _____ , and csc $(3\pi/2)$ = (6) _____ .

(1) -1   (2) 0   (3) undefined   (4) 0   (5) undefined   (6) -1

738 Find the numerical values (if they exist) for the six functions of 2π,
     i.e., sin 2π = (1) _____ , cos 2π = (2) _____ , tan 2π =
     (3) _____ , cot 2π = (4) _____ , sec 2π = (5) _____ , and
     csc 2π = (6) _____ .

(1) 0   (2) 1   (3) 0   (4) undefined   (5) 1   (6) undefined

739 Find the numerical values (if they exist) for the six functions of 3π,
     i.e., sin 3π = (1) _____ , cos 3π = (2) _____ , tan 3π =

continued →

(3)_____ , cot 3π = (4)_____ , sec 3π = (5)_____ , and
csc 3π = (6)_____ .

(1) 0   **(2)** -1   **(3)** 0   **(4)** undefined   **(5)** -1   **(6)** undefined

740   Find the numerical values (if they exist) for the six functions of -8π,
i.e., sin (-8π) = (1)_____ , cos (-8π) = (2)_____ ,
tan (-8π) = (3)_____ , cot (-8π) = (4)_____ , sec (-8π) =
(5)_____ , and csc (-8π) = (6)_____ .

(1) 0   **(2)** 1   **(3)** 0   **(4)** undefined   **(5)** 1   **(6)** undefined

741   When the secant, cosecant, and cotangent functions were introduced,
we remarked that they are not as frequently used as the sine, co-
sine, and tangent. If sin θ, cos θ, and tan θ are known, the other
three can be found immediate thus: (1) sec θ = 1/____ ,
(2) csc θ = 1/____ , and (3) cot θ = 1/____ .   Copy the entire
equations as you answer.   For this reason we do not give as much
attention to sec θ, csc θ, and cot θ as we would otherwise.

(1) sec $\theta = \dfrac{1}{\cos \theta}$ **(2)** csc $\theta = \dfrac{1}{\sin \theta}$ **(3)** cot $\theta = \dfrac{1}{\tan \theta}$

742   An important trigonometric identity states that for any angle θ if
tan θ and sec θ exist, then $\underline{1 + \tan^2 \theta = \sec^2 \theta}$. Supply reasons
for the following proof:
Starting with the left member

1. $1 + \tan^2 \theta = 1 + \dfrac{\sin^2 \theta}{\cos^2 \theta}$ (1)_____

2. $= \dfrac{\cos^2 \theta + \sin^2 \theta}{\cos^2 \theta}$ (2)_____

3. $= \dfrac{1}{\cos^2 \theta}$ (3)_____

4. $= \sec^2 \theta$ (4)_____

(1) tan $\theta = \dfrac{\sin \theta}{\cos \theta}$, definition of tangent

(2) collecting terms or simplifying

(3) $\sin^2 \theta + \cos^2 \theta = 1$, an identity

(4) $\dfrac{1}{\cos \theta}$ = sec θ, definition of secant

743 Write a proof similar to the one in frame 742 showing that for any angle θ if cot θ and csc θ exist, then $1 + \cot^2 \theta = \csc^2 \theta$.

Starting with the left member

1. $1 + \cot^2 \theta = \dfrac{\cos^2 \theta}{\sin^2 \theta}$ 1. definition of cotangent

2. $= \dfrac{\sin^2 \theta + \cos^2 \theta}{\sin^2 \theta}$ 2. collecting and simplifying

3. $= \dfrac{1}{\sin^2 \theta}$ 3. $\sin^2 \theta + \cos^2 \theta = 1$

4. $= \csc^2 \theta$ 4. definition of cosecant

744 We frequently want to express $\sin^2 \theta$ in terms of $\cos^2 \theta$ and vice versa. This we have done in previous frames. Given $\sin^2 \theta + \cos^2 \theta = 1$, then $\sin^2 \theta =$ (1) _____ and $\sin \theta =$ (2)_____ .

(1) $1 - \cos^2 \theta$ (2) $\pm\sqrt{1 - \cos^2 \theta}$

Note: $\sin \theta$ is positive in quadrants I and II and negative in III and IV, thus the double sign.

745 Given $\sin^2 \theta + \cos^2 \theta = 1$, then $\cos^2 \theta =$ (1) _____ and $\cos \theta =$ (2)_____ . $\cos \theta$ is positive in quadrants (3)_____ and (4)_____ .

(1) $1 - \sin^2 \theta$ (2) $\pm\sqrt{1 - \sin^2 \theta}$ (3) I   (4) IV

746 Given $1 + \tan^2 \theta = \sec^2 \theta$, then $\tan^2 \theta =$ (1)_____ and $\tan \theta =$ (2)_____ . (3) In which quadrants is tan θ positive?

(1) $\sec^2 \theta - 1$ (2) $\pm\sqrt{\sec^2 \theta - 1}$ (3) I and III

747 Given $\cot^2 \theta + 1 = \csc^2 \theta$, then $\cot^2 \theta =$ (1) _____ and $\cot \theta =$ (2)_____ . $\cot \theta$ is positive in quadrants (3)_____ and (4)_____ .

(1) $\csc^2 \theta - 1$ (2) $\pm\sqrt{\csc^2 \theta - 1}$ (3) I   (4) III

748 Prove that cot $(-\theta)$ = -cot θ (if cot θ exists).

> Working from the left member
>
> $$\cot(-\theta) = \frac{\cos(-\theta)}{\sin(-\theta)} \qquad \text{by definition of cotangent}$$
>
> $$= \frac{\cos\theta}{-\sin\theta} \qquad \begin{array}{l} \text{since } \cos(-\theta) = \cos\theta \text{ and} \\ \sin(-\theta) = -\sin\theta \end{array}$$
>
> $$= -\cot\theta \qquad \text{by definition of cotangent}$$

 749 Prove that sec $(-\theta)$ = sec θ (if sec θ exists).

> Working from left member
>
> $$\sec(-\theta) = \frac{1}{\cos(-\theta)} \qquad \text{by definition of secant}$$
>
> $$= \frac{1}{\cos\theta} \qquad \text{since } \cos(-\theta) = \cos\theta$$
>
> $$= \sec\theta \qquad \text{by definition of secant}$$

750 Prove that csc $(-\theta)$ = -csc θ (if csc θ exists).

> Working from left member
>
> $$\csc(-\theta) = \frac{1}{\sin(-\theta)} \qquad \text{by definition of cosecant}$$
>
> $$= \frac{1}{-\sin\theta} \qquad \text{since } \sin(-\theta) = -\sin\theta$$
>
> $$= -\csc\theta \qquad \text{by definition of cosecant}$$

751 Let $\alpha = 90°$. Simplify the statement
$$\cos(\alpha - \beta) = \cos\alpha\cos\beta + \sin\alpha\sin\beta$$

> $\cos(90° - \beta) = \sin\beta$
> *Solution:* $\cos(90° - \beta) = \cos 90° \cos\beta + \sin 90° \sin\beta$
> $$= 0 \cdot \cos\beta + 1 \cdot \sin\beta = \sin\beta$$

752 Let $\alpha = 90°$. Simplify the statement
$$\sin(\alpha - \beta) = \sin\alpha\cos\beta - \cos\alpha\sin\beta$$

> $\sin(90 - \beta) = \cos\beta$
> *Solution:* $\sin(90 - \beta) = \sin 90° \cos\beta - \cos 90° \sin\beta$
> $$= 1 \cdot \cos\beta - 0 \cdot \sin\beta = \cos\beta$$

753 From frames 751 and 752 we have cos $(90° - \beta)$ = sin β and sin $(90° - \beta)$ = cos β. Find tan $(90° - \beta)$.

---

tan $(90° - \beta)$ = cot β

One solution: By definition tan x = sin x/cos x for any angle x for which cos $x \neq 0$.

$$\tan (90° - \beta) = \frac{\sin (90° - \beta)}{\cos (90° - \beta)} = \frac{\cos \beta}{\sin \beta} = \cot \beta$$

See frame 754 for further discussion.

---

754 Explain why you cannot show that tan $(90° - \beta)$ = cot β by use of the formula

$$\tan (\alpha - \beta) = \frac{\tan \alpha - \tan \beta}{1 + \tan \alpha \tan \beta}$$

---

tan 90° is undefined; hence, you cannot express directly tan $(90° - \beta)$ in terms of

$$\frac{\tan 90° - \tan \beta}{1 - \tan 90° \tan \beta}$$

---

755 Use the relationship cot x = 1/tan x, tan $x \neq 0$, to show that cot $(90° - \beta)$ = tan β.

---

1. replace x by $(90° - \beta)$ $\cot (90° - \beta) = \dfrac{1}{\tan (90° - \beta)}$

2. since tan $(90° - \beta)$ = cot β by previous proof $= \dfrac{1}{\cot \beta}$

3. replace $\dfrac{1}{\cot \beta}$ with tan β $= \tan \beta$

---

756 By similar reasoning we should be able to see that sec $(90 - \beta)$ = (1)_____ and csc $(90 - \beta)$ = (2)_____. Refer to the definitions for secant and cosecant if necessary. Recall the reduction formula for sin $(90 - \beta)$ and cos $(90 - \beta)$.

---

(1) csc β (2) sec β

757 Although the six statements we have discussed, sin (90 - β),
cos (90 - β), etc., are true for all values of β, they have special
significance when β is an acute angle. For example, if β = 40°,
then sin (90 - 40°) = cos 40°, i.e., sin 50° = cos 40°; if β = 32°,
then tan (90 - 32°) = cot 32°, i.e., tan 58° = cot 32°. We may
state this observation in the following manner: If two angles α and
β are complementary, sin α = cos β, tan α = cot β, and sec α =
csc β. Verify from Panel 1 the following statements: sin 50° =
(1)_____ and cos 40° = (2)_____ . Therefore, sin 50° = cos 40°.

(1) 0.766   (2) 0.766

758 We sometimes refer to the following pairs of
functions as _cofunctions_ (complements'
function): sine and cosine, tangent and cotangent, and secant and cosecant. If α and β
are any two complementary angles
(α = 90° - β),
        sin α = sin (90° - β) = cos β
        cos α = (1)_____
        tan α = (2)_____
        cot α = (3)_____
        sec α = (4)_____
        csc α = (5)_____

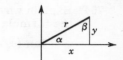

(1) cos (90° - β) = sin β   (2) tan (90° - β) = cot β
(3) cot (90° - β) = tan β   (4) sec (90° - β) = csc β
(5) csc (90° - β) = sec β

▽759 These formulas may also be called reduction formulas, when we
can state the functions of an angle in terms of the functions of a
smaller angle. Using just the left half of Panel 1, find sin 80°,
cos 75°, and sin 47° thus:
(1) sin 80° = cos 10°   = _____
(2) cos 75° = (a) _____ = (b) _____
(3) sin 47° = (a) _____ = (b) _____
Verify your results by reading from the right half of Panel 1.

(1) 0.985   (2) (a) sin 15°, (b) 0.259   (3) (a) cos 43°, (b) 0.731

760 Referring only to the part of Panel 1 giving sine, cosine, and tangent for angles 0 ≤ α ≤ 45°, find: (1) sin 68°, (2) cos 68°,
(3) tan 68°, (4) cot 68°, (5) sec 68°, and (6) csc 68°. Recall
definitions of cotangent, secant, and cosecant.

(1) sin 68° = cos 22° = 0.927   (2) cos 68° = sin 22° = 0.375

continued →

(3) $\tan 68° = \cot 22° = \dfrac{1}{\tan 22°} = \dfrac{1}{0.404} = 2.475$

(4) $\cot 68° = \tan 22° = 0.404$

(5) $\sec 68° = \dfrac{1}{\cos 68°} = \dfrac{1}{\sin 22°} = 2.667$

(6) $\csc 68° = \dfrac{1}{\sin 68°} = \dfrac{1}{\cos 22°} = 1.079$

761 Consider the effect on the value of the functions of α by adding $\pi/2$ radians. For example, $\sin(\pi/2 + \alpha) =$ (1)_____ and $\cos(\pi/2 + \alpha) =$ (2) _____ . Apply the proper addition formula and simplify.

(1) $\cos \alpha$

Solution: $\sin\left(\dfrac{\pi}{2} + \alpha\right) = \sin\dfrac{\pi}{2} \cos \alpha + \cos\dfrac{\pi}{2} \sin \alpha$

$$= 1\cdot\cos \alpha + 0\cdot\sin \alpha = \cos \alpha$$

(2) $-\sin \alpha$

Solution: $\cos\left(\dfrac{\pi}{2} + \alpha\right) = \cos\dfrac{\pi}{2} \cos \alpha - \sin\dfrac{\pi}{2} \sin \alpha$

$$= 0\cdot\cos \alpha - 1\cdot\sin \alpha = -\sin \alpha$$

762 In frame 761 we found that $\sin(\pi/2 + \alpha) = \cos \alpha$ and $\cos(\pi/2 + \alpha) = -\sin \alpha$. Use this information to get a statement for $\tan(\pi/2 + \alpha) =$ (1)_____ and $\cot(\pi/2 + \alpha) =$ (2)_____ .

(1) $-\cot \alpha$

Solution: $\tan\left(\dfrac{\pi}{2} + \alpha\right) = \dfrac{\sin(\pi/2 + \alpha)}{\cos(\pi/2 + \alpha)} = \dfrac{\cos \alpha}{-\sin \alpha} = -\cot \alpha$

(2) $-\tan \alpha$

Solution: $\cot\left(\dfrac{\pi}{2} + \alpha\right) = \dfrac{\cos(\pi/2 + \alpha)}{\sin(\pi/2 + \alpha)} = \dfrac{-\sin \alpha}{\cos \alpha} = -\tan \alpha$

763 As a numerical example, find (1) $\sin(5\pi/8)$, (2) $\cos(5\pi/8)$, and (3) $\cot(5\pi/8)$, given $\sin(\pi/8) = 0.383$, $\cos(\pi/8) = 0.924$, and $\tan(\pi/8) = 0.416$.

(1) $\sin\dfrac{5\pi}{8} = \cos\dfrac{\pi}{8} = 0.924$ (2) $\cos\dfrac{5\pi}{8} = -\sin\dfrac{\pi}{8} = -0.383$

(3) $\cot\dfrac{5\pi}{8} = -\tan\dfrac{\pi}{8} = -0.416$

$\longrightarrow \alpha \sin\dfrac{5\pi}{8} = \sin\dfrac{3\pi}{8}$

764 Show that $\tan (\theta + \pi) = \tan \theta$ (if both exist).

One solution:

$$\tan (\theta + \pi) = \frac{\tan \theta + \tan \pi}{1 - \tan \theta \tan \pi} \qquad \text{Panel 8II(5)}$$

$$= \frac{\tan \theta + 0}{1 - \tan \theta \cdot 0} = \frac{\tan \theta}{1} = \tan \theta \qquad \text{simplifying}$$

Another solution:

$$\tan (\theta + \pi) = \frac{\sin (\theta + \pi)}{\cos (\theta + \pi)} \qquad \text{definition of tangent}$$

$$= \frac{\sin \theta \cos \pi + \cos \theta \sin \pi}{\cos \theta \cos \pi - \sin \theta \sin \pi}$$

$$= \frac{\sin \theta(-1) + \cos \theta \cdot 0}{\cos \theta(-1) - \sin \theta \cdot 0}$$

$$= \frac{-\sin \theta}{-\cos \theta} = \tan \theta \qquad \begin{array}{l}\text{simplifying definition}\\\text{of tangent}\end{array}$$

765 Show that $\cot (\theta + \pi) = \cot \theta$ (if both exist).

$$\cot (\theta + \pi) = \frac{\cos (\theta + \pi)}{\sin (\theta + \pi)} \qquad \text{definition of cotangent}$$

$$= \frac{\cos \theta \cos \pi - \sin \theta \sin \pi}{\sin \theta \cos \pi + \cos \theta \sin \pi} \qquad \text{Panel 8II(3), (1)}$$

$$= \frac{\cos \theta (-1) - \sin \theta \cdot 0}{\sin \theta (-1) + \cos \theta \cdot 0} \qquad \text{simplifying}$$

$$= \frac{-\cos \theta}{-\sin \theta} = +\cot \theta \qquad \text{definition of cotangent}$$

THREE THEOREMS FROM GEOMETRY

766 We shall make use of some of the formulas that we have derived to prove three theorems from geometry.

Theorem GI. Heron's formula: Given sides a, b, and c of triangle ABC and $s = \frac{1}{2}(a + b + c)$, then area of $ABC = \sqrt{s(s - a)(s - b)(s - c)}$.

continued →

It will be necessary to state and prove preliminary facts regarding the triangle. We must show that:

1. $\dfrac{1 - \cos \alpha}{2} = \dfrac{(a + b - c)(a - b + c)}{4bc}$

2. $\dfrac{1 + \cos \alpha}{2} = \dfrac{(b + c + a)(b + c - a)}{4bc}$

3. $\sin \dfrac{\alpha}{2} = \sqrt{\dfrac{(s - b)(s - c)}{bc}}$

4. $\cos \dfrac{\alpha}{2} = \sqrt{\dfrac{s(s - a)}{bc}}$

Make a copy of Theorem GI and Facts 1, 2, 3, and 4.

Have a correct copy of Theorem GI and Facts 1, 2, 3, 4.

767 To prove Fact 1 in frame 766

$$\frac{1 - \cos \alpha}{2} = \frac{(a + b - c)(a - b + c)}{4bc}$$

we start with the left member and transform it into the right by making a substitution for $\cos \alpha$ in terms of a, b, and c. Recall the law of cosines $a^2 = b^2 + c^2 - 2bc \cos \alpha$. Solving for $\cos \alpha$, we have $\cos \alpha =$ (1)_____ . Substitute this value for $\cos \alpha$ below and reduce the resulting expression to the one that appears on the right above. Copy the entire equation as you answer.

(2) $\dfrac{1 - \cos \alpha}{2} = \dfrac{1 -}{2}$

(1) $\dfrac{b^2 + c^2 - a^2}{2bc}$

(2) see frame 768 if you were not able to complete the solution. If you completed the proof, compare your work with frame 768, but do not rewrite the proof.

768 Proof (*continued*). We now have

$$\frac{1 - \cos \alpha}{2} = \frac{1 - (b^2 + c^2 - a^2)/2bc}{2bc}$$

continued →

Study the remaining steps:

$$\frac{1 - \cos \alpha}{2} = \frac{2bc - b^2 - c^2 + a^2}{4bc}$$ simplifying the complex fraction

$$= \frac{a^2 - (b^2 - 2bc + c^2)}{4bc}$$

$$= \frac{a^2 - (b - c)^2}{4bc}$$ rearranging the terms and factoring

$$= \frac{[a - (b - c)][a + (b - c)]}{4bc}$$

$$= \frac{(a - b + c)(a + b - c)}{4bc}$$ this is the required form

Now try completing your own proof without referring to this.

Check your work with the proof given above.

769 The proof for Fact 2 in frame 766 is similar to that for Fact 1. Write your own proof for

$$\frac{1 + \cos \alpha}{2} = \frac{(b + c + a)(b + c - a)}{4bc}$$

Working from the left member

$$\frac{1 + \cos \alpha}{2} = \frac{1 + (b^2 + c^2 - a^2)/2bc}{2}$$ substituting for $\cos \alpha$ from law of cosines

$$= \frac{2bc + b^2 + c^2 - a^2}{4bc}$$ simplifying

$$= \frac{(b^2 + 2bc + c^2) - a^2}{4bc}$$ simplifying

$$= \frac{(b + c - a)(b + c + a)}{4bc}$$ simplifying

770 Prove Fact 3: $\dfrac{\alpha}{2} = \sqrt{\dfrac{(s - b)(s - c)}{bc}}$ where $s = \frac{1}{2}(a + b + c)$

Note 1: Since α is an angle of a triangle, then $\sin (\alpha/2)$ will be positive.

Note 2: If $s = \frac{1}{2}(a + b + c)$, then $2s = a + b + c$, $2s - c = a + b$, and $2s - b = a + c$.

continued →

$$\sin \frac{\alpha}{2} = \sqrt{\frac{1 - \cos \alpha}{2}}$$ Panel 8IV(2)

$$= \sqrt{\frac{(a + b - c)(a - b + c)}{4bc}}$$ (1) Why?

$$= \sqrt{\frac{(2s - c - c)(2s - b - b)}{4bc}}$$ (2) Why?

$$= \sqrt{\frac{2(s - c)\, 2(s - b)}{4bc}}$$

simplifying

$$= \sqrt{\frac{(s - c)(s - b)}{bc}}$$

(1) see Fact 1 on the list you copied from frame 766.

$$\frac{1 - \cos \alpha}{2} = \frac{(a + b - c)(a - b + c)}{4bc}$$

(2) See Note 2 above.

771 Prove Fact 4: $\cos \dfrac{\alpha}{2} = \sqrt{\dfrac{s(s - a)}{bc}}$

Note 1. If α is an angle of a triangle, then $\cos (\alpha/2)$ is positive.
Note 2. If $s = \frac{1}{2}(a + b + c)$, then $2s = a + b + c$ and $2s - a = b + c$.
Working on the left member

$\cos \dfrac{\alpha}{2} =$ (1)_____ Panel 8IV(1)

$=$ (2)_____ substituting
Fact 2 from
frame 766

$=$ (3)_____ substituting from
Note 2 above

$=$ (4)_____ simplifying

(1) $\sqrt{\dfrac{1 + \cos \alpha}{2}}$ (2) $\sqrt{\dfrac{(b + c + a)(b + c - a)}{4bc}}$

(3) $\sqrt{\dfrac{(2s - a + a)(2s - a - a)}{4bc}}$ (4) $\sqrt{\dfrac{2s(2s - 2a)}{4bc}} = \sqrt{\dfrac{s(s - a)}{bc}}$

772 Now we can prove that the area of a triangle ABC, given a, b, and c and $\sin \frac{1}{2}(a + b + c)$, is:

$$\text{area} = \sqrt{s(s - a)(s - b)(s - c)}$$

continued →

Note 1: Recall the area formula: area of triangle $ABC =$ $\frac{1}{2}bc \sin \alpha.$

Note 2: Recall the double-angle formula: $\sin 2\theta = 2 \sin \theta \cos \theta.$

Note 3: When $\alpha = 2\theta$, the double-angle formula in Note 2 may be written: $\sin \alpha = 2 \sin (\alpha/2) \cos (\alpha/2).$

Proof:

1. area $ABC = \frac{1}{2}bc \sin \alpha$ **(1)** Why?

2. $= \frac{1}{2}bc \left(2 \sin \dfrac{\alpha}{2} \cos \dfrac{\alpha}{2} \right)$ **(2)** Why?

3. $= \frac{1}{2}bc \cdot 2\sqrt{\dfrac{(s-b)(s-c)}{bc}} \sqrt{\dfrac{s(s-a)}{bc}}$ **(3)** Why?

4. $= $ **(4)**_____   simplifying

---

(1) see Note 1   **(2)** see Note 3

(3) $\sin \dfrac{\alpha}{2} = \sqrt{\dfrac{(s-b)(s-c)}{bc}}$, $\cos \dfrac{\alpha}{2}\sqrt{\dfrac{s(s-a)}{bc}}$

(4) $\sqrt{s(s-a)(s-b)(s-c)}$

---

773 *Theorem* GII from geometry: If r is the radius of a circle inscribed in a triangle having sides a, b, and c, then

   area of triangle $ABC = rs$ where $s = \frac{1}{2}(a+b+c)$

Recall that the angle bisectors meet at the center of the inscribed circle; hence,

   area $AOB = \frac{1}{2}rc$ Area $= \frac{1}{2}$ base $\cdot$ altitude
   area $AOC = $ **(1)**_____
   area $BOC = $ **(2)**_____

(Copy the entire equation below as you answer.)

(3) area ABC

   $= \frac{1}{2}rc + $ _____ $+$ _____   whole $=$ sum of the parts

   $= $ **(4)**_____

---

(1) $\frac{1}{2}rb$ **(2)** $\frac{1}{2}ra$ **(3)** area $ABC = \frac{1}{2}rc + \frac{1}{2}rb + \frac{1}{2}ra$

(4) $\frac{1}{2}r(c+b+a) = \frac{1}{2}r(2s) = rs$

---

774 Theorem GIII from geometry: If r is the radius of the inscribed circle in a triangle having sides a, b, and c, then

$$r = \sqrt{\dfrac{(s-a)(s-b)(s-c)}{s}}$$

continued →

From frames 772 and 773 you know

1. area of triangle $ABC = \sqrt{s(s-a)(s-b)(s-c)}$
2. area of triangle $ABC = rs$

Equate statements 1 and 2 and solve for r.

$$rs = \sqrt{s(s-a)(s-b)(s-c)}$$

$$r = \sqrt{\frac{s(s-a)(s-b)(s-c)}{s^2}} = \sqrt{\frac{(s-a)(s-b)(s-c)}{s}}$$

SELF-TEST 3   ANS. pg 649

1 Express the following in terms of sin θ only: **(a)** csc θ = _____,
   (b) cos θ = _____, **(c)** sec θ = _____, **(d)** tan θ = _____,
   and **(e)** cot θ = _____ .

2 Prove the identity $1 - 2 \sin^2 \theta = 2 \cos^2 \theta - 1$.

3 Indicate which of the following are identities.

$$2x + 3 = 6$$
$$\sin^2 x + \cos^2 x = 1$$
$$(x^2 - 1) = (x - 1)(x + 1)$$
$$\tan \theta = \frac{\sin \theta}{\cos \theta}$$
$$\cot \theta = \pm\sqrt{\csc^2 \theta + 1}$$

4 Reduce $\sin \theta \, (\csc \theta - \sin \theta)$ to $\cos^2 \theta$.

5 Prove the identity $\cos^2 \theta - \sin^2 \theta = \dfrac{1 - \tan^2 \theta}{1 + \tan^2 \theta}$.

6 Prove the identity $1 - 2 \sin^2 \theta + \sin^4 \theta = \cos^4 \theta$.

7 Prove $\dfrac{\sin^2 (x/2) + \cos x}{\cos^2 (x/2)} = 1$.

8 Prove $\dfrac{1 - \cos 2\theta}{\sin 2\theta} = \tan \theta$.

9 **(a)** Express the product $\cos 90° \sin 45°$ as a sum (or difference).
   (b) Find the numerical value of the result.

10 **(a)** Express the sum $\cos (\pi/3) + \cos (\pi/6)$ as a product.
    (b) Prove $\dfrac{\sin 100° - \sin 40°}{\cos 100° + \cos 40°} = \tan 30°$.

11 Prove sin $(270° + \theta) = -\cos \theta$.

12 Reduce each of the following to the function of a positive angle less than 90°: (a) sin (-50°), (b) cos 130°, and (c) tan 312°.
In Probs. 13 and 14 solve the equations for all values of x in the interval $0° \le x \le 360°$.

13 $2 \sin x - 3 \cot x = 0$.

14 $2 \sin x - \sin x - \sin^2 x + \cos^2 x = 0$.

15 Show by substitution whether 45° is one of the solutions of the equation $8 \sin^4 x - 6 \sin^2 x + 1 = 0$.

16 Solve and check the following equation for all values of x in the interval $0° \le x \le 360°$: $\sin x = 2 \sin (x + \pi/3)$.

17 Prove the identity sin $(x + 60°) - \cos (x + 30°) = \sin x$.

18 If x is a positive acute angle, which of the following are true statements?
     $\cos (180° + x) = \cos (180° - x)$ $\sin (x - 180°) = \sin x$
     $\tan (90° + x) = \cot (180° - x)$ $\cos (x - 180°) = -\cos x$

19 Compare the value of 2 sin θ with sin 2θ when $\theta = 45°$.

20 An arc of a circle cut off by a central angle is 8π units in length and the radius of the circle is 6 units. (a) Find the radian measure of the angle. (b) Find the area of the sector of the circle having the arc mentioned in part (a).

21 (a) What is the largest numerical value for $1 + \sin \theta$? (b) What is the value of θ at this point $(0 \le \theta \le 2\pi)$?

22 If a man 5.8 ft tall casts a shadow 8.3 ft long, what is the angle of elevation of the sun?

UNIT 2 ▍ Trigonometric Identities

775 In mathematics, equations may be classified under the headings *identities* and *conditional* equations. *Identities* are equations which are true for all permissible values of the variables in a given domain. *Conditional equations* (or *equations,* as we shall refer to them) are true for a limited number of values (if any) of the variables. *Examples:*
(1) $x - 2 = 6$ is true if and only if $x = $ (a)___; hence, it is called a(n) (b) _____.
(2) $(x - 2)(x + 2) = x^2 - 4$ is true for all values of x; therefore, it is called a(n) _____.

> (1) (a) 8, (b) equation or conditional equation   (2) identity

776 Trigonometric *equations* resemble trigonometric *identities* in appearance, but there is an important difference between them. An *identity* is a statement which is true for (1) _____ values of the variable in a given domain; whereas an _____ is a statement which is true for (2) _____ values of the variable in a given domain.

> (1) all permissible   (2) a limited number of or not all

777 It should be understood that when we apply the definition of identity to trigonometric statements, certain values of the variable may have to be excluded. For example, in the interval $0 \leq \theta \leq 2\pi$, $\tan \theta$ is undefined when $\theta = $ (1) _____ or (2) _____. We say that these are not permissible values of θ. Hence, in any identity in which conditions of this sort occur, the restriction will

continued →

239

be assumed even though no comment is made regarding it. If we say that tan θ = sin θ/cos θ is an identity, we mean that it is true for all values of θ, $0 \le \theta \le 2\pi$, except **(3)** _____ and **(4)** _____.

(1) $\frac{\pi}{2}$ or 90°   **(2)** $\frac{3\pi}{2}$ or 270°   **(3)** $\frac{\pi}{2}$ or 90°   **(4)** $\frac{3\pi}{2}$ or 270°

778   Consider the following: 2 cos x - 1 = 0. We may solve for cos x thus: 2 cos x = 1 or cos x = $\frac{1}{2}$. **(1)** For what values of x, $0 \le x \le 360°$, is this statement true? **(2)** Is 2 cos x - 1 = 0 an identity?

(1) 60°, 300°
(2) no, it is not true for all values of $0 \le x \le 360°$

779   In the domain $0 \le \theta < 360°$ there are only two values of θ for which the statement 2 sin θ - 1 = 0 is true, namely, θ = **(1)** ____ and **(2)** ____ . **(3)** Since the statement is true for a limited number of values of θ, should we call 2 sin θ - 1 = 0 an equation or an identity?

(1) 30°   **(2)** 150°
(3) equation (it is not true for all permissible values of θ)

780   We have shown that $\sin^2 \theta + \cos^2 \theta = 1$ is true for all values of θ (when θ is a real number); hence, we refer to this statement as a(n) _____.

identity

Comment

In this section we shall discuss trigonometric identities. The discussion of equations will appear later. In many branches of mathematics, the calculus, for example, it is necessary to change the form of a trigonometric expression. By means of a set of fundamental identities and the operations of algebra, we may do this. Unfortunately there is no simple set of rules by which we can establish new identities or make transformations from one form to another. Skill comes through practice. Here we shall start with a review of the general procedure for proving an identity and then go from examples based on the fundamental identities to the identities for composite functions. This practice will serve three purposes:
1. You will become more familiar with the definitions and formulas of the trigonometric functions.

2. You will review old algebraic techniques and learn new ones.
3. You will have a knowledge of identities useful in more advanced mathematics.

781 There are eight identities which we refer to as fundamental identities. They are listed in Panel 8IA, B, C. They are used so frequently that you should be thoroughly familiar with them. Sometimes they appear in slightly different forms, and it is important that you be able to recognize them also. Three of the fundamental identities in Panel 8I are called the Pythagorean relations. List them.

$$\sin^2 \alpha + \cos^2 \alpha = 1, \tan^2 \alpha + 1 = \sec^2 \alpha, 1 + \cot^2 \alpha = \csc^2 \alpha$$

782 (1) Solve $\sin^2 \alpha + \cos^2 \alpha = 1$ for $\sin \alpha$
(2) Solve $\sin^2 \alpha + \cos^2 \alpha = 1$ for $\cos \alpha$
Note: These are two very useful forms in which this identity may appear.

(1) $\sin \alpha = \pm\sqrt{1 - \cos^2 \alpha}$ **(2)** $\cos \alpha = \pm\sqrt{1 - \sin^2 \alpha}$

783 Given the identity $\sin \alpha = \pm\sqrt{1 - \cos^2 \alpha}$, answer the following questions regarding signs:

(1) If $0 < \alpha \leq \frac{\pi}{2}$, which sign should precede the radical?

(2) If $\frac{\pi}{2} \leq \alpha < \pi$, which sign should precede the radical?

(3) If $\pi < \alpha \leq \frac{3\pi}{2}$, which sign should precede the radical?

(4) If $\frac{3\pi}{2} \leq \alpha < 2\pi$, which sign should precede the radical?

(1) positive sign (+)   **(2)** positive sign (+)
(3) negative sign (-)   **(4)** negative sign (-)

784 Given the identity $\cos \alpha = \pm\sqrt{1 - \sin^2 \alpha}$, answer the following questions regarding signs:

(1) If $0 \leq \alpha < \frac{\pi}{2}$, which sign should precede the radical?

(2) If $\frac{\pi}{2} < \alpha \leq \pi$, which sign should precede the radical?

continued →

(3) If $\pi \le \alpha < \dfrac{3\pi}{2}$, which sign should precede the radical?

(4) If $\dfrac{3\pi}{2} < \alpha \le 2\pi$, which sign should precede the radical?

(1) positive sign (+)   (2) negative sign (-)
(3) negative sign (-)   (4) positive sign (+)

785   Solve $\tan^2 \alpha + 1 = \sec^2 \alpha$ for (1) $\tan \alpha$ and (2) $\sec \alpha$.

(1) $\tan \alpha = \pm \sqrt{\sec^2 \alpha - 1}$ (2) $\sec \alpha = \pm \sqrt{\tan^2 \alpha + 1}$

786   (1) If α is an angle terminating in quadrant II or IV, the identity
$\tan \alpha = \pm \sqrt{\sec^2 \alpha - 1}$ should have which sign, + or -, preceding the radical?
(2) If α is an angle terminating in quadrant II, the identity
$\sec \alpha = \pm \sqrt{\tan^2 \alpha + 1}$ should have which sign, + or -, preceding the radical?
(3) If α is an angle terminating in quadrant IV, the identity
$\sec \alpha = \pm \sqrt{\tan^2 \alpha + 1}$ should have which sign, + or -, preceding the radical?

(1) - in quadrant II, - in quadrant IV
(2) - in quadrant II   (3) + in quadrant IV

▽787   Solve $1 + \cot^2 \alpha = \csc^2 \alpha$ for (1) $\cot \alpha$ and (2) $\csc \alpha$. Which sign, + or -, should precede the radical (3) if α terminates in quadrant II in part (1)?   (4) If α terminates in quadrant II in part (2)?

(1) $\cot \alpha = \pm \sqrt{\csc^2 \alpha - 1}$ (2) $\csc \alpha = \pm \sqrt{1 + \cot^2 \alpha}$
(3) -   (4) +

788   Refer to the eight fundamental identities on Panel 8. List the (1) tangent and (2) cotangent relations. (3) What values of $(0 \le \alpha < 2\pi)$ are not *permissible* values in each of these identities?

(1) $\tan \alpha = \dfrac{\sin \alpha}{\cos \alpha}$ (2) $\cot \alpha = \dfrac{\cos \alpha}{\sin \alpha}$
(3) $\dfrac{\pi}{2}, \dfrac{3\pi}{2}$ in the first identity; $0, \pi$ in the second identity

789 (1) Solve $\tan \alpha = \sin \alpha / \cos \alpha$ for $\sin \alpha$.
(2) Solve $\tan \alpha = \sin \alpha / \cos \alpha$ for $\cos \alpha$.

(1) $\sin \alpha = \cos \alpha \tan \alpha$ (2) $\cos \alpha = \dfrac{\sin \alpha}{\tan \alpha}$

▽**790** Solve $\cot \alpha = \cos \alpha / \sin \alpha$ for (1) $\sin \alpha$ and (2) $\cos \alpha$.

(1) $\sin \alpha = \dfrac{\cos \alpha}{\cot \alpha}$ (2) $\cos \alpha = \sin \alpha \cot \alpha$

791 Refer to Panel 8IC. The reciprocal relations are

$$\sin \alpha = (1) \, \frac{1}{?} \qquad \csc \alpha = (2) \, \frac{1}{?}$$

$$\cos \alpha = (3) \, \frac{1}{?} \qquad \sec \alpha = (4) \, \frac{1}{?}$$

$$\tan \alpha = (5) \, \frac{1}{?} \qquad \cot \alpha = (6) \, \frac{1}{?}$$

(By the reciprocal of a quantity we mean the result obtained when 1 is divided by that quantity. Thus the reciprocal of a is $1/a$.)

(1) $\csc \alpha$ (2) $\sin \alpha$ (3) $\sec \alpha$
(4) $\cos \alpha$ (5) $\cot \alpha$ (6) $\tan \alpha$

792 $\sin \alpha \cdot \csc \alpha = 1$ is another form in which we may write the identity $\sin \alpha = 1/\csc \alpha$. This is one of the_____ relations.

reciprocal (fundamental)

▽ **793** Refer to the reciprocal relations listed on Panel 8IC. Complete the following identities: $\cos \alpha \cdot (1)(\underline{\hspace{1cm}}) = 1$ and $\tan \alpha \cdot (2)(\underline{\hspace{1cm}}) = 1$.

(1) $\sec \alpha$ (2) $\cot \alpha$

794 Note the three headings under the fundamental identities: Pythagorean relations, tangent and cotangent relations, and reciprocal relations. The headings will help you to remember the fundamental identities. By means of the eight fundamental identities, any one of the trigonometric functions can be expressed in terms of any other specified function. For example, to express $\csc \theta$ in terms of $\sin \theta$,

continued →

we refer to the reciprocal relations and see that csc θ = 1/sin θ.
To express csc θ in terms of cot θ, we refer to the (1)_____
relations and see that csc^2 θ = (2)_____; hence, csc θ =
(3)_____ .

(1) Pythagorean   **(2)** 1 + cot^2 θ **(3)** $\pm\sqrt{1 + \cot^2\theta}$

795 **(1)** In order. to express cos θ in terms of sin θ, under which of the
the headings, Pythagorean, tangent and cotangent, or reciprocal,
will you find the necessary information?
(2) Express cos θ in terms of sin θ.
(3) Now to express cos θ in terms of csc θ, we can make a substitution from the reciprocal relations into the answer to **(1)** above
and get cos θ = _____.

(1) Pythagorean   **(2)** cos θ = $\pm\sqrt{1 - \sin^2\theta}$

(3) cos θ = $\pm\sqrt{1 - \dfrac{1}{\csc^2\theta}}$ or $\pm\dfrac{\sqrt{\csc^2\theta - 1}}{\csc\theta}$

796 Refer to the Pythagorean relations. If an equation or identity contains the expression $\pm\sqrt{1 - \sin^2\theta}$, we may replace this expression
by the simpler expression_____.

cos θ

797 To express sec θ in terms of sin θ, we note first from the reciprocal relations that sec θ = **(1)**___/_____. Then substituting the
value of cos θ mentioned in frame 796, cos θ = $\pm\sqrt{1 - \sin^2\theta}$, we
can express sec θ in terms of sin θ thus sec θ = **(2)**___/_____.

(1) $\dfrac{1}{\cos\theta}$ **(2)** $\dfrac{1}{\pm\sqrt{1 - \sin^2\theta}}$

798 To express tan θ in terms of sin θ, note first from the tangent and
cotangent relations that tan θ = **(1)**_____/_____. Then substituting the value of cos θ obtained from the Pythagorean relations, we
have tan θ = **(2)**_____/_____.

(1) $\dfrac{\sin\theta}{\cos\theta}$ **(2)** $\dfrac{\sin\theta}{\pm\sqrt{1 - \sin^2\theta}}$

For numerical calculations you may prefer to have the answer

continued →

written in the form

$$\pm \frac{\sin\theta \sqrt{1 - \sin^2\theta}}{1 - \sin^2\theta}$$

Either answer is acceptable here. This remark applies to other problems of this sort.

799   In a similar manner express $\cot\theta$ in terms of $\sin\theta$.

$$\cot\theta = \frac{\cos\theta}{\sin\theta} = \frac{\pm\sqrt{1 - \sin^2\theta}}{\sin\theta}$$

▽800   As a review complete the statements below showing each of the functions expressed in terms of $\sin\theta$. Do not refer to previous answers.

$\csc\theta = $ **(1)** _____ $\cos\theta = $ **(2)** _____ $\sec\theta = $ **(3)** _____

$\tan\theta = $ **(4)** _____ $\cot\theta = $ **(5)** _____

(1) $\dfrac{1}{\sin\theta}$ **(2)** $\pm\sqrt{1 - \sin^2\theta}$

(3) $\dfrac{1}{\pm\sqrt{1 - \sin^2\theta}}$ or $\dfrac{\pm\sqrt{1 - \sin^2\theta}}{1 - \sin^2\theta}$

(4) $\dfrac{\sin\theta}{\pm\sqrt{1 - \sin^2\theta}}$ or $\dfrac{\pm\sin\theta\sqrt{1 - \sin^2\theta}}{1 - \sin^2\theta}$

(5) $\dfrac{\pm\sqrt{1 - \sin^2\theta}}{\sin\theta}$

Keep this list for use in later frames.

801   Look at your list from frame 800. (Remember that division by 0 is impossible.)
(1) If $0 \le \theta < 2\pi$, $\sec\theta$ is undefined when $\theta = $ **(a)** ____ or **(b)** ____.
(2) If $0 \le \theta < 2\pi$, $\tan\theta$ is undefined when $\theta = $ **(a)** ____ or **(b)** ____.
(3) If $0 \le \theta < 2\pi$, $\cot\theta$ is undefined when $\theta = $ **(a)** ____ or **(b)** ____.
(4) Are these examples of values of θ which we referred to as *not permissible* values in a given identity?

(1)(a) $\dfrac{\pi}{2}$, (b) $\dfrac{3\pi}{2}$ **(2)**(a) $\dfrac{\pi}{2}$, (b) $\dfrac{3\pi}{2}$ **(3)**(a) 0, (b) π **(4)** yes

802 Given $\theta = 30°$, then $\sin \theta =$ ____. Refer to the list from frame 800 where you expressed the functions in terms of $\sin \theta$. Use this list to calculate numerical values for all the other functions of $30°$.

$$\sin 30° = \frac{1}{2} \qquad\qquad \csc 30° = \frac{1}{1/2} = 2$$

$$\cos 30° = \sqrt{1 - \left(\frac{1}{2}\right)^2} = \sqrt{\frac{3}{2}} \qquad \sec 30° = \frac{1}{\sqrt{3}/2} = \frac{2}{\sqrt{3}}$$

$$\tan 30° = \frac{1/2}{\sqrt{3}/2} = \frac{1}{\sqrt{3}} \qquad\qquad \cot 30° = \frac{\sqrt{3}/2}{1/2} = \sqrt{3}$$

803 In frames 803 to 808 you will be asked to express each of the trigonometric functions in terms of $\cos \theta$. First, use one of the fundamental identities to express $\sec \theta$ in terms of $\cos \theta$; that is, $\sec \theta = $ __ / _____ .

$$\frac{1}{\cos \theta}$$

804 By means of the fundamental identities express $\sin \theta$ in terms of $\cos \theta$.

$$\sin \theta = \pm \sqrt{1 - \cos^2 \theta}$$

805 Express $\csc \theta$ in terms of $\cos \theta$.

$$\csc \theta = \frac{1}{\sin \theta} = \frac{1}{\pm \sqrt{1 - \cos^2 \theta}}$$

806 Express $\tan \theta$ in terms of $\cos \theta$.

$$\tan \theta = \frac{\pm \sqrt{1 - \cos^2 \theta}}{\cos \theta}$$

807 Express $\cot \theta$ in terms of $\cos \theta$.

$$\cot \theta = \frac{\cos \theta}{\sin \theta} = \frac{\cos \theta}{\pm \sqrt{1 - \cos^2 \theta}}$$

▽ 808 Complete the following by expressing each function in terms of cos θ: sec θ = (1)_____, sin θ = (2)_____, csc θ = (3)_____, tan θ = (4)_____, and cot θ = (5)_____. Keep the list for use in later frames.

(1) $\dfrac{1}{\cos \theta}$ (2) $\pm \sqrt{1 - \cos^2 \theta}$ (3) $\dfrac{1}{\pm \sqrt{1 - \cos^2 \theta}}$

(4) $\dfrac{\pm \sqrt{1 - \cos^2 \theta}}{\cos \theta}$ (5) $\dfrac{\cos \theta}{\pm \sqrt{1 - \cos^2 \theta}}$

809 Refer to the list from frame 808. Csc θ is undefined when θ = (1)___ or (2)___ ($0 \le \theta < 2\pi$), since (3) csc___ or csc___ = $\pm 1/\sqrt{1 - ?}$ = $\pm 1/\sqrt{?}$. Copy the entire equation in (3) as you answer.

(1) 0 (2) π (3) csc 0 or csc π = $\pm \dfrac{1}{\sqrt{1 - 1}} = \dfrac{1}{\sqrt{0}}$

810 In frames 810 to 815 you will be finding a way to express each function in terms of tan θ. Keep a record of the correct answers for later frames. First, express cot θ in terms of tan θ.

cot θ = $\dfrac{1}{\tan \theta}$

811 Express sec θ in terms of tan θ.

sec θ = $\pm \sqrt{\tan^2 \theta + 1}$

812 Express cos θ in terms of tan θ.

cos θ = $\dfrac{1}{\sec \theta}$ = $\dfrac{1}{\pm \sqrt{\tan^2 \theta + 1}}$

813 Express csc θ in terms of tan θ.

csc θ = $\pm \sqrt{\dfrac{\tan^2 \theta + 1}{\tan^2 \theta}}$ or $\dfrac{1}{\tan \theta} \sqrt{\tan^2 \theta + 1}$

continued →

Solution: $\csc^2 \theta = 1 + \cot^2 \theta = 1 + \left(\dfrac{1}{\tan \theta}\right)^2 = \dfrac{\tan^2 \theta + 1}{\tan^2 \theta}$

$\csc \theta = \pm \sqrt{\dfrac{\tan^2 \theta + 1}{\tan^2 \theta}}$ or $\dfrac{1}{\tan \theta} \sqrt{\tan^2 \theta + 1}$

814 Express $\sin \theta$ in terms of $\tan \theta$. *Suggestion:* Start with $\sin \theta / \cos \theta = \tan \theta$.

$\sin \theta = \dfrac{\tan \theta}{\pm \sqrt{\tan^2 \theta + 1}}$ or $\pm \dfrac{\tan \theta \sqrt{\tan^2 \theta + 1}}{\tan^2 \theta + 1}$

Solution: $\sin \theta = \tan \theta \cos \theta = \tan \theta \cdot \dfrac{1}{\pm \sqrt{\tan^2 \theta + 1}}$

$= \dfrac{\tan \theta}{\pm \sqrt{\tan^2 \theta + 1}}$ or $\pm \dfrac{\tan \theta \sqrt{\tan^2 \theta + 1}}{\tan^2 \theta + 1}$

815 Without referring to any list, complete the following statements showing how each function can be expressed in terms of $\tan \theta$:
$\cot \theta = $ **(1)** _____, $\sec \theta = $ **(2)** _____, $\cos \theta = $ **(3)** _____,
$\csc \theta = $ **(4)** _____, and $\sin \theta = $ **(5)** _____.
Keep this list for use in later frames.

(1) $\dfrac{1}{\tan \theta}$ **(2)** $\pm \sqrt{\tan^2 \theta + 1}$ **(3)** $\dfrac{1}{\pm \sqrt{\tan^2 \theta + 1}}$

(4) $\pm \dfrac{1}{\tan \theta} \sqrt{\tan^2 \theta + 1}$ **(5)** $\pm \dfrac{\tan \theta}{\sqrt{\tan^2 \theta + 1}}$

816 Given $\tan \theta = \frac{5}{12}$, refer to your list from frame 815 and give the numerical values for all the other functions of θ.

$\cot \theta = \frac{12}{5}$, $\sec \theta = \pm\frac{13}{12}$, $\cos \theta = \pm\frac{12}{13}$, $\csc \theta = \pm\frac{13}{5}$, $\sin \theta = \pm\frac{5}{13}$

817 Refer to your answers in frame 816. If $\tan \theta = \frac{5}{12}$, then θ is an angle terminating in quadrant I or **(1)** _____. **(2)** Discuss the choice of signs in these two quadrants for each of the functions.

(1) III
(2) All functions are positive in quadrant I. All functions, except $\tan \theta$ and $\cot \theta$, are negative in quadrant III.

818   The example below shows how to reduce $\sin \theta \cdot \sec \theta$ to $\tan \theta$.

Step 1. $\sin \theta \sec \theta = \sin \theta \cdot \dfrac{1}{\cos \theta}$

Step 2. $= \dfrac{\sin \theta}{\cos \theta}$

Step 3. $= \tan \theta$

(1) The substitution in Step 1 comes from what fundamental identity? Step 2 is merely a change of form as a result of algebraic multiplication. (2) The substitution in Step 3 comes from what fundamental identity?

(1) $\sec \theta = \dfrac{1}{\cos \theta}$,   (2) $\tan \theta = \dfrac{\sin \theta}{\cos \theta}$.

819   Show how to reduce $\cos \theta \cdot \csc \theta$ to $\cot \theta$. In this and following frames you need *not* give a reason for each step of a proof unless you are specifically asked to give reasons.

$\cos \theta \cdot \csc \theta = \cos \theta \cdot \dfrac{1}{\sin \theta} = \dfrac{\cos \theta}{\sin \theta} = \cot \theta$

820   Show the steps in reducing $\tan \theta \cdot \cos \theta$ to $\sin \theta$.

$\tan \theta \cdot \cos \theta = \dfrac{\sin \theta}{\cancel{\cos \theta}} \cdot \dfrac{\cancel{\cos \theta}}{1} = \dfrac{\sin \theta}{1} = \sin \theta$

821   Reduce $\tan \theta / \cot \theta$ to $\tan^2 \theta$.

$\dfrac{\tan \theta}{\cot \theta} = \dfrac{\tan \theta}{1/\tan \theta} = \dfrac{\tan \theta}{1} \cdot \dfrac{\tan \theta}{1} = \tan^2 \theta$

▽ 822   Reduce $2 - \cos^2 \theta$ to $\sin^2 \theta + 1$.

$2 - \cos^2 \theta = 2 - (1 - \sin^2 \theta) = 2 - 1 + \sin^2 \theta = 1 + \sin^2 \theta$
$= \sin^2 \theta + 1$

823 Reduce $(\tan \theta + \cot \theta)^2$ to $\sec^2 \theta + \csc^2 \theta$.

$$
\begin{aligned}
(\tan \theta + \cot \theta)^2 &= \tan^2 \theta + 2 \tan \theta \cot \theta + \cot^2 \theta \\
&= \tan^2 \theta + 2 \tan \theta \, \frac{1}{\tan \theta} + \cot^2 \theta \\
&= \tan^2 \theta + 2 \cdot 1 + \cot^2 \theta \\
&= \tan^2 \theta + 2 + \cot^2 \theta \\
&= (\tan^2 \theta + 1) + (1 + \cot^2 \theta) \\
&= \sec^2 \theta + \csc^2 \theta
\end{aligned}
$$

824 Reduce $\csc \theta - \sin \theta$ to $\cot \theta \cos \theta$.

$$
\begin{aligned}
\csc \theta - \sin \theta &= \frac{1}{\sin \theta} - \sin \theta = \frac{1 - \sin^2 \theta}{\sin \theta} = \frac{\cos^2 \theta}{\sin \theta} \\
&= \frac{\cos \theta}{\sin \theta} \cdot \cos \theta = \cot \theta \cos \theta
\end{aligned}
$$

825 Reduce $(1 - \sin^2 \theta)/\cot \theta$ to $\sin \theta \cos \theta$.

$$
\frac{1 - \sin^2 \theta}{\cot \theta} = \frac{\cos^2 \theta}{\cos \theta / \sin \theta} = \frac{\overset{\cos \theta}{\cancel{\cos^2 \theta}}}{1} \cdot \frac{\sin \theta}{\cancel{\cos \theta}} = \cos \theta \sin \theta
$$

826 Reduce $(\sec^2 \theta - 1)/\sin^2 \theta$ to $\sec^2 \theta$.

$$
\begin{aligned}
\frac{\sec^2 \theta - 1}{\sin^2 \theta} &= \frac{\tan^2 \theta}{\sin^2 \theta} = \frac{\sin^2 \theta / \cos^2 \theta}{\sin^2 \theta} = \frac{\overset{1}{\cancel{\sin^2 \theta}}}{\cos^2 \theta} \cdot \frac{1}{\cancel{\sin^2 \theta}} \\
&= \frac{1}{\cos^2 \theta} = \sec^2 \theta
\end{aligned}
$$

827 Reduce $(1 + \tan^2 \theta)/\csc^2 \theta$ to $\tan^2 \theta$.

$$
\begin{aligned}
\frac{1 + \tan^2 \theta}{\csc^2 \theta} &= \frac{\sec^2 \theta}{\csc^2 \theta} = \frac{1/\cos^2 \theta}{1/\sin^2 \theta} = \frac{1}{\cos^2 \theta} \cdot \frac{\sin^2 \theta}{1} \\
&= \frac{\sin^2 \theta}{\cos^2 \theta} = \tan^2 \theta
\end{aligned}
$$

828   Simplify $\cos \theta \tan \theta \csc \theta$ by use of the fundamental identities.

$$\cos \theta \tan \theta \csc \theta = \cos \theta \cdot \frac{\sin \theta}{\cos \theta} \cdot \frac{1}{\sin \theta} = 1$$

829   Simplify $\sin \theta / \cos \theta \tan \theta$ by use of the fundamental identities.

$$\frac{\sin \theta}{\cos \theta \tan \theta} = \frac{\sin \theta}{\cos \theta \cdot \dfrac{\sin \theta}{\cos \theta}} = \frac{\sin \theta}{\sin \theta} = 1$$

830   Reduce $\csc \theta \tan \theta$ to a form involving $\sin \theta$ or $\cos \theta$ only. Simplify as much as possible.

$$\csc \theta \tan \theta = \frac{1}{\sin \theta} \cdot \frac{\sin \theta}{\cos \theta} = \frac{1}{\cos \theta}$$

831   Simplify $(1 - \cos^2 \theta)(1 + \cot^2 \theta)$ by use of the fundamental identities.

$$(1 - \cos^2 \theta)(1 + \cot^2 \theta) = \sin^2 \theta \csc^2 \theta = \sin^2 \theta \cdot \frac{1}{\sin^2 \theta} = 1$$

832   Reduce $(\cot \theta - \cos \theta)/(1 - \sin \theta)$ to a form involving $\sin \theta$ and $\cos \theta$ only. Simplify as much as possible.

$$\frac{\cot \theta - \cos \theta}{1 - \sin \theta} = \frac{\cos \theta / \sin \theta - \cos \theta}{1 - \sin \theta}$$

$$= \frac{(\cos \theta - \sin \theta \cos \theta)/\sin \theta}{1 - \sin \theta}$$

$$= \frac{\cos \theta (1 - \sin \theta)}{\sin \theta (1 - \sin \theta)} = \frac{\cos \theta}{\sin \theta}$$

Comment

Proving a trigonometric identity is somewhat like proving a theorem in geometry. Here you are given a statement of equality involving trigonometric terms. By means of fundamental identities and algebraic operations you transform one member of the equation until its form is identical to the other. The suggestions below will be helpful in making proofs, but, as we have mentioned before, there is no simple set of rules for proving identities.

1. It often is better to try to change the more complicated member of the equation into the form of the other.
2. If one member of the equation contains only one trigonometric function, you might be able to express the functions of the other member in terms of this single function.
3. You may change all functions to sines and cosines.
4. It is usually better to avoid introducing terms involving radicals.
5. Simplify as far as possible by algebraic processes. This will include performing indicated multiplications and divisions. Multiplying numerator and denominator by the same term, factoring, etc.
6. Keep in view the member of the equation you are working toward. If your first attempt is unsuccessful, try another.
7. If you believe that the equation is not an identity, you may show that this is indeed the case by producing one specific example for which it is not true (excluding, of course, inadmissible values). Although you may "disprove" an identity (or any theorem in mathematics) by showing that it fails to hold in just one case, you may *not* prove an identity by showing that it works in one case (or in a few specific cases).
8. It is wrong to "cross-multiply" across the equality sign when proving identities; doing so tacitly assumes that the two members are equivalent.

833 Study the proof below showing how the left member has been changed into the right.

Problem: Prove $1/\cos \theta - \cos \theta = \tan \theta \sin \theta$

Solution: $\dfrac{1}{\cos \theta} - \cos \theta = \dfrac{1 - \cos^2 \theta}{\cos \theta} = \dfrac{\sin^2 \theta}{\cos \theta}$

$$= \frac{\sin \theta}{\cos \theta} \cdot \sin \theta = \tan \theta \sin \theta$$

This completes the proof.

Prove the identity $1/\sin \theta - \sin \theta = \cot \theta \cos \theta$.

$$\frac{1}{\sin \theta} - \sin \theta = \frac{1 - \sin^2 \theta}{\sin \theta} = \frac{\cos^2 \theta}{\sin \theta} = \frac{\cos \theta}{\sin \theta} \cdot \cos \theta$$

$$= \cot \theta \cos \theta$$

834   Below is an example showing how to express
$(\sin \theta + \tan \theta)/(\sec \theta + 1)$ in terms of $\sin \theta$ only.

Part 1.   From Panel 8 we substitute $\sin \theta/\cos \theta$ for $\tan \theta$ and
$1/\cos \theta$ for $\sec \theta$. Thus,

$$\frac{\sin \theta + \tan \theta}{\sec \theta + 1} = \frac{\sin \theta + \sin \theta/\cos \theta}{1/\cos \theta + 1}$$

Part 2.   We simplify the complex fraction thus:

a. $\dfrac{\sin \theta + \sin \theta/\cos \theta}{1/\cos \theta + 1} = \dfrac{(\sin \theta \cos \theta + \sin \theta)/\cos \theta}{(1 + \cos \theta)/\cos \theta}$

b. $\qquad\qquad = \dfrac{[\sin \theta (\cos \theta + 1)]/\cos \theta}{(1 + \cos \theta)/\cos \theta}$

c. $\qquad\qquad = \dfrac{\sin \theta \,\cancel{(\cos \theta + 1)}}{\cancel{\cos \theta}} \; \dfrac{\overset{1}{\cancel{\cos \theta}}}{\underset{1}{\cancel{1 + \cos \theta}}}$

$$\qquad\qquad = \sin \theta$$

Therefore, $\dfrac{\sin \theta + \tan \theta}{\sec \theta + 1} = \sin \theta$.

Note: In Part 1 we were able to express the entire problem in
terms of what two functions? In Part 2 the simplification depended
on the familiar operations of algebra, addition, factoring, and
division.

$\sin \theta$ and $\cos \theta$
Part 2 is the simplification of a complex fraction.

835   Show the necessary steps to express $(\tan \theta + \cot \theta)/(\sec \theta \sin \theta)$ in
terms of $\cos \theta$ only. *Suggestions:*
Step 1.   Change $\tan \theta$, $\cot \theta$, and $\sec \theta$ to equivalent forms involving
only $\sin \theta$ and $\cos \theta$.
Step 2.   Use the usual operations of algebra and any other substitution necessary from Panel 8 to reduce to a form involving
only $\cos \theta$.

$$\frac{\tan \theta + \cot \theta}{\sec \theta \sin \theta} = \frac{\sin \theta/\cos \theta + \cos \theta/\sin \theta}{1/\cos \theta \cdot \sin \theta}$$

$$= \frac{(\sin^2 \theta + \cos^2 \theta)/\sin \theta \cos \theta}{\sin \theta/\cos \theta}$$

$$= \frac{1}{\sin \theta \,\cancel{\cos \theta}} \cdot \frac{\overset{1}{\cancel{\cos \theta}}}{\sin \theta}$$

$$= \frac{1}{\sin^2 \theta} = \frac{1}{1 - \cos^2 \theta}$$

836 Prove that $\tan \theta + \cot \theta = \sec \theta \cdot \csc \theta$ is an identity, starting with the left member and showing that it is identically equal to the right.

$$\tan \theta + \cot \theta = \frac{\sin \theta}{\cos \theta} + \frac{\cos \theta}{\sin \theta} = \frac{\sin^2 \theta + \cos^2 \theta}{\sin \theta \cos \theta}$$

$$= \frac{1}{\cos \theta \cdot \sin \theta} = \frac{1}{\cos \theta} \cdot \frac{1}{\sin \theta}$$

$$= \sec \theta \cdot \csc \theta$$

837 Prove that $1/(\tan \theta + \cot \theta) = \sin \theta \cos \theta$ is an identity.

$$\frac{1}{\tan \theta + \cot \theta} = \frac{1}{\sin \theta/\cos \theta + \cos \theta/\sin \theta}$$

$$= \frac{1}{(\sin^2 \theta + \cos^2 \theta)/\sin \theta \cos \theta}$$

$$= \frac{1}{1/\sin \theta \cos \theta} = \sin \theta \cos \theta$$

838 Working on the right member, prove that the following equation is an identity: $1 - 2 \sin^2 \theta = 2 \cos^2 \theta - 1$.

$$2 \cos^2 \theta - 1 = 2(1 - \sin^2 \theta) - 1 = 2 - 2 \sin^2 \theta - 1$$

$$= 1 - 2 \sin^2 \theta$$

Therefore, $1 - 2 \sin^2 \theta = 2 \cos^2 \theta - 1$

839 Prove the identity $\sin \theta \cos \theta \sec \theta \csc \theta = 1$.

$$\frac{1}{\cancel{\sin \theta}} \cdot \frac{1}{\cancel{\cos \theta}} \cdot \frac{1}{\cancel{\cos \theta}} \cdot \frac{1}{\cancel{\sin \theta}} = \frac{1}{1} = 1$$

▽ 840 Prove the identity $\sin \theta \tan \theta + \cos \theta = 1/\cos \theta$.

$$\sin \theta \tan \theta + \cos \theta = \sin \theta \frac{\sin \theta}{\cos \theta} + \cos \theta = \frac{\sin^2 \theta + \cos^2 \theta}{\cos \theta}$$

$$= \frac{1}{\cos \theta}$$

841 Prove the identity $\cos^4 \theta - \sin^4 \theta = \cos^2 \theta - \sin^2 \theta$. *Suggestion:* Factor the left member and simplify.

$$\cos^4 \theta - \sin^4 \theta = (\cos^2 \theta - \sin^2 \theta)(\cos^2 \theta + \sin^2 \theta)$$
$$= (\cos^2 \theta - \sin^2 \theta) \cdot 1 = \cos^2 \theta - \sin^2 \theta$$

842 Use the factoring method to simplify (and prove) the following identity:

$$\frac{2 \sin^2 \theta + 2 \cos^2 \theta}{\tan \theta} = \frac{2}{\tan \theta}$$

$$\frac{2 \sin^2 \theta + 2 \cos^2 \theta}{\tan \theta} = \frac{2(\sin^2 \theta + \cos^2 \theta)}{\tan \theta} = \frac{2 \cdot 1}{\tan \theta} = \frac{2}{\tan \theta}$$

843 Prove the following identity:

$$\frac{\tan^4 \theta - 1}{\tan^2 \theta - 1} = \sec^2 \theta$$

$$\frac{\tan^4 \theta - 1}{\tan^2 \theta - 1} = \frac{(\tan^2 \theta - 1)(\tan^2 \theta + 1)}{\tan^2 \theta - 1}$$
$$= \frac{(\tan^2 \theta - 1) \sec^2 \theta}{\tan^2 \theta - 1} = \sec^2 \theta$$

844 Prove the identity

$$\frac{1 - \cos \theta}{\sin \theta} = \frac{\sin \theta}{1 + \cos \theta}$$

Suggestion: change the left member by multiplying both numerator and denominator of the fraction by $(1 + \cos \theta)$, then see what substitutions you can make.

$$\frac{1 - \cos \theta}{\sin \theta} = \frac{(1 - \cos \theta)(1 + \cos \theta)}{\sin \theta (1 + \cos \theta)} = \frac{1 - \cos^2 \theta}{\sin \theta (1 + \cos \theta)}$$
$$= \frac{\sin^2 \theta}{\sin \theta (1 + \cos \theta)} = \frac{\sin \theta}{1 + \cos \theta}$$

845 Prove the identity $(1 + \tan^2 \theta)/\tan^2 \theta = \csc^2 \theta.$

$$\frac{1 + \tan^2 \theta}{\tan^2 \theta} = \frac{\sec^2 \theta}{\tan^2 \theta} = \frac{1/\cos^2 \theta}{\sin^2 \theta/\cos^2 \theta} = \frac{1}{\cos^2 \theta} \cdot \frac{\cos^2 \theta}{\sin^2 \theta}$$

$$= \frac{1}{\sin^2 \theta} = \csc^2 \theta$$

846 Complete the proof of the identity

$$(\csc \theta - \cot \theta)^2 = \frac{1 - \cos \theta}{1 + \cos \theta}$$

We can show that the left member is identically equal to the right as follows:

$$(\csc \theta - \cot \theta)^2 = \left(\frac{1}{\sin \theta} - \frac{\cos \theta}{\sin \theta}\right)^2 = \left(\frac{1 - \cos \theta}{\sin \theta}\right)^2$$

$$= \frac{(1 - \cos \theta)(1 - \cos \theta)}{\sin^2 \theta}$$

$$= (1)\underline{\hspace{2cm}} = (2)\underline{\hspace{2cm}} = (3)\underline{\hspace{1.5cm}}$$

(1) $\dfrac{(1 - \cos \theta)(1 - \cos \theta)}{1 - \cos^2 \theta}$ **(2)** $\dfrac{(1 - \cos \theta)(1 - \cos \theta)}{(1 - \cos \theta)(1 + \cos \theta)}$

(3) $\dfrac{1 - \cos \theta}{1 + \cos \theta}$

▽ **847** Prove the identity $(\sec \theta - \tan \theta)^2 = (1 - \sin \theta)/(1 + \sin \theta).$

$$(\sec \theta - \tan \theta)^2 = \left(\frac{1}{\cos \theta} - \frac{\sin \theta}{\cos \theta}\right)^2 = \left(\frac{1 - \sin \theta}{\cos \theta}\right)^2$$

$$= \frac{(1 - \sin \theta)(1 - \sin \theta)}{\cos^2 \theta}$$

$$= \frac{(1 - \sin \theta)(1 - \sin \theta)}{1 - \sin^2 \theta}$$

$$= \frac{(1 - \sin \theta)(1 - \sin \theta)}{(1 - \sin \theta)(1 + \sin \theta)} = \frac{1 - \sin \theta}{1 + \sin \theta}$$

848 Prove the identity $(1 - \tan^2 \theta)/(1 + \tan^2 \theta) = 1 - 2 \sin^2 \theta$.

$$\frac{1 - \tan^2 \theta}{1 + \tan^2 \theta} = \frac{1 - \tan^2 \theta}{\sec^2 \theta} = \frac{1}{\sec^2 \theta} \cdot (1 - \tan^2 \theta)$$

$$= \cos^2 \theta \left(1 - \frac{\sin^2 \theta}{\cos^2 \theta}\right)$$

$$= \cos^2 \theta \frac{(\cos^2 \theta - \sin^2 \theta)}{\cos^2 \theta} = \cos^2 \theta - \sin^2 \theta$$

$$= 1 - \sin^2 \theta - \sin^2 \theta = 1 - 2 \sin^2 \theta$$

849 Prove the identity $\sec \theta \csc \theta - 2 \cos \theta \csc \theta = \tan \theta - \cot \theta$. Reduce each member of this problem to a common form. Be careful to simplify each member independently.

Left member	Right member
$\sec \theta \csc \theta - 2 \cos \theta \csc \theta$	$\tan \theta - \cot \theta$
$\dfrac{1}{\cos \theta} \cdot \dfrac{1}{\sin \theta} - \dfrac{2 \cos \theta}{\sin \theta}$	$\dfrac{\sin \theta}{\cos \theta} - \dfrac{\cos \theta}{\sin \theta}$
$\dfrac{1 - 2 \cos^2 \theta}{\cos \theta \sin \theta}$	$\dfrac{(1 - \cos^2 \theta) - \cos^2 \theta}{\cos \theta \sin \theta}$
	$\dfrac{1 - 2 \cos^2 \theta}{\cos \theta \sin \theta}$

Therefore, $\sec \theta \csc \theta - 2 \cos \theta \csc \theta = \tan \theta - \cot \theta$

850 Prove the identity $\sin \theta /(\csc \theta - \cot \theta) = 1 + \cot \theta$.

Remember that there may be several ways by which you may prove an identity. The proof given as an answer should be examined carefully as it may illustrate methods you have not tried.

Working on the left member

$$\frac{\sin \theta}{\csc \theta - \cot \theta} = \frac{\sin \theta}{\csc \theta - \cot \theta} \cdot \frac{\csc \theta + \cot \theta}{\csc \theta + \cot \theta}$$

$$= \frac{\sin \theta (\csc \theta + \cot \theta)}{\csc^2 \theta - \cot^2 \theta}$$

$$= \frac{\sin \theta (1/\sin \theta + \cos \theta/\sin \theta)}{1} = \frac{1 + \cos \theta}{1}$$

$$= 1 + \cos \theta$$

851 We have indicated various devices for simplifying trigonometric expressions. Some of them are reviewed in the questions below.
(1) What substitution can be made for $\sin^2 \theta + \cos^2 \theta$?
(2) What substitution can be made for $\sec^2 \theta - \tan^2 \theta$?
(3) How can you change $(\sin \theta - \sin \theta \cos \theta)/(1 - \cos^2 \theta)$ to the form $\sin \theta/(1 + \cos \theta)$?

> **(1)** 1   **(2)** 1
> **(3)** factor numerator and denominator; then reduce the fraction

852 Prove the identity

$$\frac{(\cos^2 \theta - \sin^2 \theta)^2}{\cos^4 \theta - \sin^4 \theta} = 1 - 2 \sin^2 \theta$$

> $$\frac{(\cos^2 \theta - \sin^2 \theta)^2}{\cos^4 \theta - \sin^4 \theta} = \frac{(\cos^2 \theta - \sin^2 \theta)(\cos^2 \theta - \sin^2 \theta)}{(\cos^2 \theta - \sin^2 \theta)(\cos^2 \theta + \sin^2 \theta)}$$
>
> $$= \frac{\cos^2 \theta - \sin^2 \theta}{\cos^2 \theta + \sin^2 \theta} = \frac{\cos^2 \theta - \sin^2 \theta}{1}$$
>
> $$= 1 - \sin^2 \theta - \sin^2 \theta = 1 - 2 \sin^2 \theta$$

853 Use the plan outlined below to prove the identity

$$1 + \cot \theta = \frac{(1 - \cot^2 \theta) \sin \theta}{\sin \theta - \cos \theta}$$

Outline of proof: Divide both numerator and denominator of the right member by $\sin \theta$.

$$\frac{(1 - \cot^2 \theta) \sin \theta}{\sin \theta - \cos \theta} = \frac{[(1 - \cot \theta) \sin \theta]/\sin \theta}{(\sin \theta/\sin \theta) - (\cos \theta/\sin \theta)}$$

$$= \text{(1)}\underline{\hspace{3cm}}/\underline{\hspace{3cm}}$$

(2) Express your result in terms of $\cot \theta$ and simplify.

> **(1)** $\dfrac{1 - \cot^2 \theta}{1 - \cos \theta/\sin \theta}$ **(2)** $\dfrac{(1 - \cot \theta)(1 + \cot \theta)}{(1 - \cot \theta)} = 1 + \cot \theta$

854 Prove the identity $1 + \tan \theta = \dfrac{(\tan^2 \theta - 1) \cos \theta}{\sin^2 \theta - \cos \theta}$ ~~$\sin \theta$~~ not $\dfrac{\sin \theta}{\sin^2}$

$$\frac{(\tan^2 \theta - 1) \cos \theta}{\sin \theta - \cos \theta} = \frac{(\tan^2 \theta - 1) \cos \theta / \cos \theta}{\sin \theta / \cos \theta - \cos \theta / \cos \theta}$$

$$= \frac{\tan^2 \theta - 1}{\tan \theta - 1}$$

$$= \frac{(\tan \theta - 1)(\tan \theta + 1)}{(\tan \theta - 1)} = \tan \theta + 1$$

855 Prove the identity

$$\frac{\sec \theta + \tan \theta}{\cos \theta - \tan \theta - \sec \theta} = - \csc \theta$$

$$\frac{\sec \theta + \tan \theta}{\cos \theta - \tan \theta - \sec \theta} = \frac{1/\cos \theta + \sin \theta / \cos \theta}{\cos \theta - \sin \theta / \cos \theta - 1/\cos \theta}$$

$$= \frac{(1 + \sin \theta)/\cos \theta}{(\cos^2 \theta - \sin \theta - 1)/\cos \theta}$$

$$= \frac{(1 + \sin \theta)/\cos \theta}{(1 - \sin^2 \theta - \sin \theta - 1)/\cos \theta}$$

$$= \frac{1 + \sin \theta}{- \sin^2 \theta - \sin \theta} = \frac{1 + \sin \theta}{- \sin \theta (\sin \theta + 1)}$$

$$= \frac{1}{\sin \theta} = - \csc \theta$$

856 Prove the identity below without using the double-angle formulas.

$$\frac{\sin \theta \cos \theta + \cos \theta \sin \theta}{\cos \theta \cos \theta - \sin \theta \sin \theta} = \frac{\tan \theta + \tan \theta}{1 - \tan \theta \tan \theta}$$

Suggestion: You can first simplify terms by addition and by multiplication before making trigonometric substitutions.

Left member after terms are collected	*Right member after terms are collected*
$\dfrac{2 \sin \theta \cos \theta}{\cos^2 \theta - \sin^2 \theta}$	$\dfrac{2 \tan \theta}{1 - \tan^2 \theta}$
	$= \dfrac{2 \sin \theta / \cos \theta}{1 - \sin^2 \theta / \cos^2 \theta}$
	$= \dfrac{(2 \sin \theta / \cos \theta)(\cos^2 \theta / 1)}{[(\cos^2 \theta - \sin^2 \theta)/\cos^2 \theta](\cos^2 \theta / 1)}$
	$= \dfrac{2 \sin \theta \cos \theta}{\cos^2 \theta - \sin^2 \theta}$

857   Refer to the double-angle formulas in Panel 8. (1) In what simpler
      form can you write the left member:

$$\frac{2 \sin \theta \cos \theta}{\cos^2 \theta - \sin^2 \theta} = \frac{2 \tan \theta}{1 - \tan^2 \theta}$$

(2) Explain how you know that the resulting statement is an identity.

(1) $\dfrac{\sin 2\theta}{\cos 2\theta} = \tan 2\theta$

(2) this is a form of the identity $\tan \alpha = \sin \alpha / \cos \alpha$ where α is
    replaced by 2θ.

858   Justify each step of the proof below:

$$\frac{\sin^2 \theta}{\sec \theta - 1} - \cos \theta = \cos^2 \theta$$

1. $\dfrac{\sin^2 \theta}{\sec \theta - 1} - \cos \theta = \dfrac{1 - \cos^2 \theta}{\sec \theta - 1} - \cos \theta$ (1)_____

2. $= \dfrac{(1 - \cos \theta)(1 + \cos \theta)}{\sec \theta - 1} - \cos \theta$ (2)_____

3. $= \dfrac{(1 - \cos \theta)(1 + \cos \theta)}{1/\cos \theta - 1} - \cos \theta$ (3)_____

4. $= \dfrac{(1 - \cos \theta)(1 + \cos \theta)}{(1 - \cos \theta)/\cos \theta} - \cos \theta$ (4)_____

5. $= [(1 + \cos \theta) \cos \theta] - \cos \theta$ (5)_____

6. $= \cos^2 \theta$ (6)_____

(1) substituting from the identity $1 - \cos^2 \theta = \sin^2 \theta$
(2) algebraic factoring
(3) substituting from the identity $1/\cos \theta = \sec \theta$
(4) algebraic addition
(5) simplification of complex fraction
(6) collecting terms (algebraic multiplication and addition)

859   Prove the identity $\tan^2 \theta /(1 + \sec \theta) = \sec \theta - 1$.

$$\frac{\tan^2 \theta}{1 + \sec \theta} = \frac{\sec^2 \theta - 1}{\sec \theta + 1} = \frac{(\sec \theta - 1)(\sec \theta + 1)}{\sec \theta + 1}$$

$$= \sec \theta - 1$$

▼ 860   Prove the identity $1 - [\cos^2 \theta/(1 + \sin \theta)] = \sin \theta$.

$$1 - \frac{\cos^2 \theta}{1 + \sin \theta} = 1 - \frac{1 - \sin^2 \theta}{1 + \sin \theta} = 1 - \frac{(1 - \sin \theta)(1 + \sin \theta)}{1 + \sin \theta}$$

$$= 1 - (1 - \sin \theta) = \sin \theta$$

861   Prove the identity

$$\frac{1 + 2 \sin \theta \cos \theta}{\sin \theta + \cos \theta} = \sin \theta + \cos \theta$$

Suggestion: Write the right member in the form $(\sin \theta + \cos \theta)/1$ and multiply both numerator and denominator by $\sin \theta + \cos \theta$; then reduce the result until it is identical with the given left member.

$$\frac{\sin \theta + \cos \theta}{1} = \frac{(\sin \theta + \cos \theta)^2}{\sin \theta + \cos \theta}$$

$$= \frac{\sin^2 \theta + 2 \sin \theta \cos \theta + \cos^2 \theta}{\sin \theta + \cos \theta}$$

$$= \frac{\sin^2 \theta + \cos^2 \theta + 2 \sin \theta \cos \theta}{\sin \theta + \cos \theta}$$

$$= \frac{1 + 2 \sin \theta \cos \theta}{\sin \theta + \cos \theta}$$

862   Prove that the following equation is an identity:

$$\frac{1 + 2 \sin \theta - 3 \sin^2 \theta}{\cos^2 \theta} = \frac{1 + 3 \sin \theta}{1 + \sin \theta}$$

$$\frac{1 + 2 \sin \theta - 3 \sin^2 \theta}{\cos^2 \theta} = \frac{(1 + 3 \sin \theta)(1 - \sin \theta)}{1 - \sin \theta}$$

$$= \frac{(1 + 3 \sin \theta)(1 - \sin \theta)}{(1 - \sin \theta)(1 + \sin \theta)}$$

$$= \frac{1 + 3 \sin \theta}{1 + \sin \theta}$$

863 Prove that the equation below is an identity:

$$\frac{1 - \tan^4 \theta}{\sec^2 \theta (\sin \theta + \cos \theta)} = \sec \theta - \tan \theta \sec \theta$$

$$\frac{1 - \tan^4 \theta}{\sec^2 \theta (\sin \theta + \cos \theta)}$$

$$= \frac{(1 - \tan^2 \theta)(1 + \tan^2 \theta)}{(1 + \tan^2 \theta)(\sin \theta + \cos \theta)}$$

$$= \frac{(1 - \tan \theta)(1 + \tan \theta)}{\sin \theta + \cos \theta}$$

$$= \frac{(1 - \sin \theta/\cos \theta)(1 + \sin \theta/\cos \theta)}{\sin \theta + \cos \theta}$$

$$= \frac{[(\cos \theta - \sin \theta)/\cos \theta][(\cos \theta + \sin \theta)/\cos \theta]}{(\sin \theta + \cos \theta)/1}$$

$$= \left(\frac{\cos \theta - \sin \theta}{\cos \theta}\right)\left(\frac{\cos \theta + \sin \theta}{\cos \theta}\right) \cdot \frac{1}{\sin \theta + \cos \theta}$$

$$= (1 - \tan \theta)\frac{1}{\cos \theta} \qquad \frac{\cos\theta - \sin\theta}{\cos\theta} \cdot \frac{1}{\cos\theta}$$

$$= (1 - \tan \theta)\sec \theta \qquad \left(\frac{\cos\theta}{\cos\theta} - \frac{\sin\theta}{\cos\theta}\right)\sec\theta$$

▽ **864** Prove that the following equation is an identity:

$$4 \sin^2 \theta \cos^2 \theta + (\cos^2 \theta - \sin^2 \theta)^2 = 1$$

$$4 \sin^2 \theta \cos^2 \theta + (\cos^2 \theta - \sin^2 \theta)^2$$

$$= 4 \sin^2 \theta \cos^2 \theta + \cos^4 \theta - 2 \sin^2 \theta \cos^2 \theta + \sin^4 \theta$$

$$= \cos^4 \theta + 2 \sin^2 \theta \cos^2 \theta + \sin^4 \theta$$

$$= (\cos^2 \theta + \sin^2 \theta)^2 = (1)^2 = 1$$

865 Supply reasons for the proof below.

$$\frac{(1 - \tan \theta)^2}{\csc^2 \theta} + 2 \frac{\sin \theta \cos \theta}{\cot^2 \theta} = \tan^2 \theta$$

The left member may be rewritten as follows:

$(1 - \tan \theta)^2 \sin^2 \theta + 2 \sin \theta \cos \theta \frac{\sin^2 \theta}{\cos^2 \theta}$ **(1)**_____

$(1 - 2 \tan \theta + \tan^2 \theta) \sin^2 \theta + 2 \sin^2 \theta \frac{\sin \theta}{\cos \theta}$ **(2)**_____

$\sin^2 \theta(1 - 2 \tan \theta + \tan^2 \theta + 2 \tan \theta)$ **(3)**_____

continued →

$\sin^2 \theta (1 + \tan^2 \theta)$ **(4)**_____

$\sin^2 \theta \sec^2 \theta$ **(5)**_____

$\dfrac{\sin^2 \theta}{\cos^2 \theta} = \tan^2 \theta$ **(6)**_____

(1) substitute $\sin^2 \theta$ for $1/\csc^2 \theta$; $\sin^2 \theta/\cos^2 \theta$ for $1/\cot^2 \theta$
(2) perform the indicated multiplications.
(3) factor and substitute $\tan \theta$ for $\sin \theta/\cos \theta$
(4) collect terms
(5) substitute $\sec^2 \theta$ for $1 + \tan^2 \theta$
(6) substitute $1/\cos^2 \theta$ for $\sec^2 \theta$; $\tan^2 \theta$ for $\sin^2 \theta/\cos^2 \theta$

866 Prove that the following equation is an identity for all permissible values of α and β:

$$\frac{\sin \alpha \cos \beta}{\sin \beta \cos \alpha} = \frac{\tan \alpha}{\tan \beta}$$

$$\frac{\sin \alpha \cos \beta}{\sin \beta \cos \alpha} = \frac{\sin \alpha}{\cos \alpha} \cdot \frac{\cos \beta}{\sin \beta} = \tan \alpha \cot \beta = \frac{\tan \alpha}{\tan \beta}$$

867 Prove that the following equation is an identity:

$$\frac{\tan \alpha + \tan \beta}{\cot \alpha + \cot \beta} = \tan \alpha \tan \beta$$

$$\frac{\tan \alpha + \tan \beta}{\cot \alpha + \cot \beta} = \frac{\sin \alpha/\cos \alpha + \sin \beta/\cos \beta}{\cos \alpha/\sin \alpha + \cos \beta/\sin \beta}$$

$$= \frac{\dfrac{\sin \alpha \cos \beta + \cos \alpha \sin \beta}{\cos \alpha \cos \beta}}{\dfrac{\cos \alpha \sin \beta + \sin \alpha \cos \beta}{\sin \alpha \sin \beta}}$$

$$= \frac{\sin \alpha \sin \beta}{\cos \alpha \cos \beta} = \tan \alpha \tan \beta$$

∇868 Prove that the following equation is an identity:

$$\frac{\tan \alpha + \tan \beta}{1 - \tan \alpha \tan \beta} = \frac{\sin \alpha \cos \beta + \cos \alpha \sin \beta}{\cos \alpha \cos \beta - \sin \alpha \sin \beta}$$

$$\frac{\tan \alpha + \tan \beta}{1 - \tan \alpha \tan \beta} = \frac{\sin \alpha/\cos \alpha + \sin \beta/\cos \beta}{1 - (\sin \alpha/\cos \alpha)\cdot(\sin \beta/\cos \beta)}$$

$$= \frac{\dfrac{\sin \alpha \cos \beta + \cos \alpha \sin \beta}{\cos \alpha \cos \beta}}{\dfrac{\cos \alpha \cos \beta - \sin \alpha \sin \beta}{\cos \alpha \cos \beta}}$$

$$= \frac{\sin \alpha \cos \beta + \cos \alpha \sin \beta}{\cos \alpha \cos \beta - \sin \alpha \sin \beta}$$

869 Supply reasons for the proof in which the left member of the following equation is transformed:

$$\csc^2 \theta \sec \theta - \cot \theta \csc \theta + \csc \theta \sec \theta - \cot \theta = \sec \theta + \tan \theta$$

Working on left member, we may write   Reasons

1. $\csc^2 \theta \sec \theta - \cot \theta \csc \theta + \csc \theta \sec \theta - \cot \theta$

    $= \csc \theta \sec \theta (\csc \theta + 1) - \cot \theta (\csc \theta + 1)$ (1)_____

2. $= (\csc \theta \sec \theta - \cot \theta)(\csc \theta + 1)$ (2)_____

3. $= \left(\dfrac{1}{\sin \theta} \cdot \dfrac{1}{\cos \theta} - \dfrac{\cos \theta}{\sin \theta}\right)\left(\dfrac{1}{\sin \theta} + 1\right)$ (3)_____

4. $= \left(\dfrac{1 - \cos^2 \theta}{\sin \theta \cos \theta}\right)\left(\dfrac{1 + \sin \theta}{\sin \theta}\right)$ (4)_____

5. $= \dfrac{\sin^2 \theta}{\sin \theta \cos \theta} \cdot \left(\dfrac{1 + \sin \theta}{\sin \theta}\right)$ (5)_____

6. $= \dfrac{1}{\cos \theta} (1 + \sin \theta)$ (6)_____

7. $= \dfrac{1}{\cos \theta} + \dfrac{\sin \theta}{\cos \theta}$ (7)_____

8. $= \sec \theta + \tan \theta$ (8)_____

(1) factoring
(2) factoring
(3) substituting from fundamental relations
(4) algebraic addition of fractions
(5) substituting from fundamental relations
(6) multiplication of fractions
(7) multiplication of fractions
(8) substituting from fundamental relations

870 Frames 870 to 872 are optional. They are good practice problems. Prove the identity

$$\sin \theta + \cos \theta + \frac{\sin \theta}{\cot \theta} = \sec \theta + \csc \theta - \frac{\cos \theta}{\tan \theta}$$

Reduction of left member	*Reduction of right member*
$\sin \theta + \cos \theta + \dfrac{\sin \theta}{\cot \theta}$	$\sec \theta + \csc \theta - \dfrac{\cos \theta}{\tan \theta}$
$\sin \theta + \cos \theta + \dfrac{\sin \theta}{1} \cdot \dfrac{\sin \theta}{\cos \theta}$	$\dfrac{1}{\cos \theta} + \dfrac{1}{\sin \theta} - \dfrac{\cos \theta}{1} \cdot \dfrac{\cos \theta}{\sin \theta}$
$\dfrac{\sin \theta \cos \theta + \cos^2 \theta + \sin^2 \theta}{\cos \theta}$	$\dfrac{1}{\cos \theta} + \dfrac{1 - \cos^2 \theta}{\sin \theta}$
$\dfrac{\sin \theta \cos \theta + 1}{\cos \theta}$	$\dfrac{1}{\cos \theta} + \dfrac{\sin^2 \theta}{\sin \theta}$
	$\dfrac{1}{\cos \theta} + \sin \theta$
	$\dfrac{1 + \cos \theta \sin \theta}{\cos \theta}$

Therefore, $\sin \theta + \cos \theta + \dfrac{\sin \theta}{\cot \theta} = \sec \theta + \csc \theta - \dfrac{\cos \theta}{\tan \theta}$

871 Optional. Prove the identity

$$\frac{\sec \theta + \tan \theta}{\cos \theta - \tan \theta - \sec \theta} = - \csc \theta$$

$$\frac{\sec \theta + \tan \theta}{\cos \theta - \tan \theta - \sec \theta} = \frac{1/\cos \theta + \sin \theta/\cos \theta}{\cos \theta - 1/\cos \theta - \sin \theta/\cos \theta}$$

$$= \frac{(1 + \sin \theta)/\cos \theta}{(\cos^2 \theta - 1 - \sin \theta)/\cos \theta}$$

$$= \frac{(1 + \sin \theta)/\cos \theta}{(- \sin^2 \theta - \sin \theta)/\cos \theta}$$

$$= \frac{1 + \sin \theta}{\cos \theta} \cdot \frac{\cos \theta}{- \sin \theta (1 + \sin \theta)}$$

$$= \frac{1}{- \sin \theta} = - \csc \theta$$

872 Optional. Prove that the following equation is an identity:

$$1 + \cot \theta = \frac{(1 - \cot^2 \theta) \sin \theta}{\sin \theta - \cos \theta}$$

Reduction of left member	*Reduction of right member*
$1 + \cot \theta$	$\dfrac{(1 - \cot^2 \theta) \sin \theta}{\sin \theta - \cos \theta}$
$= 1 + \dfrac{\cos \theta}{\sin \theta}$	$= \dfrac{(1 - \cos^2 \theta / \sin^2 \theta) \sin \theta}{\sin \theta - \cos \theta}$
$= \dfrac{\sin \theta + \cos \theta}{\sin \theta}$	$= \dfrac{\dfrac{\sin^2 \theta - \cos^2 \theta}{\sin^2 \theta} \cdot \sin \theta}{\sin \theta - \cos \theta}$
	$= \dfrac{(\sin \theta - \cos \theta)(\sin \theta + \cos \theta)}{\sin \theta (\sin \theta - \cos \theta)}$
	$= \dfrac{\sin \theta + \cos \theta}{\sin \theta}$

Therefore $1 + \cot \theta = \dfrac{(1 - \cot^2 \theta) \sin \theta}{\sin \theta - \cos \theta}$

873 The identities you will be working with next will require the formulas for
1. the sum of two angles
2. the double angle
3. the half angle
4. sums or differences to products
5. reduction
You should be able to write the formulas for the sum of two angles from memory. Try it. Then check your answers with Panel 8.

$\sin(\alpha + \beta) = (1)$ _____ $\cos(\alpha - \beta) = (2)$ _____
$\sin(\alpha - \beta) = (3)$ _____ $\tan(\alpha + \beta) = (4)$ _____
$\cos(\alpha + \beta) = (5)$ _____ $\tan(\alpha - \beta) = (6)$ _____

See Panel 8 for the answer.

874 Recall that we obtained a formula for the sine of twice an angle, i.e., $\sin 2\alpha = 2 \sin \alpha \cos \alpha$, from the formula for $\sin(\alpha + \beta)$. Derive the formula for $\sin 2\alpha$.

If $\beta = \alpha$, then $\sin(\alpha + \beta) = \sin(\alpha + \alpha) = \sin 2\alpha$
$\qquad\qquad\qquad\qquad = \sin \alpha \cos \alpha + \cos \alpha \sin \alpha$
$\qquad\qquad\qquad\qquad = 2 \sin \alpha \cos \alpha$

Therefore, $\sin 2\alpha = 2 \sin \alpha \cos \alpha$

875   Derive the identity (formula) for cos 2α. Follow the plan used in frame 874 for sin 2α.

Let $\alpha = \beta$, then, $\cos(\alpha + \beta) = \cos(\alpha + \alpha)$

$$= \cos \alpha \cos \alpha - \sin \alpha \sin \alpha$$

$$= \cos^2 \alpha - \sin^2 \alpha$$

Therefore, $\cos 2\alpha = \cos^2 \alpha - \sin^2 \alpha$

876   Change the right member of $\cos 2\alpha = \cos^2 \alpha - \sin^2 \alpha$ to a form involving only cos α.

$\cos 2\alpha = \cos^2 \alpha - \sin^2 \alpha = \cos^2 \alpha - (1 - \cos^2 \alpha)$

$$= \cos^2 \alpha - 1 + \cos^2 \alpha = 2 \cos^2 \alpha - 1$$

▽877   Derive the identity (formula) for tan 2α.

Let $\alpha = \beta$, then $\tan(\alpha + \beta) = \tan(\alpha + \alpha) = \tan 2\alpha$

$$= \frac{\tan \alpha + \tan \alpha}{1 - \tan \alpha \tan \alpha} = \frac{2 \tan \alpha}{1 - \tan^2 \alpha}$$

Therefore, $\tan 2\alpha = \dfrac{2 \tan \alpha}{1 - \tan^2 \alpha}$

878   Is $45°$ a permissible value for α in tan $2\alpha = 2 \tan \alpha /(1 - \tan^2 \alpha)$? Explain your answer.

no

$\tan 2(45°) = \dfrac{2 \tan 45°}{1 - \tan^2 45°} = \dfrac{2 \cdot 1}{1 - (1)^2} = \dfrac{2}{0}$ undefined

or $\tan 2(45°) = \tan 90°$ which is undefined

879   Can you use the identity tan $2\alpha = 2 \tan \alpha /(1 - \tan^2 \alpha)$ to find tan 2α if $\alpha = 90°$? Explain your answer.

no

Since tan $90°$ is undefined the following statement is meaningless

$$\tan 2(90°) = \frac{2 \tan 90°}{1 - \tan^2 90°}$$

880 Refer to the answer in frame 879. Although you cannot compute tan 180° by means of the double-angle formula, you know from previous work that tan 180° = _____. (Give a numerical answer.)

0

881 What are two values other than 90° for α, $0 \le \alpha < 360°$, which are not permissible values in the identity $\tan 2\alpha = 2 \tan \alpha /(1 - \tan^2 \alpha)$.

any two of the list $\alpha = 135°, 225°, 315°, 270°$

Example: $\alpha = 135°$, $\tan 2(135°) = \dfrac{2 \tan 135°}{1 - \tan^2 135°} = \dfrac{2(-1)}{1 - (-1)}$

$$= \dfrac{-2}{0} \quad \text{undefined}$$

882 Let $\alpha = 30°$. Use the fact that $\tan 30° = 1/\sqrt{3}$ and the double-angle formula to find tan 60°. Write your answer in simple radical form.

$\tan 60° = \sqrt{3}$

Solution: $\tan 2(30°) = \dfrac{2 \tan 30°}{1 - \tan^2 30°}$

$$\tan 60° = \dfrac{2 \cdot 1/\sqrt{3}}{1 - \frac{1}{3}} = \dfrac{2/\sqrt{3}}{\frac{2}{3}} = \dfrac{3}{\sqrt{3}} = \sqrt{3}$$

883 Note that $\tan 2\theta \ne 2 \tan \theta$. Let $\theta = 30°$.

tan 2θ means tan $2 \cdot 30°$ = tan 60°   = (1)_____
2 tan θ means 2 tan 30° = (2) 2(____) = (3)_____

(1)   3   (2) $\dfrac{1}{\sqrt{3}}$ (3) $\dfrac{2}{\sqrt{3}}$ or $\dfrac{2\sqrt{3}}{3}$

884 Let $\alpha = 60°$. Use the double-angle formula to find tan 120°.

$\tan 120° = -\sqrt{3}$

Solution: $\tan 120° = \tan 2(60°) = \dfrac{2 \tan 60°}{1 - \tan^2 60°} = \dfrac{2(\sqrt{3})}{1 - (\sqrt{3})}$

$$= \dfrac{2\sqrt{3}}{1 - 3} = \dfrac{2\sqrt{3}}{-2} = -\sqrt{3}$$

885 Let $\alpha = 45°$. Use the double-angle formula to find $\sin 90°$.

> $\sin 90° = 1$
>
> *Solution:* $\sin 90° = \sin 2(45°) = 2 \sin 45° \cos 45° = 2 \frac{\sqrt{2}}{2} \cdot \frac{\sqrt{2}}{2}$
>
> $$= \frac{2 \cdot 2}{2 \cdot 2} = 1$$

886 Let $\alpha = 90°$. Use the double-angle formula to find $\cos 180°$.

> $\cos 180° = -1$
>
> *Solution:* $\cos 180° = \cos 2(90°) = 2 \cos^2 90° - 1 = 2 \cdot 0 - 1 = -1$

887 You know that $\sin 135° = $ (1)_____ and $\cos 135° = $ (2)_____.
Use this information and the double-angle formulas to find
(3) $\sin 270°$ and (4) $\cos 270°$.

> (1) $\frac{\sqrt{2}}{2}$ (2) $\frac{-\sqrt{2}}{2}$
>
> (3) $\sin 270° = -1$
>
> *Solution:* $\sin 270° = \sin 2(135°) = 2 \sin 135° \cos 135°$
>
> $$= 2 \frac{\sqrt{2}}{2} \cdot \frac{-\sqrt{2}}{2} = -1$$
>
> (4) $\cos 270° = 0$
>
> *Solution:* $\cos 270° = \cos 2(135°) = 2 \cos^2 135° - 1 = 2\left(\frac{-\sqrt{2}}{2}\right)^2 - 1$
>
> $$= \frac{2 \cdot 2}{4} - 1 = 0$$

888 Show how to derive the half-angle formula

$$\sin \frac{\theta}{2} = \pm \sqrt{\frac{1 - \cos \theta}{2}}$$

> 1. $\cos 2\alpha = 1 - 2 \sin^2 \alpha$
> 2. $2 \sin^2 \alpha = 1 - \cos 2\alpha$
> 3. $\sin^2 \alpha = \frac{1 - \cos 2\alpha}{2}$
> 4. $\sin \alpha = \pm \sqrt{\frac{1 - \cos 2\alpha}{2}}$

continued →

Now let $\theta = 2\alpha$ and $\theta/2 = \alpha$ and substitute these values in Step 4 above.

5. $\sin \dfrac{\theta}{2} = \pm \sqrt{\dfrac{1 - \cos \theta}{2}}$

Be sure that you understand the substitution to get Step 5.

889 Start with the half-angle formula and show that the following is true: $2 \sin^2 4\alpha = 1 - \cos 8\alpha$.

1. let $8\alpha = \theta$, then $4\alpha = \theta/2$ and the half-angle formula may be written thus: $\sin 4\alpha = \pm \sqrt{(1 - \cos 8\alpha)/2}$
2. square both members, $\sin^2 4\alpha = (1 - \cos 8\alpha)/2$
3. finally multiply by 2, $2 \sin^2 4\alpha = 1 - \cos 8\alpha$

890 Review the formula for $\cos (\theta/2)$ by showing how it is derived from one of the double-angle formulas.

Use the formula $\cos 2\alpha = 2 \cos^2 \alpha - 1$

$2 \cos^2 \alpha = 1 + \cos 2\alpha$ $\cos \alpha = \pm \sqrt{\dfrac{1 + \cos 2\alpha}{2}}$

Let $\theta = 2\alpha, \dfrac{\theta}{2} = \alpha$

$\cos \dfrac{\theta}{2} = \pm \sqrt{\dfrac{1 + \cos \theta}{2}}$

This is the half-angle formula for $\cos \frac{1}{2}\theta$ found on Panel 8IV(1).

891 In frame 700 a method for finding alternate forms for the formula

$\tan \dfrac{\theta}{2} = \pm \sqrt{\dfrac{1 - \cos \theta}{1 + \cos \theta}}$

which did not contain radicals was given. In this frame, other (perhaps easier) ways to derive these formulas are given.

(1) Multiply both numerator and denominator of the right member by $\sqrt{1 - \cos \theta}$ and simplify the result.
(2) Multiply both numerator and denominator of the right member by $\sqrt{1 + \cos \theta}$ and simplify.

(1) $\tan \dfrac{\theta}{2} = \dfrac{1 - \cos \theta}{\sin \theta}$ (2) $\tan \dfrac{\theta}{2} = \dfrac{\sin \theta}{1 + \cos \theta}$

892 Refer to your formulas for tan $(\theta/2)$. The sign of tan $(\theta/2)$ will be positive if $\theta/2$ is an angle terminating in quadrants (1)_____ or (2)_____ and negative if $\theta/2$ terminates in quadrants (3)_____ or (4)_____. (5) Have we allowed for this variation of sign in the formula tan $(\theta/2) = (1 - \cos \theta)/\sin \theta$ or should we write tan $(\theta/2) = \pm (1 - \cos \theta)/\sin \theta$?

(1) I **(2)** III **(3)** II **(4)** IV
(5) the double sign is not necessary. If you check with angles terminating in the first, second, third, and fourth quadrants, you will see that the double sign is not needed. Furthermore, in the derivation in frame 700 the double sign did not appear in the alternate form.

893 Remember that you have three forms in which you can express tan $(\theta/2)$. Sometimes one of the forms will make the solution of a particular problem easier than another. List all three forms.

$$\tan \frac{\theta}{2} = \pm \sqrt{\frac{1 - \cos \theta}{1 + \cos \theta}} = \frac{1 - \cos \theta}{\sin \theta} = \frac{\sin \theta}{1 + \cos \theta}$$

894 If you are given the numerical value for cos $44°$ and are required to find cos $22°$, the half-angle formula tells you that cos $22° =$ _____. Try to answer frames 895 to 898 without looking at the list of identities.

$$\sqrt{\frac{1 + \cos 44°}{2}}$$

895 Given the numerical value for cos $210°$, complete the following formula by inserting the correct function preceded by the proper sign.

$$\underline{\qquad} 105° = \sqrt{\frac{1 - \cos 210°}{1 + \cos 210°}}$$

-tan   *Note:* $105°$ is an angle terminating in quadrant II.

896 Express $(1 - \cos 38°)/\sin 38°$ as a function of $19°$.

tan $19°$

897 Express $2 \cos^2(\theta/2)$ in terms of θ.

$2 \cos^2 \frac{\theta}{2} = 1 + \cos \theta$

Solution: $2 \cos^2 \frac{\theta}{2} = 2 \left(\sqrt{\frac{1 + \cos \theta}{2}} \right)^2 = 2 \left(\frac{1 + \cos \theta}{2} \right) = 1 + \cos \theta$

898 Express $\tan^2(\theta/2)$ in terms of θ.

$\tan^2 \frac{\theta}{2} = \frac{1 - \cos}{1 + \cos}$

899 Such substitutions as the following are useful when working with trigonometric functions:

Given $\sin(x/2) = \pm\sqrt{(1 - \cos x)/2}$. If we replace $x/2$ by θ and x by 2θ, then $\sin \theta = \pm\sqrt{(1 - \cos 2\theta)/2}$.

Be sure that you understand the substitution! Let $x/2 = 2\beta$, write the resulting form of the above identity.

$\sin 2\beta = \pm\sqrt{\frac{1 - \cos 4\beta}{2}}$

900 Let $x = 2\theta$, then rewrite the following identities in terms of θ:

(1) $\tan \frac{x}{2} = \pm\sqrt{\frac{1 - \cos x}{1 + \cos x}}$ **(2)** $\cos \frac{x}{2} = \pm\sqrt{\frac{1 + \cos x}{2}}$

(1) $\tan \theta = \pm\sqrt{\frac{1 - \cos 2\theta}{1 + \cos 2\theta}}$ **(2)** $\cos \theta = \pm\sqrt{\frac{1 + \cos 2\theta}{2}}$

901 Let $\cos \theta = \frac{1}{2}$. **(1)** Find $\cos(\theta/2)$ using the half-angle formula. **(2)** Explain why the double sign is needed in your answer.

(1) $\cos \frac{\theta}{2} = \pm \frac{\sqrt{3}}{2}$

(2) If $0° \le \theta \le 360°$ and $\cos \theta = \frac{1}{2}$, then $\theta = 60°$ or $\theta = 300°$. Hence $\theta/2 = 30°$ or $\theta/2 = 150°$. $\cos 30°$ is positive and $\cos 150°$ is negative.

902 Let $\cos \theta = \frac{1}{2}$.
(1) Find $\sin(\theta/2)$ using the half-angle formula.
(2) If $\cos \theta$ is positive and $0° \leq \theta \leq 360°$, then θ is an angle terminating in quadrant (a)_____ or (b)_____. Therefore, $\theta/2$ is an angle terminating in quadrant (c)_____ or (d)_____.
(e) Will $\sin(\theta/2)$ be positive or negative?
(3) Suppose $\theta = 420°$, then $\theta/2 =$ (a)_____ and now $\theta/2$ terminates in quadrant (b)_____. (c) Is $\sin(\theta/2)$ positive or negative?

(1) $\sin \dfrac{\theta}{2} = \pm\dfrac{1}{2}$ (2)(a) I,   (b) IV,   (c) I,   (d) II,   (e) positive

(3)(a) $210°$,   (b) III,   (c) negative

903 Let $\cos \theta = \frac{1}{2}$. (1) Find $\tan(\theta/2)$ using the half-angle formula.
(2) Make a statement regarding the sign of the result.

(1) $\tan \dfrac{\theta}{2} = \pm\sqrt{\dfrac{1 - \frac{1}{2}}{1 + \frac{1}{2}}} = \dfrac{1}{\sqrt{3}}$

(2) the answer should have double sign. If θ is an angle terminating in quadrant I, then $\theta/2$ will terminate in quadrant I or III and $\tan(\theta/2)$ will be positive. If θ terminates in quadrant IV, then $\theta/2$ will terminate in quadrant II or IV and $\tan(\theta/2)$ will be negative. Check these statements with angles greater than $360°$.

904 If you are given $\tan \theta = a$ and asked to find $\sin 2\theta$ in terms of a, you would first have to find values of $\sin \theta$ and $\cos \theta$ in terms of a to substitute in the formula for $\sin 2\theta$. Thus:
Given $\tan \theta = a = a/1$ and θ terminates in quadrant I, then
$y =$ (1)_____, $x =$ (2)_____, $r =$ (3)_____, and
$\sin \theta =$ (4)_____/_____ and $\cos \theta =$ (5)_____/_____.
This problem will be continued in frame 905.

(1) a (2) 1   (3) $\sqrt{a^2 + 1}$ (4) $\dfrac{a}{\sqrt{a^2 + 1}}$ (5) $\dfrac{1}{\sqrt{a^2 + 1}}$

905   Use the information in frame 904 to find sin 2θ. (Remember that θ terminates in quadrant I, check the sign of your answer.)

$$\sin 2\theta = \frac{2a}{1 + a^2}$$

Solution: $\sin 2\theta = 2 \sin \theta \cos \theta$

$$= 2\left(\frac{a}{\sqrt{a^2 + 1}} \cdot \frac{1}{\sqrt{a^2 + 1}}\right) = \frac{2a}{a^2 + 1}$$

See frame 906 for a discussion on signs.

906   (1) Consider $\tan \theta = a$ as positive. Then θ terminates in quadrant I or III, and 2θ may terminate in quadrant (a)_____ or (b)_____, and sin 2θ has (c)_____ sign.   Check using angles in the form $(\theta + k \cdot 360)$.

(2) Consider $\tan \theta = a$ as negative. Then θ terminates in quadrant II or IV, and 2θ may terminate in quadrant (a)_____ or (b)_____, and sin 2θ has (c)_____ sign.   Check using angles in the form $(\theta + k \cdot 360)$.

(1)(a) I,   (b) II,   (c) positive
(2)(a) III,   (b) IV,   (c) negative

907   Prove that $\cot \theta/2 = (1 + \cos \theta)/\sin \theta$ is an identity.

$$\cot \frac{\theta}{2} = \frac{1}{\tan (\theta/2)} = \frac{1}{\sin \theta/(1 + \cos \theta)} = \frac{1 + \cos \theta}{\sin \theta}$$

908   Prove $\sin^2 (\theta/2) = (\sec \theta - 1)/2 \sec \theta$.

$$\sin^2 \frac{\theta}{2} = \frac{1 - \cos \theta}{2} = \frac{1 - 1/\sec \theta}{2} = \frac{\sec \theta - 1}{2 \sec \theta}$$

909   Prove $\dfrac{\cos^2 (x/2) - \cos x}{\sin^2 (x/2)} = 1$

$$\frac{\cos^2 (x/2) - \cos x}{\sin^2 (x/2)} = \frac{(1 + \cos x)/2 - \cos x}{(1 - \cos x)/2}$$

$$= \frac{(1 + \cos x - 2 \cos x)/2}{(1 - \cos x)/2}$$

$$= \frac{(1 - \cos x)/2}{(1 - \cos x)/2} = 1$$

910 Prove $\dfrac{\sin 2\theta + \sin \theta}{\cos 2\theta + \cos \theta + 1} = \tan \theta$

$$\frac{\sin 2\theta + \sin \theta}{\cos 2\theta + \cos \theta + 1} = \frac{2 \sin \theta \cos \theta + \sin \theta}{2 \cos^2 \theta - 1 + \cos \theta + 1}$$

$$= \frac{\sin \theta (2 \cos \theta + 1)}{\cos \theta (2 \cos \theta + 1)} = \tan \theta$$

911 Prove $\tan \dfrac{A}{2} \sin A = \dfrac{\tan A - \sin A}{\sin A \sec A}$

Reduce each member to a common form.

Reduce left and right members as follows:

Left member

$\tan \frac{1}{2} A \sin A$

$= \dfrac{1 - \cos A}{\sin A} \cdot \sin A$

$= 1 - \cos A$

Right member

$\dfrac{\tan A - \sin A}{\sin A \sec A}$

$= \dfrac{\sin A / \cos A - \sin A}{\sin A \sec A}$

Divide by $\sin A$

$= \dfrac{1/\cos A - 1}{\sec A}$

$= \dfrac{1 - \cos A}{\cos A} \cdot \dfrac{\cos A}{1}$

$1 - \cos A = 1 - \cos A$

912 Prove $\left(\cos \dfrac{\theta}{2}\right)^4 + \left(\sin \dfrac{\theta}{2}\right)^4 = \dfrac{2 - \sin^2 \theta}{2}$

$$\left(\cos \frac{\theta}{2}\right)^4 + \left(\sin \frac{\theta}{2}\right)^4 = \left(\frac{1 + \cos \theta}{2}\right)^2 + \left(\frac{1 - \cos \theta}{2}\right)^2$$

$$= \frac{1 + 2\cos \theta + \cos^2 \theta}{4} + \frac{1 - 2\cos \theta + \cos^2 \theta}{4}$$

$$= \frac{2 + 2\cos^2 \theta}{4} = \frac{1 + \cos^2 \theta}{2}$$

$$= \frac{1 + (1 - \sin^2 \theta)}{2} = \frac{2 - \sin^2 \theta}{2}$$

913 Prove $8 \sin^2 \frac{1}{2}x \cos^2 \frac{1}{2}x = 1 - \cos 2x$

$$8 \sin^2 \tfrac{1}{2}x \cos^2 \tfrac{1}{2}x = 8 \frac{(1 - \cos x)}{2} \cdot \frac{(1 + \cos x)}{2} = 2(1 - \cos^2 x)$$
$$= 2 - 2 \cos^2 x = 1 - (2 \cos^2 x - 1)$$
$$= 1 - \cos 2x$$

914 Express $\sin 3\theta$ in terms of $\sin \theta$. Start with $\sin 3\theta = \sin(2\theta + \theta)$.

$$\sin 3\theta = \sin(2\theta + \theta) = \sin 2\theta \cos \theta + \cos 2\theta \sin \theta$$
$$= (2 \sin \theta \cos \theta) \cos \theta + (1 - 2 \sin^2 \theta) \sin \theta$$
$$= 2 \sin \theta \cos^2 \theta + \sin \theta - 2 \sin^3 \theta$$
$$= 2 \sin \theta (1 - \sin^2 \theta) + \sin \theta - 2 \sin^3 \theta$$
$$= 2 \sin \theta - 2 \sin^3 \theta + \sin \theta - 2 \sin^3 \theta$$
$$= 3 \sin \theta - 4 \sin^3 \theta$$

915 Show that $\cos 3\theta = 4 \cos^3 \theta - 3 \cos \theta$.

$$\cos 3\theta = \cos(2\theta + \theta) = \cos 2\theta \cos \theta - \sin 2\theta \sin \theta$$
$$= (2 \cos^2 \theta - 1) \cos \theta - 2 \sin \theta \cos \theta \sin \theta$$
$$= \cos \theta (2 \cos^2 \theta - 1 - 2 \sin^2 \theta)$$
$$= \cos \theta [2 \cos^2 \theta - 1 - 2(1 - \cos^2 \theta)]$$
$$= \cos \theta [2 \cos^2 \theta - 1 - 2 + 2 \cos^2 \theta]$$
$$= \cos \theta [4 \cos^2 \theta - 3] = 4 \cos^3 \theta - 3 \cos \theta$$

916 Express $\sin 4\theta$ in terms of $\sin \theta$ and $\cos \theta$.

You may begin with either the addition formula (Step 1 below) or double-angle formula (Step 2).

1. $\sin 4\theta = \sin(2\theta + 2\theta)$
2. $\quad\quad = 2 \sin 2\theta \cos 2\theta$
3. $\quad\quad = 2[2 \sin \theta \cos \theta (\cos^2 \theta - \sin^2 \theta)]$
4. $\quad\quad = 4(\sin \theta \cos^3 \theta - \sin^3 \theta \cos \theta)$
   $\quad$ or $4 \sin \theta \cos\theta (\cos^2 \theta - \sin^2 \theta)$

continued →

Alternate forms:

1. Starting with step 3

$$= 2[2 \sin \theta \cos \theta (2 \cos^2 \theta - 1)]$$
$$= 4 \sin \theta \cos \theta (2 \cos^2 \theta - 1)$$

2. Starting with step 3

$$= 2[2 \sin \theta \cos \theta (1 - 2 \sin^2 \theta)]$$
$$= 4 \sin \theta \cos \theta (1 - 2 \sin^2 \theta)$$

917 Express $\cos 4\theta$ in terms of $\cos \theta$.

$$\cos 4\theta = 2 \cos^2 2\theta - 1 = \boxed{2(2 \cos^2 \theta - 1)^2 - 1}$$
$$= 2(4 \cos^4 \theta - 4 \cos^2 \theta + 1) - 1$$
$$= 8 \cos^4 \theta - 8 \cos^2 \theta + 2 - 1$$
$$= 8 \cos^4 \theta - 8 \cos^2 \theta + 1$$

918 Prove $(1 - \cos 2\theta)/\sin 2\theta = \tan \theta$.

Solution 1: Start with the identity

$$\tan \frac{x}{2} = \frac{1 - \cos x}{\sin x}$$

Let $\theta = x/2$, then $2\theta = x$. Substituting these values, we have

$$\tan \theta = \frac{1 - \cos 2\theta}{\sin 2\theta}$$

Solution 2: Transform the right member

$$\frac{1 - \cos 2\theta}{\sin 2\theta} = \frac{1 - (2 \cos^2 \theta - 1)}{2 \sin \theta \cos \theta} = \frac{2(1 - \cos^2 \theta)}{2 \sin \theta \cos \theta}$$

$$= \frac{\sin^2 \theta}{\sin \theta \cos \theta} = \frac{\sin \theta}{\cos \theta} = \tan \theta$$

919 Prove $\csc 2\theta - \cot 2\theta = \tan \theta$. Express the left member in terms of $\sin 2\theta$ and $\cos 2\theta$. Recall the identity of frame 918.

$$\csc 2\theta - \cot 2\theta = \frac{1}{\sin 2\theta} - \frac{\cos 2\theta}{\sin 2\theta} = \frac{1 - \cos 2\theta}{\sin 2\theta}$$

$$= \tan \theta \quad \text{(from frame 918)}$$

920 Prove $\tan 3\theta = \dfrac{3 \tan \theta - \tan^3 \theta}{1 - 3 \tan^2 \theta}$

$$\tan (3\theta) = \tan (2\theta + \theta) = \frac{\tan 2\theta + \tan \theta}{1 - \tan 2\theta \tan \theta}$$

$$= \frac{2 \tan \theta / (1 - \tan^2 \theta) + \tan \theta}{1 - [2 \tan \theta / (1 - \tan^2 \theta)] \tan \theta}$$

$$= \frac{2 \tan \theta + \tan \theta - \tan^3 \theta}{1 - \tan^2 \theta - 2 \tan^2 \theta} = \frac{3 \tan \theta - \tan^3 \theta}{1 - 3 \tan^2 \theta}$$

921 Prove $\sin 2\theta / \sin \theta - \cos 2\theta / \cos \theta = \sec \theta$.

$$\frac{\sin 2\theta}{\sin \theta} - \frac{\cos 2\theta}{\cos \theta} = \frac{2 \sin \theta \cos \theta}{\sin \theta} - \frac{2 \cos^2 \theta - 1}{\cos \theta}$$

$$= \frac{2 \cos^2 \theta - 2 \cos^2 \theta + 1}{\cos \theta} = \frac{1}{\cos \theta} = \sec \theta$$

See frame 922 for a discussion of this problem.

922 An alternate proof of $\sin 2\theta / \sin \theta - \cos 2\theta / \cos \theta = \sec \theta$ is suggested below.

1. Express the left member with a common denominator; thus,

$$\frac{\sin 2\theta \cos \theta - \cos 2\theta \sin \theta}{\sin \theta \cos \theta}$$

2. Identify the addition formula represented in the numerator; thus,

$$\frac{\sin (2\theta - \theta)}{\sin \theta \cos \theta}$$

3. Simplify and reduce to $\sec \theta$.

$$\frac{\sin (2\theta - \theta)}{\sin \theta \cos \theta} = \frac{\sin \theta}{\sin \theta \cos \theta} = \frac{1}{\cos \theta} = \sec \theta$$

923 Prove $\sin 3\theta / \cos \theta + \cos 3\theta / \sin \theta = 2 \cot 2\theta$. Use the plan suggested in frame 922.

$$\frac{\sin 3\theta}{\cos \theta} + \frac{\cos 3\theta}{\sin \theta} = \frac{\sin 3\theta \sin \theta + \cos 3\theta \cos \theta}{\sin \theta \cos \theta}$$

$$= \frac{\cos 2\theta}{\sin \theta \cos \theta} = \frac{\cos 2\theta}{\frac{1}{2} \sin 2\theta} = 2 \cot 2\theta$$

$$\frac{2 \; \cos 2\theta}{2 \sin \theta \cos \theta} = \frac{\cos 2\theta}{\frac{1}{2} \sin} \qquad X \, 2$$

924 In frames 924 to 930 you are to apply the product-to-sum formulas to specific examples. (1) Use Panel 9VA(3) to change the product $\cos 60°\cos 30°$ to a sum; i.e., $\cos 60°\cos 30°$ = _____. (2) Show that the result is correct by substituting numerical values in both members of equation (1).

(1) $\frac{1}{2}[\cos(60° + 30°) + \cos(60° - 30°)] = \frac{1}{2}[\cos 90° + \cos 30°]$

(2) $\frac{1}{2} \cdot \frac{\sqrt{3}}{2} = \frac{1}{2}\left[0 + \frac{\sqrt{3}}{2}\right], \qquad \frac{\sqrt{3}}{4} = \frac{\sqrt{3}}{4}$

925 Change $\cos 2\theta \sin 4\theta$ to a sum (or difference).

$\cos 2\theta \sin 4\theta = \frac{1}{2}[\sin 6\theta - \sin(-2\theta)]$ or $\frac{1}{2}(\sin 6\theta + \sin 2\theta)$

926 Change $\sin 75° \cos 15°$ to a sum and find the value of the result. Leave the answer in simple radical form.

$\sin 75° \cos 15° = \frac{1}{2}(\sin 90° + \sin 60°) = \frac{1}{2}\left(1 + \frac{\sqrt{3}}{2}\right)$

$= \frac{1}{2}\left(\frac{2}{2} + \frac{\sqrt{3}}{2}\right) = \frac{2 + \sqrt{3}}{4}$

927 Change $\sin 37\frac{1}{2}° \sin 7\frac{1}{2}°$ to a sum (or difference) and evaluate the result. Leave your answer in simple radical form.

$\sin 37\frac{1}{2}° \sin 7\frac{1}{2}° = -\frac{1}{2}[\cos 45° - \cos 30°] = -\frac{1}{2}\left[\frac{\sqrt{2}}{2} - \frac{\sqrt{3}}{2}\right]$

$= -\frac{1}{2}\left(\frac{\sqrt{2} - \sqrt{3}}{2}\right) = \frac{-\sqrt{2} + \sqrt{3}}{4}$

928 (1) Change the product $4\cos(\pi/3)\cos(\pi/6)$ to a sum. (2) Evaluate your answer. Be careful, here we have *four times* the product of two trigonometric functions!

(1) $4\cos\frac{\pi}{3}\cos\frac{\pi}{6} = 4\left[\frac{1}{2}\cos\frac{\pi}{2} + \cos\frac{\pi}{6}\right] = 2\cos\frac{\pi}{2} + \cos\frac{\pi}{6}$

(2) $2\left(0 + \frac{\sqrt{3}}{2}\right) = \sqrt{3}$

929 A remark should be made about applications of the formulas of this section. A great many applications of trigonometry are to subjects

continued →

for which trigonometry is a prerequisite; hence, it is not expected that a student will be familiar with such subjects! However, we may motivate the problem here by saying that in Fourier analysis, for purposes of integration, the expression cos mx cos nx must be changed to a sum, instead of a product, of trigonometric functions. Show that you can make the transfer from product to sum: cos mx cos nx = _____ .

$$\cos mx \cos nx = \tfrac{1}{2}[\cos(mx + nx) + \cos(mx - nx)]$$
$$= \tfrac{1}{2}[\cos(m + n)x + \cos(m - n)x]$$

930 In physics we have the following formula for an FM (frequency modulation) wave:

$$i = I(1 + m \sin at)\sin bt$$

Show that the right member of this equation can be expressed as the sum of sines and cosines.

$$i = I \sin bt + Im \sin at \sin bt$$
$$= I \sin bt + Im(-\tfrac{1}{2})[\cos(at + bt) - \cos(at - bt)]$$
$$= I \sin bt - \frac{Im}{2}\cos(a + b)t + \frac{Im}{2}\cos(a - b)t$$

931 Use one of the sum-to-product formulas to show that sin 55° + sin 5° = cos 25°.

Use VB(1) of Panel 8

$$\sin 55° + \sin 5° = 2[\sin \tfrac{1}{2}(55° + 5°)\cos \tfrac{1}{2}(55° - 5°)]$$
$$= 2(\sin 30° \cos 25°) = 2(\tfrac{1}{2}\cos 25°) = \cos 25°$$

932 Use one of the sum-to-product formulas to change the sum cos $(\pi/3)$ + cos $(\pi/2)$ to a product.

Use VB(3) of Panel 8

$$\cos \frac{\pi}{3} + \cos \frac{\pi}{2} = 2\left[\cos \frac{1}{2}\left(\frac{\pi}{3} + \frac{\pi}{2}\right)\cos \frac{1}{2}\left(\frac{\pi}{3} - \frac{\pi}{2}\right)\right]$$
$$= 2 \cos \frac{5\pi}{12} \cos \frac{-\pi}{12} = 2 \cos \frac{5\pi}{12} \cos \frac{\pi}{12}$$

933   Express the following difference as a product: $\sin 50° - \sin 12°$.

$$\sin 50° - \sin 12° = 2 \cos \tfrac{1}{2}(50° + 12°) \sin \tfrac{1}{2}(50° - 12°)$$
$$= 2 \cos 31° \sin 19°$$

934   Express the following difference as a product: $\cos 65° - \cos 55°$.

$$\cos 65° - \cos 55° = -2 \sin \tfrac{1}{2}(65° + 55°) \sin \tfrac{1}{2}(65° - 55°)$$
$$= -2 \sin 60° \sin 5° = -2\frac{\sqrt{3}}{2} \sin 5°$$
$$= -\sqrt{3} \sin 5°$$

935   Express the following sum as a product: $\sin 3x + \sin 7x$.

$$\sin 3x + \sin 7x = 2 \sin 5x \cos (-2x) = 2 \sin 5x \cos 2x$$

▽**936**   Change $\cos 165° - \cos 75°$ to a product and evaluate the result. Leave the result in simple radical form.

$$\cos 165° - \cos 75° = -2 \sin 120° \sin 45° = -2 \frac{\sqrt{3}}{2} \cdot \frac{\sqrt{2}}{2} = \frac{-\sqrt{6}}{2}$$

▽**937**   Change $2 \cos 45° \cos 15°$ to a sum (or difference) and evaluate the result. Leave the result in simple radical form.

$$2 \cos 45° \cos 15° = 2 \cdot \tfrac{1}{2}(\cos 60° + \cos 30°) = 1\left(\frac{1}{2} + \frac{\sqrt{3}}{2}\right)$$
$$= \frac{(1 + \sqrt{3})}{2}$$

938   Use the sum-to-product formulas to show that
$$\frac{\sin 80° + \sin 10°}{\cos 80° + \cos 10°} = 1$$

$$\frac{\sin 80° + \sin 10°}{\cos 80° + \cos 10°} = \frac{2 \sin \tfrac{1}{2}(80° + 10°) \cos \tfrac{1}{2}(80° - 10°)}{2 \cos \tfrac{1}{2}(80° + 10°) \cos \tfrac{1}{2}(80° - 10°)}$$
$$= \frac{2(\sqrt{2}/2) \cos 35°}{2(\sqrt{2}/2) \cos 35°} = 1$$

939   Express $\sin(\pi/9 + y) - \sin(\pi/9 - y)$ as a product.

$2 \cos \dfrac{\pi}{9} \sin y$ *Solution:* Use VA(2) or VB(2) in Panel 8.

940   Prove the identity $\dfrac{\sin 8\theta + \sin 2\theta}{\cos 8\theta + \cos 2\theta} = \tan 5\theta$

$\dfrac{\sin 8\theta + \sin 2\theta}{\cos 8\theta + \cos 2\theta} = \dfrac{2 \sin 5\theta \cos 3\theta}{2 \cos 5\theta \cos 3\theta} = \tan 5\theta$

941   Below is an example showing how to change the sum of four terms to a product. Supply reasons for Steps 3, 4, 5, and 6. Grouping the first two and last two terms and using VB(1) in Panel 8, we have

1. $\sin \theta + \sin 3\theta + \sin 5\theta + \sin 7\theta$

$= 2 \sin \left(\dfrac{\theta + 3\theta}{2}\right) \cos \left(\dfrac{\theta - 3\theta}{2}\right) + 2 \sin \left(\dfrac{5\theta + 7\theta}{2}\right) \cos \left(\dfrac{5\theta - 7\theta}{2}\right)$

2. $= 2 \sin 2\theta \cos(-\theta) + 2 \sin 6\theta \cos(-\theta)$ (See reasons below.)

3. $= 2(\sin 2\theta \cos \theta + \sin 6\theta \cos \theta)$

4. $= 2 \cos \theta(\sin 2\theta + \sin 6\theta)$

5. $= 2 \cos \theta[2 \sin 4\theta \cos(-2\theta)]$

6. $= 4 \cos \theta \sin 4\theta \cos 2\theta$

3. factoring, and $\cos(-\theta) = \cos \theta$
4. factoring
5. using VB(1) Panel 8
6. $\cos(-2\theta) = \cos 2\theta$

942   Prove the identity $\dfrac{\sin \theta + \sin 3\theta + \sin 5\theta}{\cos \theta + \cos 3\theta + \cos 5\theta} = \tan 3\theta$

1. Rearrange the terms thus: $\dfrac{(\sin \theta + \sin 5\theta) + \sin 3\theta}{(\cos \theta + \cos 5\theta) + \cos 3\theta}$

continued →

2. Use the sum-to-product formulas on the first two terms of the numerator and denominator.
3. Simplify.

$$\frac{\sin \theta + \sin 3\theta + \sin 5\theta}{\cos \theta + \cos 3\theta + \cos 5\theta} = \frac{(\sin \theta + \sin 5\theta) + \sin 3\theta}{(\cos \theta + \cos 5\theta) + \cos 3\theta}$$

$$= \frac{2 \sin 3\theta \cos (-2\theta) + \sin 3\theta}{2 \cos 3\theta \cos (-2\theta) + \cos 3\theta}$$

$$= \frac{2 \sin 3\theta \cos 2\theta + \sin 3\theta}{2 \cos 3\theta \cos 2\theta + \cos 3\theta}$$

$$= \frac{\sin 3\theta (2 \cos 2\theta + 1)}{\cos 3\theta (2 \cos 2\theta + 1)} = \tan 3\theta$$

▽ **943** Make use of the appropriate identities in Panel 8 to solve the problems on the following frames:

$$\frac{\sin 3\theta - \sin \theta}{\cos^2 \theta - \sin^2 \theta} = 2 \sin \theta$$

$$\frac{\sin 3\theta - \sin \theta}{\cos^2 \theta - \sin^2 \theta} = \frac{2 \cos 2\theta \sin \theta}{\cos 2\theta} = 2 \sin \theta$$

▽ **944** Prove that $\tan (x - \pi/4) + \cot (x + \pi/4) = 0.$

$$\tan \left(x - \frac{\pi}{4}\right) + \cot \left(x + \frac{\pi}{4}\right)$$

$$= \frac{\tan x - \tan (\pi/4)}{1 + \tan x \tan (\pi/4)} + \frac{1/[\tan x + \tan (\pi/4)]}{1 - \tan x \tan (\pi/4)}$$

$$= \frac{\tan x - 1}{1 + \tan x \cdot 1} + \frac{1/(\tan x + 1)}{1 - \tan x \cdot 1}$$

$$= \frac{\tan x - 1}{1 + \tan x} + \frac{1 - \tan x}{\tan x + 1} = 0$$

▽ **945** Prove $\dfrac{\cos 4x + \cos 3x + \cos 2x}{\sin 4x + \sin 3x + \sin 2x} = \cot 3x.$

$$\frac{\cos 4x + \cos 3x + \cos 2x}{\sin 4x + \sin 3x + \sin 2x} = \frac{(\cos 4x + \cos 2x) + \cos 3x}{(\sin 4x + \sin 2x) + \sin 3x}$$

$$= \frac{2 \cos 3x \cos x + \cos 3x}{2 \sin 3x \cos x + \sin 3x}$$

$$= \frac{\cos 3x (2 \cos x + 1)}{\sin 3x (2 \cos x + 1)} = \cot 3x$$

946 Prove $\sin (x + y) \sin (x - y) = \cos^2 y - \cos^2 x$. *Suggestion:* Work on the left member, using VA(4) in Panel 8 with $\alpha = x + y$ and $\beta = x - y$. Then use III(2) in Panel 8.

Let $x + y = \alpha$ and $x - y = \beta$, substitute in VA(4)

$\sin (x + y) \sin (x - y)$

$= -\tfrac{1}{2}[\cos (x + y + x - y) - \cos (x + y - x + y)]$

$= -\tfrac{1}{2}(\cos 2x - \cos 2y)$

$= -\tfrac{1}{2}[(2 \cos^2 x - 1) - (2 \cos^2 y - 1)]$

$= -\tfrac{1}{2}(2 \cos^2 x - 2 \cos^2 y) = -\cos^2 x + \cos^2 y$

947 Prove $\cos (x + y) \cos (x - y) = \cos^2 x - \sin^2 y$.

$\cos (x + y) \cos (x - y)$

$= \tfrac{1}{2}[\cos (x + y + x - y) + \cos (x + y - x + y)]$

$= \tfrac{1}{2}(\cos 2x + \cos 2y)$

$= \tfrac{1}{2}[(2 \cos^2 x - 1) + (1 - 2 \sin^2 y)]$

$= \tfrac{1}{2}(2 \cos^2 x - 1 + 1 - 2 \sin^2 y) = (\cos^2 x - \sin^2 y)$

948 Prove $\dfrac{\sin 3x}{\sin 2x} - \dfrac{\cos 3x}{\cos 2x} = \dfrac{2 \sin x}{\sin 4x}$

Suggestion: Work on the left member. Find a common denominator. Use II(1) in Panel 8, then III(1).

$$\dfrac{\sin 3x}{\sin 2x} - \dfrac{\cos 3x}{\cos 2x} = \dfrac{\sin 3x \cos 2x - \cos 3x \sin 2x}{\sin 2x \cos 2x}$$

$$= \dfrac{\sin (3x - 2x)}{\tfrac{1}{2} \cdot \sin 4x} = \dfrac{2 \sin x}{\sin 4x}$$

949 Prove $\dfrac{\cos 2x}{\sin 3x} - \dfrac{\sin 2x}{\cos 3x} = \dfrac{2 \cos 5x}{\sin 6x}$

$$\dfrac{\cos 2x}{\sin 3x} - \dfrac{\sin 2x}{\cos 3x} = \dfrac{\cos 3x \cos 2x - \sin 3x \sin 2x}{\sin 3x \cos 3x}$$

$$= \dfrac{\cos (3x + 2x)}{\tfrac{1}{2} \sin 6x} = \dfrac{2 \cos 5x}{\sin 6x}$$

950   Prove $\cos^4 \theta - \sin^4 \theta = \sin 4\theta / 2 \sin 2\theta$. *Suggestion:* Reduce both right and left members to a common form.

Working on the left member, we get
$$\cos^4 \theta - \sin^4 \theta = (\cos^2 \theta - \sin^2 \theta)(\cos^2 \theta + \sin^2 \theta)$$
$$= (\cos^2 \theta - \sin^2 \theta) \cdot 1 = \cos 2\theta$$

Working on the right member, we get
$$\frac{\sin 4\theta}{2 \sin 2\theta} = \frac{2 \sin 2\theta \cos 2\theta}{2 \sin 2\theta} = \cos 2\theta$$

Therefore, $\cos^4 \theta - \sin^4 \theta = \dfrac{\sin 4\theta}{2 \sin 2\theta}$

∇ **951**   Prove $\sin 2\theta = 2 \cot \theta / (1 + \cot^2 \theta)$.

Working on the right member
$$\frac{2 \cot \theta}{1 + \cot^2 \theta} = \frac{2 \cos \theta / \sin \theta}{\csc^2 \theta} = \frac{2 \cos \theta / \sin \theta}{1 / \sin^2 \theta}$$
$$= 2 \cos \theta \sin \theta = \sin 2\theta$$

∇ **952**   Prove $\sin x + \tan x = \sin x \tan x / \tan \frac{1}{2} x$. *Suggestion:* Use a substitution for $\tan \frac{1}{2} x$ which does not contain a radical.

Working on the right member
$$\frac{\sin x \tan x}{\tan \frac{1}{2} x} = \frac{\sin x \sin x / \cos x}{\sin x / (1 + \cos x)} = \frac{\sin^2 x}{\cos x} \cdot \frac{1 + \cos x}{\sin x}$$
$$= \frac{\sin x + \sin x \cos x}{\cos x} \left(= \frac{\sin x}{\cos x} + \sin x \right)$$
$$= \tan x + \sin x$$

953 Prove $\dfrac{\sin^3 x - \cos^3 x}{\sin x - \cos x} = \dfrac{2 + \sin 2x}{2}$

Suggestion: The factors of $\sin^3 x - \cos^3 x$ are $(\sin x - \cos x)$ $(\sin^2 x + \sin x \cos x + \cos^2 x)$.

$$\dfrac{\sin^3 x - \cos^3 x}{\sin x - \cos x} = \dfrac{(\sin x - \cos x)(\sin^2 x + \sin x \cos x + \cos^2 x)}{(\sin x - \cos x)}$$

$$= \dfrac{(\sin^2 x + \cos^2 x) + \sin x \cos x}{1}$$

$$= 1 + \sin x \cos x = 1 + \tfrac{1}{2}\sin 2x$$

$$= \dfrac{2 + \sin 2x}{2}$$

954 Prove $\dfrac{\cos 2\theta - \sin 2\theta}{\sin \theta \cos \theta} = \cot \theta - \tan \theta - 2$

This problem could be solved by reducing both left and right members to a common form, but notice the method used on the second line of the proof below.

$$\dfrac{\cos 2\theta - \sin 2\theta}{\sin \theta \cos \theta} = \dfrac{\cos^2 \theta - \sin^2 \theta - 2 \sin \theta \cos \theta}{\sin \theta \cos \theta}$$

$$= \dfrac{\cos^2 \theta}{\sin \theta \cos \theta} - \dfrac{\sin^2 \theta}{\sin \theta \cos \theta} - \dfrac{2 \sin \theta \cos \theta}{\sin \theta \cos \theta}$$

$$= \dfrac{\cos \theta}{\sin \theta} - \dfrac{\sin \theta}{\cos \theta} - 2 = \cot \theta - \tan \theta - 2$$

955 Prove $\dfrac{\sin (\theta + 300°) - \sin (\theta + 60°)}{\cos (\theta + 30°) + \cos (\theta - 30°)} = -1$

Suggestion: Use VB(2) and (3) in Panel 8.

$$\dfrac{\sin (\theta + 300°) - \sin (\theta + 60°)}{\cos (\theta + 30°) + \cos (\theta - 30°)} = \dfrac{2 \cos \tfrac{1}{2}(2\theta + 360°) \sin \tfrac{1}{2}(240°)}{2 \cos \tfrac{1}{2}(2\theta) \cos \tfrac{1}{2}(60°)}$$

$$= \dfrac{\cos (\theta + 180°) \sin 120°}{\cos \theta \cos 30°}$$

$$= \dfrac{(\cos \theta)(\sqrt{3}/2)}{(\cos \theta)(\sqrt{3}/2)} = -1$$

956   Prove $4 \sin 3x \cos 3x \sin x = \cos 5x - \cos 7x$. *Suggestion:*
Group the terms in the left member thus: $4 \sin x (\sin 3x \cos 3x)$
and use the proper identities from V in Panel 8.

$$
\begin{aligned}
4 \sin 3x \cos 3x \sin x &= 4 \sin x(\sin 3x \cos 3x) \\
&= 4 \sin x(\tfrac{1}{2} \sin 6x) \\
&= 2 \sin 6x \sin x \\
&= 2[-\tfrac{1}{2}(\cos 7x - \cos 5x)] \\
&= -\cos 7x + \cos 5x
\end{aligned}
$$

957   Prove $\dfrac{\sin \alpha - \sin \beta}{\sin \alpha + \sin \beta} = \dfrac{\tan \tfrac{1}{2}(\alpha - \beta)}{\tan \tfrac{1}{2}(\alpha + \beta)}$

$$
\begin{aligned}
\frac{\sin \alpha - \sin \beta}{\sin \alpha + \sin \beta} &= \frac{2 \cos \tfrac{1}{2}(\alpha + \beta) \sin \tfrac{1}{2}(\alpha - \beta)}{2 \sin \tfrac{1}{2}(\alpha + \beta) \cos \tfrac{1}{2}(\alpha - \beta)} \\
&= \cot \tfrac{1}{2}(\alpha + \beta) \tan \tfrac{1}{2}(\alpha - \beta) \\
&= \frac{1}{\tan \tfrac{1}{2}(\alpha + \beta)} \cdot \tan \tfrac{1}{2}(\alpha - \beta) \\
&= \frac{\tan \tfrac{1}{2}(\alpha - \beta)}{\tan \tfrac{1}{2}(\alpha + \beta)}
\end{aligned}
$$

Comment

An important application of the addition formulas is made when we
develop the identities for reductions such as functions of $(90° - \theta)$
to functions of θ. These will be reviewed now.

958   Recall the reduction formulas for $(90 - \theta)$. They are especially
useful when θ is an acute angle, but they are true for any angle
(providing the function is defined).
If $\sin 10°$ $= 0.174$, then $\cos (1)$ _____ $= 0.174$
If $\cos 22°$ $= 0.927$, then (2) _____ $68°$ $= 0.927$
If $\tan 35°$ $= 0.700$, then $\cot (3)$ _____ $= 0.700$
If $\sin 90°$ $= 1.000$, then $\cos (4)$ _____ $= 1.000$
If $\cos 135°$ $= -\dfrac{\sqrt{2}}{2}$, then (5) _____ $(90° - 135°) = -\dfrac{\sqrt{2}}{2}$

or (6) _____ $= -\dfrac{\sqrt{2}}{2}$

(1) $80°$ (2) $\sin$ (3) $55°$
(4) 0 (5) $\sin$ (6) $\sin(-45)$

959 Consult Panel 1 for numerical values when necessary.

(1) sin 14°   = (a)_____ = cos (b)_____
(2) cos 40°   = (a)_____ = sin (b)_____
(3) sin 80°   = (a)_____ = cos (b)_____
(4) cos (a)_____ = 0.970   = sin (b)_____
(5) Does sin 240° = cos (90° - 240°)?
(6) Does sin 270° = cos (90° - 270°)?

(1)(a) 0.242, (b) 76°   (2)(a) 0.766 (b) 50°
(3)(a) 0.985, (b) 10°   (4)(a) 14°   (b) 76°
(5) yes   (6) yes
Note: sin θ = cos (90° - θ) for any θ.

960 Reduce the following functions of (90° + θ) to functions of θ by
means of the addition formulas: sin (90° + θ) = (1)_____,
cos (90° + θ) = (2)_____, and tan (90° + θ) = (3)_____.
You may be able to write the above identities without going through
all the steps each time. Remember that you can establish each of
them by means of the addition formulas.

(1) cos θ (2) - sin θ (3) - cot θ
Verification that cos (90° + θ) = - sin θ:

cos (90° + θ) = cos 90° cos θ - sin 90° sin θ

= 0 · cos θ - 1 · sin θ = - sin θ

961 If you know the numerical values of the trigonometric functions of θ
when θ = 80°, then the identities in frame 960 tell you how to find
the functions of _____ . (Give a numerical answer.)

90° + 80° = 170°

962 Reduce the following functions of (180° - θ) to functions of θ by
means of the addition formulas: sin (180° - θ) = (1)_____,
cos (180° - θ) = (2)_____, and tan (180° - θ) = (3)_____.

(1) sin θ (2) - cos θ (3) - tan θ
Verification that tan (180° - θ) = - tan θ:

$$\tan (180° - \theta) = \frac{\tan 180° - \tan \theta}{1 + \tan 180° \tan \theta}$$

$$= \frac{0 - \tan \theta}{1 + 0 \cdot \tan \theta} = - \tan \theta$$

963 If $\theta = 30°$, (a) express the following in terms of functions of 30° and (b) evaluate your answer:
(1) sin (180° - θ) = (a) _____ = (b) _____
(2) cos (180° - θ) = (a) _____ = (b) _____
(3) tan (180° - θ) = (a) _____ = (b) _____

(1)(a) sin 30°, (b) $\frac{1}{2}$ (2)(a) - cos 30°, (b) $\frac{-\sqrt{3}}{2}$

(3)(a) - tan 30°, (b) $\frac{-\sqrt{3}}{3}$

964 If $\theta = 70°$, (a) express the following in terms of functions of 70°; (b) refer to Panel 1 to evaluate:
(1) sin (180° - θ) = (a) _____ = (b) _____
(2) cos (180° - θ) = (a) _____ = (b) _____
(3) tan (180° - θ) = (a) _____ = (b) _____

(1)(a) sin 70°, (b) 0.940 (2)(a) - cos 70°, (b) - 0.342
(3)(a) - tan 70°, (b) 2.747

965 Given cos 40° = 0.766 and sin 40° = 0.643. (1) What is the cos (180° - 40°)? (2) What is the cos (90° - 40°)?

(1) cos (180° - 40°) = - 0.766   (2) cos (90° - 40°) = 0.643

▽ **966** Given sin θ = 0.914 and cos θ = 0.407. Fill in the table below.

	90° - θ	90° + θ	180° - θ
sin	0.407		
cos	0.914		

	90° - θ	90° + θ	180° - θ
sin	0.407	0.407	0.914
cos	0.914	- 0.914	- 0.407

967 Reduce the following functions of $(180° + \theta)$ to functions of θ by means of the addition formulas: $\sin(180° + \theta) = $ (1)_____, $\cos(180° + \theta) = $ (2)_____, and $\tan(180° + \theta) = $ (3)_____.

(1) $-\sin\theta$ (2) $-\cos\theta$ (3) $\tan\theta$
Verification that $\sin(180° + \theta) = -\sin\theta$:

$$\sin(180° + \theta) = \sin 180° \cos\theta + \cos 180° \sin\theta$$
$$= 0 \cdot \cos\theta + (-1)\sin\theta = -\sin\theta$$

968 Reduce the following functions of $(270° - \theta)$ to functions of θ by means of the addition formulas: $\sin(270° - \theta) = $ (1)_____, $\cos(270° - \theta) = $ (2)_____, and $\tan(270° - \theta) = $ (3)_____.

(1) $-\cos\theta$ (2) $-\sin\theta$ (3) $\cot\theta$

969 Which of the following are identities?

$\sin(270° + \theta) = \cos\theta$ $\sin(270° + \theta) = \sin\theta$
$\sin(270° + \theta) = -\cos\theta$ $\sin(270° + \theta) = -\sin\theta$

$\sin(270° + \theta) = -\cos\theta$

970 Prove that $\cos(270° + \theta) = \sin\theta$.

$$\cos(270° + \theta) = \cos 270° \cos\theta - \sin 270° \sin\theta$$
$$= 0 \cdot \cos\theta - (-1)\sin\theta = \sin\theta$$

971 Prove that $\tan(270° + \theta) = -\cot\theta$.

$$\tan(270° + \theta) = \frac{\sin(270° + \theta)}{\cos(270° + \theta)} = \frac{-\cos\theta}{+\sin\theta} = -\cot\theta$$

▽972 Check the accuracy of the following. Indicate which, if any, are not true. Let $\theta = 210°$, then
1. $\sin(90° - 210°) = \cos 210°$
2. $\sin(90° + 210°) = \cos 210°$
3. $\sin(180° - 210°) = \cos 210°$
4. $\sin(180° + 210°) = \cos 210°$
5. $\sin(270° - 210°) = \cos 210°$
6. $\sin(270° + 210°) = \cos 210°$

the following are false: 3, 4, 5, 6

973 Reduce the following functions of $(360° - \theta)$ to functions of θ by means of the addition formulas: $\sin(360° - \theta) = $ (1)_____, $\cos(360° - \theta) = $ (2)_____, and $\tan(360° - \theta) = $ (3)_____.

> **(1)** $-\sin\theta$ **(2)** $\cos\theta$ **(3)** $-\tan\theta$

974 Reduce the following functions of $-\theta$ to functions of θ by means of the addition formulas: $\sin(-\theta) = $ (1)_____, $\cos(-\theta) = $ (2)_____, and $\tan(-\theta) = $ (3)_____.

Let $\alpha = 0$ and $\beta = \theta$ in the formula

$$\sin(\alpha - \beta) = \sin\alpha\cos\beta - \cos\alpha\sin\beta$$

and simplify.

> **(1)** $-\sin\theta$ **(2)** $\cos\theta$ **(3)** $-\tan\theta$
> Verification for (1):
>
> $$\sin(0 - \theta) = \sin 0\cos\theta - \cos 0\sin\theta$$
> $$= 0\cdot\cos\theta - 1\sin\theta = -\sin\theta$$

975 Prove $\sin(\pi - A - B) = \sin A\cos B + \cos A\sin B$.
Arrange the terms as shown below and use the correct reduction formula thus:

$$\sin(\pi - A - B) = \sin[\pi - (A + B)] = \sin((1)\underline{\hspace{3cm}})$$
$$= (2)\underline{\hspace{3cm}}$$

> **(1)** $A + B$ **(2)** $\sin A\cos B + \cos A\sin B$
> *Solution:* Let $(A + B) = x$, then
>
> $$\sin[\pi - (A - B)] = \sin(\pi - x) = \sin\pi\cos x - \cos\pi\sin x$$
> $$= 0\cdot\cos x - (-1)\sin x = \sin x$$
>
> But $A + B = x$; therefore,
>
> $$\sin[\pi - (A + B)] = \sin(A + B) = \sin A\cos B + \cos A\sin B$$

976 Prove $\cos(\pi/2 + A - B) = \cos A\sin B - \sin A\cos B$.

> $$\cos\left(\frac{\pi}{2} + A - B\right) = \cos\left[\frac{\pi}{2} + (A - B)\right] = -\sin(A - B)$$
> $$= -(\sin A\cos B - \cos A\sin B)$$
> $$= \cos A\sin B - \sin A\cos B$$

▽977 Prove $\cos (\pi + A - B) = -\cos A \cos B - \sin A \sin B$.

$$\cos (\pi + A - B) = \cos [\pi + (A - B)] = -\cos (A - B)$$
$$= -(\cos A \cos B + \sin A \sin B)$$
$$= -\cos A \cos B - \sin A \sin B$$

978 Prove $\tan (45° + \theta) = (\cos \theta + \sin \theta)/(\cos \theta - \sin \theta)$. Work on the left member, using the identity $\tan \alpha = \sin \alpha /\cos \alpha$.

$$\tan (45° + \theta) = \frac{\sin (45° + \theta)}{\cos (45° + \theta)} = \frac{\sin 45° \cos \theta + \cos 45° \sin \theta}{\cos 45° \cos \theta - \sin 45° \sin \theta}$$
$$= \frac{(\sqrt{2}/2) \cos \theta + (\sqrt{2}/2) \sin \theta}{(\sqrt{2}/2) \cos \theta - (\sqrt{2}/2) \sin \theta}$$
$$= \frac{(\sqrt{2}/2)(\cos \theta + \sin \theta)}{(\sqrt{2}/2)(\cos \theta - \sin \theta)}$$

979 Reduce each of the following to the function of an angle less than 90°: $\sin 162° = (1)$_____, $\cos 345° = (2)$_____, and $\tan (7\pi/6) = (3)$_____. Check your result with a sketch.

(1) $\sin (180° - 162°) = \sin 18°$ or $\cos 72°$
(2) $\cos (360° - 345°) = \cos 15°$ or $\sin 75°$
(3) $\tan \left(\pi + \dfrac{\pi}{6}\right) = \tan \dfrac{\pi}{6}$ or $\cot \dfrac{\pi}{3}$

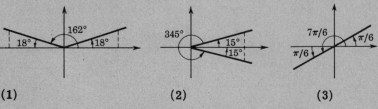

(1)   (2)   (3)

980 Reduce each of the following to the function of a positive angle less than 90°: $\sin (-18°) = (1)$_____, $\cos (-40°) = (2)$_____, and $\tan (-145°) = (3)$_____.

(1) $-\sin 18°$ (2) $\cos 40°$ (3) $\tan 35°$

UNIT 3 | Trigonometric Equations

981 Recall the difference between a trigonometric equation and an identity. A relationship which holds for some, but not all, of the permissible values of the quantities involved is a(n) **(1)**_____. A relationship which holds for all permissible values of the quantities involved is a(n) **(2)**_____.

> **(1)** equation (conditional equation) **(2)** identity

982 To solve a trigonometric equation means to find all the values of the variable which satisfy the equation (make a true statement when substituted into the equation). The general procedure for finding the solution is to use algebraic methods already familiar to you and to make substitutions from identities. We shall start with the simplest type of equation, the one in which a function is equal to a constant. Examples are $\sin x = \frac{1}{2}$, $\cos \theta = \sqrt{3}/2$, and $\tan \alpha = -1$. You know that in the interval from 0 to $360°$, if $\sin x = \frac{1}{2}$, then $x = $ **(1)**___$°$ or **(2)**___$°$.

> **(1)** 30 **(2)** 150

983 From frame 982 you have two values $x = 30°$ and $x = 150°$ satisfying the condition $\sin x = \frac{1}{2}$. Any angle coterminal with $30°$ (or $150°$) also satisfies the condition $\sin x = \frac{1}{2}$. What are two other values that x may have?

> $x = 390°$ and $x = 510°$ or $x = (30° \pm n \cdot 360°)$ and $x = (150° \pm n \cdot 360)$ where n is an integer

Comment

In solving trigonometric equations, we often limit the number of solutions to values of the variable in the range 0 to 2π (0 to 360°). However, you should remember that if the equation has at least one solution in the range 0 to 2π, then it actually has many solutions when the range is unlimited, since any angle coterminal with this one will also be a solution.

984 If $\sin x = 1/\sqrt{2}$, then $x = \pi/4$ or $3\pi/4$ or any angle coterminal with $\pi/4$ or $3\pi/4$. (1) Name two angles coterminal with $\pi/4$. (2) Name two angles coterminal with $3\pi/4$.

(1) Possible answers are

$$\frac{\pi}{4} + 2\pi = \frac{9\pi}{4}, \frac{\pi}{4} + 4\pi = \frac{17\pi}{4}$$

$$\frac{\pi}{4} - 2\pi = \frac{-7\pi}{4} \ (405°, 765°, -315°)$$

(2) Possible answers are

$$\frac{3\pi}{4} + 2\pi = \frac{11\pi}{4}, \frac{3\pi}{4} + 4\pi = \frac{19\pi}{4}$$

$$\frac{3\pi}{4} - 2\pi = \frac{-5\pi}{4} \ (495°, 855°, -225°)$$

985 Look at the answers for (1) in frame 984. The set of all numbers of the form $\pi/4$, $\pi/4 + 2\pi$, $\pi/4 + 4\pi$, $\pi/4 - 2\pi$, etc., can be written thus: $\pi/4 + 2\pi n$, where n is an integer.
If $n = \ \ 0$, then $\pi/4 + 2\pi n = $ **(1)**_____
If $n = \ \ 1$, then $\pi/4 + 2\pi n = $ **(2)**_____
If $n = \ \ 2$, then $\pi/4 + 2\pi n = $ **(3)**_____
If $n = -1$, then $\pi/4 + 2\pi n = $ **(4)**_____

(1) $\frac{\pi}{4}$ **(2)** $\frac{\pi}{4} + 2\pi$ or $\frac{9\pi}{4}$

(3) $\frac{\pi}{4} + 4\pi$ or $\frac{17\pi}{4}$ **(4)** $\frac{\pi}{4} - 2\pi$ or $-\frac{7\pi}{4}$

986 Here are some answers to the solution for $\sin x = \frac{1}{2}$ (frame 984, question (2)): $3\pi/4$, $3\pi/4 + 2\pi$, $3\pi/4 + 4\pi$, $3\pi/4 - 2\pi$, etc. Make a general statement in terms of n for all numbers of this type.

$\frac{3\pi}{4} + 2\pi n$, where n is an integer

987 A sketch showing the possible solutions to an equation is often an advantage in deciding the general form. Suppose we wish to find all solutions to the equation sin x = $-\frac{1}{2}$. The sketch shows two solutions. Express each of these as an angle in radians. The general form will be discussed in frame 988.

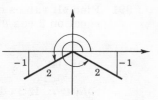

$$\frac{7\pi}{6}, \quad \frac{11\pi}{6}$$

988 Refer to frame 987. The sine of any angle coterminal with $7\pi/6$ or $11\pi/6$ also has a numerical value of $-\frac{1}{2}$. Therefore any multiple of 2π added to $7\pi/6$ or $11\pi/6$ is a solution for the equation sin x = $-\frac{1}{2}$. We write these two answers in the general form as follows: Adding $2\pi n$ to $7\pi/6$, we have $7\pi/6 + 2\pi n$. Adding $2\pi n$ to $11\pi/6$, we have _____, where n is any integer.

$$\frac{11\pi}{6} + 2\pi n$$

989 Find all values of x in the interval $0 \leq x < 2\pi$ which satisfy the equation tan x = 1.

$$\frac{\pi}{4}, \quad \frac{5\pi}{4}$$

990 Refer to frame 989. Write the general form which gives *all* angles satisfying the equation tan x = 1. The sketch shows three of the many angles.

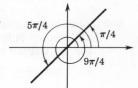

$\frac{\pi}{4} + n\pi$, where n is an integer

Note: These angles differ by π radians, so that instead of writing the two forms $\pi/4 + 2n\pi$ and $5\pi/4 + 2n\pi$, we can give the simpler answer shown above.

991   Find all values of θ in the interval $0 \le \theta < 2\pi$ which satisfy the equation $2 \cos \theta - 1 = 0$.

$\dfrac{\pi}{3}$ or $60°$, $\dfrac{5\pi}{3}$ or $300°$

Solution: If $2 \cos \theta - 1 = 0$, then $\cos \theta = \frac{1}{2}$ and $\theta = \dfrac{\pi}{3}$, $\dfrac{5\pi}{3}$

992   Refer to frame 991. Write the general forms for the solutions to the equation $2 \cos \theta - 1 = 0$.

$\dfrac{\pi}{3} + 2n\pi$, $\dfrac{5\pi}{3} + 2n\pi$, where n is an integer

▽993   (1) Solve the following equation for all values of x in the interval $0 \le x < 2\pi$: $2 \sin x = \sqrt{3}$. (2) Write the general forms for your solutions showing *all* values of x which satisfy the equation in (1).

(1) $\dfrac{\pi}{3}$, $\dfrac{2\pi}{3}$ (2) $\dfrac{\pi}{3} + 2n\pi$, $\dfrac{2\pi}{3} + 2n\pi$

994   (1) Find all values of x satisfying the equation $\tan x - \sqrt{3} = 0$. First give the angles in the interval $0 \le x < 2\pi$ and (2) then the general form.

(1) $\dfrac{\pi}{3}$, $\dfrac{4\pi}{3}$ (2) $\dfrac{\pi}{3} + n\pi$

995   The first three steps in the solution of the equation $4 \sin^2 \theta - 3 = 0$ are shown below. Study them carefully, then complete the solution for all values of   in the interval $0 \le \theta < 2\pi$.

1. $4 \sin^2 \theta = 3$ rearranging terms

2. $\sin^2 \theta = \frac{3}{4}$ dividing by 4

3. $\sin \theta = \dfrac{\sqrt{3}}{2}$, $\sin \theta = \dfrac{-\sqrt{3}}{2}$ taking the square root of both members

If $\sin \theta = \dfrac{\sqrt{3}}{2}$, $\theta = $ (1)_____, (2)_____.

If $\sin \theta = \dfrac{-\sqrt{3}}{2}$, $\theta = $ (3)_____, (4)

(1) $\dfrac{\pi}{3}$ (2) $\dfrac{2\pi}{3}$ (3) $\dfrac{4\pi}{3}$ (4) $\dfrac{5\pi}{3}$

996 To be sure that the values of θ you have obtained do satisfy the original equation, you should check by substitution. From frame 995, $\pi/3$ was one value of θ. When it is substituted in $4\sin^2\theta - 3 = 0$, we get

$$4\sin^2\frac{\pi}{3} - 3 \stackrel{?}{=} 0$$

$$4\left(\frac{\sqrt{3}}{2}\right)^2 - 3 \stackrel{?}{=} 0 \left.\begin{array}{c} \\ \\ \\ \end{array}\right\}$$ The question marks indicate what we are attempting to check.

$$4 \cdot \frac{3}{4} - 3 \stackrel{?}{=} 0$$

$$3 - 3 = 0$$

Write out the check showing that $4\pi/3$ satisfies the original equation.

$4\sin^2\dfrac{4\pi}{3} - 3 \stackrel{?}{=} 0, \ 4\left(\dfrac{-\sqrt{3}}{2}\right)^2 - 3 \stackrel{?}{=} 0, \ 4\cdot\dfrac{3}{4} - 3 \stackrel{?}{=} 0, \ 3 - 3 = 0$

997 Find all values of x satisfying the equation $\sin^2 x = 4$.

there are none. *Note:* If $\sin^2 x = 4$, $\sin x = \pm 2$, but $\sin x$ is never greater than 1 nor less than -1.

998 Solve the following equation for all values of θ, $0 \le \theta < 360°$: $4\sin^2\theta = 1$.

$\dfrac{\pi}{6}, \ \dfrac{5\pi}{6}, \ \dfrac{7\pi}{6}, \ \dfrac{11\pi}{6}$

Solution: $4\sin^2\theta = 1$, $\sin^2\theta = \frac{1}{4}$, $\sin\theta = \frac{1}{2}$ or $\sin\theta = -\frac{1}{2}$

If $\sin\theta = \frac{1}{2}$, then $\theta = \dfrac{\pi}{6}, \dfrac{5\pi}{6}$. If $\sin\theta = -\frac{1}{2}$, then $\theta = \dfrac{7\pi}{6}, \dfrac{11\pi}{6}$.

Note: There is an angle in each quadrant, since $\sin\theta = \pm\frac{1}{2}$.

999   Refer to frame 998. Make a general statement for *all* values of θ which satisfy the equation $4 \sin^2 \theta = 1$. A sketch may help you.

$\dfrac{\pi}{6} + n\pi$ The sketch indicates that these angles differ by π radians.

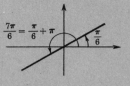

$\dfrac{5\pi}{6} + n\pi$ The sketch indicates how much is added each time.

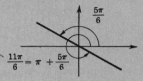

1000   Find *all* values of θ for which the following equation is true: $\sin^2 \theta - 1 = 0$. *Note:* After you have found the values of θ between 0 and 2π go on to frame 1001.

$\dfrac{\pi}{2}, \dfrac{3\pi}{2}$

Solution: $\sin^2 \theta - 1 = 0$, $\sin^2 \theta = 1$, $\sin \theta = 1$ or $\sin \theta = -1$

Therefore, $\theta = \dfrac{\pi}{2}$ or $\theta = \dfrac{3\pi}{2}$

1001   In frame 1000 we found that when $\sin^2 \theta - 1 = 0$, then $\theta = \pi/2$ or $\theta = 3\pi/2$. Write the general form for *all* angles satisfying the equation above.

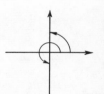

$\dfrac{\pi}{2} + n\pi$, where n is an integer

1002   Let $n = 3$, check that $\theta = (\pi/2 + n\pi)$ satisfies the equation $\sin^2 \theta - 1 = 0$.

$\sin^2 \left(\dfrac{\pi}{2} + 3\pi \right) - 1 \overset{?}{=} 0$, $(-1)^2 - 1 \overset{?}{=} 0$, $1 - 1 = 0$

1003 Find all values of x for which the following equation is true: $\tan^2 x - 3 = 0$.

> $\tan^2 x - 3 = 0$, $\tan^2 x = 3$, $\tan x = \sqrt{3}$ or $\tan x = -\sqrt{3}$
>
> Between 0 and 2π the values of x are
>
> $$x = \frac{\pi}{3}, \frac{4\pi}{3} \text{ or } x = \frac{2\pi}{3}, \frac{5\pi}{3}$$
>
> Therefore, $x = \frac{\pi}{3} + \pi n$ or $\frac{2\pi}{3} + \pi n$ where n is an integer

1004 Solve for all values of x: $4 \cos x = 8 - 2(\cos x + 1)$.

> *Solution:* $4 \cos x = 8 - 2(\cos x + 1)$, $4 \cos x = 8 - 2 \cos x - 2$,
>
> $6 \cos x = 6$, $\cos x = 1$, $x = 0$
>
> General form: $0 + 2n = 2n$

1005 Recall from algebra that certain equations are solved by transforming the equation so that one member is zero. The other member is factored and the solution is completed by setting each factor equal to zero, then finding the roots of the simpler equations. This method is used on the trigonometric equation below. Study it and complete the solution.

Given $2 \sin \theta \tan \theta = \sqrt{3} \tan \theta$, find values of θ between 0 and 2π.

Solution:
1. $2 \sin \theta \tan \theta - \sqrt{3} \tan \theta = 0$
2. $\tan \theta (2 \sin \theta - \sqrt{3}) = 0$
3. $\tan \theta = 0$, or $2 \sin \theta - \sqrt{3} = 0$
4. $\theta = (1)\underline{\hspace{1cm}}$, $(2)\underline{\hspace{1cm}}$ or $\sin \theta = \frac{\sqrt{3}}{2}$, $\theta = (3)\underline{\hspace{1cm}}$, $(4)\underline{\hspace{1cm}}$

> (1) 0   (2) π (3) $\frac{\pi}{3}$ (4) $\frac{2\pi}{3}$

1006 Find values for θ, $0 \le \theta < 2\pi$, for which the following equation is true: $\tan \theta \sin \theta + \tan \theta = 0$. Keep your work for frame 1007. These answers will be checked.

> $0, \pi, \frac{3\pi}{2}$ *Solution:* $\tan \theta (\sin \theta + 1) = 0$
>
> If $\tan \theta = 0$, then $\theta = 0$, π
>
> If $\sin \theta = -1$, then $\theta = \frac{3\pi}{2}$

1007 Which of the values for θ (0, π, and $3\pi/2$) do not check in the equation tan θ sin θ + tan θ = 0. Keep your work for frame 1008.

$\dfrac{3\pi}{2}$ does not check

Check 0: tan 0 sin 0 + tan 0 $\overset{?}{=}$ 0, 0 · 0 + 0 = 0

Check π: tan π sin π + tan π $\overset{?}{=}$ 0, 0 · 0 + 0 = 0

Check $\dfrac{3\pi}{2}$: tan $\dfrac{3\pi}{2}$ sin $\dfrac{3\pi}{2}$ + tan $\dfrac{3\pi}{2}$ $\overset{?}{=}$ 0

It does not check since tan $\dfrac{3\pi}{2}$ is undefined.

1008 Find the general form for the values of θ which satisfy the equation in frame 1007.

$\theta = (0 + \pi n)$, where n is an integer

1009 Solve for all values of θ: $\cos^2 \theta - 3 \cos \theta = 0$.

$\dfrac{\pi}{2}, \dfrac{3\pi}{2}$

$$\cos^2 \theta - 3 \cos \theta = 0, \cos \theta (\cos \theta - 3) = 0$$

If cos θ = 0, then $\theta = \dfrac{\pi}{2}, \dfrac{3\pi}{2}$

If cos θ = 3, there are no values of θ for which cos θ = 3 is true.

General form: $= \dfrac{\pi}{2} + \pi n$

▽ **1010** Solve for values of θ between 0 and 2π: $2 \cos^2 \theta - \sqrt{3} \cos \theta = 0$.

$\dfrac{\pi}{2}, \dfrac{3\pi}{2}, \dfrac{\pi}{6}, \dfrac{11\pi}{6}$

$$\cos \theta (2 \cos \theta - \sqrt{3}) = 0$$

If cos θ = 0, then $\theta = \dfrac{\pi}{2}, \dfrac{3\pi}{2}$

If 2 cos θ = $\sqrt{3}$ and cos θ = $\dfrac{\sqrt{3}}{2}$, then $\theta = \dfrac{\pi}{6}, \dfrac{11\pi}{6}$

1011 Solve for values of x, $0 \leq x < 360°$: $2 \tan^2 \theta - \tan \theta = 0$. Use Panel 1 for an approximate answer.

0, $180°$, $27°$, $207°$

Solution: $2 \tan^2 \theta - \tan \theta = 0$, $\tan \theta (2 \tan \theta + 1) = 0$

If $\tan \theta = 0$, then $\theta = 0°$, $180°$

If $2 \tan \theta - 1 = 0$ and $\tan \theta = \frac{1}{2}$, then $\theta \approx 27°$, $207°$

1012 Solve for values of x in the interval $0 \leq x < 2\pi$: $4 \sin^3 x - \sin x = 0$.

0, π, $\dfrac{\pi}{6}$, $\dfrac{5\pi}{6}$, $\dfrac{7\pi}{6}$, $\dfrac{11\pi}{6}$ (0, $180°$, $30°$, $150°$, $210°$, $330°$)

Solution: $4 \sin^3 x - \sin x = 0$, $\sin x (4 \sin^2 x - 1) = 0$

If $\sin x = 0$, then $x = 0, \pi$

If $4 \sin^2 x - 1 = 0$, $\sin^2 x = \frac{1}{4}$, and $\sin x = \pm\frac{1}{2}$,

then $x = \dfrac{\pi}{6}$, $\dfrac{5\pi}{6}$, $\dfrac{7\pi}{6}$, $\dfrac{11\pi}{6}$

1013 Solve for values of θ in the interval $0 \leq \theta < 2\pi$: $2 \sin \theta \cos \theta + \sin \theta = 0$.

0, π, $\dfrac{2\pi}{3}$, $\dfrac{4\pi}{3}$ (0, $180°$, $120°$, $240°$)

1014 Solve for values of x between 0 and 2π: $2 \cos^2 x + 5 \cos x + 2 = 0$. *Suggestion:* Factor the left member as the product of two binomials. This problem will be continued in frame 1015.

$\dfrac{2\pi}{3}$, $\dfrac{4\pi}{3}$

$2 \cos^2 x + 5 \cos x + 2 = 0$, $(2 \cos x + 1)(\cos x + 2) = 0$

If $\cos x = -\frac{1}{2}$, then $x = \dfrac{2\pi}{3}$, $\dfrac{4\pi}{3}$

If $\cos x = -2$, there is no solution for $\cos x = -2$, since the value of the cosine is never less than -1.

1015 Check the two answers from frame 1014 $2\pi/3$ and $4\pi/3$ in the equation $2 \cos^2 x + 5 \cos x + 2 = 0$.

Check $\dfrac{2\pi}{3}$: $2 \cos^2 \dfrac{2\pi}{3} + 5 \cos \dfrac{2\pi}{3} + 2 = 2(-\tfrac{1}{2})^2 + 5(-\tfrac{1}{2}) + 2 = 0$

Check $\dfrac{4\pi}{3}$: $2 \cos^2 \dfrac{4\pi}{3} + 5 \cos \dfrac{5\pi}{3} + 2 = 2(-\tfrac{1}{2})^2 + 5(-\tfrac{1}{2}) + 2 = 0$

1016 Solve for values of x between 0 and 2π: $2 \sin^2 x - 5 \sin x + 2 = 0$.

$\dfrac{\pi}{6}$, $\dfrac{5\pi}{6}$

▽**1017** Solve for values of x between 0 and 360°: $4 \sin^2 x + 3 \sin x = 1$. You will be asked to write the check in frame 1018.

14.5°, 165.5°, 270°

Solution: $4 \sin^2 x + 3 \sin x = 1, (4 \sin x - 1)(\sin x + 1) = 0$

If $\sin x = \tfrac{1}{4}$, then from Panel 1, $x \approx 14.5°, 165.5°$

If $\sin x = -1$, then $x = 270°$

1018 Check all three of the answers in frame 1017 for the equation $4 \sin^2 x + 3 \sin x = 1$.

Check   14.5°: $4 \sin^2 (14.5°) + 3 \sin 14.5° = 4(\tfrac{1}{4})^2 + 3(\tfrac{1}{4}) = 1$

Check 165.5°: $4 \sin^2 (165.5) + 3 \sin 165.5° = 4(\tfrac{1}{4})^2 + 3(\tfrac{1}{4}) = 1$

Check 270°   : $4 \sin^2 (270°) + 3 \sin 270° = 4(-1)^2 + 3(-1) = 1$

1019 Solve for all values of x, $0 \le x < 360°$: $3 \tan^2 x + 2 \tan x = 3$
Note: Recall the quadratic formula

$$x = \frac{-b \pm \sqrt{b^2 - 4ac}}{2a}$$

which you used to solve an equation of the form $ax^2 + bx + c = 0$ when you were unable to use the factoring method. See frame 1020 for a discussion on checking this problem.

36°, 216°, 126°, 306°

continued →

Solution: $3 \tan^2 x + 2 \tan x = 3$. Substituting in the quadratic formula:

$$\tan x = \frac{-2 \pm \sqrt{4 + 36}}{6} = \frac{-2 \pm 2\sqrt{10}}{6} = \frac{-1 \pm \sqrt{10}}{3}$$

$$= \frac{-1 \pm 3.162}{3} = 0.721 \quad x \approx 36°, 216°$$

$$\text{or} \quad = -1.387 \quad x \approx 126°, 306°$$

1020 Since the solutions to the equation $3 \tan^2 x + 2 \tan x = 3$ were not exact numbers, the check will be approximate, but you can judge whether certain apparent roots must be rejected because they do not satisfy the given equation. Check the answer $x \approx 36°$ in the equation $3 \tan^2 x + 2 \tan x = 3$.

$3 \tan^2 36° + 2 \tan x \overset{?}{=} 3$, $3(0.721)^2 + 2(0.721) \overset{?}{=} 3$,

$1.560 + 1.442 \approx 3$

1021 Solve for all values of x in the interval $0 \le x < 360°$: $3 \cos^2 x - 7 \cos x = 6$. Although we shall not call for a check on each problem, a complete solution would include a check on each answer.

$132°, 228°$

Solution: $3 \cos^2 x - 7 \cos x - 6 = 0$, $(3 \cos x + 2)(\cos x - 3) = 0$

If $\cos x = \frac{-2}{3}$, then $x \approx 132°, 228°$

If $\cos x = 3$, there is no solution for $\cos x = 3$.

1022 Solve for values of x in the interval $0 \le x < 360°$: $\tan^2 x + \tan x + 1 = 0$. Use the quadratic formula.

this equation has no real solution. Using the quadratic formula, we get

$$\tan x = \frac{-1 \pm \sqrt{1 - 4}}{2} = \frac{-1 \pm \sqrt{-3}}{2}$$

This indicates that the roots of this equation are complex numbers.

▽ 1023   Solve for all values of x in the interval $0 \leq x < 360°$:
$\sin^2 x + 5 \sin x + 2 = 0$.

206°, 334°

Solution: Using the quadratic formula, we get

$$\sin x = \frac{-5 \pm \sqrt{25 - 8}}{2} = \frac{-5 \pm \sqrt{17}}{2} \approx \frac{-5 \pm 4.123}{2}$$

$$\approx -0.439 \text{ or } -4.562$$

If $\sin x \approx -0.439$, then $x \approx 206°, 334°$

If $\sin x \approx -4.562$, there is no solution

1024   Below is shown a solution where you substitute from one of the trigonometric identities to reduce the equation to a factorable form. Complete the solution for values of x in the interval $0 \leq x < 360°$

$\sin 2x - \cos x = 0$

$2 \sin x \cos x - \cos x = 0$ $\left\{ \begin{array}{l} \text{substituting } 2 \sin x \cos x \\ \text{for } \sin 2x, \text{ see} \\ \text{Panel 8III(1).} \end{array} \right.$

90°, 270°, 30°, 150°

Solution: $\cos x (2 \sin x - 1) = 0$

If $\cos x = 0$, then $x = 90°, 270°$

If $2 \sin x - 1 = 0$ and $\sin x = \frac{1}{2}$, then $x = 30°, 150°$

1025   Check the four values for x, 90°, 270°, 30°, 150°, in the equation $\sin 2x - \cos x = 0$.

Check $x = 90°$: $\sin 2(90°) - \cos 90° = 0 - 0 = 0$

Check $x = 270°$: $\sin 2(270°) - \cos 270° = 0 - 0 = 0$

Check $x = 30°$: $\sin 2(30°) - \cos 30° = \dfrac{\sqrt{3}}{2} - \dfrac{\sqrt{3}}{2} = 0$

Check $x = 150°$: $\sin 2(150°) - \cos 150° = \dfrac{-\sqrt{3}}{2} - \left(\dfrac{-\sqrt{3}}{2} \right) = 0$

1026 Solve for values of x between 0 and 360°: $\cos 2x = \sin x$.

30°, 150°, 270°

Solution: Substitute $1 - 2 \sin^2 x$ for $\cos 2x$

$1 - 2 \sin^2 x = \sin x, 2 \sin^2 x + \sin x - 1 = 0,$

$(2 \sin x - 1)(\sin x + 1) = 0$

If $\sin x = \frac{1}{2}$, then $x = 30°, 150°$

If $\sin x = -1$, then $x = 270°$

▽ **1027** Solve for all values of x in the interval $0 \le x < 360°$:
$\cos 2x + \cos x + 1 = 0.$

90°, 270°, 120°, 240°

Solution: Substitute $2 \cos^2 x - 1$ for $\cos 2x$

$(2 \cos^2 x - 1) + \cos x + 1 = 0, 2 \cos^2 x + \cos x = 0,$

$\cos x(2 \cos x + 1) = 0$

If $\cos x = 0$, then $x = 90°, 270°$

If $2 \cos x = -1$, then $x = 120°, 240°$

1028 Solve for values of x between 0 and 2π: $\sin^2 x - \cos x + 5 = 0$.
Suggestion: Substitute $1 - \cos^2 x$ for $\sin^2 x$ so that the equation
is in terms of $\cos x$ only and continue as usual.

no answers

Solution: $\sin^2 x - \cos x + 5 = 0, (1 - \cos^2 x) - \cos x + 5 = 0,$

$\cos^2 x + \cos x - 6 = 0,$

$(\cos x + 3)(\cos x - 2) = 0$

$\cos x = -3$ or $\cos x = 2$

There are no values for x in either case.

1029 (1) Solve for values of x in the interval $0 \le x < 2\pi$:
$\cos^2 (x/2) = \cos x.$
(2) Check your answers.

(1) 0

Solution: $\left(\pm \sqrt{\dfrac{1 + \cos x}{2}} \right)^2 = \cos x, \dfrac{1 + \cos x}{2} = \cos x,$

$1 + \cos x = 2 \cos x, \cos x = 1, x = 0$

continued →

(2) *Check* $x = 0$: $\cos^2 \dfrac{0}{2} = \cos 0,\ 1^2 = 1,\ 1 = 1$

1030   Solve for all values of θ in the interval $0 \leq \theta < 2\pi$: $\sin \theta = \cos \theta$.
       Suggestion: Divide both members of the equation by $\cos \theta$. (This
       division is possible for all values of θ except those for which
       $\cos \theta = 0$.) Then simplify the result.

$\dfrac{\pi}{4},\ \dfrac{5\pi}{4}$

Solution: $\sin \theta = \cos \theta$

$\dfrac{\sin \theta}{\cos \theta} = 1$ except when $\cos \theta = 0$

$\tan \theta = 1,\ \theta = \dfrac{\pi}{4},\ \dfrac{5\pi}{4}$

Note: $\cos (\pi/4) \neq 0$ and $\cos (5\pi/4) \neq 0$; hence, the division was
permissible.

1031   The solution in frame 1030 for the equation $\sin \theta = \cos \theta$ was
       $\theta = \pi/4,\ 5\pi/4$ if θ is between 0 and 2π. What is the general form
       for this answer if θ is any number.

$\theta = \dfrac{\pi}{4} + \pi n$, where n is an integer

1032   (1) Solve for all values of θ in the interval $0 \leq \theta < 360°$:
       $\sin \theta \cos \theta = \sin \theta$. (2) Explain why you should not try to solve
       this equation by dividing both members of the given equation by
       $\sin \theta$.

(1) $0°$, $180°$

Solution: $\sin \theta \cos \theta - \sin \theta = 0$, $\sin \theta (\cos \theta - 1) = 0$

If $\sin \theta = 0$ and $\theta = 0$, then $\theta = 0°$, $180°$

If $\cos \theta - 1 = 0$ and $\cos \theta = 1$, then $\theta = 0°$

(2) Since $\sin \theta = 0$ when $\theta = 0$ or $180°$, dividing by $\sin \theta$ is equiv-
    alent to dividing by 0. or (When you divide both members of an
    expression involving the variable you may "lose roots" of the
    equation.)

1033 Solve $2 \sin^2 y = 3 \cos y$ for all values of y in the interval $0 \leq y < 2\pi$. *Suggestion:* Express the left member in terms of $\cos y$.

$\dfrac{\pi}{3}, \dfrac{5\pi}{3}$

Solution: $2(1 - \cos^2 y) = 3 \cos y$, $2 - 2 \cos^2 y = 3 \cos y$,

$\quad 2 \cos^2 y + 3 \cos y - 2 = 0$, $(2 \cos y - 1)(\cos y + 2) = 0$

If $\cos y = \frac{1}{2}$, then $y = \dfrac{\pi}{3}, \dfrac{5\pi}{3}$

If $\cos y = -2$, then there is no solution

1034 Solve for all values of x between 0 and $360°$: $\sin x = \cos^2 x - \sin^2 x$.

$30°, 150°, 270°$

Solution: Start with $\sin x = (1 - \sin^2 x) - \sin^2 x$ and complete as before.

1035 In the remaining frames on solutions of equations, solve for all values in the interval 0 to $360°$ only, unless you are directed otherwise. Solve for x: $4 \sin x + \csc x - 4 = 0$. *Suggestion:* Make a substitution from one of the reciprocal relations.

$30°, 150°$

Solution: $4 \sin x + \dfrac{1}{\sin x} - 4 = 0$, $4 \sin^2 x + 1 - 4 \sin x = 0$,

$\quad 4 \sin^2 x - 4 \sin x + 1 = 0$, $(2 \sin x - 1)^2 = 0$

If $\sin x = \frac{1}{2}$, then $x = 30°, 150°$

1036 Solve for x: $\sec x + \cos x + 2 = 0$.

$180°$

1037 Solve for x: $\tan x + \sec x + \cos x = 0$.

no answers

Solution: $\dfrac{\sin x}{\cos x} + \dfrac{1}{\cos x} + \cos x = 0$, $\sin x + 1 + \cos^2 x = 0$,

$\sin x + 1 + 1 - \sin^2 x = 0$, $\sin^2 x - \sin x - 2 = 0$,

$(\sin x - 2)(\sin x + 1) = 0$

If $\sin x = 2$, there is no answer

If $\sin x = -1$, then $x = 270°$, but $\tan x$ and $\sec x$ are undefined at $x = 270°$; hence $270°$ is not a root.

▽**1038** Solve for x: $\cot x + 2 \sin x = \csc x$.

$120°, 240°$

Solution: $\dfrac{\cos x}{\sin x} + 2 \sin x = \dfrac{1}{\sin x}$, $\cos x + 2 \sin^2 x = 1$,

$\cos x + 2(1 - \cos^2 x) = 1$, $\cos x + 2 - 2 \cos^2 x = 1$,

$2 \cos^2 x - \cos x - 1 = 0$, $(2 \cos x + 1)(\cos x - 1) = 0$

If $\cos x = -\frac{1}{2}$, then $x = 120°, 240°$

If $\cos x = 1$, then $x = 0°$, but $\cot x$ and $\csc x$ are undefined at $x = 0$

▽ **1039** Solve for x: $4 \sin^2 x + 3 \csc^2 x = 7$.

$60°,\ 120°,\ 240°,\ 300°,\ 90°,\ 270°$

Solution: $4 \sin^2 x + \dfrac{3}{\sin^2 x} = 7$, $4 \sin^4 x - 7 \sin^2 x + 3 = 0$,

$(4 \sin^2 x - 3)(\sin^2 x - 1) = 0$,

If $\sin^2 x = \frac{3}{4}$ and $\sin x = \pm\dfrac{\sqrt{3}}{2}$, then $x = 60°, 120°, 240°, 300°$

If $\sin^2 x = 1$ and $\sin^2 x = \pm 1$, then $x = 90°, 270°$

1040 Two methods for solving the equation $\cos \frac{1}{2}x - \sin x = 0$ will be suggested. Try each of them. First method, substitute $\pm\sqrt{(1 + \cos x)/2}$ for $\cos \frac{1}{2} x$ and complete the solution. The second method will be given in frame 1041.

$60°,\ 300°,\ 180°$

Solution: $\pm\sqrt{\dfrac{1 + \cos x}{2}} - \sin x = 0,\ \pm\sqrt{\dfrac{1 + \cos x}{2}} = \sin x,$

$\dfrac{1 + \cos x}{2} = \sin^2 x = 1 - \cos^2 x,\ 1 + \cos x = 2 - 2\cos^2 x,$

$2\cos^2 x + \cos x - 1 = 0$

If $\cos x = \frac{1}{2}$, then $x = 60°, 300°$

If $\cos x = -1$, then $x = 180°$

1041 Second method for solving the equation $\cos \frac{1}{2}x - \sin x = 0$. In the double-angle formula $\sin 2\theta = 2 \sin \theta \cos \theta$, if we substitute x for 2θ and $\frac{1}{2}x$ for θ, we have $\sin x = 2 \sin\frac{1}{2}x \cos\frac{1}{2}x$. Use $2 \sin\frac{1}{2} x \cos\frac{1}{2} x$ as a replacement for $\sin x$ above and complete the solution.

$180°,\ 60°,\ 300°$

Solution: $\cos\frac{1}{2}x - 2 \sin\frac{1}{2} x \cos\frac{1}{2}x = 0$

$\cos\frac{1}{2} x\, (1 - 2 \sin\frac{1}{2}x) = 0$

If $\cos\frac{1}{2}x = 0, \frac{1}{2}x = 90°$, then $x = 180°$

If $2 \sin\frac{1}{2} x = 1$, $\sin\frac{1}{2}x = \frac{1}{2}$, and $\frac{1}{2}x = 30°, 150°$, then $x = 60°, 300°$

1042 Solve for x: $\sin x + 1 = \cos x$. *Suggestion:* Square both members of the equation, then make a substitution so that the equation is in terms of either sines or cosines only. Squaring may introduce apparent solutions which will not satisfy the original equation. Check all answers where this method has been used.

$0,\ 270°$

Solution: $(\sin x + 1)^2 = \cos^2 x,\ \sin^2 x + 2 \sin x + 1 = 1 - \sin^2 x,$

$2 \sin^2 x + 2 \sin x = 0,\ 2 \sin x\, (\sin x + 1) = 0,$

If $2 \sin x = 0$, then $x = 0°, 180°$

If $\sin x = -1$, then $x = 270°$

continued →

Check $x = 0°$: $\sin 0° + 1 \overset{?}{=} \cos 0°, 0 + 1 = 1$

Check $x = 180°$: $\sin 180° + 1 \overset{?}{=} \cos 180°, 0 + 1 \neq -1$

Check $x = 270°$: $\sin 270° + 1 = \cos 270°, -1 + 1 = 0$

1043   Solve for x: $\sin x - 1 = \cos x$.

90°, 180°   One apparent root, $x = 0°$, will not check.

1044   Solve for x: $\sin x - 2 = \cos x$.

no answers   *Note:* The method suggested in frame 1042 leads
to an equation in which the apparent solutions are complex
numbers, i.e.,

Solution: $(\sin x - 2)^2 = \cos^2 x$, $\sin^2 x - 4 \sin x + 4 = 1 - \sin^2 x$,

$2 \sin^2 x - 4 \sin + 3 = 0$, $\sin x = \dfrac{+4 \pm \sqrt{16 - 24}}{4}$

$= \dfrac{+4 \pm \sqrt{-8}}{4} = \dfrac{2 \pm \sqrt{-2}}{2}$

▽1045 Solve for x: $2 \sin x + 1 = \cos x$. Check your answers.

0°, 233°

Solution: Squaring both members and simplifying the result
leads to the apparent solutions

If $\sin x = 0$, then $x = 0°$, 180°

and if $5 \sin x + 4 = 0$, then $x = 233°$, 307°

but if $x = 180°$,

$2 \sin 180° + 1 \neq \cos 180°, 2 \cdot 0 + 1 \neq -1$

and if $x = 307°$,

$2 \sin 307° + 1 \neq \cos 307°, 2(-\tfrac{4}{5}) + 1 \neq 0.6018$

▽ 1046   Solve for x: $2 \cos^2 x + 2 \cos 2x = 1$.

$45°$, $135°$, $225°$, $315°$

Solution: $2 \cos^2 x + 2(2 \cos^2 x - 1) = 1$,

$2 \cos^2 x + 4 \cos^2 x - 2 = 1$, $6 \cos^2 x = 3$, $\cos^2 x = \frac{1}{2}$

If $\cos x = + \dfrac{1}{\sqrt{2}}$, then $x = 45°$, $315°$

If $\cos x = - \dfrac{1}{\sqrt{2}}$, then $x = 135°$, $225°$

1047   Solve for θ: $6 \sin^2 \theta + \cos 2\theta = 2$.

$30°$, $150°$, $210°$, $330°$

Comment

Sometimes a sum-to-product formula can be used to simplify a trigonometric equation. An example is shown below. Study the solution carefully, in particular steps 1 and 4.

Solve the equation $\cos 3x + \cos x = 0$

1. If we let $\theta = 3x$ and $\phi = x$ in the formula

$$\cos \theta + \cos \phi = 2 \cos \tfrac{1}{2}(\theta + \phi) \cos \tfrac{1}{2}(\theta - \phi)$$

and substitute in the given equation, we have

$$\cos 3x + \cos x = 2 \cos \tfrac{1}{2}(3x + x) \cos \tfrac{1}{2}(3x - x) = 0$$

2. This simplifies to $2 \cos 2x \cos x = 0$

3. If $\cos x = 0$, then $x = 90°$, $270°$

4. If $\cos 2x = 0$, then

$$2x = 90°, 270°, 450°, 630°$$
$$x = 45°, 135°, 225°, 315°$$

or

If $\cos 2x = 0$, then

$$2 \cos^2 x - 1 = 0, \cos^2 x = \tfrac{1}{2}$$
$$\cos x = +1/\sqrt{2}, -1/\sqrt{2}$$
$$x = 45°, 135°, 225°, 315°$$

If $\cos 2x = 0$, there are four values of x in the interval 0 to $360°$ which satisfy the equation. We must be careful to include all of these values in the answer. It is always wise to take time to consider all the possible answers before leaving a problem.

1048 If $\cos 2x = \frac{1}{2}$, what are values of x in the interval 0 to 360°?

> 30°, 150°, 210°, 330°
>
> *Solution:* $\cos 2x = \frac{1}{2}$
>
> $$2x = 60°, 300°, (60 + 360°), (300 + 360°)$$
> $$x = 30°, 150°, 210°, 330°$$

▽**1049** If $\sin 2x = 0$, what are the values for x in the interval 0 to 360° which satisfy the equation?

> 0°, 90°, 180°, 270°
>
> *Solution:* $\sin 2x = 0$
>
> $$2x = 0°, 180°, (0 + 360°), (180 + 360°)$$
> $$x = 0°, 90°, 180°, 270°$$

1050 Solve for x: $\sin 5x + \sin 3x = 0$.

> 0°, 45°, 90°, 135°, 180°, 225°, 270°, 315°
>
> *Solution:* $\sin 5x + \sin 3x = 2 \sin 4x \cos x = 0$
>
> If $2 \sin 4x = 0$ and $\sin 4x = 0$, then
>
> $$4x = 0, 180°, (0 + 180°n), \ldots, \text{ where } n = 2, 3, 4, 5, 6, 7$$
> $$x = 0, 45°, 90°, 135°, 180°, 225°, 270°, 315°$$
> $$\text{or } (n \cdot 45°, \text{ where } n = 0, 1, 2, 3, \ldots, 7)$$
>
> If $\cos x = 0$, then $x = 90°, 270°$

1051 Solve the equation $\cos 3x - \cos x = 0$.

> 0, 90°, 180°, 270°
>
> *Solution:* Using VB(4) in Panel 8
>
> $$\cos 3x - \cos x = -2 \sin 2x \sin x = 0$$
>
> If $-2 \sin 2x = 0$ and $\sin 2x = 0$, then
>
> $$2x = 0°, 180°, 360°, 540°$$
> $$x = 0°, 90°, 180°, 270°$$
> $$\text{or } (n \cdot 90°, \text{ where } n = 0, 1, 2, 3)$$
>
> If $\sin x = 0$, then $x = 0°, 180°$

▼1052   (1) Solve for x: $\sin 4x - \sin 2x = \cos 3x$.
(2) If $150°$ is one of your answers check it.

(1) $30°$, $90°$, $150°$, $210°$, $270°$, $330°$

Solution: $\sin 4x - \sin 2x = 2 \cos 3x \sin x = \cos 3x$

$$\cos 3x (2 \sin x - 1) = 0$$

If $\cos 3x = 0$, then

$$3x = 90°, 270°, (90 + 180n) \ldots n = 2, 3, 4, 5$$
$$x = 30°, 90°, 150°, 210°, 270°, 330°$$
$$\text{or } [(30° + 60°n) \text{ where } n = 0, 1, 2, 3, 4, 5]$$

If $2 \sin x - 1 = 0$ and $\sin x = \frac{1}{2}$, then $x = 30°, 150°$

(2) *Check* $x = 150°$: $\sin 4(150°) - \sin 2(150°) = \cos 3(150°)$

$$-\frac{\sqrt{3}}{2} - \left(-\frac{\sqrt{3}}{2}\right) = 0$$

1053   Solve for x: $\sin^3 x \sec^3 x = 4 \tan^2 x$. *Suggestion:* Use the reciprocal relations for a substitution for $\sec^3 x$, then express the equation in terms of $\tan x$.

$0°$, $180°$ $76°$, $256°$

Solution: $\sin^3 x \cdot \dfrac{1}{\cos^3 x} = 4 \tan^2 x$, $\tan^3 x - 4 \tan^2 x = 0$

$$\tan^2 x (\tan x - 4) = 0$$

If $\tan^2 x = 0$, then $x = 0, 180°$

If $\tan x - 4 = 0$, then $x \approx 76°, 256°$

Comment

In the following frames where you are finding solutions to equations, you may use any of the methods which have been suggested. If a solution is shown with the answer, it may not be the only way to solve the problem. However, the *answers* should agree. (A check in the original equation verifies your answer.)

1054 Solve for x: $\cos 2x + 2 \cos^2(x/2) = 1$.

$60°$, $180°$, $300°$

Solution: $(2 \cos^2 x - 1) + 2\left(\sqrt{\dfrac{1 + \cos x}{2}}\right)^2 = 1$

$2 \cos^2 x - 1 + 1 + \cos x = 1$, $2 \cos^2 x + \cos x - 1 = 0$,

$(2 \cos x - 1)(\cos x + 1) = 0$

If $\cos x = \frac{1}{2}$, then $x = 60°$, $300°$

If $\cos x = -1$, then $x = 180°$

1055 Solve for x: $\tan x + \sec x = 1$.

$0°$

Solution: $\dfrac{\sin x}{\cos x} + \dfrac{1}{\cos x} = 1$, $\sin x + 1 = \cos x$

Squaring both members

$\sin^2 x + 2 \sin x + 1 = \cos^2 x$,

$\sin^2 x + 2 \sin x + 1 = 1 - \sin^2 x$, $2 \sin^2 x + 2 \sin x = 0$

$2 \sin x (\sin x + 1) = 0$

If $2 \sin x = 0$, then $x = 0°$, $180°$

If $\sin x = -1$, then $x =$ $270°$

$180°$ and $270°$ do not satisfy the original equation.

1056 Solve for x: $\tan \frac{1}{2}x + 2 \sin 2x = \csc x$.

$30°$, $90°$, $150°$, $210°$, $270°$, $330°$

Solution: $\dfrac{(1 - \cos x)}{\sin} + 4 \sin x \cos x = \dfrac{1}{\sin x}$,

$1 - \cos x + 4 \sin^2 x \cos x = 1$, $\cos x(4 \sin^2 x - 1) = 0$

If $\cos x = 0$, then $x = 90°$, $270°$

If $4 \sin^2 x - 1 = 0$, $\sin^2 x = \frac{1}{4}$, and $\sin x = \pm\frac{1}{2}$, then

$x = 30°$, $150°$, $210°$, $330°$

1057   Solve for x: $\csc x \cot x = \sqrt{2}$.

$45°$, $315°$

Solution: $\dfrac{1}{\sin x} \cdot \dfrac{\cos x}{\sin x} = \sqrt{2}$, $\dfrac{\cos x}{\sin^2 x} = \sqrt{2}$,

$\cos x = \sqrt{2} \sin^2 x = \sqrt{2}\,(1 - \cos^2 x)$,

$\sqrt{2} \cos^2 x + \cos x - \sqrt{2} = 0$, $(\sqrt{2} \cos x - 1)(\cos x + \sqrt{2}) = 0$

If $\cos x = \dfrac{1}{\sqrt{2}}$, then $x = 45°, 315°$

If $\cos x = -\sqrt{2}$, there is no solution.

1058   Solve for x: $2 \sin^4 x - \cos^2 x = 0$.

$45°$, $135°$, $225°$, $315°$

Solution: $2 \sin^4 x - (1 - \sin^2 x) = 0$, $2 \sin^4 x + \sin^2 x - 1 = 0$

$(2 \sin^2 x - 1)(\sin^2 x + 1) = 0$

If $\sin^2 x = \frac{1}{2}$, then $\sin x = \pm \dfrac{1}{\sqrt{2}}$ and $x = 45°, 135°, 225°, 315°$

If $\sin^2 x = -1$, there is no solution.

1059   Solve for x: $4 \cos^4 x = (\sin 2x)^2$.

$45°$, $90°$, $135°$, $225°$, $270°$, $315°$

Solution: $4 \cos^4 x = (2 \sin x \cos x)^2$, $4 \cos^4 x = 4 \sin^2 x \cos^2 x$,

$\cos^4 x - \sin^2 x \cos^2 x = 0$, $\cos^2 x\,(\cos^2 x - \sin^2 x) = 0$,

$\cos^2 x \cdot \cos 2x = 0$

If $\cos^2 x = 0$, then $x = 90°, 270°$

If $\cos 2x = 0$, then $2x = 90°, 270°, 450°, 630°$ and

$x = 45°, 135°, 225°, 315°$

1060   Solve for x: $\cos x + 4 \sin x - \sin 2x = 2$.

30°, 150°

Solution: $\cos x + 4 \sin x - 2 \sin x \cos x - 2 = 0$,

$\cos x - 2 \sin x \cos x - 2 + 4 \sin x = 0$,

$\cos x (1 - 2 \sin x) - 2 (1 - 2 \sin x) = 0$,

$(\cos x - 2)(1 - 2 \sin x) = 0$

If $\cos x = 2$, there is no solution.

If $2 \sin x = 1$, then, $\sin x = \frac{1}{2}$ and $x = 30°, 150°$

UNIT 4 ▌ Miscellaneous Problems

Comment

In frames 1061 to 1124 you will find miscellaneous problems, some
are numerical and some require proofs. You have panels to which
you may refer, but try to solve the problems without constant use of
this source of information. The problems are review exercises. If
you cannot answer the question with the information given when the
problem is first presented, read the suggestions given with the
answer (or in the next frame) and try the problem again.

1061 Without using a table, state the following in fractional or radical
form: (1) $\sin 30°$, (2) $\cos 30°$, (3) $\tan 30°$, (4) $\cot 30°$, (5) $\sec 30°$,
and (6) $\csc 30°$.

> (1) $\sin 30° = \frac{1}{2}$ (2) $\cos 30° = \frac{\sqrt{3}}{2}$ (3) $\tan 30° = \frac{1}{\sqrt{3}}$
>
> (4) $\cot 30° = \sqrt{3}$ (5) $\sec 30° = \frac{2}{\sqrt{3}}$ (6) $\csc 30° = 2$
>
> If all of your answers are correct, skip to frame 1063.
> If all of your answers are not correct, go on to frame 1062.

1062 (1) Make a sketch as shown here and indicate the
numerical values of the sides of triangle
OPQ. Recall that in a right triangle the side
opposite the 30° angle is one-half the
hypotenuse. Refer to Panel 8 (I) (C) for
formulas for $\cot \theta$, $\sec \theta$, and $\csc \theta$.

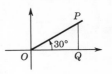

continued ➔

317

(2) Write again the numerical values for (a) sin 30°, (b) cos 30°, (c) tan 30°, (d) cot 30°, (e) sec 30°, and (f) csc 30°.

---

(1)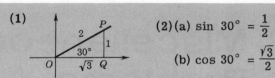

(2)(a) $\sin 30° = \dfrac{1}{2}$

(b) $\cos 30° = \dfrac{\sqrt{3}}{2}$

(c) $\tan 30° = \dfrac{1}{\sqrt{3}}$

(d) $\cot 30° = \dfrac{\cos 30°}{\sin 30°} = \dfrac{\sqrt{3}/2}{1/2} = \sqrt{3}$

(e) $\sec 30° = \dfrac{1}{\cos 30°} = \dfrac{1}{\sqrt{3}/2} = \dfrac{2}{\sqrt{3}}$

(f) $\csc 30° = \dfrac{1}{\sin 30°} = \dfrac{1}{1/2} = 2$

1063 Give numerical values for (1) sin 60°, (2) cos 60°, (3) tan 60°, (4) cot 60°, (5) sec 60°, and (6) csc 60°.

---

(1) $\sin 60° = \dfrac{\sqrt{3}}{2}$ (2) $\cos 60° = \tfrac{1}{2}$ (3) $\tan 60° = \sqrt{3}$

(4) $\cot 60° = \dfrac{1}{\sqrt{3}}$ (5) $\sec 60° = 2$ (6) $\csc 60° = \dfrac{2}{\sqrt{3}}$

If all of your answers are correct, skip to frame 1065.
If all of your answers are not correct, go on to frame 1064.

1064 (1) Write the definitions for (a) cot θ, (b) sec θ, and (c) csc θ. (2) Place correct numerical values on the sides of the triangle OPQ. (3) Give the numerical values for (a) sin 60°, (b) cos 60°, (c) tan 60°, (d) cot 60°, (e) sec 60°, and (f) csc 60°.

---

(1)(a) $\cot \theta = \dfrac{\cos \theta}{\sin \theta}$, (b) $\sec \theta = \dfrac{1}{\cos \theta}$, (c) $\csc = \dfrac{1}{\sin \theta}$

(2)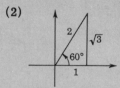

(3)(a) $\sin 60° = \dfrac{\sqrt{3}}{2}$, (b) $\cos 60° = \tfrac{1}{2}$,

(c) $\tan 60° = \sqrt{3}$, (d) $\cot 60° = \dfrac{1}{\sqrt{3}}$

(e) $\sec 60° = 2$, (f) $\csc 60° = \dfrac{2}{\sqrt{3}}$

1065   Prove $\tan (\pi/2 - \theta) = \cot \theta$, providing $\tan (\pi/2 - \theta)$ and $\cot \theta$ exist.

You should avoid using Panel 8II(5) since tangent is undefined at $\pi/2$. Proof will appear in frame 1066.

Suggestions: Recall
1. Definition of tangent, i.e., $\tan (\pi/2 - \theta) = \dfrac{\sin (\pi/2 - \theta)}{\cos (\pi/2 - \theta)}$

2. Refer to Panel 8 II (2)(4) for substitutions and simplify.

1066   If your proof for $\tan (\pi/2 - \theta) = \cot \theta$ was not completed in frame 1065, work it out now.

Starting with the left member

$$\tan \left(\frac{\pi}{2} - \theta\right) = \frac{\sin (\pi/2 - \theta)}{\cos (\pi/2 - \theta)} \qquad \begin{array}{l}\text{definition} \\ \text{of tangent}\end{array}$$

$$= \frac{\sin (\pi/2) \cos \theta - \cos (\pi/2) \sin \theta}{\cos (\pi/2) \cos \theta + \sin (\pi/2) \sin \theta} \qquad \text{Panel 8II(2)(4)}$$

$$= \frac{1 \cdot \cos \theta - 0 \cdot \sin \theta}{0 \cdot \cos \theta + 1 \cdot \sin \theta} \qquad \text{simplifying}$$

$$= \frac{\cos \theta}{\sin \theta} \qquad \text{simplifying}$$

$$= \cot \theta \qquad \begin{array}{l}\text{definition} \\ \text{of cot}\end{array}$$

Therefore, $\tan \left(\dfrac{\pi}{2} - \theta\right) = \cot \theta$

1067   Given $\sin \alpha = -\frac{2}{3}$ and α terminates in quadrant III, find **(1)** $\cos \alpha$ and **(2)** $\tan \alpha$.

(1) $\cos = -\dfrac{\sqrt{5}}{3}$ (2) $\tan = \dfrac{2}{\sqrt{5}}$

If both of your answers are correct, skip to frame 1069.
If both of your answers are not correct, go on to frame 1068.

1068   To find $\cos \alpha$ and $\tan \alpha$ given $\sin \alpha = -\frac{2}{3}$ when α terminates in quadrant III, make a sketch similar to either of those shown below and use the suggestion accompanying the sketch you have selected.

continued →

1. Use the distance formula to find
   OQ. Then find cos α and tan α.

or

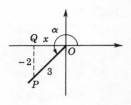

2. Use the distance formula to find
   cos α, then compute tan α using
   the definition of tan α.

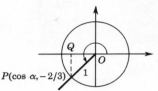

$$\cos \alpha = -\frac{\sqrt{5}}{3} \quad \tan \alpha = \frac{2}{\sqrt{5}} \text{ or } \frac{2\sqrt{5}}{5}$$

Solution 1: $\quad x = -\sqrt{3^2 - (-2)^2} = -\sqrt{5}$ (for quadrant III)

$$\cos \alpha = \frac{x}{r} = -\frac{\sqrt{5}}{3} \quad \tan \alpha = \frac{y}{x} = \frac{-2}{-\sqrt{5}} = \frac{2}{\sqrt{5}} \text{ or } \frac{2\sqrt{5}}{5}$$

Solution 2: $\quad 1^2 = \sin^2 \alpha + \cos^2 \alpha$

$$\cos \alpha = -\sqrt{1^2 - \left(\frac{-2}{3}\right)^2} = \frac{-\sqrt{5}}{3}$$

$$\tan \alpha = \frac{\sin \alpha}{\cos \alpha} = \frac{-2/3}{-\sqrt{5}/3} = \frac{2\sqrt{5}}{5}$$

1069   Find to the nearest inch the perimeter of a regular polygon of nine
sides inscribed in a circle whose radius is 40 in.

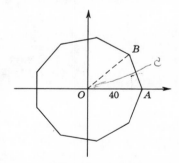

$P \approx 246$ in.
You will find suggestions for three ways to solve this problem in
frames 1070 and 1071. Read through all the solutions even though
you may have the correct answer.

1070 *Solution* I: Refer to the sketch in frame 1069. Let AB represent one side of a regular polygon of nine sides inscribed in a circle of radius = 40. Then angle AOB = (1)___°. Since AB is the chord which this central angle subtends, we may use the formula chord = $r\sqrt{2 - 2\cos\theta}$, to find the length of one side. The length of $AB \approx$ (2)_____. Perimeter of polygon then $\approx$ (3)_____. Other solutions are shown in frame 1071.

> (1) 40°   (2) 27.360   (3) 246

1071 *Solution* II: Refer to the sketch in frame 1069. Let AB represent one side of a regular inscribed polygon of nine sides. Then angle AOB = (1)_____. Let OC be perpendicular to AB, then angle AOC = (2)_____. Now compute the length of (3) AC,   (4) AB, and (5) the perimeter of the polygon.
> *Solution* III: Use law of cosines in triangle AOB to find side AB.

> *Solution* II:
>   (1) 40°   (2) 20°   (3) $\approx$ 13.68   (4) $\approx$ 27.36   (5) $\approx$ 246
> *Solution* III:
>   In triangle AOB, $AB^2 = 40^2 + 40^2 - 2(40)(40)\cos 40°$,
> $$AB \approx 27.4, \text{ and perimeter} \approx 247$$

1072 If a central angle of 3 radians intercepts an arc of 18 in. on a circle, then the radius of the circle is ___ in.

> 6   *Solution:*   The definition of a radian-measure:
> Central angle in radians = $\dfrac{\text{arc}}{\text{radius}}$.

▽**1073** Find the radius of a circle if a central angle of 1.57 radians intercepts an arc of 17.898 in.

> radius = 11.4 in.

1074 In triangle ABC, $\alpha = 90°$, $\beta = 38°$, and $a = 14$, find (1) γ (2) b, and (3) c.

> (1) γ = 52°   (2) $b \approx 8.6$ (3) $c \approx 11.0$
> *Suggestion:* To find b and c use the law of sines or
> $$\sin 38° = \frac{y}{14} \qquad \cos 38° = \frac{x}{14}$$

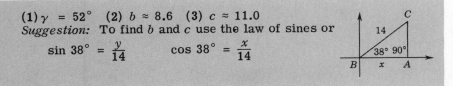

1075 Change an angle reading of 25°36′ to an equivalent radian reading in terms of π.

25°36′ = $\dfrac{32\pi}{225}$ radians

If your answer is correct, skip to frame 1077.
If your answer is not correct, go on to frame 1076.

1076 To change 25°36′ to radians, we should first write 25°36′ in decimal or fractional form as (1)_____°. (2) Then use the fact that 1° = $\pi/180$ radians to find the number of radians equivalent to 25°36′.

(1) 25.6° or 25$\frac{3}{5}$°   (2) 25.6 $\dfrac{\pi}{180}$ = $\dfrac{32\pi}{225}$ radians

1077 Express each of the following as functions of positive acute angles: (1) sin 250°, (2) tan 165°, and (3) cos 327°. Attach the proper sign.

(1) sin 250° = |sin (250° − 180°)| = − sin 70°
(2) tan 165° = |tan (180° − 165°)| = − tan 15°
(3) cos 327° = |cos (360° − 327°)| =   cos 33°

1078 Express each of the following as the same function of a positive acute angle: (1) cos (− 200°), (2) sin (− 40°), (3) tan (− 7π/4), (4) cos (− π/6), and (5) sin (− 2π/3). Indicate the correct sign.

(1) cos (− 200°) = − cos 20°   (2) sin (− 40°) = − sin 40°

(3) tan $\dfrac{-7\pi}{4}$ = tan $\dfrac{\pi}{4}$ (4) cos $\dfrac{-\pi}{6}$ = cos $\dfrac{\pi}{6}$

(5) sin $\dfrac{-2\pi}{3}$ = − sin $\dfrac{\pi}{3}$

▽**1079** Find the value of sin (3π/2) + tan (7π/4) · cos π.

sin $\dfrac{3\pi}{2}$ + tan $\dfrac{7\pi}{4}$ · cos π = 0

Solution: (− 1) + (− 1) · (− 1) = (− 1) + (+ 1) = 0

1080 Prove that sec $(\pi/2 - \theta)$ = csc θ, if sec $(\pi/2 - \theta)$ and csc θ exist.

> See frame 1081 for a proof. If you have not succeeded in making a proof, follow these suggestions:
> 1. Recall the definition for secant.
> 2. See Panel 8II(4) or ID(1).
> 3. Recall the definition for cosecant.

1081 Using the suggestions in frame 1080 if necessary, complete the proof for sec $(\pi/2 - \theta)$ = csc θ.

> 1. $\sec\left(\dfrac{\pi}{2} - \theta\right) = \dfrac{1}{\cos(\pi/2 - \theta)}$
>
> 2. $\qquad\qquad = \dfrac{1}{\cos(\pi/2)\cos\theta + \sin(\pi/2)\sin\theta}$
>
> 3. $\qquad\qquad = \dfrac{1}{0\cdot\cos\theta + \sin(\pi/2)\sin\theta}$
>
> 4. $\qquad\qquad = \dfrac{1}{\sin\theta}$
>
> 5. $\sec\left(\dfrac{\pi}{2} - \theta\right) = \csc\theta$
>
> A shorter proof uses ID(1):
>
> $$\sec\left(\frac{\pi}{2} - \theta\right) = \frac{1}{\cos(\pi/2 - \theta)} = \frac{1}{\sin\theta} = \csc\theta$$

1082 Prove that $\dfrac{1 + \sin\alpha}{\cos\alpha} = \dfrac{\cos\alpha}{1 - \sin\alpha}$ where $\cos\alpha \neq 0$ and

$1 - \sin\alpha \neq 0$.

> If you have not succeeded in making a proof, follow these suggestions:
> 1. Multiply both numerator and denominator of the right member by $1 + \sin\alpha$
> 2. Simplify the result.
> See frame 1083 for an alternative proof.

1083 Carry out the suggestions below to show that $\dfrac{1 + \sin\alpha}{\cos\alpha} =$

$\dfrac{\cos\alpha}{1 - \sin\alpha}$

continued ➙

1. Multiply both numerator and denominator of the *left* member by 1 - sin α
2. Simplify the result.

$$\frac{(1 + \sin \alpha)}{\cos \alpha} \frac{(1 - \sin \alpha)}{(1 - \sin \alpha)} = \frac{1 - \sin^2 \alpha}{\cos \alpha \, (1 - \sin \alpha)}$$

$$= \frac{\cos^2 \alpha}{\cos \alpha \, (1 - \sin \alpha)}$$

$$= \frac{\cos \alpha}{1 - \sin \alpha}$$

Therefore, $\dfrac{1 + \sin \alpha}{\cos \alpha} = \dfrac{\cos \alpha}{1 - \sin \alpha}$

1084 If sin $\alpha = \frac{12}{13}$, cos $\beta = \frac{4}{5}$, and x and y are acute, find the value of sin $(\alpha - \beta)$.

sin $(\alpha - \beta) = \frac{33}{65}$

If your answer is correct, skip to frame 1086.
If your answer is not correct, go on to frame 1085.

1085 Find the value for sin $(\alpha - \beta)$, given sin $\alpha = \frac{12}{13}$, cos $\beta = \frac{4}{5}$.

1. Make a sketch of α in standard position and compute cos α.
2. Make a sketch of β in standard position and compute sin β.
3. Consult Panel 8 if necessary for formula for sin $(\alpha - \beta)$.

sin $(\alpha - \beta) = \frac{12}{13} \cdot \frac{4}{5} - \frac{5}{13} \cdot \frac{3}{5} = \frac{33}{65}$

1086 Show by repeated applications of the product-to-sum formulas that

$$\sin \frac{\pi}{12} \cdot \sin \frac{\pi}{4} \cdot \sin \frac{5\pi}{12} \cdot \sin \frac{7\pi}{12} \cdot \sin \frac{3\pi}{4} \cdot \sin \frac{11\pi}{12} = \frac{1}{32}$$

Use formula VA(4)

$$\sin \alpha \sin \beta = -\tfrac{1}{2}[\cos (\alpha + \beta) - \cos (\alpha - \beta)]$$

$$= \tfrac{1}{2}[\cos (\alpha - \beta) - \cos (\alpha + \beta)]$$

continued →

$$\sin \frac{\pi}{12} \, \sin \frac{\pi}{4} = \frac{1}{2} \left(\cos \frac{-\pi}{6} - \cos \frac{\pi}{3} \right)$$

$$= \frac{1}{2} \left(\frac{\sqrt{3}}{2} - \frac{1}{2} \right) = \frac{\sqrt{3} - 1}{4}$$

$$\sin \frac{5\pi}{12} \, \sin \frac{7\pi}{12} = \left(\frac{1}{2} \cos \frac{-\pi}{6} - \cos \pi \right)$$

$$= \frac{1}{2} \left(\frac{\sqrt{3}}{2} + 1 \right) = \frac{\sqrt{3} + 2}{4}$$

$$\sin \frac{3\pi}{4} \, \sin \frac{11\pi}{12} = \frac{1}{2} \left(\cos \frac{-\pi}{6} - \cos \frac{5\pi}{3} \right)$$

$$= \frac{1}{2} \left(\frac{\sqrt{3}}{2} - \frac{1}{2} \right) = \frac{\sqrt{3} - 1}{4}$$

$$\frac{\sqrt{3} - 1}{4} \cdot \frac{\sqrt{3} + 2}{4} \cdot \frac{\sqrt{3} - 1}{4} = \frac{1}{32}$$

1087 Find (1) $\sin \theta$, (2) $\cos \theta$, and (3) $\tan \theta$ if the terminal side of θ in standard position goes through the point $(-2, -3)$.

(1) $\sin \theta = \frac{-3}{\sqrt{13}}$

(2) $\cos \theta = \frac{-2}{\sqrt{13}}$

(3) $\tan \theta = \frac{3}{2}$

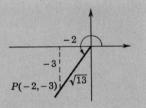

1088 Find (1) $\sin \theta$, (2) $\cos \theta$, and (3) $\tan \theta$ if the terminal side of θ in standard position goes through the point $(-3, 0)$.

(1) $\sin \theta = 0$

(2) $\cos \theta = -1$

(3) $\tan \theta = 0$

Note: $\theta = \pi$

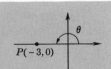

1089 Find (1) sin θ, (2) cos θ, and (3) tan θ if the terminal side of θ in standard position goes through the point (0, - 3).

(1) sin θ = -1

(2) cos θ = 0

(3) tan θ undefined

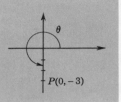

1090 Prove $\tan^2 \theta/\sec^2 \theta + \cot^2 \theta/\csc^2 \theta = 1$

By definition of functions

$$\frac{\tan^2 \theta}{\sec^2 \theta} + \frac{\cot^2 \theta}{\csc^2 \theta} = \frac{\sin^2 \theta/\cos^2 \theta}{1/\cos^2 \theta} + \frac{\cos^2 \theta/\sin^2 \theta}{1/\sin^2 \theta}$$

$$= \sin^2 \theta + \cos^2 \theta = 1$$

Therefore, $\dfrac{\tan^2 \theta}{\sec^2 \theta} + \dfrac{\cot^2 \theta}{\csc^2 \theta} = 1$

1091 Prove $\sin (x + y) \cos y - \cos (x + y) \sin y = \sin x$. *Suggestion:* Consider the left member as a form of sin $(\alpha - \beta)$, Panel 8II(2).

Proof 1: Let $x + y = \alpha$ and $\beta = y$, then

$\sin (x + y) \cos y - \cos (x + y) \sin y = \sin [(x + y) - y] = \sin x$

Proof 2: A longer proof is shown below.

$\sin (x + y) \cos y - \cos (x + y) \sin y$

$= (\sin x \cos y + \cos x \sin y) \cos y$

$\quad - (\cos x \cos y - \sin x \sin y) \sin y$

$= \sin x \cos^2 y + \cos x \sin y \cos y - \cos x \sin y \cos y$

$\quad + \sin x \sin^2 y$

$= \sin x (\cos^2 y + \sin^2 y) = \sin x \cdot 1 = \sin x$

1092 Two observers C and A are on a line through the base of a tower. The angles of elevation of the top of the tower from the observers who are 410 ft apart are 65° and 55°. Find (1) the height

continued $\rightarrow$

of the tower, (2) the distance of observer A from the foot of the tower, and (3) the distance of observer C from the foot of the tower. (Assume that the observers are on opposite sides of the tower.)

(1) $h \approx 351$ ft   (2) $AD \approx 246$ ft   (3) $CD \approx 164$ ft
If all of your answers are correct, skip to frame 1094.
If all of your answers are not correct, go on to frame 1093.

1093   Consider the problem in frame 1092 again. Look at the sketch. Find angle ABC. Apply the law of sines to find AB in triangle ABC. Continue the solution using triangle ADB.

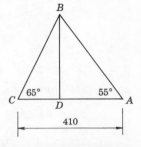

In triangle ABC, angle $ABC = 180° - (55° + 65°) = 60°$

$\dfrac{AB}{\sin 65°} = \dfrac{410}{\sin 60°}$, $AB \approx 429$ ft

In triangle ABD, $\sin 55° = \dfrac{h}{429}$, $h \approx 351$ ft

$\cos 55° = \dfrac{AD}{429}$, $AD \approx 246$ ft, $CD \approx 410 - 246 \approx 164$ ft

1094   Assume that both observers are on the same side of the tower in the problem in frame 1092 instead of on opposite sides; otherwise, the data are the same; i.e., two observers 410 ft apart are in a line with the base of a tower, and the angles of elevation of the top of the tower are 65° and 55°, respectively. Find (1) the height of the tower, (2) the distance of observer A from the base of the tower, and (3) the distance of observer C from the base of the tower.

(1) $h \approx 1,749$ ft
(2) $AD \approx 1,226$ ft
(3) $CD \approx 816$ ft

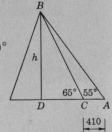

Solution: In $\triangle ABC < ACB = 115°, < CBA = 10°$

$\dfrac{BC}{\sin 55°} = \dfrac{410}{\sin 10°}$ $BC \approx 1,930$ ft

$\cos 65° = DC/BC,\ DC \approx 816$ ft

$\sin 65° = h/BC,\ h \approx 1,749$ ft

$DA = CA + DC,\ DA \approx 1,226$ ft

1095   A central angle θ intercepts an arc of $11\pi/3$ in.
in a circle whose radius is 6 in. **(1)** Find the
measure of θ in radians. **(2)** Find the area of
the sector of the circle which has θ as its angle.

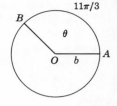

$$A = \frac{\alpha r^2}{2}$$

(1) $\theta = \dfrac{11\pi}{18}$ *Solution:* θ in radians $= \dfrac{\text{arc}}{\text{radius}}$

$$\theta = \frac{11\pi/3}{6} = \frac{11\pi}{18} \text{ radians}$$

(2) area of sector $= 11\pi$ sq in.

Solution: The sector having a central angle of $\dfrac{11\pi}{18}$ radians

represents $\frac{11}{36}$ of the circle since $\dfrac{11\pi/18}{2\pi}$ reduces to $\frac{11}{36}$. If the

area of the circle is 36π, i.e., (πr^2), then the area of the sector
is $\frac{11}{36} \cdot 36\pi = 11\pi$ sq in.

1096   Express as functions of positive acute angles, each of the following:
$\cos 295°10' =$ (1)_____, $\tan 340°20' =$ (2)_____, and
$\sin 284°50' =$ (3)_____.

(1) $\cos 64°50'$ **(2)** $-\tan 19°40'$ **(3)** $-\sin 75°10'$

1097   Find the value of $\cos (\pi/2) - \csc (5\pi/3) + \tan (5\pi/4) + \sec (5\pi/6)$.

1

If your answer is correct, skip to frame 1099.
If your answer is not correct, go on to frame 1098.

1098   Find the value of $\cos (\pi/2) - \csc (5\pi/3) + \tan (5\pi/4) + \sec (5\pi/6)$,
following these suggestions: Recall definitions for $\csc \theta$ and $\sec \theta$.
Make sketches to determine the numerical values, *do not* refer to
Panel 1.

$$\cos \frac{\pi}{2} - \csc \frac{5\pi}{3} + \tan \frac{5\pi}{4} + \sec \frac{5\pi}{6}$$

$$= \cos \frac{\pi}{2} - \frac{1}{\sin (5\pi/3)} + \tan \frac{5\pi}{4} + \frac{1}{\cos (5\pi/6)}$$

$$= 0 - \frac{1}{-\sqrt{3}/2} + 1 + \frac{1}{-\sqrt{3}/2} = 0 + \frac{2}{\sqrt{3}} + 1 - \frac{2}{\sqrt{3}} = 1$$

▽ **1099** Given θ any angle, what is (1) the largest value for $1 - \cos \theta$? (2) The smallest?

(1) 2 *Solution:* $1 - \cos \pi = 1 - (-1) = 2$
(2) 0 *Solution:* $1 - \cos 0 = 1 - 1 = 0$

▽ **1100** (1) For any angle θ, find (a) the largest and (b) the smallest values for $1 - \sin \theta$. (2) Indicate the value of θ in the interval $0 \leq \theta < 2\pi$ when these values occur.

(1)(a) 2, (b) 0 (2)(a) $\theta = \dfrac{3\pi}{2}$, (b) $\theta = \dfrac{\pi}{2}$

1101 Prove $\cos \pi/(1 - \sin^2 \theta) = \sec \theta$. *Note:* In the exercises which follow, it is assumed that the identity holds for all values of θ for which left and right members are defined.

$$\frac{\cos \theta}{1 - \sin^2 \theta} = \frac{\cos \theta}{\cos^2 \theta} = \frac{1}{\cos \theta} = \sec \theta$$

1102 Prove $\cos^2 \theta/(1 - \sin^2 \theta) = 1 + \sin \theta$.

$$\frac{\cos^2 \theta}{1 - \sin \theta} = \frac{1 - \sin^2 \theta}{1 - \sin \theta} = \frac{(1 - \sin \theta)(1 + \sin \theta)}{1 - \sin \theta} = 1 + \sin \theta$$

1103 Occasionally an identity can be proved by substituting from either the double-angle formula or the half-angle formula. Follow the suggestions in this frame and in frame 1104 for an example. Prove that $\tan \theta = \sin 2\theta/(1 + \cos 2\theta)$ by substituting from the formulas for the double angle into the right member. See frame 1104 for an alternate proof.

$$\frac{\sin 2\theta}{1 + \cos 2\theta} = \frac{2 \sin \theta \cos \theta}{1 + (2 \cos^2 \theta - 1)} = \frac{2 \sin \theta \cos \theta}{2 \cos^2 \theta} = \frac{\sin \theta}{\cos \theta} = \tan \theta$$

1104 An alternate proof for $\tan \theta = \sin 2\theta/(1 + \cos 2\theta)$ is outlined below. Refer to Panel 8IV. Use the half-angle formula (3) $\tan \frac{1}{2}\alpha = \sin \alpha/(1 + \cos \alpha)$. Let $\frac{1}{2}\alpha = \theta$, then $\alpha = 2\theta$.

The proof consists of the two steps.
1. Let $\frac{1}{2}\alpha = \theta$, then $\alpha = 2\theta$.

continued →

2. Substitute these values in the identity

$$\tan \tfrac{1}{2}\alpha = \frac{\sin \alpha}{1 + \cos \alpha}$$

to get the required form

$$\tan \theta = \frac{\sin 2\theta}{1 + \cos 2\theta}$$

1105   What are the values of θ in the interval $0 \le \theta < 2\pi$ for which $\sin 2\theta = 0$?

$0, \dfrac{\pi}{2}, \pi, \dfrac{3\pi}{2}$

Check $\theta = 0$: $\sin 2 \cdot 0 = \sin 0 = 0$

Check $\theta = \dfrac{\pi}{2}$: $\sin 2\left(\dfrac{\pi}{2}\right) = \sin \pi = 0$

Check $\theta = \pi$: $\sin 2(\pi) = \sin 2\pi = 0$

Check $\theta = \dfrac{3\pi}{2}$: $\sin 2\left(\dfrac{3\pi}{2}\right) = \sin 3\pi = 0$

See frame 1106 for a discussion of this problem.

1106   To find values of θ in the interval $0 \le \theta < 2\pi$ for which $\sin 2\theta = 0$, consider the formula $\sin 2\theta = 2 \sin \theta \cos \theta$. (1) The numerical value of $\sin 2\theta$ will be zero if either $\sin \theta = 0$ or $\cos \theta = 0$. Why? (2) $\sin \theta = 0$ if $\theta = $ (a)_____ or (b)_____. (3) $\cos \theta = 0$ if $\theta = $ (a)_____ or (b)_____.

(1) if one of the factors of a product is 0, then the product is 0.

(2)(a) 0, (b) π (3)(a) $\dfrac{\pi}{2}$, (b) $\dfrac{3\pi}{2}$

1107   What are the values of θ in the interval $0 \le \theta < 2\pi$ for which $\cos 2\pi = 0$?

$\dfrac{\pi}{4}, \dfrac{3\pi}{4}, \dfrac{5\pi}{4}, \dfrac{7\pi}{4}$

Check $\theta = \dfrac{\pi}{4}$: $\cos 2\left(\dfrac{\pi}{4}\right) = \cos\left(\dfrac{\pi}{2}\right) = 0$

Check $\theta = \dfrac{3\pi}{4}$: $\cos 2\left(\dfrac{3\pi}{4}\right) = \cos\left(\dfrac{3\pi}{2}\right) = 0$

continued →

Check $\theta = \dfrac{5\pi}{4}$: $\cos 2\left(\dfrac{5\pi}{4}\right)= \cos \dfrac{5\pi}{2} = \cos \dfrac{\pi}{2} = 0$

Check $\theta = \dfrac{7\pi}{4}$: $\cos 2\left(\dfrac{7\pi}{4}\right)= \cos \dfrac{7\pi}{2} = \cos \dfrac{3\pi}{2} = 0$

1108   Simplify $\tan 4\alpha / \sec 4\alpha$

$$\frac{\tan 4\alpha}{\sec 4\alpha} = \frac{\sin 4\alpha/\cos 4\alpha}{1/\cos 4\alpha} = \frac{\sin 4\alpha}{\cos 4\alpha} \cdot \frac{\cos 4\alpha}{1} = \sin 4\alpha$$

▽**1109**   Prove $\tan \theta \sin 2\theta = 2 \sin^2 \theta$.

$$\tan \theta \sin 2\theta = \frac{\sin \theta}{\cos \theta} \cdot \frac{2 \sin \theta \cos \theta}{1} = 2 \sin^2 \theta$$

1110   Prove that $\sin 4\theta = 4 \sin \theta \cos \theta \cos 2\theta$.

$$\begin{aligned}
\sin 4\theta &= \sin [2(2\theta)] = 2 \sin 2\theta \cos 2\theta & \text{Panel 8III(1)}\\
&= 2 (2 \sin \theta \cos \theta) \cos 2\theta & \text{Panel 8III(1)}\\
&= 4 \sin \theta \cos \theta \cos 2\theta
\end{aligned}$$

1111   Prove that $3 \sin \theta - \sin 3\theta = 4 \sin^3 \theta$. *Suggestion:* Let $\sin 3\theta = \sin (2\theta + \theta)$.

$$\begin{aligned}
3 \sin \theta - \sin 3\theta &= 3 \sin \theta - (\sin 2\theta \cos \theta + \cos 2\theta \sin \theta)\\
&= 3 \sin \theta - [2 \sin \theta \cos \theta \cos \theta\\
&\quad + (\cos^2 \theta - \sin^2 \theta) \sin \theta]\\
&= 3 \sin \theta - [2 \sin \theta \cos^2 \theta + \sin \theta \cos^2 \theta\\
&\quad - \sin^3 \theta]\\
&= 3 \sin \theta - 3 \sin \theta \cos^2 \theta + \sin^3 \theta\\
&= 3 \sin \theta (1 - \cos^2 \theta) + \sin^3 \theta\\
&= 3 \sin \theta \sin^2 \theta + \sin^3 \theta = 4 \sin^3 \theta
\end{aligned}$$

1112   A circle with center O and radius
       r is inscribed in triangle ABC
       whose dimensions are shown in
       the sketch. Find (1) r, (2) d,
       (3) angle CAB, and (4) the area
       of triangle ABC.

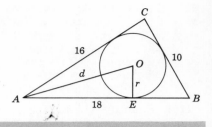

> (1) $r \approx 3.619$ (2) $d \approx 13$ (3) angle $ABC \approx 34°$
> (4) area $ABC \approx 80$
> If all of your answers are correct, skip to frame 1114.
> If all of your answers are not correct, go on to frame 1113.

1113   (1) To find r, see Panel 9E. (2) To find angle CAB, use the law of
       cosines. (3) To find d, consider triangle AOE in which angle
       $E = 90°$, angle $OAE = \frac{1}{2}CAB$, and r as found in part (1). (4) To
       find the area of ABC, see Panel 9D(2).

> (1) $r = \sqrt{\dfrac{(22 - 10)(22 - 16)(22 - 18)}{22}} = \dfrac{12\sqrt{11}}{11} \approx 3.619$
>
> (2) $\cos \alpha = \dfrac{16^2 + 18^2 - 10^2}{2(16)(18)} \approx 0.833, \quad \alpha \approx 33.6° \approx 34°$
>
> (3) $\sin \frac{1}{2}\alpha = \dfrac{r}{d}$ Therefore, $\sin 16.8° = \dfrac{3.619}{d}, \quad d \approx 12.6 \approx 13$
>
> (4)   area $= \sqrt{22(22 - 10)(22 - 16)(22 - 18)} \approx 79.6 \approx 80$

1114   A tree is located on a hillside as
       shown in the sketch. The hill has a
       slope of 24° (i.e., the hill forms
       an angle of 24° with the horizontal).
       From a certain point D along the
       hillside the angle of elevation of
       the top of the tree is 40°. From
       a point 50 ft closer to the tree
       the angle of elevation of the top

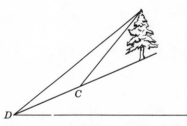

       is 52°. Find the height of the tree. *Note:* At point D, the angle of
       elevation of the tree top is the angle between a horizontal line and
       the line drawn to the top of the tree.

> approximately 34 ft
> If your answer is correct, skip to frame 1116.
> If your answer is not correct, go on to frame 1115.

1115 In triangle ABC, angle ACB =
(1)___°. In triangle DBC, angle
BCD = (2)___°, angle BDC =
(3)___°, angle DBC = (4)___°.
Apply law of sines to (5) find
length of BC of triangle DBC, and
(6) BA of triangle CAB.

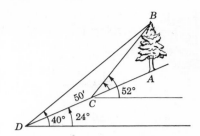

(1) 28   (2) 152   (3) 16   (4) 12   (5) $BC \approx 66.3$ (6) $BA \approx 34$

1116 Express the following sums or differences as products:
(1) $\cos 7x + \cos 3x$ and (2) $\sin 50° + \sin 12°$.

(1) $\cos 7x + \cos 3x = 2 \cos \frac{1}{2}(10x) \cos \frac{1}{2}(4x) = 2 \cos 5x \cos 2x$

(2) $\sin 50° + \sin 12° = 2 \sin \frac{1}{2}(62°) \cos \frac{1}{2}(38°) =$
$2 \sin 31° \cos 19°$

1117 Prove that $\dfrac{\cos 3\theta - \cos \theta}{\sin \theta - \sin 3\theta} = \tan 2\theta$

$$\frac{\cos 3\theta - \cos \theta}{\sin \theta - \sin 3\theta} = \frac{-2 \sin \frac{1}{2}(4\theta) \sin \frac{1}{2}(2\theta)}{2 \cos \frac{1}{2}(4\theta) \sin \frac{1}{2}(-2\theta)}$$ Panel 8 V(4), (2)

$$= \frac{-2 \sin 2\theta \sin \theta}{2 \cos 2\theta(-\sin \theta)} = \frac{\sin 2\theta}{\cos 2\theta} = \tan 2\theta$$

▽**1118** An observer on a tower notes that two objects on a level road below
have angle of depression of 60° and 30°, respectively. If the height
of the tower is 120 ft and the road runs directly away from the observer, find the distance between the objects.

≈ 134 ft
One of several possible solutions
is shown here. In triangle CBD

$\tan 60° = \dfrac{120}{BD}$

$BD = \dfrac{120}{\sqrt{3}} = 40\sqrt{3}$

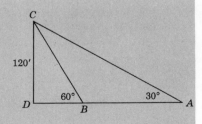

continued ➤

In triangle CAD

$$\tan 30° = \frac{120}{AD}$$

$$AD = \frac{120}{1/\sqrt{3}} = 120\sqrt{3}$$

$$AB = AD - BD = 120\sqrt{3} - 40\sqrt{3} = 80\sqrt{3} \approx 139$$

1119 How many triangles are possible if $b = 120$, $c = 145$, and angle $B = 21°$?

two triangles, ABC' and ABC
Explanation: When B is acute and the side opposite angle B is less than side C but greater than the height $h = C \sin B$, then there are two triangles.

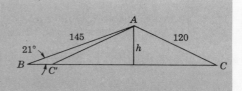

1120 Find angles (1) C and (2) $BC'A$.

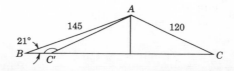

(1) $C \approx 26°$ (2) $BC'A \approx 154°$

$$\frac{145}{\sin C} = \frac{120}{\sin 21°}, \quad \sin C \approx 0.433, \quad C \approx 26°,$$

$$BC'A \approx 180° - 26° \approx 154°$$

1121 Complete the solutions for triangles ABC and ABC' by finding (1) angle BAC (2) angle BAC', (3) length of BC, and (4) length of BC'.

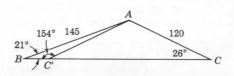

(1) angle $BAC = 133°$ (2) angle $BAC' = 5°$ (3) $BC \approx 245$
(4) $BC' \approx 29$

1122 Does $\sec(\alpha + \beta) = \sec \alpha \sec \beta/(1 - \tan \alpha \tan \beta)$? If your answer is yes, show the proof. If your answer is no, give your reason.

yes, Starting with the left member

$$\frac{\sec \alpha \sec \beta}{1 - \tan \alpha \tan \beta} = \frac{(1/\cos \alpha)(1/\cos \beta)}{1 - (\sin \alpha/\cos \beta) \cdot (\sin \alpha/\cos \beta)}$$

$$= \frac{1/(\cos \alpha \cdot \cos \beta)}{\cos \alpha \cos \beta - \sin \alpha \sin \beta/\cos \alpha \cos \beta}$$

$$= \frac{1}{\cos \alpha \cos \beta - \sin \alpha \sin \beta}$$

$$= \frac{1}{\cos(\alpha + \beta)}$$

Therefore, $\sec(\alpha + \beta) = \sec(\alpha + \beta)$

1123 *Optional.* A movie screen of height s is located on top of a tower of height t. At what distance d from the foot of the tower will the observer be located if the angle θ subtended by the tower is equal to the angle θ subtended by the screen. Express d in terms of s and t.

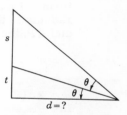

$$d = t\sqrt{\frac{s + t}{s - t}}$$

Solution:

1. $\tan \theta = \dfrac{t}{d}$

2. $\tan 2\theta = \dfrac{s + t}{d}$

3. Since $\tan 2\theta = \dfrac{2 \tan \theta}{1 - \tan^2 \theta}$, then $\dfrac{2 \tan \theta}{1 - \tan^2 \theta} = \dfrac{s + t}{d}$

4. Substitute from step 1 into the left member of step 3.

$$\frac{2(t/d)}{1 - (t/d)^2} = \frac{s + t}{d}$$

5. $\dfrac{2t/d}{(d^2 - t^2)/d^2} = \dfrac{s + t}{d}$

6. $\dfrac{2td}{d^2 - t^2} = \dfrac{s + t}{d}$

7. $2td = (d^2 - t^2)(s + t)$

8. $2td^2 = sd^2 + d^2t - st^2 - t^3$

continued →

9. $st^2 + t^3 = sd^2 - d^2t$

10. $t^2(s + t) = d^2(s - t)$

11. $d^2 = \dfrac{t^2(s + t)}{s - t}$

12. $d = t\sqrt{\dfrac{s + t}{s - t}}$

Note: To make a sensible answer, s must be larger than t.

1124 *Optional.* Two points A and B are located on opposite sides of a circular pond of radius r. An athlete swims from point A to a point P on the shore of the pond and then walks along arc PB to point B. Express the total distance d he travels in terms of θ and r, where θ expressed in radians is the angle between diameter AB and AP, the line of swimming.

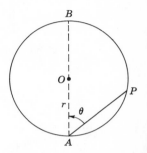

$d = 2r(\theta + \cos\ \theta)$
Here is one solution:

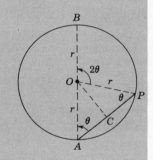

1. A central angle in radians $= \dfrac{\text{arc}}{\text{radians}}$

Therefore $2\theta = \dfrac{\text{arc } BP}{r}$

$r(2\theta) = \widehat{BP}$

2. In right triangle AOC

$\cos\ \theta = \dfrac{\frac{1}{2}\ \text{chord } AP}{r}$

Therefore, $2r\cos\ \theta = \text{chord } AP$

3. $d = \widehat{BP} + \text{chord } AP$

$\quad = 2r\theta + 2r\cos\ \theta$

$\quad = 2r(\theta + \cos\ \theta)$

SELF-TEST 4

1 Find (a) $\sin 9\pi$ and (b) $\cos 9\pi$.

2 What is the period for (a) $\sin \theta$ and (b) $\cos \theta$ when θ represents any real number?

3 (a) If f is a function having period 5, express $f(12)$ in terms of a number x where x is in the interval $0 \le x < 5$. (b) Express $f(-4)$ as a function of x in the same interval as part (a). (c) Express $f(21.2)$ as a function of x as in part (a).

4 A function has the period 3π. What are two values of x in the interval $0 \le x \le 5\pi$ such that $f(13\pi) = f(x)$?

5 What period has the function represented by (a) $\sin 2x$, (b) $\sin \frac{1}{2}x$, (c) $\sin ax$?

6 The arcs given below have their initial points at $(1,0)$ on a unit circle and are measured in a counterclockwise direction on the circle. What are the coordinates of the end points? (a) $A = \pi/6$, (b) $B = \pi/4$, (c) $C = \pi/3$, (d) $D = \pi/2$, (e) $E = 2\pi/3$, (f) $F = 3\pi/4$, (g) $G = 5\pi/6$, and (h) $H = \pi$.

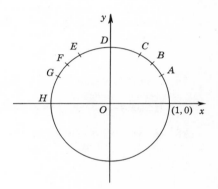

7 Make a statement comparing the graph of $y = \sin x$ with the graph of $y = 3 \sin x$.

8 Fill in the table:

x	0	$\pi/2$	π	$3\pi/2$	2π	$5\pi/2$	3π	$7\pi/2$	4π
$\frac{1}{2}x$									
$\sin \frac{1}{2}x$									

9 What is the period for (a) $\cos 2x$, (b) $\cos (x/3)$, (c) $\cos ax$?

10 Discuss the effect produced on the graph of $y = \sin x$ when $\pi/2$ is added to x thus: $y = \sin(x + \pi/2)$.

11 Sketch the graph of $y = 2 \sin(x - \pi/2)$ for one period.

12   Fill in the table:

Formula	Amplitude	Period	Phase shift
$y = \cos x$			
$y = 3 \sin 4x$			
$y = 2 \sin (3x + \pi/2)$			

13   Answer true or false for the following: (a) $\sin (-x) = \sin x$, (b) $\cos (-\theta) \tan \theta = \sin \theta$, (c) $\sin 30° + \sin 60° = \sin 90°$, (d) $2 \cos 30° = \cos 60°$, and (e) $\tan 25° = \sqrt{1 - \cos 50°/1 + \cos 50°}$.

14   Sketch the graph of $y = \cos x - \sin x$.

15   Fill in the table:

x	0	$\pi/6$	$\pi/4$	$\pi/3$	$\pi/2$
$\cot x$					

16   Find the value of $\tan (\pi/3) - \cot (\pi/3) + \sec 0$.

17   If $\tan A = 3$ and $\tan B = 2$, find the value of $\tan (A - B)$.

18   (a) Prove $\sin 2A (\sec A + \csc A) = 2(\sin A + \cos A)$. (b) Prove $\sin (x + y) \sin (x - y) + \cos (x + y) \cos (x - y) = \cos 2y$.

PART
TWO

UNIT 5 ▌Circular Functions

CIRCULAR FUNCTIONS DEFINED

1125 Introduction to *circular functions*. In the first part of this program we developed the concept of the trigonometric functions of directed angles. Each of the trigonometric functions has for its domain a set of angles and for its range a set of real numbers. For example, the functions which we refer to as the sine functions make the following association: Given any angle θ (positive or negative) expressed in degrees or radians, there is associated a real number which we call sin θ. Look at Panel 1 and report the real numbers representing sin θ when θ in radians is (1) $\pi/12$, (2) $\pi/9$, and (3) $\pi/5$.

> (1) $\sin \dfrac{\pi}{12} = 0.259$ (2) $\sin \dfrac{\pi}{9} = 0.342$ (3) $\sin \dfrac{\pi}{5} = 0.588$

Comment

In frames 1126 to 1133 the terms "function," "domain," "range," and "real numbers" are reviewed.

1126 *Function.* Whenever there is a relationship between two collections (sets) of objects or numbers so that to each element of the first set there is assigned one and only one element of the second set, we call the relationship a *function*. Let the first set be the set of all angles (in degrees or radians) and the second set be the set of real numbers. We refer to the sine as a (1)_____ because it

continued →

assigns to each angle θ one and only one real number, namely, $\sin \theta$. (2) Can a similar statement be made for the other trigonometric functions you have studied? [For example, may we speak of the *cosine as a function;* i.e., is there assigned to each angle θ (an element of the first set) a unique element of the second set, namely, $\cos \theta$?]

(1) function (2) yes

1127 *Function.* Sometimes we refer to a function as a *set of ordered pairs* since the "rule" or "association," mentioned in frame 1126 results in *pairs* of numbers. They are called *ordered pairs* since we write them so that the first component of each pair is from the first set and the second component of each pair is from the second set, thus: $(\theta, \sin \theta)$. Look at Panel 1. We could make a list showing the sine function as *ordered pairs* in this manner:

$$(0°, 0),\ (1°, 0.018),\ (2°, 0.035),\ (3°, 0.052).$$

Continue the list using (1) $4°$, (2) $5°$, (3) $6°$, and (4) $7°$ as first components respectively.

(1) $(4°, 0.070)$ (2) $(5°, 0.087)$ (3) $(6°, 0.105)$ (4) $(7°, 0.122)$

1128 *Domain and range of a function.* Let A represent one set (collection) and B represent a second set. If there is a rule which associates with each element of set A one and only one element of set B, then the set of ordered pairs thus formed is called a function. The set A is the *domain* of the function and the elements of B which appear as second components is the *range* of the function. The *domain* for the sine function as we have been studying it is the set of all directed angles expressed in radians or degrees. The *range* of the *sine* function is the set of real numbers from (1)_____ to (2)_____ inclusive. (Recall that $\sin \theta$ is never less than (3)_____ nor greater than (4)_____.)

(1) -1 (2) 1 (3) -1 (4) 1

1129 In stating the *domain* for the *tangent* function, we must exclude (1)_____ radians and (2)_____ radians (and all angles coterminal with them) from the set of all angles, because the tangent is not defined for these angles. The *range* for the *tangent* function is (3)_____.

(1) $\dfrac{\pi}{2}$ (2) $\dfrac{3\pi}{2}$

continued →

(3) all real numbers (Look at Panel 7; the line representing the tangent extends indefinitely in both positive and negative directions.)

1130 *Real numbers.* The composition of the system of *real numbers* is indicated in the following outline

Real-number system
  Rational numbers
    Integers (..., -2, -1, 0, 1, 2 ...)
    Fractions ($\frac{1}{2}$, $\frac{4}{5}$, $-\frac{2}{3}$, -2, 0.08, etc.)
  Irrational numbers ($\sqrt{3}$, $\sqrt[3]{11}$, π, $-\sqrt[5]{4}$, etc.)

The real numbers can be represented by points on a line, as indicated below, starting first with the integers. Let the distance from 0 to 1 be one unit.

The points on the line between the integers represent real numbers that are not integers, i.e., fractions and irrational numbers. For example, you know that 1.5 is a point on the line half way between 1 and 2. The fraction $\frac{3}{4}$ could be represented by a point _____ (describe its location). In your study of geometry you learned how to represent some of the irrational numbers, such as $\sqrt{2}$ and $\sqrt{3}$, using a straight edge and a compass. Considering the entire real-number system, we have this important fact: There is a one-to-one correspondence between the points on a line and the set of real numbers.

$\frac{3}{4}$ of the distance between 0 and 1

1131 When we say that there is a one-to-one correspondence between the points on a line and the set of *real numbers,* we mean that to each point on a line there corresponds exactly one real number and for each real number there is a point. (The points and the real numbers are "paired off.") This is one of the basic assumptions of analytic geometry. Consider just the *integers.* It is true that each integer can be made to correspond to a point on a number line, but what can you say about the converse "each point of the line has an integer assigned to it"?

The converse is not true.
There are many points of a real-number line to which *no* integer is assigned.
or
The integers represent only a few of the points of a number line.

1132 Consider the *rational* numbers ($\frac{1}{2}$, $\frac{5}{3}$, 2, $4\frac{7}{9}$, etc.). **(1)** Is it true that each rational number can be made to correspond to a point on a number line? **(2)** Is the converse true "each point of the number line has a rational number assigned to it"? (A rational number is a number which can be written in the form a/b where a and b are integers, $b \neq 0$. See the introduction to complex numbers in Unit 8 for a further discussion on rational numbers.

(1) yes
(2) No, there are many points of a real-number line to which *no* rational number is assigned. Consider the length which represents the diagonal of a square 1 in. on a side.

1133 Here is a table in which you are to summarize some of the statements in frames 1127 to 1132. Complete the table.

Function	Domain of θ	Range
$\sin \theta = y$	all angles	$-1 \leq$ all real numbers ≤ 1
$\cos \theta =$		
$\tan \theta =$		

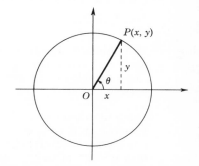

Function	Domain of θ	Range
$\sin \theta = y$	all angles	$-1 \leq$ all real numbers ≤ 1
$\cos \theta = x$	all angles	$-1 \leq$ all real numbers ≤ 1
$\tan \theta = y/x$	all angles for which $x \neq 0$	all real numbers

1134 We shall soon be ready to define a set of functions which we shall call *circular functions*. They are very closely related to the trigonometric functions; in fact, they will have the same names, sine, cosine, tangent, etc. They differ from the trigonometric functions by having as their domains the set of real numbers (as we think of them) on a number line, instead of a set of angles. It may seem confusing to say that two functions will be given the same

continued →

name, but if you will follow closely what we are saying, you should have no difficulty. We start with a circle of radius 1 in., with its center at the origin of a coordinate system. Make a sketch; label the axes u and v instead of x and y.

We shall explain later why we are using u and v instead of x and y for the axes.

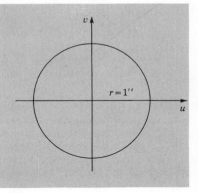

1135 Recall these facts about the circle with $r = 1$.
  1. The circle having a radius of one unit is called a *unit circle*.
  2. The distance from any point $P(u, v)$ on the unit circle to the origin is one unit ($OP = 1$).
  3. Making use of the distance formula, we have the equation

$$u^2 + v^2 = 1.$$

This is called the *equation of a unit circle* whose center is at the origin of u, v coordinate system.

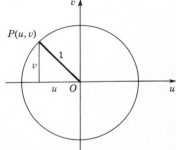

(1) Is $P(0, 1)$ a point on the unit circle? (2) Is $P(\frac{1}{2}, \frac{1}{2})$?

(1) yes, $0^2 + 1^2 = 1$ (2) no, $(\frac{1}{2})^2 + (\frac{1}{2})^2 \neq 1$

1136 Facts regarding the unit circle (*continued*).
  4. Any point whose coordinates satisfy the equation $u^2 + v^2 = 1$ is on the unit circle, and conversely the coordinates of any point on the unit circle satisfy the equation.

(1) Is $P(-1, 0)$ a point on the unit circle? (2) Is $P(1, 1)$? (3) Is $P(\frac{1}{2}, \sqrt{3}/2)$

(1) yes, $(-1)^2 + 0 = 1$ (2) no, $1^2 + 1^2 \neq 1$
(3) yes, $\left(\frac{1}{2}\right)^2 + \left(\frac{\sqrt{3}}{2}\right)^2 = 1$

1137 Facts regarding the unit circle (*continued*).
5. The length of the circumference of any circle is given by the formula $C = 2\pi r$. For a *unit circle* the circumference is equal in length to $2\pi \cdot 1 = 2\pi$ units.

On a unit circle, one-half the circumference = **(1)**_____ units. If $\pi \approx 3.14$ and $r = 1$ in., then the circumference $\approx$ **(2)**_____ and one-half the circumference $\approx$ **(3)**_____ in.

(1) π **(2)** 6.28   **(3)** 3.14

1138 Let S be the real number 2. The accompanying sketch shows the approximate location of a point P when an arc S of 2 in. is laid off along the circle, starting at the point $A(1, 0)$, in a counter-clockwise direction. Make a similar sketch showing the location of point P when S represents the real number π.

$\alpha = \dfrac{S}{r}$

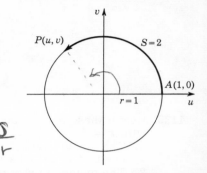

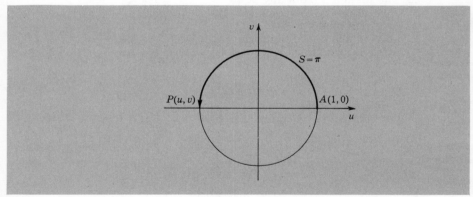

1139 To get an intuitive idea of the length of an arc on a circle, think of laying a piece of string along the arc. When the string is straightened out, you can measure its length. Suppose you want to represent the arc s on a unit circle which corresponds to the real number 1. Make a sketch showing such an arc with $A(1, 0)$ its

continued →

initial point. *Note:* A precise interpretation of the length of an arc along a curve involves the concept of limits, a topic in the calculus.

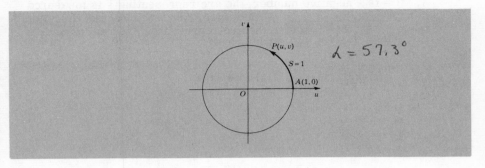

1140 In frame 1139 we suggested laying a piece of string along a circle in order to determine the length of an arc. If you think of "wrapping" or "winding" around a circle a line on which the real numbers are represented, you can see that for each real number there is a corresponding point on the circle. Start with 0 on the number line at $A(1, 0)$ on the circle. When you wind the line once around the circle, what number on the line will now coincide with the point A?

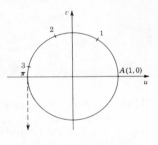

2π

1141 This sketch helps to show where certain real numbers of a straight line R will fall as the line is wrapped around the unit circle when 0 on the real line corresponds to $A(1, 0)$ on the circle. Every point on R (positive or negative) will correspond to a point on the circle. For instance, 0 corresponds to $(1, 0)$. $\pi/2$ corresponds to **(1)** _____, and $-\pi/2$ corresponds to **(2)** _____.

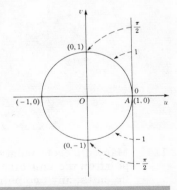

(1) $(0, 1)$ **(2)** $(0, -1)$

1142 If s is a positive number, the arc representing s is laid off in a **(1)**_____ (clockwise, counterclockwise) direction from A. If s is a negative number, the arc representing s is measured in a **(2)**_____ (clockwise, counterclockwise) direction from A. Show by a sketch the arc representing the real number s when **(3)** $s = -\pi/2$ and **(4)** $s = 3.14$.

(1) counterclockwise   **(2)** clockwise

(3)

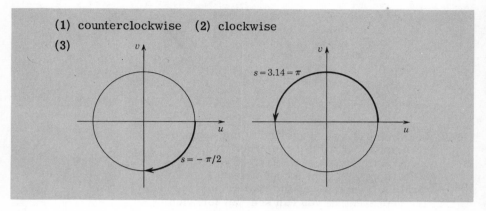

1143 The measure of the length of the arc may be larger than the circumference, e.g., if $s > |2\pi|$. Show by a sketch the arc representing the real number s when **(1)** $s = -3\pi$, **(2)** $s = 5\pi/2$, and **(3)** s is positive and the arc is a fourth-quadrant arc. *Note:* The arc having length s will be called arc s and will be referred to as first-quadrant arc if it terminates in quadrant I, etc.

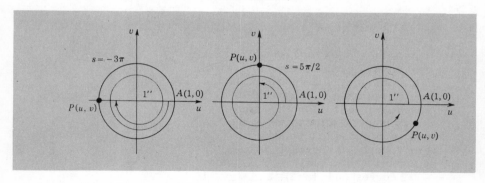

1144 Many different points on the real-number line "wrap" to the same point on the unit circle. Since the circumference of the circle is 2π units, any two points on the real-number line that are 2π units apart will "wrap" to the same point on the unit circle. If 0 on the real-number line is at the point $(1, 0)$ on the circle, then $0 \pm$ **(1)**_____ on the real line will also be at the point $(1, 0)$ on the circle if we wrap the line tightly. The points $\pi/2$ and $\pi/2 \pm$ **(2)**_____ on the

continued →

real-number line will wrap to the point (3) (___ , ___) of the unit circle if we keep 0 on the real line at the point (1, 0) on the circle.

(1) 2π or $2n\pi$ (2) 2π or $2n\pi$ (3) (0, 1)

1145 Any two points of the real-number line differing by an integral multiple of 2π will have what position with respect to each other as the line is "wrapped" around the circle? That is, if $P(u, v)$ represents the point on the circle corresponding to the real number s, what point on the circle will correspond to $s + 2\pi n$?

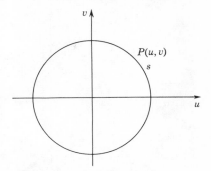

Two points on the real-number line differing by an integral multiple of 2π will coincide as the line is wrapped around the unit circle since $C = 2\pi$. If $P(u, v)$ is the point corresponding to s, then $P(u, v)$ is also the point corresponding to $s + 2\pi n$.

1146 If n is an integer and s represents a real number, then the terminal point of an arc of length s will coincide with the terminal point of the arc of length $s \pm 2n\pi$ when the arcs have the same initial point on a unit circle. This statement is true because a complete rotation around the circle returns a point to its original position and, for the unit circle, one rotation is equivalent to an arc equal to the circumference or 2π. (n rotations will mean $n \cdot 2\pi$ or $2n\pi$.) Suppose $n = -2$ and $s = -3$. Check the terminal points for an arc = -3 (real number) and an arc = $-3 + (-2 \cdot n\pi)$ on a unit circle.

Explanation: The terminal point for $s_1 = -3$ is $P(u, v)$ in the sketch (approximately). If $n = -2$, then $s_2 = -3 + (-2 \cdot 2\pi)$ which is two complete rotations from $P(u, v)$ in a clockwise direction.

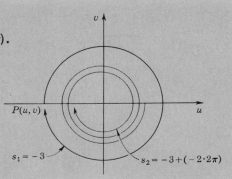

1147 Coterminal arcs are arcs on the unit circle which have their initial
point at $(1, 0)$ and have the *same* point $P(u, v)$ as their terminal
point. (1) Are $\pi/2$ and $-3\pi/2$ coterminal arcs? (2) Are π and 3π
coterminal arcs? (3) Make a sketch of two third-quadrant arcs
which are coterminal.

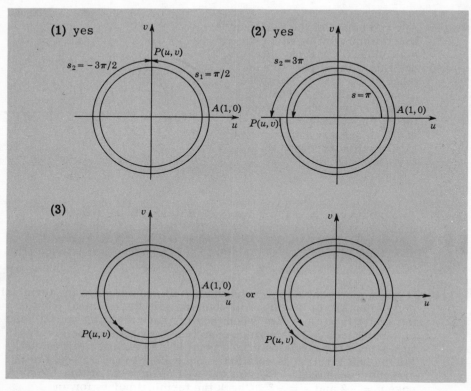

(1) yes

$s_2 = -3\pi/2$

$P(u, v)$

$s_1 = \pi/2$

$A(1, 0)$

(2) yes

$s_2 = 3\pi$

$s = \pi$

$A(1, 0)$

$P(u, v)$

(3)

$A(1, 0)$

$P(u, v)$ or

$P(u, v)$

1148 Locate the following points on a circle with a 1-in. radius (show
the circle on a coordinate system): $s = 1, 2, 3, 4, 5, 6$. On the
circle you have drawn, mark the points as P_1, P_2, etc.

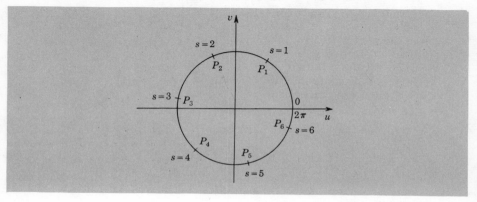

$s = 2$ $s = 1$

P_2 P_1

$s = 3$ P_3

0

2π u

P_6

$s = 6$

P_4

$s = 4$ P_5

$s = 5$

1149 You now know how to locate approximately any real number on the unit
circle. Next, if we let P represent a
moving point which starts at A and
moves in a circular path around the
unit circle a distance s equal to any
real number, we can describe the
location of P by giving its u, v coordinates. Thus we are associating with
each real number s a point $P(u, v)$ on
the circle. For example, if $s = \pi/2$,
then point P has coordinates $u = 0$
and $v = 1$, and we write $P(0, 1)$. Make a similar statement for
$s = \pi$.

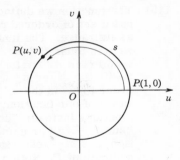

If $s = \pi$, then point P has moved to the point with coordinates
$u = -1$ and $v = 0$, and we write $P(-1, 0)$.

1150 With each arc *length s* on the circle we
are associating the *pair of numbers*
(u, v) which are the coordinates of
point P. Recall your definition of function: "Whenever there is a relationship
between two sets of numbers so that to
each element of the *first set* there is
assigned one and only one element of
the *second set*, we call the relationship
a *function*." Here the *first set* we are
using is the set of real numbers, since
s represents any real number. The
second set consists of the *pairs* (u, v) of numbers which represent
the coordinates of point P. Think this through: For each real number (an arc of length s) there is assigned one and only one pair of
numbers (u, v) on the unit circle when the point P moves on the
circle the distance s. Therefore, we say that this circular motion
of P defines a function. (1) When $s = 3\pi/2$, what pair of numbers
on the circle does this function associate with s? (2) Make a
sketch.

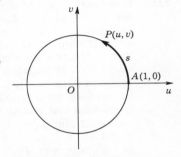

(1) $(0, -1)$ (2)

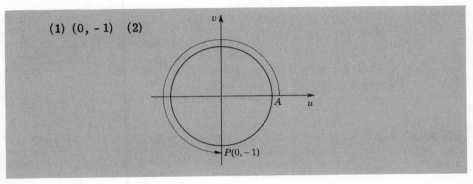

1151   The function we defined in frame 1150
has a set of ordered pairs of numbers
as its range. The function might be
written thus: "*P: s* → (*u, v*)," and we
would read it "the function *P* associates
s with the ordered pair (*u, v*)." In
order to avoid the ordered pair in the
range of our function, we define two
functions instead: "cos: *s* → *u*" and
"sin: *s* → *v*" or using previous notation, cos *s* = abscissa of *P* and sin *s* =
ordinate of *P*. Notice that cos *s* = *u*,
where *u* is the (1)_____ (first,
second) component of the ordered pair, and sin *s* = *v*, where *v* is
the (2)_____ (first, second) of the ordered pair.

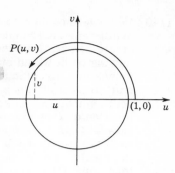

(1) first   (2) second

1152   If we take a few of the familiar values
for *s* such as 0, $\pi/2$, π, and $3\pi/2$, we
can write our new functions with the
correct numerical values assigned to
them. Remember that if *P* is a function which associates *s* with the
ordered pair (*u, v*), i.e., *P: s* →
(*u, v*), then we defined the two functions sine and cosine thus: cos: *s*
→ *u* and sin: *s* → *v*, that is, cos *s* =
u and sin *s* = *v*. Now if *s* is an arc
of length 0, then *P*: 0 → (1, 0), and
we have cos 0 = 1 and sin 0 = 0. If *s* is an arc of length $\pi/2$, then
P: $\pi/2$ → (0, 1) and cos ($\pi/2$) = (1)_____ and sin ($\pi/2$) = (2)_____.

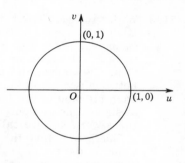

(1) 0   (2) 1

1153   Supply the correct numerical values
for the blanks.

If *s* = π, then

    cos π = (1)_____
    sin π = (2)_____

If *s* = $3\pi/2$, then

    cos $3\pi/2$ = (3)_____
    sin $3\pi/2$ = (4)_____

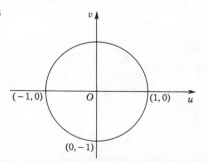

(1) -1   (2) 0   (3) 0   (4) -1

1154 This is a summary of the values of the circular functions for the real numbers 0, $\pi/2$, π, $3\pi/2$ which you have been studying.

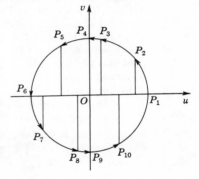

$\sin 0 = $ **(1)**_____,

$\cos 0 = $ **(2)**_____

$\sin \dfrac{\pi}{2} = $ **(3)**_____,

$\cos \dfrac{\pi}{2} = $ **(4)**_____

$\sin \pi = $ **(5)**_____, $\cos \pi = $ **(6)**

$\sin \dfrac{3\pi}{2} = $ **(7)**_____, $\cos \dfrac{3\pi}{2} = $ **(8)**

(1) 0   **(2)** 1   **(3)** 1   **(4)** 0   **(5)** 0   **(6)** –1   **(7)** –1   **(8)** 0

1155 As a point P moves around the circle in a counterclockwise direction, the points P_1, P_2, P_3, P_{-1}, P_{-2}, P_{-3}, etc., represent the end points of arcs of length s in the interval $0 \le s < 2\pi$. The length of the perpendicular from each point will correspond to the ordinate of the point and hence represent the $\sin s$. Thus, as the arc s increases from 0 to $\pi/2$, **(1)** $\sin s$ increases from **(a)**_____ at P_1 to **(b)**_____ at P_4.

(1)(a) 0, **(b)** 1

1156 **(1)** As s increases from $\pi/2$ to π, the lengths of the perpendiculars from P decrease in length from **(a)**_____ to **(b)**_____. **(2)** Hence, $\sin s$ decreases from **(a)**_____ to **(b)**_____in the interval $\pi/2 \le s \le \pi$. **(3)** In the interval $\pi \le s \le 3\pi/2$, $\sin s$

continued →

decreases from **(a)**_____to
(b)_____. **(4)** In the interval
$3\pi/2 \le s \le 2\pi$, sin s increases
from **(a)**_____ to **(b)**_____ .

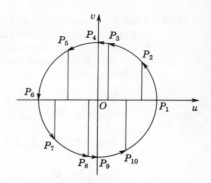

(1)(a) 1, **(b)** 0 **(2)(a)** 1, **(b)** 0
(3)(a) 0, **(b)** - 1 **(4)(a)** - 1, **(b)** 0

1157 To study the changes in the values
of cos s as s increases from 0
to $\pi/2$, we look at the abscissa of
points P_1, P_2, P_3, etc. Namely,
OP_1, OQ, OQ_2, etc. These segments **(1)**_____ (decrease, increase) in length as s increases
from 0 to $\pi/2$. cos 0 = **(2)**_____
and cos $(\pi/2)$ = **(3)**_____. *Note:*
Corresponding to each real number
s in the interval $0 \le s \le \pi/2$,
there is assigned a real number
$u = \cos s$ in the interval $1 \ge u \ge 0$.

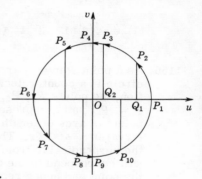

(1) decrease   **(2)** 1   **(3)** 0

1158 **(1)** As s increases over the interval
$\pi/2 \le s \le \pi$, observe that the abscissa $u = \cos s$ of the points indicated by P_4, P_5, etc., are real numbers decreasing from **(a)**_____ to
(b)_____. **(2)** Discuss the range of
u as s continues to increase over the
interval $\pi \le s \le 3\pi/2$. **(3)** Discuss
the range of u as s increases from
$3\pi/2$ to 2π.

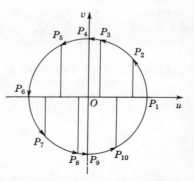

(1)(a) 0, **(b)** - 1   **(2)** u increases from - 1 to 0
(3) u increases from 0 to 1

1159 As we continue to locate points on the unit circle corresponding to the real numbers greater than or equal to 2π, we can find the values of their circular functions (sine and cosine) by referring to the set of values for points such that $0 \le s \le 2\pi$. Recall that the terminal points for arcs of length s and $s \pm 2n\pi$ coincide on the unit circle. We can extend the table thus:

Since:

$2\pi = 0 + 2\pi$,   **(1)** $\sin 2\pi = \sin 0 = $ (a)____, $\cos 2\pi = \cos 0 = $ (b)____

$\dfrac{5\pi}{2} = \dfrac{\pi}{2} + 2\pi$ **(2)** $\sin \dfrac{5\pi}{2} = \sin \dfrac{\pi}{2} = $ (a)____, $\cos \dfrac{5\pi}{2} = \cos \dfrac{\pi}{2} = $ (b)____

$3\pi = \pi + 2\pi$ **(3)** $\sin 3\pi = \sin \pi = $ (a)____, $\cos 3\pi = \cos \pi = $ (b)____

$\dfrac{7\pi}{2} = \dfrac{3\pi}{2} + 2\pi$ **(4)** $\sin \dfrac{7\pi}{2} = \sin \dfrac{3\pi}{2} = $ (a)____, $\cos \dfrac{7\pi}{2} = \cos \dfrac{3\pi}{2} = $ (b)____

(1)(a) 0, (b) 1   **(2)**(a) 1,   (b) 0
(3)(a) 0, (b) - 1   **(4)**(a) - 1, (b) 0

1160 If the real number is 8π, we can find $\sin 8\pi$ thus:

(1) $8\pi = 0 + 2 \cdot 4\pi$; therefore, $\sin 8\pi = \sin 0$ = _____

(2) $\dfrac{17}{2\pi} = \dfrac{\pi}{2} + 2 \cdot 4\pi$; therefore, $\sin \dfrac{17}{2\pi} = \sin$ (a)_____ = (b)_____

(3) $9\pi = $ (a)_____; therefore, $\sin 9\pi = \sin$ (b)_____ = (c)_____

(4) $\dfrac{19}{2\pi} = $ (a)_____; therefore, $\sin \dfrac{19}{2\pi} = \sin$ (b)_____ = (c)_____

Note: Either $2n\pi$ or $n \cdot 2\pi$ is correct.

(1) 0   **(2)**(a) $\dfrac{\pi}{2}$, (b) 1   **(3)**(a) $\pi + 2 \cdot 4\pi$, (b) π, (c) 0

(4)(a) $\dfrac{3\pi}{2} + 2 \cdot 4\pi$, (b) $\dfrac{3\pi}{2}$, (c) - 1

1161 If we are given the real number $-\pi/2$, we locate the corresponding point on the unit circle by moving $\pi/2$ units in a **(1)**_____ direction from $A(1, 0)$. This arc is coterminal with an arc represented by the positive real number **(2)**_____. Therefore, $\sin(-\pi/2) = $ **(3)**_____ and $\cos(-\pi/2) = $ **(4)**_____.

(1) clockwise   **(2)** $\dfrac{3\pi}{2}$ **(3)** - 1 or $\sin \dfrac{3\pi}{2}$ **(4)** 0 or $\cos \dfrac{3\pi}{2}$

1162 (1) (a) Find sin (-5π) and (b) cos (-5π). (2) (a) Find sin $\dfrac{-9\pi}{2}$ and (b) cos $(-9\pi/2)$. Make a sketch if you are not sure.

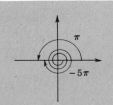

(1) (a) sin $(-5\pi) = 0$

   (b) cos $(-5\pi) = -1$

Solution: $-5\pi = \pi - 2 \cdot 3\pi$

Therefore, sin $\dfrac{-5\pi}{2}$ = sin   = 0

(2) (a) sin $\dfrac{-9\pi}{2} = -1$

   (b) cos $\dfrac{-9\pi}{2} = 0$

Solution: $\dfrac{-9\pi}{2} = \dfrac{3\pi}{2} - 3 \cdot 2\pi$

Therefore, sin $\dfrac{-9\pi}{2}$ = sin $\dfrac{3\pi}{2}$ = -1

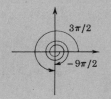

1163 (1) (a) Find sin 780π and (b) cos 780π. (2) (a) Find sin 781π and (b) cos 781π.

(1) (a) sin $780\pi = 0$, (b) cos $780\pi = 1$

Solution: $780\pi = 0 + 2 \cdot 390\pi$; therefore, sin 780π = sin 0 = 0

Note: A line segment corresponding to the real number 780π will "wrap" around the unit circle exactly 390 times.

(2) (a) sin $781\pi = 0$, (b) cos $781\pi = -1$

Solution: $781\pi = \pi + 2 \cdot 390\pi$; therefore, sin 781π = sin π = 0

1164   Remember that s may be any real number; thus, we say that the domain for each of our functions is the set of all real numbers. Since P always lies on the circle of radius 1, the co-ordinates of P (abscissa u and ordinate v) are also real numbers ranging from -1 to 1 inclusive.

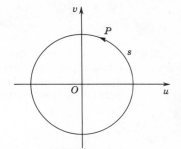

continued →

Complete the table.

Function	Domain	Range
cos s		
sin s		

Function	Domain	Range
cos s	all real numbers	$-1 \leq s \leq 1$
sin s	all real numbers	$-1 \leq s \leq 1$

1165 Here we point out the relationship between the circular functions cos s and sin s which we have just defined and the trigonometric functions cos θ and sin θ which you studied earlier in the program. Study the sketch. If arc s represents a real number and P is the position of a point which has moved in a circular path for a distance s from A, then cos s = **(1)**_____
_____ and sin s =
(2)_____.

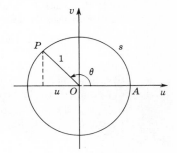

If we connect point P with the origin O, we have constructed the angle θ in the unit circle, and we know from previous definitions that cos θ = **(3)**_____ and sin θ = **(4)**_____.

(1) u or abscissa or first component
(2) v or ordinate or second component
(3) u or abscissa   **(4)** v or ordinate

1166 In frame 1165 we pointed out that if θ is the angle with vertex at the center of a unit circle and s is the length of the arc subtending θ, then sin θ = v = sin s (i.e., sin θ = sin s) and cos θ = r = cos s (i.e., cos θ = cos s). You recall that we have a unit of measure for angles such

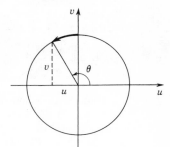

continued →

that the number of angular units in the measure of θ is equal to the number of linear units in the subtending arc of the unit circle. State the name of the unit.

radian

1167   If we are thinking of any real number, a, for example, the sin a can be interpreted (1) as the value of the *circular* function sine for the real number a or (2) as the value of the trigonometric function sine for an angle whose radian measure is a. The values of the functions are the same whichever interpretation is made; for this reason the same names are used for the circular functions as for the trigonometric functions. You can usually decide from the context whether you are dealing with the circular functions or the trigonometric functions. Note that the values of the circular functions can be found by referring to Panel 1 and using the column labeled *radians*. Look at Panel 1. Suppose the length of s is 0.524; then sin 0.524 = 0.500 and cos 0.524 = 0.866 since sin s = sin θ and cos s = cos θ.

(1) If $s = 1.047$, find (a) sin s and (b) cos s
(2) If $s = 1.571$, find (a) sin s and (b) cos s.

(1)(a) sin 1.047 = 0.866, (b) cos 1.047 = 0.500
(2)(a) sin 1.571 = 1.000, (b) cos 1.571 = 0.000
Note: 1.571 $\approx \pi/2$ and we have already identified this arc with the ordered pair (1, 0).

1168   The other circular functions tangent, cotangent, secant, and cosecant are defined in terms of *sine* and *cosine* as the trigonometric functions were: tan s = (1)_____, sec s = (2)_____, cot s = (3)_____, and csc s = (4)_____. Supply the correct words for the blanks. Consult the reference panel only if necessary.

(1) $\dfrac{\sin s}{\cos s}$ (2) $\dfrac{1}{\cos s}$

(3) $\dfrac{\cos s}{\sin s}$ or $\dfrac{1}{\tan s}$ (4) $\dfrac{1}{\sin s}$

Remember that the function is undefined when the denominator has a numerical value of 0.

1169   So that there is no doubt about using θ and s as we have done, let us review. In the first part of the program we defined radian measure thus: θ in radians = (1)_____, where θ is the central angle in a circle whose radius is r and where s is the length of the arc which

continued →

θ intercepts on the circle. If θ is the central angle in a *unit* circle, then $r = 1$ and our definition may be written θ in radians = (2)_____. Hence the measure of an angle in (3)_____ is equal to the length of the corresponding arc on the unit circle.

(1) $\dfrac{s}{r}$ **(2)** $\dfrac{s}{1} = s$ **(3)** radians

1170 If an arc s on a unit circle represents the real number 1, then the central angle θ is 1 radian. If an arc s on a unit circle represents the real number 2, then the central angle is 2 radians, etc.

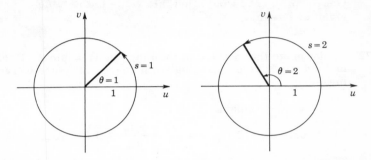

Make a sketch using the real number 3 for the arc s and indicate the corresponding central angle θ.

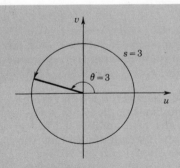

Note: The arc representing the real number 3 is slightly less than π (3.14) which is one-half the circumference.

1171 We have now shown that although there is a definite relationship between the so-called trigonometric functions (angle functions) and

continued →

the circular functions (real-number
functions), we can work with the circular functions without thinking of the
angles associated with them. In the
sketch we have shown 2 as the measure
of the arc on a unit circle. Is it meaningful to ask for the numerical value
of sin 2?

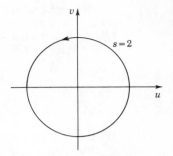

yes   *Note:* You would find this value in the table of sines
given in radians.

1172   Do not make the mistake of thinking sin 2° = sin 2. Recall the
method you have of changing from degree measure to radian
measure.

$$1° = \frac{\pi}{180} \text{ radians}$$

Therefore $2° = 2 \cdot \frac{\pi}{180} = \frac{\pi}{90} \approx \frac{3.14}{90} \approx 0.035$ radians

Then sin 2° ≈ sin 0.035 radian or sin 0.035 (a real number) ≈
(1)_____ (see Panel 1). (2) Can you find in Panel 1 a value for
sin 2? If so, what is it?

(1) 0.035
(2) sin 2 ≈ 0.910. Your answer probably was "no." The approxi-
      mate answer can be obtained by a method which will be ex-
      plained in the following frames.

1173   We asked you about the sin 2 in frame
1172. The information in Panel 1 extends only to the real number 1.571 (or
1.571 radians). To find sin 2 study the
following: We know from previous
work that sin (π - θ) = sin θ where θ
and π are expressed in radians.

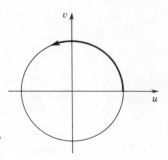

Therefore, sin (π - 2) = sin 2

If π = 3.142, then sin (3.142 - 2) ≈ sin 2,
sin (1.142) ≈ sin 2, sin (1.142) ≈ _____.
(See Panel 1.)

0.910   Since 1.142 is not one of the numbers in Panel 1, a process called *interpolation* was used for approximating the sin 1.142.
See frame 1174 for an explanation.

1174 *Interpolation.* In Panel 1 we find

sin 1.135 = 0.906
sin 1.152 = 0.914

To find sin 1.142, we proceed as follows: Find the differences indicated

$$0.018\left[0.008\left[\begin{matrix}\sin 1.134 = 0.906\\ \sin 1.142 = \quad x\\ \sin 1.152 = 0.914\end{matrix}\right] x - 0.906\right]0.008$$

We assume the differences (over a small interval) in the left member are proportional to those on the right. Therefore,

$$\frac{0.008}{0.018} = \frac{x - 0.906}{0.008}$$

$$\frac{4}{9} = \frac{x - 0.906}{0.008}$$

$$0.910 = x$$

hence, sin 1.140 = 0.910

A more complete explanation appears in Appendix A. Interpolation is not a completely satisfactory process when tables have only the accuracy shown in Panel 1. No answer required unless you want to try a problem on interpolation. *Suggested problem:* Find sin 0.828, using Panel 1 and interpolating for three-digit accuracy.

$$0.018\left[0.008\left[\begin{matrix}\sin 0.820 = 0.731\\ \sin 0.828 = \quad x\\ \sin 0.838 = 0.743\end{matrix}\right] x - 0.731\right]0.012$$

$$\frac{0.008}{0.018} = \frac{x - 0.731}{0.012}$$

$$x = 0.736$$

Therefore, sin 0.826 $\approx$ 0.736

Note: sin 0.828 must lie between sin 0.820 and 0.838, i.e., $0.731 < 0.736 < 0.743$.

1175 *Optional.* Use interpolation to find cos 0.658.

$$0.017\left[0.012\left[\begin{matrix}\cos 0.646 = 0.799\\ \cos 0.658 = \quad x\\ \cos 0.663 = 0.788\end{matrix}\right] x - 0.799\right] -0.011$$

$$\frac{0.012}{0.017} = \frac{x - 0.799}{-0.011}$$

$$0.791 \approx x \qquad\qquad \text{Therefore, cos 0.658} \approx 0.791$$

Note: cos θ decreases as θ increases.

1176 *Optional.* Find tan 1.200.

$$0.017\left[0.013\left[\begin{array}{l}\tan 1.187 = 2.475 \\ \tan 1.200 = \quad x \\ \tan 1.204 = 2.605\end{array}\right] x - 2.475\right]0.130$$

$$\frac{0.013}{0.017} = \frac{x - 2.475}{0.130}$$

$$2.574 = x$$

Therefore, tan 1.200 = 2.574

Consult Appendix A for further work on interpolation.

1177 We said previously that by means of the circular functions, mathematicians and scientists may study many of the properties of periodic motion or phenomena (alternating electric currents, sound waves, uniform motion on a circle, etc.). When we speak of periodic motion, we mean that the motion has the property of repeating itself at regular intervals. The measure of the interval is referred to as the period of the motion, and the motion itself is said to be periodic. Below are listed two familiar examples of periodic motion. You are to indicate the period for each (the time required for one complete cycle).

(1) The rotation of the earth on its axis.
(2) The movement of the earth around the sun.

(1) 24 hr   (2) 1 year—app. 365 days

1178 Our study of periodic motion is concerned with *circular* periodicities where the simplest example is that of a wheel turning on its axis. If you mark a point on the wheel, you notice that it travels over a certain path and returns to its initial position. You may think of the distance traversed by the point in one complete cycle as the period, or if the wheel is turning at a regular speed, you may think of the time required for one rotation as the period. Using a clock as an example, think of a motion you see there and describe the period of that motion.

You have several:
1. The distance traveled by the tip of the minute hand in 1 cycle (or the hour hand).
2. The time required by the minute hand to make a complete revolution (1 hr).
3. The time for the hour hand to make a complete revolution (12 hr).
4. If it is a pendulum clock, the swing back and forth of the pendulum represents one period.

1179 We have already stated that the circular functions sine and cosine are *periodic* and that the period for each is 2π. (Recall that as point P moves around the unit circle, with each real number s, $0 \leq s < 2\pi$, there is associated a unique pair of numbers (u, v), the co-ordinates of a point P on the circle. The first coordinate we designated as cos s and the second coordinate as sin s). When stating the period for a circular function, we try to state the *smallest* interval which includes all the elements of the *range* of the function. A movement of **(1)**_____ units is required to make a complete cycle on a circle; hence, the period for sine and cosine is **(2)**_____ .

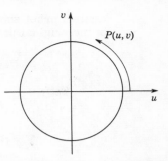

(1) 2π **(2)** 2π

Comment

Since we shall be working later with functions whose period is not 2π, we shall digress at this point to make two general statements about periodicity.

1. Functions which have the property of repeating themselves at equal intervals are said to be *periodic*.
2. The function f is said to be periodic with a period a, if the value of the function f at x is equal to the value of the function f at $(x + a)$ for all real numbers x, assuming $a \neq 0$ (and a is smallest number for which this is true).

In symbols this is written: $f(x) = f(x + a), a \neq 0$, for all x.

Example: Each successive addition of a unit of time ($a = 1$ min) brings the second hand of the watch back to a designated point x on the dial.

1180 Given the function f having period a, $a \neq 0$, such that $f(x) = f(x + a)$ for all x,

I. Prove that $f(x + 2a) = f(x)$ when $a > 0$.

Study the following proof: Starting with the left member, we can write

1. $f(x + 2a) = f(x + a + a)$ applying the associative
              $= f((x + a) + a))$ law of addition
2. $= f(x + a)$ since the period for f is
                                 a by hypothesis
3. $= f(x)$ reasoning again as in Step 2.

continued →

Write a proof showing that $f(x + 3a) = f(x)$, using the hypothesis of the original problem.

Here is a short proof:

Proof

1. $f(x + 3a) = f((x + 2a) + a)$ starting with the left member as in the proof for I

   $= f(x + 2a)$ by hypothesis f has period a

   $= f(x)$ applying statement I

A longer proof would be the repetition here of the steps for statement I.

1181 By continuing the reasoning shown in frame 1180, we can state that in general $f(x + na) = f(x)$, where $n = 1, 2, 3, \ldots$, if f is a function with period a, $a \neq 0$, for all real numbers x. Suppose n is *negative*. Study the following to see whether $f(x) = f(x + na)$ where $a > 0$ and $n = -1, -2, -3, \ldots$.

Proof:

1. First note that
   $f(x) = f((x - a) + a)$ since $[(s - a) + a] = x$

2. $= f(x - a)$ f is a function having period a by hypothesis

3. $f(x - a) = f((x - 2a) + a)$ since $[(x - 2a) + a] = x - a$

4. $= f(x - 2a)$ same as Step 2

5. $f(x - 2a) = f((x - 3a) + a)$ Why?_____

6. $= f(x - 3a)$ Why?_____

7. Therefore, $f(x) = f(x - 3a)$ from Steps 2, 4, and 6

5. $[(x - 3a) + a] = x - 2a$
6. same as Step 2

1182 Continuing the reasoning in frame 1180 and 1181, we arrive at the general statement: If f is a periodic function, with $a > 0$, then $f(x) = f(x + na)$ where n is any integer. This means then that we can determine all the values for f if we know the values of the function for the interval $0 \leq x < a$.

Example 1: f is a function whose period is 3, i.e., $f(x) = f(x + 3)$.

Express $f(10)$ in terms of $f(x)$ where x is in the interval $0 \leq x < 3$.
Solution: $f(10) = f(1 + 3 \cdot 3) = f(1)$ since $f(x) = f(x + na)$.

continued →

Example 2. Express $f(-4)$ as a function of a number in the interval $0 \leq x < 3$.

Solution: $f(-4) = f(2 + (-2) \cdot 3) = f(2)$.

Express $f(11)$ as a function of a number in the interval $0 \leq x < 3$.

$f(11) = f(2 + 3 \cdot 3) = f(2)$

1183 f is a function having period $a = 4$; i.e., $f(x) = f(x + 4)$, $0 \leq x < 4$. Express the following as a function of a number in the indicated interval: **(1)** $f(5)$ and **(2)** $f(7)$.

(1) $f(5) = f(1 + 1 \cdot 4) = f(1)$
(2) $f(7) = f(3 + 1 \cdot 4) = f(3)$

1184 f is a function whose period is 4. **(1)** Express $f(23)$ as in frame 1183. **(2)** Express $f(-1)$.

(1) $f(23) = f(3 + 5 \cdot 4) = f(3)$
(2) $f(-1) = f(3 + (-1) \cdot 4) = f(3)$

1185 f is a function having period $a = 4$. **(1)** Express $f(5.3)$ as in frame 1183 and 1184. **(2)** Express $f(6\frac{2}{3})$.

(1) $f(5.3) = f(1.3 + 1 \cdot 4) = f(1.3)$
(2) $f(6\frac{2}{3}) = f(2\frac{2}{3} + 1 \cdot 4) = f(2\frac{2}{3})$

1186 Express f as a function of a number in the indicated interval: f is a function having period $a = 2\pi$; i.e., $f(x) = f(x + 2\pi)$, $0 \leq x < 2\pi$. **(1)** $f(7\pi)$ and **(2)** $f(-7\pi)$.

(1) $f(7\pi) = f(\pi + 3 \cdot 2\pi) = f(\pi)$
(2) $f(-7\pi) = f(\pi + (-4) \cdot 2\pi) = f(\pi)$
Note: You may not need the formula for solving these exercises, but it gives a systematic way of working.

1187 Sine is a function whose period is 2π; i.e., $\sin x = \sin (x + 2\pi)$, $0 \leq x < 2\pi$. Express the following as functions of a number in the indicated interval: **(1)** $\sin 12\pi$ and **(2)** $\sin (9\pi/4)$.

(1) $\sin 12\pi = \sin (0 + 6 \cdot 2\pi) = \sin 0$
(2) $\sin \frac{9\pi}{4} = \sin\left(\frac{\pi}{4} + 1 \cdot 2\pi\right) = \sin \frac{\pi}{4}$

1188   Cosine is a function having period $a = 2\pi$; i.e., $\cos x = \cos(x + 2\pi)$, $0 \leq x < 2\pi$. **(1)** Express $\cos(17\pi/3)$ as in frame 1187. **(2)** Express $\cos 15.56$. *Note:* $\pi \approx 3.14$ and $2\pi \approx 6.28$.

(1) $\cos \dfrac{17\pi}{3} = \cos\left(\dfrac{5\pi}{3} + 2 \cdot 2\pi\right) = \cos \dfrac{5\pi}{3}$

(2) $\cos 15.56 = \cos(3 + 2 \cdot 2\pi) = \cos 3$
or $= \cos(3 + 2 \cdot 6.28) = \cos 3$

1189   The function f has period $a = \pi$; i.e., $f(x) = f(x + \pi)$, $0 \leq x \leq \pi$. **(1)** Express $f(9\pi/2)$ as in frames 1187 and 1188. **(2)** Express $f(-13\pi)$.

(1) $f\left(\dfrac{9\pi}{2}\right) = f\left(\dfrac{\pi}{2} + 4 \cdot \pi\right) = f\left(\dfrac{\pi}{2}\right)$

(2) $f(-13\pi) = f(\pi + (-14)\pi) = f(\pi)$

1190   Suppose we have a function whose period is 2π. What are two values of x in the interval $0 \leq x < 4\pi$ such that $f(12\pi) = f(x)$?

$x = 0$, $x = 2\pi$

Solution: $f(12\pi) = f(0 + 6 \cdot 2\pi) = f(0)$
Since the period is 2π, $f(2\pi) = f(0 + 2\pi) = f(0)$
So that in the interval $0 \leq x < 4\pi$, $f(12\pi) = f(0) = f(2\pi)$

1191   If a function f has the period 2π, find two values of x in the interval $0 \leq x < 4\pi$ such that $f(-\pi/2) = f(x)$.

$x = \dfrac{3\pi}{2}$, $x = \dfrac{7\pi}{2}$

Solution: $f\left(\dfrac{-\pi}{2}\right) = f\left(\dfrac{3\pi}{2} + (-1) \cdot 2\pi\right) = f\left(\dfrac{3\pi}{2}\right)$

and $f\left(\dfrac{3\pi}{2} + 2\pi\right) = f\left(\dfrac{7\pi}{2}\right)$

1192   If the function f has the period 2π, state two values of x in the interval $0 \leq x < 4\pi$ such that $f(15\pi) = f(x)$.

$x = \pi$, $x = 3\pi$

1193 We have been discussing functions with a specified period such as the sine function with period 2π, i.e., $\sin x = \sin(x + 2n\pi)$ for all x. Our next problem is to *find* the period for $\sin 2x$.

1. Let $2x = z$. Since the period for the sine function is 2π, we know that $\sin z$ completes exactly one cycle in the interval $0 \leq z < 2\pi$.
2. Note that if we begin the cycle with $z = 0$ so that $\sin z = 0$, then we end the cycle with $z = 2\pi$ so that again $\sin z = 0$.
3. Since $2x = z$, we know that the cycle for $\sin 2x$ starts with $2x = 0$, or $x = 0$, and ends with $2x = 2\pi$, or $x = \pi$.
4. Therefore, the period for $\sin 2x$ is the interval from 0 to π, or simply π.

Repeat these steps to find the period for $\sin \frac{1}{2} x$

the period for $\sin \frac{1}{2} x$ is 4π.
Solution:
1. Let $\frac{1}{2} x = z$
2. Since $\sin z$ has period 2π, cycle begins with $z = 0$ when $\sin z = 0$; cycle ends with $z = 2\pi$ when $\sin z = 0$.
3. Substituting from Steps 1 to 2 and solving for x
   $\frac{1}{2} x = 0$ Therefore $x = 0$
   $\frac{1}{2} x = 2\pi$ Therefore $x = 4\pi$
4. The period for $\sin \frac{1}{2} x$ is $4\pi - 0$ or 4π.

1194 You know the period for $\sin x$ or $\cos x$ is 2π. Apply the method in frame 1193 to find the period for $\sin 4x$.

the period for $\sin 4x$ is $\dfrac{\pi}{2}$
Solution:
1. Let $z = 4x$
2. If $z = 0$, $\sin z = 0$ $\Big\}$ sine has period of 2π
   If $z = 2\pi$, $\sin z = 0$
3. Therefore, $4x = 0$ and $x = 0$ substituting from step 1 to
   $4x = 2\pi$ and $x = \dfrac{\pi}{2}$ 2 and solving for x
4. The period for $\sin 4x$ is $\dfrac{\pi}{2} - 0 = \dfrac{\pi}{2}$

1195 Find the period for the function represented by $\cos \frac{1}{2} x$ when you know that $\cos x$ has period 2π.

$\cos \frac{1}{2} x$ has period 4π.

1196　What period has the function represented by $\cos \frac{1}{3} x$ if $\cos x$ has period 2π?

> $\sin \frac{1}{3} x$ has period 6π
>
> *Note:* Later in this program you will graph the functions $\sin x$, $\sin 2x$, $\sin \frac{1}{2}x$, etc., and you will see the importance of being able to find the period easily.

1197　If two functions f and g have the same period a for any real number x, we can show that the *sum* of the two functions f and g also has period a as follows:

$\rightarrow$

　1. $\left.\begin{array}{l} f(x) = f(x + a) \\ g(x) = g(x + a) \end{array}\right\}$ 　　　　　　　by hypothesis and the definition of periodic property

　2. $f(x) + g(x) = f(x + a) + g(x + a)$ 　　　addition axiom

　3. $(f + g)(x) = (f + g)(x + a)$ 　　　by definition of addition of functions

　4. Therefore, $f + g$ has period a 　　　by definition of the periodic property

Since the sine and cosine are two functions having period 2π, what will be the period for the sum of these two functions?

> the sum will have period 2π 　　*Note:* This idea will be useful when graphs of sums of functions are made.

1198　*Multiplication of functions f and g is defined thus for any real x:*

$$f(x) \cdot g(x) = (f \cdot g)(x)$$

To show that if f and g have period a, then $f \cdot g$ also has period a, we make a proof thus:

$\Rightarrow$

　1. $f(x) = f(x + a)$ 　　　　　　by hypothesis and the
　　 $g(x) = g(x + a)$ 　　　　　　property of periodic functions

　2. $f(x) \cdot g(x) = f(x + a) \cdot g(s + a)$ 　Why?_____

　3. $(f \cdot g)(x) = (f \cdot g)(x + a)$ 　　Why?_____

　4. Therefore, $f \cdot g$ has period a 　　by definition of the periodic property

> 2. multiplication axiom
> 3. definition of multiplication of functions (and substitution)

1199 In frame 1198 we stated and proved the following property regarding multiplication of functions: If f and g are functions having period a, then $f \cdot g$ also has period a. Sine and cosine are functions having period 2π for all real numbers x. What period has the product of these two function?

the product also has period 2π

1200 If you have studied composition of functions [notation $g(f(x))$ or $g \circ f$] read frame 1200. If you have not, skip to frame 1201. The following is a brief discussion of *composition* of functions as it applies to the periodic property of sines and cosines. *Statement:* If g and f are two functions and f has period a, then the composite function $g(f(x))$ also has period a for any meaningful choice of a with respect to g.

Proof:

1. $f(x) = f(x + a)$ by hypothesis

2. $g(x) = g(x)$ if g is defined for x

3. $g(f(x)) = g(f(x + a))$ definition of composition and substitution

4. Therefore, $g(f(x))$ has period a definition of periodic principle.

If sin x has period 2π, what is the period for cos (sin x)?

2π

1201 How can we be sure that the sine and cosine functions can have no positive period less than 2π? *Suggestion:* What can you say about the coordinates (u, v) of point P for any real number s in the interval $0 \leq s < 2\pi$?

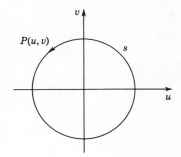

For any real number s in the interval $0 \leq s < 2\pi$, the terminal point P represents a unique point on the unit circle. All points of the unit circle are represented, as s assumes all real numbers in the interval $0 \leq s < 2\pi$.

1202   For what real numbers s in the interval
$0 \leq s < 2\pi$ does $\sin s = \cos s$?
Suggestion: Since $\cos s = u$ and $\sin s$
$= v$, you must determine the real number s such that the coordinates u and
v of P are equal. Two points are located
approximately in the sketch. **(1)** What
is the length of s, which terminates at
P_1, and **(2)** s_2, which terminates at P_2?

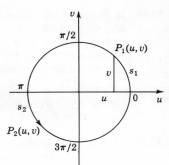

(1) $s_1 = \dfrac{\pi}{4}$ **(2)** $s_2 = \dfrac{5\pi}{4}$

1203   Find the real numbers s in the interval
$0 \leq s < 2\pi$ for which $\sin s = -\cos s$.
Suggestion: Recall in which quadrants
the sine and cosine functions have opposite signs. Apply the ideas that were
used in frame 1202.

$s_1 = \dfrac{3\pi}{4}$, $s_3 = \dfrac{7\pi}{4}$

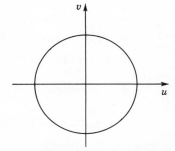

GRAPHS OF CIRCULAR FUNCTIONS

1204 We shall now discuss the process of graphing the circular functions defined thus: $u = \cos s$, $v = \sin s$; i.e., $P(u, v)$ a point on the unit circle is associated with the real number s. Since we have established that each function has period 2π, we can devote most of our attention to the graphs of the interval $0 \leq s < 2\pi$. You will find that you know a great deal about these graphs since you already have constructed the graphs of cosine and sine functions of angles (in radian measure). Some properties of these functions will be reviewed first.

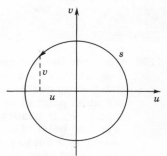

1. Since u and v are coordinates of a point on the unit circle, we know that $u^2 + v^2 = $ **(1)**_____.

2. By definition, $u = \cos s$ and $v = \sin s$; therefore, substituting step 1, we have, $\cos^2 s + \sin^2 s = $ **(2)**_____.

(1) 1   **(2)** 1

1205 If you solve $\cos^2 s + \sin^2 s = 1$ for $\cos s$, the result is $\cos^2 s = $ **(1)**_____ and $\cos s = $ **(2)**_____. If you solve $\cos^2 s + \sin^2 s = 1$ for $\sin s$, the result is $\sin^2 s = $ **(3)**_____ and $\sin s = $ **(4)**_____. *Note:* You are now thinking of s representing a measure of length on a number line, but you are getting the same statements as when s represented the measure of an angle in radians.

(1) $1 - \sin^2 s$ **(2)** $\pm\sqrt{1 - \sin^2 s}$

(3) $1 - \cos^2 s$ **(4)** $\pm\sqrt{1 - \cos^2 s}$

1206 If you examine the statements $\cos^2 s = 1 - \sin^2 s$ and $\sin^2 s = 1 - \cos^2 s$, you should be able to state the range (the set of all values) for $\sin s$ or $\cos s$ thus: **(1)**_____ $\leq \cos s \leq$ _____ and **(2)**_____ $\leq \sin s \leq$ _____ (copy the entire statements as you answer). *Note:* Recall also that by definition $\sin s$ and $\cos s$ are coordinates of points on the unit circle.

(1) $-1 \leq \cos s \leq 1$ **(2)** $-1 \leq \sin s \leq 1$

1207   We speak of the amplitude of the sine (or cosine) function meaning the maximum value of $|\sin s|$. The statement in frame 1206 tells you that the sine function has amplitude **(1)**_____. The amplitude for the cosine function is **(2)**_____. *Note:* The amplitude may be thought of as the greatest deviation of the $\sin s$ from 0, either in a positive or negative direction.

(1) 1   **(2)** 1

1208   Consider the symmetry of a circle with respect to the u axis. If you mark a point P_1 in quadrant I which is the terminal point of an arc of length s and a point P_2 in quadrant IV which is the terminal point of an arc of the same length as s but negative in direction, you should observe that the coordinates of points P_1 and P_2 are the same, except for signs. If you represent P_1 with coordinates (u, v), how should you represent P_2?

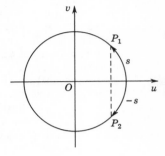

$(u, -v)$

1209   Suppose the arc of length s gives us a terminal point on the unit circle in quadrant II, and we represent P with coordinates (u, v). How would we indicate the coordinates of P_2 if it is the terminal point of an arc of the same length but extending in the opposite direction from A.

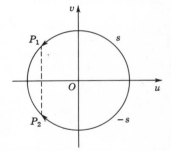

$(u, -v)$

Note: If the coordinates of P_1 are (u, v), we are indicating that u represents a *negative number* since the first coordinate of a point in quadrant II is negative. Then it follows that for the first coordinate of P_2, u represents the *same negative* number. The second coordinate of P_1 is a positive quantity, but the second coordinate of P_2 is a negative quantity.

1210 Because of the symmetric property of the circle with respect to the U axis, we can see that corresponding to any two arcs of length s and $(-s)$, $s \neq 0$, on a unit circle are two points P_1 and P_2 such that if the coordinates of P_1 are (u, v), then the coordinates of P_2 are **(1)** (__ , __). **(2)** Check this statement, if arc s terminates in quadrant IV, by sketching both arc s and $-s$ on a unit circle and writing the coordinates of point P_1 and P_2 corresponding to s and $-s$, respectively.

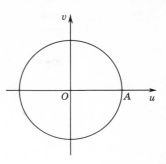

(1) $(u, -v)$ **(2)**

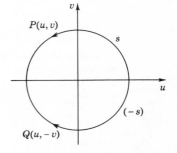

1211 By definition $\cos s$ = abscissa of P and $\sin s$ = ordinate of P. Therefore we see that for any arc of length s

$\cos (-s) = u$
$\cos s = u$

hence, $\cos (-s) = \cos s$.

But,

$\sin (-s) =$ **(1)** _____
$\sin s =$ **(2)** _____

hence, $\sin (-s) =$ **(3)** _____ .

(1) $-v$ **(2)** v **(3)** $-\sin s$
Note: We had a similar statement for sine and cosine of positive and negative *angles*.

1212 In our discussion of circular functions we used the u, v notation for the axes of the unit circle and indicated points corresponding to the real numbers s as $P(u, v)$ on the circle. In constructing graphs of the circular functions we shall return to the x, y notation, plotting

continued →

the numbers s on the x axis and their corresponding points $P(u = \cos s, v = \sin s)$ from the circle on the y axis.

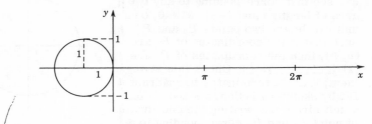

For one period of the sine (or cosine) function, the interval on the x axis is **(1)**_____ $\leq x <$ _____, on the y axis the interval is **(2)**_____ $\leq y \leq$ _____. Copy the entire statements as you answer.

(1) $0 \leq x < 2\pi$ **(2)** $-1 \leq y \leq 1$

1213   Mark off an area of length 2π and width 2 as shown below. This will be used to sketch the graph of $y = \sin x$. Divide the interval from 0 to 2π into four equal parts and label them as shown.

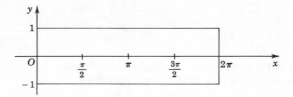

It will be helpful in this section for you to use the same scale of measurement on both x and y axes.

your graph is your answer

1214   Make a list as shown here and fill in the blanks for the values of the points you have marked on the graph. Recall that $v = \sin s$ and that the u and v axes divide the circle into four equal arcs as shown.

continued →

$\sin 0 \quad = \quad \underline{\hspace{2cm}}$

$\sin \dfrac{\pi}{2} \quad = \quad \underline{\hspace{2cm}}$

$\sin \pi \quad = \quad \underline{\hspace{2cm}}$

$\sin \dfrac{3\pi}{2} \quad = \quad \underline{\hspace{2cm}}$

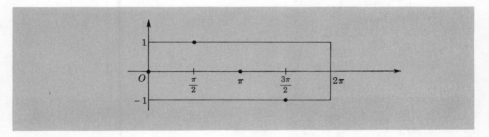

$$\sin 0 = 0, \quad \sin \dfrac{\pi}{2} = 1, \quad \sin \pi = 0, \quad \sin \dfrac{3\pi}{2} = -1$$

1215 Letting $y = v$ and $x = s$, the statement $v = \sin s$ becomes $y = \sin x$ and you can locate four points of the graph of $y = \sin x$ from the list in frame 1214. Mark these points on the graph you started in frame 1213. Also mark the point indicated by $\sin 2\pi = 0$.

Comment

If you recall the previous graph of $y = \sin \theta$, you could sketch the graph without locating additional points. However, the discussion in frames 1216 to 1225 is instructive.

1216   If each of the quarter arcs of the
circle is bisected, the arc lengths
are $\pi/4$, $3\pi/4$, **(1)**_____, and
(2)_____. The corresponding
central angles in radians are $\pi/4$,
$3\pi/4$, **(3)**_____, and **(4)**_____.

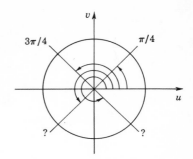

(1) $\dfrac{5\pi}{4}$ **(2)** $\dfrac{7\pi}{4}$ **(3)** $\dfrac{5\pi}{4}$ **(4)** $\dfrac{7\pi}{4}$

1217   To find the coordinates u and v of P
for the arc $\pi/4$ on the unit circle,
recall that OPA is a right triangle
with hypotenuse 1 and that $u = v$
Hence, using the equation:
$$u^2 + v^2 = 1$$
we find that
$$u = \textbf{(1)}\underline{\qquad}$$
$$v = \textbf{(2)}\underline{\qquad}$$

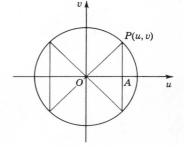

(1) $\dfrac{1}{\sqrt{2}}$ or $\dfrac{\sqrt{2}}{2}$ **(2)** $\dfrac{1}{\sqrt{2}}$ or $\dfrac{\sqrt{2}}{2}$

Solution: Since $u = v$, we can write $u^2 + v^2 = 1$ as $u^2 + u^2 = 1$
then
$$2u^2 = 1$$
$$u^2 = \tfrac{1}{2}$$
$$u = \frac{1}{\sqrt{2}}$$

For quadrant I both coordinates u and v are positive, i.e., $u = v = 1/\sqrt{2}$.

1218   List the coordinates for points **(1)** Q, **(2)** R, and **(3)** S corresponding to the arcs $3\pi/4$, $5\pi/4$, and $7\pi/4$, respectively.

continued →

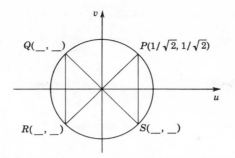

$Q(\_,\_)$ $P(1/\sqrt{2},1/\sqrt{2})$

v

u

$R(\_,\_)$ $S(\_,\_)$

(1) $\dfrac{1}{-\sqrt{2}}, \dfrac{1}{\sqrt{2}}$ **(2)** $\dfrac{1}{-\sqrt{2}}, \dfrac{1}{-\sqrt{2}}$ **(3)** $\dfrac{1}{\sqrt{2}}, \dfrac{-1}{\sqrt{2}}$

Make a sketch and label points P, Q, R with these coordinates for future use.

1219 Refer to your sketch. $\sin(\pi/4) =$ **(1)** _____, $\sin(3\pi/4) =$ **(2)** _____, $\sin(5\pi/4) =$ **(3)** _____, and $\sin(7\pi/4) =$ **(4)** _____. **(5)** Locate these points on the graph of $y = \sin x$. *Note:* $\sqrt{2} \approx 1.4$

(1) $\dfrac{1}{\sqrt{2}} \approx 0.7$ **(2)** $\dfrac{1}{\sqrt{2}} \approx 0.7$ **(3)** $\dfrac{-1}{\sqrt{2}} \approx -0.7$ **(4)** $\dfrac{-1}{\sqrt{2}} \approx -0.7$

(5)

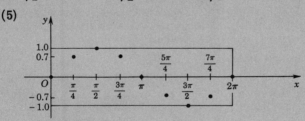

1220 In order to find additional points for the graph of $y = \sin x$, we can divide each quarter arc of the unit circle into thirds. The arc lengths for these new points are $\pi/6$, $\pi/3$, _____, _____, _____, _____, _____, _____.
Fill in the blanks for the arcs indicated in quadrants II, III, IV. Mark the corresponding points on the x *axis* of your graph.

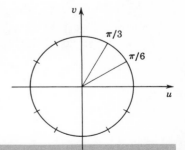

$\dfrac{2\pi}{3}, \dfrac{5\pi}{6}, \dfrac{7\pi}{6}, \dfrac{4\pi}{3}, \dfrac{5\pi}{3}, \dfrac{11\pi}{6}$

continued →

The points on the x axis should look like this:

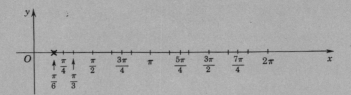

Note: $\pi/6$ and $\pi/3$ divide the segment from 0 to $\pi/2$ into three equal lengths.

1221 On a sketch of one-fourth of the unit circle we have indicated by points P and Q the arcs $\pi/6$ and $\pi/3$, respectively. Perpendiculars PA and QB are drawn to the u axis. To find the co-ordinates u and v of point P, we note that angle POA = $\pi/6$ radians or $30°$. In the right tri-angle POA if the hypotenuse OP = 1, then $PA = \frac{1}{2}$. **(1)** Find OA. Thus, we know that the coordinates of P are u = **(2)**_____ and v = **(3)**_____.

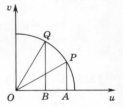

(1) $OA = \dfrac{\sqrt{3}}{2}$ **(2)** $\dfrac{\sqrt{3}}{2}$ **(3)** $\frac{1}{2}$

1222 The arc $s = \pi/3$ has a central angle of **(1)**_____ radians or **(2)**_____$°$. **(3)** Find the coordinates of Q.

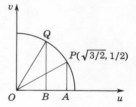

$P(\sqrt{3/2},\,1/2)$

(1) $\dfrac{\pi}{3}$ **(2)** 60 **(3)** $u = \dfrac{1}{2}$, $v = \dfrac{\sqrt{3}}{2}$

1223 Label correctly the coordinates of
the points corresponding to arcs
(1) $\pi/6$, **(2)** $\pi/3$, **(3)** $2\pi/3$, **(4)**
$5\pi/6$, **(5)** $7\pi/6$, **(6)** $4\pi/6$, **(7)** $5\pi/3$,
and **(8)** $11\pi/6$ on this unit circle.
Keep a copy of your answer.

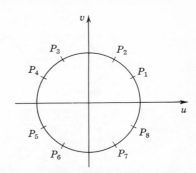

(1) $\dfrac{\sqrt{3}}{2}, \dfrac{1}{2}$ **(2)** $\dfrac{1}{2}, \dfrac{\sqrt{3}}{2}$ **(3)** $\dfrac{-1}{2}, \dfrac{\sqrt{3}}{2}$ **(4)** $\dfrac{-\sqrt{3}}{2}, \dfrac{1}{2}$

(5) $\dfrac{-\sqrt{3}}{2}, \dfrac{-1}{2}$ **(6)** $\dfrac{-1}{2}, \dfrac{-\sqrt{3}}{2}$ **(7)** $\dfrac{1}{2}, \dfrac{-\sqrt{3}}{2}$ **(8)** $\dfrac{\sqrt{3}}{2}, \dfrac{-1}{2}$

1224 Complete the following and plot the points on your graph.

$\sin \dfrac{\pi}{6}$ = **(1)** _____ $\sin \dfrac{\pi}{3}$ = **(2)** _____

$\sin \dfrac{2\pi}{3}$ = **(3)** _____ $\sin \dfrac{5\pi}{6}$ = **(4)** _____

$\sin \dfrac{7\pi}{6}$ = **(5)** _____ $\sin \dfrac{4\pi}{3}$ = **(6)** _____

$\sin \dfrac{5\pi}{3}$ = **(7)** _____ $\sin \dfrac{11\pi}{6}$ = **(8)** _____

Note: $\sqrt{3} \approx 1.73$

(1) $\dfrac{1}{2}$ **(2)** $\dfrac{\sqrt{3}}{2}$ **(3)** $\dfrac{\sqrt{3}}{2}$ **(4)** $\dfrac{1}{2}$

(5) $\dfrac{-1}{2}$ **(6)** $\dfrac{-\sqrt{3}}{2}$ **(7)** $\dfrac{-\sqrt{3}}{2}$ **(8)** $\dfrac{-1}{2}$

1225 To complete the graph of one period of the sine function, draw a
continuous line through the points you have plotted. *Note:* By
placing equal rectangular areas to the right or left of your graph,
you could show as many cycles of the sine function as you wished.

continued →

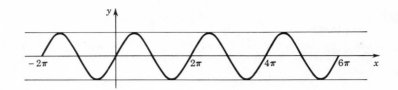

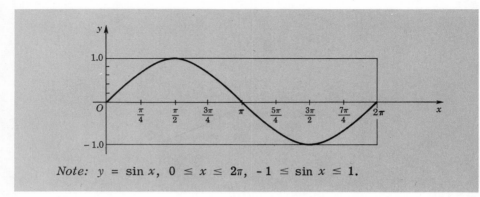

Note: $y = \sin x$, $0 \le x \le 2\pi$, $-1 \le \sin x \le 1$.

1226 You have indicated the coordinates of the points $P(u, v)$ corresponding to the following arc lengths:

$$0, \frac{\pi}{6}, \frac{\pi}{4}, \frac{\pi}{3}, \frac{\pi}{2}, \frac{2\pi}{3}, \frac{3\pi}{4}, \frac{5\pi}{6}, \pi, \frac{7\pi}{6}, \ldots, 2\pi$$

By definition $u = \cos s$; hence, you should be able to complete the following lists:

$\cos 0 =$ ____ $\cos \dfrac{\pi}{2} =$ ____ $\cos \pi =$ ____ $\cos \dfrac{3\pi}{2} =$ ____

$\cos \dfrac{\pi}{6} =$ ____ $\cos \dfrac{2\pi}{3} =$ ____ $\cos \dfrac{7\pi}{6} =$ ____ $\cos \dfrac{5\pi}{3} =$ ____

$\cos \dfrac{\pi}{4} =$ ____ $\cos \dfrac{3\pi}{4} =$ ____ $\cos \dfrac{5\pi}{4} =$ ____ $\cos \dfrac{7\pi}{4} =$ ____

$\cos \dfrac{\pi}{3} =$ ____ $\cos \dfrac{5\pi}{6} =$ ____ $\cos \dfrac{4\pi}{3} =$ ____ $\cos \dfrac{11\pi}{6} =$ ____

$\cos 0 = 1$ $\cos \dfrac{\pi}{2} = 0$ $\cos \pi = -1$ $\cos \dfrac{3\pi}{2} = 0$

$\cos \dfrac{\pi}{6} = \dfrac{\sqrt{3}}{2}$ $\cos \dfrac{2\pi}{3} = -\dfrac{1}{2}$ $\cos \dfrac{7\pi}{6} = -\dfrac{\sqrt{3}}{2}$ $\cos \dfrac{5\pi}{3} = \dfrac{1}{2}$

$\cos \dfrac{\pi}{4} = \dfrac{1}{\sqrt{2}}$ $\cos \dfrac{3\pi}{4} = -\dfrac{1}{\sqrt{2}}$ $\cos \dfrac{5\pi}{4} = -\dfrac{1}{\sqrt{2}}$ $\cos \dfrac{7\pi}{4} = \dfrac{1}{\sqrt{2}}$

$\cos \dfrac{\pi}{3} = \dfrac{1}{2}$ $\cos \dfrac{5\pi}{6} = \dfrac{-\sqrt{3}}{2}$ $\cos \dfrac{4\pi}{3} = -\dfrac{1}{2}$ $\cos \dfrac{11\pi}{6} = \dfrac{\sqrt{3}}{2}$

1227 On an x, y coordinate axes similar to the one used for the graph of the sine function, construct the graph of $u = \cos s$. First locate the quadrantal points 0, $\pi/2$, π, $3\pi/2$, 2π. Then locate a few additional points from the list in frame 1226 to check the accuracy of your work.

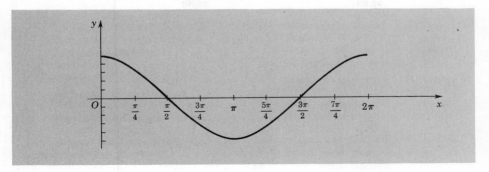

1228 To see how the graph of $y = 2 \cos x$ differs from the graph of $y = \cos x$, first prepare a table as follows and fill in the blanks.

x	$\cos x$	$2 \cos x$
0	1	$2 \cdot 1 = 2$
$\pi/6$	$\sqrt{3}/2$	$2 \cdot \sqrt{3}/2 = \sqrt{3} \approx 1.7$
$\pi/4$	$1/\sqrt{2}$	$2 \cdot \underline{\hspace{1cm}} = \underline{\hspace{1cm}}$
$\pi/3$	$1/2$	$2 \cdot \underline{\hspace{1cm}} = \underline{\hspace{1cm}}$
$\pi/2$	0	$2 \cdot \underline{\hspace{1cm}} = \underline{\hspace{1cm}}$
$2\pi/3$	$-1/2$	$\underline{\hspace{1cm}} = \underline{\hspace{1cm}}$
$3\pi/4$	$\underline{\hspace{1cm}}$	$\underline{\hspace{1cm}} = \underline{\hspace{1cm}}$
$5\pi/6$	$\underline{\hspace{1cm}}$	$\underline{\hspace{1cm}} = \underline{\hspace{1cm}}$
π	$\underline{\hspace{1cm}}$	$\underline{\hspace{1cm}} = \underline{\hspace{1cm}}$

This should be enough of the table for you to see the pattern.

x	$\cos x$	$2 \cos x$
0	1	$2 \cdot 1 = 2$
$\pi/6$	$\sqrt{3}/2$	$2 \cdot \sqrt{3}/2 = \sqrt{3} \approx 1.7$
$\pi/4$	$1/\sqrt{2}$	$2 \cdot 1/\sqrt{2} = \sqrt{2} \approx 1.4$

continued →

x	$\cos x$	$2 \cos x$
$\pi/3$	$1/2$	$2 \cdot 1/2 = 1$
$\pi/2$	0	$2 \cdot 0 = 0$
$2\pi/3$	$-1/2$	$2 \cdot (-1/2) = -1$
$3\pi/4$	$-1/\sqrt{2}$	$2 \cdot (-1/\sqrt{2}) = -\sqrt{2} \approx -1.4$
$5\pi/6$	$-\sqrt{3}/2$	$2 \cdot (-\sqrt{3}/2) = -\sqrt{3} \approx -1.7$
π	-1	$2 \cdot -1 = -2$

▽1229 If you look at the columns headed $\cos x$ and $2 \cos x$ in frame 1228, you see that each entry of $2 \cos x$ is merely two times the entry of the corresponding $\cos x$ entry. This means that the amplitude of $y = 2 \cos x$ is 2, but the period remains unchanged. On your x, y coordinate system for $y = \cos x$, extend the y axis so that you have $-2 \leq y \leq 2$, and plot the graph $y = 2 \cos x$ for one period of $\cos x$. Use dashes to represent this graph.

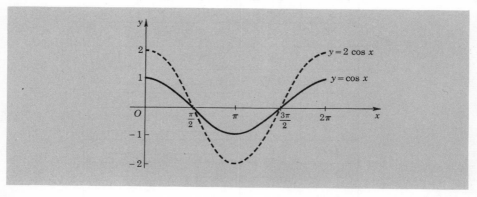

1230 Thus you see that when 2 is used as a multiplier of $\cos x$, i.e., $y = 2 \cos x$, the amplitude of the function is doubled but the period remains unchanged. In fact, any multiplier a of $\cos x$ simply multiplies each ordinate y by a without affecting the period of the function. Suppose $a = 3$, then the amplitude of $y = 3 \cos x$ is three times the amplitude of $y = \cos x$. (1) If $a = -1$, how is the graph affected? (2) With a red pencil (or a dotted line) sketch the graph of $y = (-1) \cos x$ on the same axes with $y = \cos x$ and $y = 2 \cos x$.

(1) Each value of y in $y = \cos x$ will be opposite in sign when $a = -1$, i.e., $y = -\cos x$ or the graph is inverted.
(2) see Panel 10 for the answer.

▽1231 We want to compare the graphs of the three functions: $y = \sin x$, $y = 2 \sin x$, and $y = \frac{1}{2} \sin x$. Graph them on one set of axes showing one period of each. (Refer to the table for graphing $y = \sin x$.)

see Panel 11 for the answer

1232 You should have a good idea now of how the graph changes when a constant a appears as a coefficient of a function, i.e., $y = a \cos x$ or $y = a \sin x$. You know that the maximum point on the graph of $y = \cos x$ is 1 and the minimum point is -1. **(1)** What is the maximum point and the minimum point for $y = 3 \cos x$? **(2)** For $y = \frac{2}{3} \cos x$? **(3)** For $y = -2 \cos x$?

(1) maximum 3, minimum -3 **(2)** maximum $\frac{2}{3}$, minimum $-\frac{2}{3}$
(3) maximum 2, minimum -2
Note: When $a = -2$, the graph is inverted, but the maximum and minimum values still are 2 and -2, respectively.

▽1233 We have shown on the same axis the graphs of $y = \sin x$ and $y = 2 \sin x$ over the interval $-2\pi \leq x \leq 2\pi$. To show that you understand the effect of the factors in $y = a \sin x$, make a similar sketch on which you show $y = \sin x$, $y = 2 \sin x$, $y = 3 \sin x$, and $y = 6 \sin x$.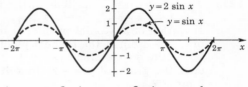

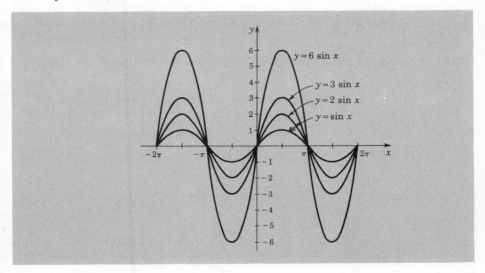

1234 If you are familiar with the variations in the sine or cosine functions and know the amplitude and period, you may avoid much of the tedious work of graphing by "sketching" the curve. To do this, locate the maximum and minimum points and the points at which the graph intercepts the x axis. For example, after you have constructed the graph for $y = \cos x$, you should be able to "sketch" quite quickly the graph of $y = a \cos x$, a being equal to any real number other than 0. Explain in your own words how the graph of $y = a \cos x$ differs from $y = \cos x$.

Here are several acceptable answers.
1. Each ordinate is multiplied by a.
2. The maximum and minimum points are changed from 1 and -1 to a and $-a$, respectively.
3. The amplitude is multiplied by a.
4. The graph is "stretched" or "compressed" vertically by the multiplier a. If a is an integer and $|a| > 1$, the graph is "stretched"; if $-1 < a < 1$, the graph is "compressed." (Also the graph is inverted if a is negative.)

1235 We say that the amplitude of the sine or cosine function defined by $y = a \sin x$ or $y = a \cos x$ is $|a|$. This indicates the greatest deviation of any point of the curve from the x axis. If $y = 2 \sin x$ or $y = -2 \sin x$, the highest point of the graph is **(1)**_____ units above the x axis since $|2| = |-2| = $ **(2)**_____. **(3)** In what way does the graph of $y = -2 \sin x$ differ from the graph of $y = 2 \sin x$?

(1) 2   **(2)** 2
(3) The graph of $y = -2 \sin x$ is the inverted form of $y = 2 \sin x$.

1236 Consider the function defined by $y = \sin 2x$. Complete the table.

If $x =$	0	$\pi/4$	$\pi/2$	$3\pi/4$	π	$5\pi/4$	$3\pi/2$	$7\pi/4$	2π
then $2x =$	0	$\pi/2$	π						
and $\sin 2x =$	0	1	0						

If $x =$	0	$\pi/4$	$\pi/2$	$3\pi/4$	π	$5\pi/4$	$3\pi/2$	$7\pi/4$	2π
then $2x =$	0	$\pi/2$	π	$3\pi/2$	2π	$5\pi/2$	3π	$7\pi/2$	4π
and $\sin 2x =$	0	1	0	-1	0	1	0	-1	0

1237 Prepare an x, y coordinate axes as in frame 1236, omitting points
$\pi/6, \pi/3, 2\pi/3$, etc., on the axis. First, construct the graph of
$y = \sin x$ on the interval $0 \leq x < 2\pi$. Refer to the table in frame
1236 and draw on the same axes the graph of $y = \sin 2x$.

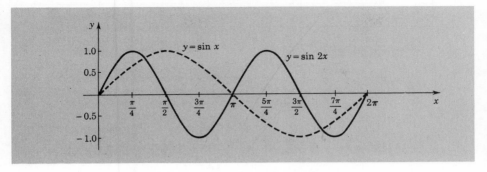

1238 When $y = \sin 2x$ defines the function, the period is π. You saw on
the graph two complete cycles in the interval $0 \leq x < 2\pi$. Let
$y = \sin 3x$, what is the period for this function?

the period is $\dfrac{2\pi}{3}$

Solution: Let $z = 3x$. We know that the cycle for $y = \sin z$
begins when $z = 0$ and ends when $z = 2\pi$. Therefore, the period
for $y = \sin 3x$ begins when $3x = 0$ and ends when $3x = 2\pi$; i.e.,
the period begins when $x = 0$ and ends when $x = 2\pi/3$. Hence,
the period for $y = \sin 3x = (2\pi/3 - 0)$ or $2\pi/3$.

1239 We have shown a detailed way to find the period for a function
having a constant a appearing as a coefficient of x, i.e., $y =
\sin ax$. What is the "short cut" (rule) for finding the period for
$y = \sin ax$?

period $= \dfrac{2\pi}{a}$

Solution: If $y = \sin x$ has period 2π,

then $y = \sin 2x$ has period $\dfrac{1}{2} \cdot 2\pi = \pi$,

and $y = \sin 3x$ has period $\dfrac{1}{3} \cdot 2\pi = \dfrac{2\pi}{3}$,

and $y = \sin ax$ has period $\dfrac{1}{a} \cdot 2\pi = \dfrac{2\pi}{a}$

1240 Complete the following table which will be used later to sketch the graph of $y = \sin 3x$:

If x =	0	$\pi/6$	$\pi/3$	$\pi/2$	$2\pi/3$	$5\pi/6$	π	$7\pi/6$	$4\pi/3$	$3\pi/2$	$5\pi/3$	$11\pi/6$	2π
then $3x$ =	0	$\pi/2$	π	$3\pi/2$	2π								
and $\sin 3x$ =	0	1	0	-1	0								

If x =	0	$\pi/6$	$\pi/3$	$\pi/2$	$2\pi/3$	$5\pi/6$	π	$7\pi/6$	$4\pi/3$	$3\pi/2$	$5\pi/3$	$11\pi/6$	2π
then $3x$ =	0	$\pi/2$	π	$3\pi/2$	2π	$5\pi/2$	3π	$7\pi/2$	4π	$9\pi/2$	5π	$11\pi/2$	6π
and $\sin 3x$ =	0	1	0	-1	0	1	0	-1	0	1	0	-1	0

1241 Refer to the table in frame 1240 and use a scale as indicated below to sketch the graph of $y = \sin 3x$. Since the period is $2\pi/3$, you should have three complete cycles in the interval $0 \le x < 2\pi$.

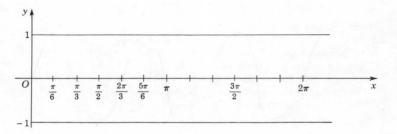

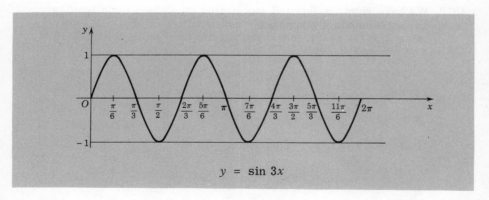

$$y = \sin 3x$$

▽**1242**   In order to remember the effect of the constant a in the statement
$y = \sin ax$, fill in the tables below and keep a copy for frames 1243
to 1246. Look carefully at the information appearing in the bottom
line of each table.

I $a = 1$

If $x =$	0	$\pi/2$	π	$3\pi/2$	2π
then $\sin x =$					

II $a = 2$

If $x =$	0	$\pi/4$	$\pi/2$	$3\pi/4$	π	$5\pi/4$	$3\pi/2$	$7\pi/2$	2π
then $2x =$	0	$\pi/2$	π	$3\pi/2$	2π				
and $\sin 2x =$									

III $a = 3$

If $x =$	0	$\pi/6$	$\pi/3$	$\pi/2$	$2\pi/3$	$5\pi/6$	π	$7\pi/6$	$4\pi/3$	$3\pi/2$	$5\pi/3$	$11\pi/6$	2π
then $3x =$	0												
and $\sin 3x =$													

I

If $x =$	0	$\pi/2$	π	$3\pi/2$	2π
then $\sin x =$	0	1	0	−1	0

II

If $x =$	0	$\pi/4$	$\pi/2$	$3\pi/4$	π	$5\pi/4$	$3\pi/2$	$7\pi/4$	2π
then $2x =$	0	$\pi/2$	π	$3\pi/2$	2π	$5\pi/2$	3π	$7\pi/2$	4π
and $\sin 2x =$	0	1	0	−1	0	1	0	−1	0

III

If $x =$	0	$\pi/6$	$\pi/3$	$\pi/2$	$2\pi/3$	$5\pi/6$	π	$7\pi/6$	$4\pi/3$	$3\pi/2$	$5\pi/3$	$11\pi/6$	2π
then $3x =$	0	$\pi/2$	π	$3\pi/2$	2π	$5\pi/2$	3π	$7\pi/2$	4π	$9\pi/2$	5π	$11\pi/2$	6π
and $\sin 3x =$	0	1	0	−1	0	1	0	−1	0	1	0	−1	0

1243 On a set of axes as shown below sketch the graph of $y = \sin x$. The information from table I in frame 1242 may be used if necessary. Extend the graph to the left to show the interval $-2\pi \le x \le 2\pi$.

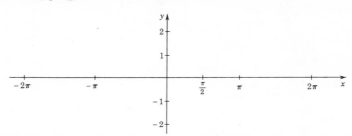

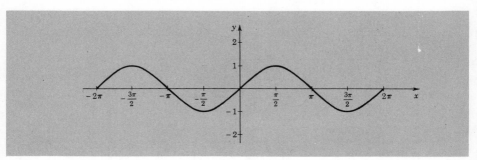

1244 On the same axis with $y = \sin x$, sketch the graph of $y = \sin 2x$ over the interval $-2\pi \le x \le 2\pi$. (Use Table II in frame 1242 and mark the additional points $\pi/4$, $3\pi/4$, etc., on the x axis to aid you.)

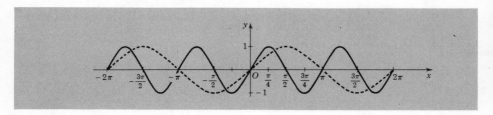

1245 On the same set of axes with $y = \sin x$ and $y = \sin 2x$, sketch the graph of $y = \sin 3x$ over the interval $-2\pi \le x \le 2\pi$. (Use Table III in frame 1242 and mark the additional points $\pi/6$, $\pi/3$, $2\pi/3$, $5\pi/6$, etc., on the x axis to aid you.)

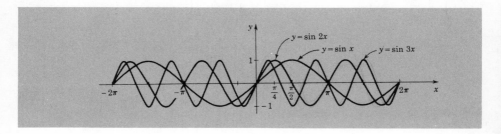

▽1246 You should think of the period before graphing a function. **(1)** What is the period for the function defined by $y = \sin \frac{1}{2} x$? **(2)** Make up a table and **(3)** sketch the graph over the interval $0 \le x \le 2\pi$.

(1) the period is 4π

(2)

$x =$	0	$\pi/2$	π	$3\pi/2$	2π	$5\pi/2$	3π	$7\pi/2$	4π
$\frac{1}{2}x =$	0	$\pi/4$	$\pi/2$	$3\pi/4$	π	$5\pi/4$	$3\pi/2$	$7\pi/4$	2π
$\sin \frac{1}{2}x =$	0	$1/\sqrt{2}$	1	$1/\sqrt{2}$	0	$-1/\sqrt{2}$	-1	$-1/\sqrt{2}$	0

(3)

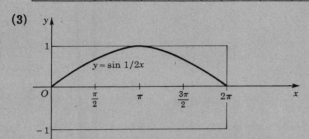

Since the period is 4π this graph shows only one-half of a cycle.

1247 Consider the function defined by $y = \sin (x + \pi/2)$. You may have an idea of the appearance it will have when it is graphed. Study the following to see if you are correct. We can find the period for this function as we did in our original discussion. If we let $z = x + \pi/2$, we know that a period for $y = \sin z$ begins when $z = 0$ and ends when $z = 2\pi$. Therefore, a period for $y = \sin (x + \pi/2)$ begins when $(x + \pi/2) = 0$ and ends when $(x + \pi/2) = 2\pi$. Solving each of these for x, we get $x = -\pi/2$ and $x = 3\pi/2$. This tells us that the cycle for $y = \sin (x + \pi/2)$ begins when $x =$ **(1)**_____ and ends when $x =$ **(2)**_____. We note that the length of this period is **(3)**_____, since the distance from $-\pi/2$ to $3\pi/2$ on the x axis is **(4)**_____.

(1) $\frac{-\pi}{2}$ **(2)** $\frac{3\pi}{2}$ **(3)** 2π **(4)** 2π

1248   To sketch the graph of $y = \sin(x + \pi/2)$, we may start the graph with any value of x we choose. A good point would be the one where $y = 0$. In frame 1247 we saw that y is 0 when $x = -\pi/2$. Complete the table below. It will give you enough points to see the pattern.

$x =$	$-\pi/2$	0	$\pi/2$	π	$3\pi/2$
$x + \pi/2 =$	0	$\pi/2$	π		
$\sin(x + \pi/2) =$	0	1			

$x =$	$-\pi/2$	0	$\pi/2$	π	$3\pi/2$
$x + \pi/2 =$	0	$\pi/2$	π	$3\pi/2$	2π
$\sin(x + \pi/2) =$	0	1	0	-1	0

Keep a copy for frame 1249.

1249   Sketch one period of the graph of $y = \sin(x + \pi/2)$ on a coordinate axis similar to this:

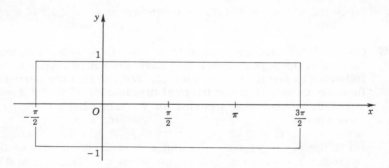

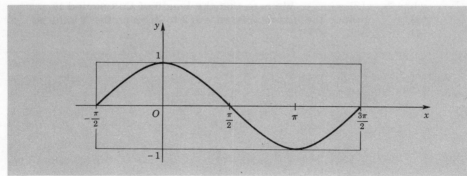

1250   Sketch the graph of $y = \sin (x - \pi/2)$ showing one complete period.

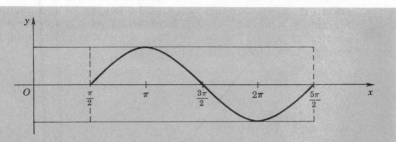

Employing the method of frames 1248 and 1249, we find that for the function defined by $y = \sin (x - \pi/2)$, if we start the cycle when $y = 0$, then the correct value for x is $\pi/2$. Thus the table:

$x =$	$\pi/2$	π	$3\pi/2$	2π	$5\pi/2$
$x - \pi/2 =$	0	$\pi/2$	π	$3\pi/2$	2π
$\sin (x - \pi/2) =$	0	1	0	-1	0

▽**1251**   You have sketched graphs of $y = \sin (x + \pi/2)$ and $y = \sin (x - \pi/2)$. Explain in your own words the effect of "adding" the constant $\pi/2$ to x.

The graph is shifted $\pi/2$ units to the *left* when $\pi/2$ is *positive* and $\pi/2$ units to the *right* when $\pi/2$ is *negative*.

1252   Here is a general statement regarding the function defined by $y = \sin (x + a)$: The graph of $y = \sin (x + a)$ differs from the graph of $y = \sin x$ in position only. The addition of a shifts the graph a units to the left if a is positive and a units to the right if a is negative. Make a statement telling how the graph of $y = \sin (x - \pi)$ differs from the graph of $y = \sin x$. A proof of the above general statement follows the steps used in the specific example where $a = \pi/2$ shown before.

the graph is shifted π units to the right

Note: Later we shall investigate the changes produced in the graph by the introduction of the constants a and b in this manner: $y = \sin (ax + b)$.

1253 Let $x = 0$. **(1)** What is the value of y if $y = \sin(x - \pi/2)$?
(2) Refer to your graph of this function and extend it to include this point. **(3)** Consider this point as the beginning of a period for the function $y = \sin(x - \pi/2)$. Indicate on your graph the end of this particular period. *Note:* We may select any point along the curve as the beginning of a period.

(1) $y = -1$

(2) and **(3)** period ends at $x = 2\pi$

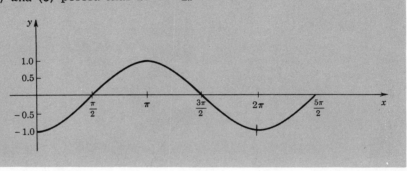

▽1254 In this frame you are asked to summarize the effect of the constant a in each of the statements below:

1. $y = a \sin x$
2. $y = \sin ax$
3. $y = \sin(x + a)$

(1) In which one is the period of the function equal to $\frac{1}{a} \cdot 2\pi$?

(2) In which one is each value of the ordinate multiplied by a?

(3) In which one is the graph of the function moved a units to the left?

(1) In statement 2 the period of the function is equal to $\frac{1}{a} \cdot 2\pi$.

(2) In statement 1 each ordinate is multiplied by a.

(3) In statement 3 the graph is shifted a units to the left.

1255 **(1)** Complete the table below and **(2)** use these points in sketching a graph of $y = \cos(x - \pi/2)$ on a set of coordinate axes.

continued →

$x =$	$\pi/2$	π	$3\pi/2$	2π	$5\pi/2$
$x - \pi/2 =$	0	$\pi/2$			
$\cos(x - \pi/2) =$	1	0			

(1)

$x =$	$\pi/2$	π	$3\pi/2$	2π	$5\pi/2$
$x - \pi/2 =$	0	$\pi/2$	π	$3\pi/2$	2π
$\cos(x - \pi/2) =$	1	0	-1	0	1

(2)

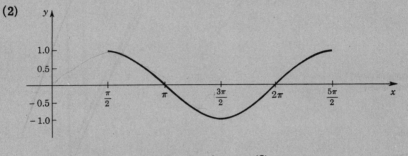

$$y = \cos(x - \pi/2)$$

Keep a copy of the graph for frame 1256.

1256 On the same set of axes as you used for plotting the graph of $y = \cos(x - \pi/2)$, sketch the graph of $y = \sin x$ for the interval $0 \le x \le 2\pi$.

Your graph of $y = \sin x$ will coincide with the graph of $y = \cos(x - \pi/2)$ from the point $x = \pi/2$ and extending to the right.

1257 In frame 1256 we called your attention to the fact that by "shifting" the graph of $y = \cos x$ to the right $\pi/2$ units, it would coincide with the graph of $y = \sin x$. The sine function and the cosine function, $y = \sin x$ and $y = \cos x$ noted previously, each has a period of **(1)**_____ and each has an amplitude of **(2)**_____. See frame 1258 for further discussion on this.

(1) 2π **(2)** 1

1258   In order to be sure that the graph of $y = \sin x$ will coincide with the graph of $y = \cos (x - \pi/2)$ when they are plotted on the same set of axes, we must be sure that $\sin x = \cos (x - \pi/2)$ for all x. Recall the addition formula for $\cos (\alpha - \beta)$—see Panel 8II(4). Let x and $\pi/2$ represent the radian measures for α and β and show that $\cos (x - \pi/2) = \sin x$.

$$\cos \left(x - \frac{\pi}{2}\right) = \cos x \cos \frac{\pi}{2} + \sin x \sin \frac{\pi}{2}$$

$$= \cos x \cdot 0 + \sin x \cdot (1) = \sin x$$

1259   We shall give several more examples of the changes produced in the graph by the constant a. First take $y = a \cos x$. Let $a = 4$. Sketch the graph of $y = 4 \cos x$ over the interval $0 \le x \le 2\pi$.

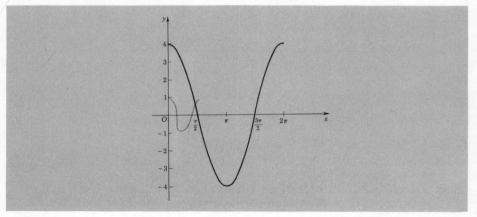

1260   On the axes in frame 1259, sketch the graph of $y = \cos 4x$ over the interval $0 \le x \le 2\pi$. Before you make the graph you should decide the effect of the constant 4 in $y = \cos 4x$.

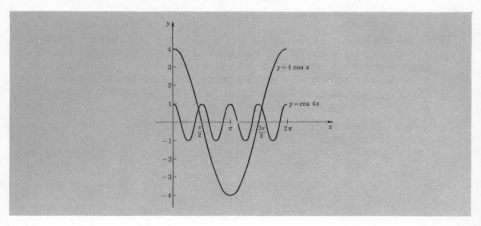

1261 In sketching the graph of the function defined by $y = \cos 4x$, you
could identify the period by applying the rule period $= 2\pi/a$ for
any function of the type $y = \cos ax$, $a \neq 0$. Hence, $2\pi/4 = \pi/2 =$
period for $y = \cos 4x$. Its graph differs from the graph of $y =$
$\cos x$ only in the fact that it has been "compressed" horizontally.
There are four cycles in the interval $0 \leq x < 2\pi$.

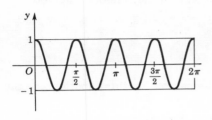

$$y = \cos 4x$$

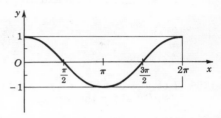

$$y = \cos x$$

Given the function defined by $y = \cos(ax + b)$, you know in general
that the value of that constant (1)_____ determines the change in
the period and the value of the constant (2)_____ shifts the graph
to the right or left.

(1) a **(2)** b

1262 When two constants a and b appear in the same function thus: $y =$
$\cos(ax + b)$, we can decide the period simply by using the statement, period $= 2\pi/a$, but this new period will influence the number
of units of "shifting" produced by b. If we go back to the original
method of analyzing the change, we can see what is happening.
1. Let $z = ax + b$.
2. Then if we begin a period of $y = \cos z$ with $z = 0$, we shall end
   the period with $z = 2\pi$, because $y = \cos z$ has period 2π.
3. We therefore let $ax + b =$ (1)_____ and $ax + b =$ (2)_____ and
   find that $x =$ (3)_____ and $x =$ (4)_____.
See frame 1263 for further discussion.

(1) 0 **(2)** 2π

(3) $-\dfrac{b}{a}$ **(4)** $\dfrac{2\pi}{a} - \dfrac{b}{a}$

Solution: $ax + b = 0$ *Solution:* $ax + b = 2\pi$

$\qquad\qquad ax = -b$ $ax = 2\pi - b$

$\qquad\qquad x = -\dfrac{b}{a}$ $x = \dfrac{2\pi}{a} - \dfrac{b}{a}$

1263 We found in frame 1262 two values of x for the function defined by $y = \cos(ax + b)$ corresponding to $y = \cos 0$ and $y = \cos 2\pi$. They were $x = -b/a$ and $(2\pi/a - b/a)$. The cycle for $y = \cos(ax + b)$ starts at $x = -b/a$. This indicates a shift to the left of b/a units on the x axis. When we find the difference between the points $x = -b/a$ and $x = 2\pi/a - b/a$ on the x axis, we have the length of the period. It is _____, as we had already verified by another method.

$$\frac{2\pi}{a}$$

▽**1264** Let $y = \cos(2x + \pi)$. Find the period for this function and the "shift" along the x axis.

From frame 1263 we found that:

Given $y = \cos(ax + b)$

$$\text{shift} = -\frac{b}{a} \qquad \text{period} = \frac{2\pi}{a}$$

Given $y = \cos(2x + \pi)$

$$\text{shift} = \frac{-\pi}{2} \qquad \text{period} = \frac{2\pi}{2} = \pi$$

If you do not remember the formula, you can work it out as you have done before.

▽**1265** State the period for the graph of (1) $y = \cos x$, (2) $y = \cos 4x$, and (3) $y = 3\cos 2x$.

(1) the period is 2π (2) the period is $\frac{\pi}{2}$ (3) the period is π

Note: The coefficient 3 multiplies each ordinate by 3 and thus gives an amplitude of 3, but it does not affect the period.

▽**1266** What is the period for the function defined by $y = \cos \pi x$?

The period is 2.   *Note:* $\frac{1}{\pi} \cdot 2\pi = 2$

1267 Discuss how the graph of the function defined by $y = \frac{1}{2}\sin\frac{1}{2}x$ differs from $y = \sin x$.

The period for $y = \frac{1}{2}\sin\frac{1}{2}x$ is 4π. The amplitude is $\frac{1}{2}$ (the maximum value of y is $\frac{1}{2}$ unit and the minimum is $-\frac{1}{2}$ unit).

1268 The next problem will be to sketch the graph of the function defined by $y = 3 \sin (x + \pi)$. Answer these questions before making the sketch. **(1)** What is the period? **(2)** What effect has the addition of π? **(3)** What effect has the coefficient 3?

(1) the period is 2π
(2) the graph is shifted π units to the left
(3) each ordinate is multiplied by 3 or the amplitude is 3

1269 Sketch the graph of one period of the function defined by $y = 3 \sin (x + \pi)$.

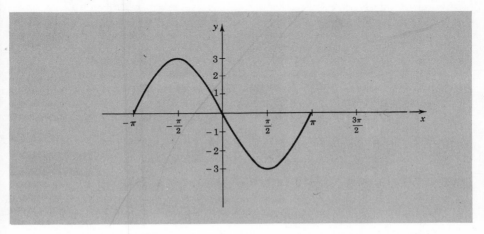

▽**1270** **(1)** Find the period for the function defined by $y = \frac{2}{3} \sin \frac{3}{2} \pi x$.
(2) What are the **(a)** maximum and **(b)** minimum values for y?

(1) the period is $\dfrac{2\pi}{a} = \dfrac{2\pi}{3\pi/2} = \dfrac{4}{3}$

(2)(a) maximum for y is $\frac{2}{3}$, **(b)** minimum for y is $-\frac{2}{3}$

▽**1271** **(1)** Find the period for the function defined by $y = \sin (2x/3 + \pi/4)$.
(2) Describe the "shift" produced by the addition of $\pi/4$.

(1) the period is 3π **(2)** the "shift" is $3\pi/8$ units to the left

continued ➛

Solution 1: period $= \dfrac{2\pi}{a} = \dfrac{2\pi}{2/3} = 3\pi$

"shift" $= \dfrac{-b}{a} = \dfrac{-\pi/4}{2/3} = \dfrac{-3\pi}{8}$, i.e., graph "shifts" $\dfrac{3\pi}{8}$ units left

Solution 2: Let $\dfrac{2x}{3} + \dfrac{\pi}{4} = 0$ and $\dfrac{2x}{3} + \dfrac{\pi}{4} = 2\pi$

Then $x = \dfrac{-3\pi}{8}$ and $x = \dfrac{21\pi}{8}$

period $= \dfrac{21\pi}{8} - \dfrac{-3\pi}{8} = 3\pi$

"shift": the period begins with $x = \dfrac{-3\pi}{8}$

1272   Below is outlined the first step in sketching the graph of $y = \sin(2x/3 + \pi/4)$. Recall that the period is 3π and that the graph is shifted $3\pi/8$ units to the left. Complete Step 1 as outlined below.

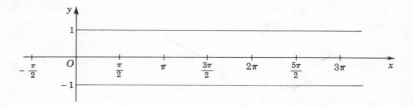

Step 1. On a set of axes similar to this one, locate the points on the x axis marking the beginning and end of one period and the midpoint of the period.
Note: Use compass to locate the midpoint.

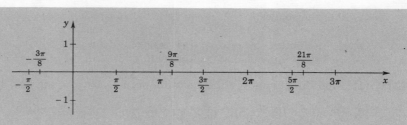

If the period begins at $-3\pi/8$ and ends at $21\pi/8$, the midpoint is at $9\pi/8$.

1273 Step 2. Locate the maximum and minimum points of the graph, marking them with points on the lines representing $y = 1$ and $y = -1$ of the graph. If you are not sure where these points will be, study the graph of $y = \sin x$ (Panel 11). Sketch the graph using the points you have marked as guides.

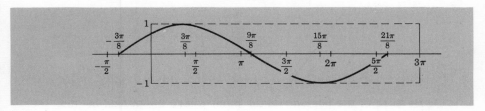

1274

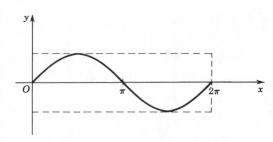

To acquire speed in sketching the *"sine curve"* notice these features.
1. Assume the graph intercepts the x axis at the beginning of a period; then, it intercepts it at the midpoint of the period and at the end of the period.
2. The maximum point occurs at the first-quarter mark and the minimum point at the third-quarter mark of the period.

If $y = \sin \frac{1}{4} x$ defines a function, we know that its period is **(1)**_____ . If $x = 0$ represents the beginning of the period, **(2)** what are the other x intercepts of the graph, and what are the values of x at which $y = \sin \frac{1}{4} x$ has **(3)** a maximum and **(4)** a minimum? Answer in words or mark the points on a coordinate system.

(1) 8π **(2)** $x = 0,\ x = 4\pi,\ x = 8\pi$ **(3)** $x = 2\pi$ **(4)** $x = 6\pi$

1275 Sketch the graph of $y = \sin \frac{1}{4} x$ for one period.

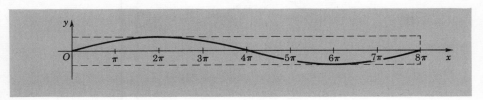

1276 Locate along the x axis the points at which the graph of the function defined by $y = \sin(3x/2 + \pi/4)$ intercepts the x axis.

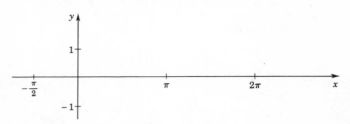

Be sure of the period and the point where the period begins.

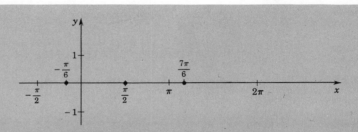

The period $\dfrac{2\pi}{3/2} = \dfrac{4\pi}{3}$

Phase shift $\dfrac{-b}{a} = \dfrac{-\pi}{4} \div \dfrac{3}{2} = \dfrac{-\pi}{6}$

The points are $\dfrac{-\pi}{6}, \dfrac{\pi}{2}, \dfrac{7\pi}{6}$

The graph is to be completed in frame 1277.

1277 After you have located the x intercepts, you can find the maximum and minimum points. Do this and sketch the graph of the function $y = \sin(3x/2 + \pi/4)$. Keep your graph for frames 1278 and 1279.

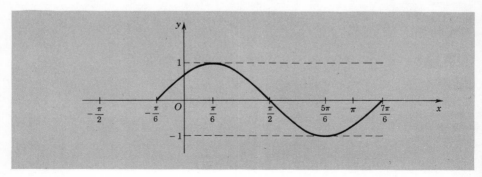

1278 In frame 1277 you sketched the graph of $y = \sin(3x/2 + \pi/4)$.
Sketch the graph of $y = \cos(3x/2 + \pi/4)$ on the set of axes with
$y = \sin(3\pi/2 + \pi/4)$.

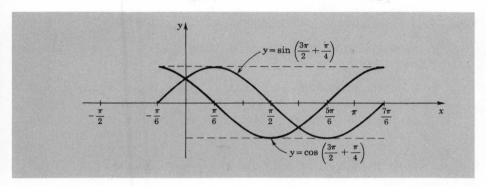

1279 Look at the graphs in frames 1277 and 1278. **(1)** The graph of
$y = \cos(3x/2 + \pi/4)$ has its maximum points when x has what
values? **(2)** The graph of $y = \cos(3\pi/2 + \pi/4)$ has a minimum
point when x has what value?

(1) $\dfrac{-\pi}{6}$ and $\dfrac{7\pi}{6}$ **(2)** $\dfrac{\pi}{2}$

▽ **1280** Sketch on one coordinate system the graphs of $y = \cos x$,
$y = 2\cos x$, and $y = \cos 2x$, over the interval $0 \le x \le 4\pi$. Use
different types of lines, dots, dashes, and solid, respectively, so
that you can distinguish the graphs.

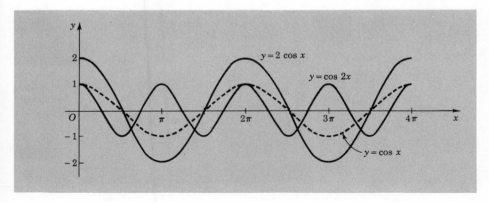

1281   If the constant $\pi/2$ is added to each x in frame 1280 thus:

1. $y = \cos \left(x + \dfrac{\pi}{2}\right)$

2. $y = 2 \cos \left(x + \dfrac{\pi}{2}\right)$

3. $y = \cos \left(2x + \dfrac{\pi}{2}\right)$

how is each graph affected? Give an explanation in words.

> The addition of $\pi/2$, as in examples 1 and 2, shifts the graph
> $\pi/2$ units to the left. The addition of $\pi/2$, as in example 3,
> shifts the graph $\pi/4$ units to the left.
> $$\text{("shift"} = \frac{-b}{a} = \frac{\pi/2}{2} = \frac{-\pi}{4}$$

1282   Various names are applied to the change of position of the graph on
the x axis produced by the addition of the constant b in the statements $y = A \cos (ax + b)$ and $y = A \sin (ax + b)$. Some terms
used are *phase shift, translation, lag,* and *crawl.* Recall that we
have an easy method for finding the amount and direction of the
shift: Given a and b positive real numbers, $a \neq 0$, and $y =
A \cos (ax + b)$

$$\text{phase shift} = -\frac{b}{a}$$

What is the phase shift for **(1)** $y = \cos x$, **(2)** $y = \cos (3x - 4)$,
and **(3)** $y = \cos (\pi x + 3\pi)$?

> **(1)** 0   **(2)** $\frac{4}{3}$ **(3)** -3

1283   We have also shown that the formula for finding the period of a
function of the general form $y = A \cos (ax + b)$ is period =
$2\pi/a$. State the period, phase shift, and amplitude for the functions
defined as follows: **(1)** $y = 3 \cos (x + \pi/2)$, **(2)** $y = \frac{1}{2} \sin 3x$, and
(3) $y = 4 \sin (\frac{1}{3} x + \pi/6)$.

	Period	Shift	Amplitude
(1)	2π	$-\dfrac{\pi}{2}$	3
(2)	$\dfrac{2\pi}{3}$	0	$\dfrac{1}{2}$
(3)	6π	$-\dfrac{\pi}{2}$	4

1284 Below are stated facts you should know regarding the positive constant A in the function defined by $y = A \cos (ax + b)$.

1. A represents the amount by which each ordinate is multiplied.

2. A and $-A$ indicate the maximum and minimum values of the function $y = A \cos (ax + b)$. Recall that 1 and -1 are the maximum and minimum values, respectively, of $y = \cos (ax + b)$; hence, $A \cdot 1$ and $A(-1) = A$ and $-A$.

3. $|A|$ gives us the amplitude of the function.

4. Changes in values of A do not change the length of period nor "shift" the graph.

Compare the graphs of $y = 3 \cos x$, $y = 3 \cos (x - \frac{1}{2})$, and $y = 3 \cos 4x$.

all three have amplitude 3 (or maximum 3 and minimum -3)

$y = 3 \cos x$ has period 2π

$y = 3 \cos (x - \frac{1}{2})$ has period 2π but is shifted right $\frac{1}{2}$ unit

$y = 3 \cos 4x$ has period $\frac{\pi}{2}$

▽1285 The summary of statements given regarding $y = A \cos (ax + b)$ applies also to $y = A \sin (ax + b)$; i.e., if a, b, and A are positive real numbers, then the function defined by $y = A \sin (ax + b)$ has period **(1)**_____, phase shift **(2)**_____, and amplitude **(3)**_____.

(1) $\frac{2\pi}{a}$ **(2)** $\frac{-b}{a}$ **(3)** A

Note: We specified in this frame that A is positive. For the general case we state that amplitude $= |A|$.

1286 If you planned to sketch the graphs of the following functions, you should have certain information as indicated by the table. Fill in the table.

continued →

	Period	Phase shift	Amplitude
$y = 2 \sin (x - \pi/6)$			
$y = 0.5 \sin (2\pi x + \pi/8)$			

	Period	Phase shift	Amplitude
$y = 2 \sin (x - \pi/6)$	2π	$\pi/6$	2
$y = 0.5 \sin (2\pi x + \pi/8)$	1	$-1/16$	0.5

Keep a copy of this table.

1287 Sketch quickly the graph of $y = 2 \sin (x - \pi/6)$ using the information from the table in frame 1286.

1. Mark on the x axis the points for the beginning and end of one period.
2. Divide the segment between these points into four equal segments.
3. Mark the maximum and minimum points.
4. Sketch the graph using a scale as shown below.

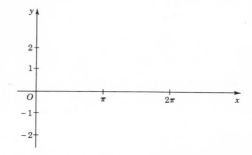

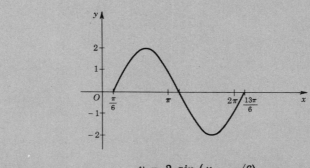

$$y = 2 \sin (x - \pi/6)$$

1288 Look again at the table from frame 1286 in which you listed the period, phase shift, and amplitude for $y = 0.5 \sin (2\pi x + \pi/8)$. The period is 1 unit (not 1π), and the phase shift is $-\frac{1}{16}$ unit (not $-\pi/16$). Locate carefully the points marking the beginning and end of a period of this function on the x axis. Complete the sketch of one period of this function.

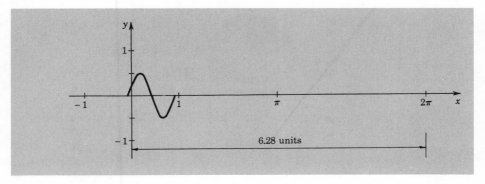

1289 Continue the graph of $y = 0.5 \sin (2\pi x + \pi/8)$ for six periods.

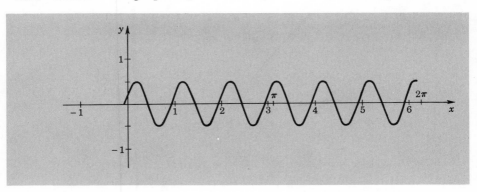

1290 Although the graphs which have been made thus far have had the same scale on both axes (one unit represented the same length on the y axis as on the x), it is not necessary to use the same scale; in fact, it is sometimes better to modify the scale. *Example:* $y = 100 \sin 4x$. The graph of this function has period (1)_____ and amplitude (2)_____. You can see that this function would be difficult to graph without modifying the scale.

(1) $\frac{\pi}{2}$ (2) 100

▽**1291**   Sketch four periods of the graph of the function defined by $y = 100 \sin 4x$, using a scale of 25 to 1 on the y axis.

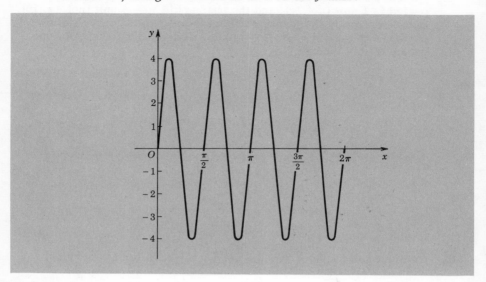

1292   When we gave the general forms $y = A \sin(ax + b)$ and $y = A \cos(ax + b)$, we restricted A, a, and b to positive constants in our discussion. If $A < 0$, the function has precisely the same graph *except* that for each value of x, those values of y which were positive are now negative and vice versa. On one coordinate system sketch the graphs of $y = A \sin \pi x$, first with $A = 2$, then $A = -2$.

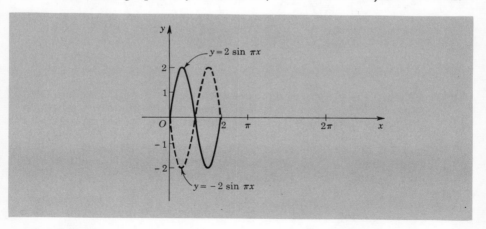

1293   Consider next the effect on the graph if $a < 0$ for the functions defined by $y = A \sin(ax + b)$ and $y = A \cos(ax + b)$. We need to recall two important facts regarding negative angles:

continued →

1. $\sin(-x) = -\sin x$
2. $\cos(-x) = \cos x$

Statement 1 can be used to make the adjustment in $y = A \sin (ax + b)$. Statement 2 shows that the graph $y = A \cos (ax + b)$ will not be affected by $a < 0$. Graph on the same axes $y = \frac{1}{2} \sin ax$, $a = 1$, $a = -1$

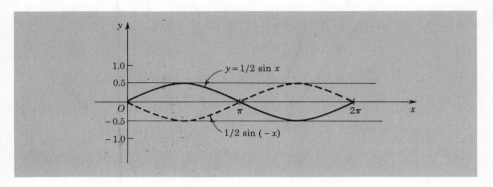

1294 First let $a = 2$, then $a = -2$, in the function defined by $y = \frac{1}{2} \cos ax$. Sketch one period of the graph of each on the same coordinate axes. Recall a previous conclusion by checking values in this table. Complete the table before making the graph.

x	0	$\pi/4$	$\pi/2$	$3\pi/4$	π
$2x$	0	$\pi/2$	π	$3\pi/2$	2π
$\cos 2x$	1				
$\cos(-2x)$					

x	0	$\pi/4$	$\pi/2$	$3\pi/4$	π
$2x$	0	$\pi/2$	π	$3\pi/2$	2π
$\cos 2x$	1	0	-1	0	1
$\cos(-2x)$	1	0	-1	0	1

continued ➙

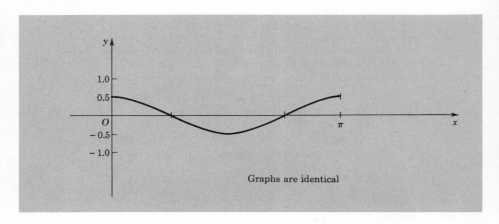

Graphs are identical

1295 This statement reviews the effect of $b < 0$ in the general forms $y = A \sin (ax + b)$ and $y = A \cos (ax + b)$. The graph is shifted to the right or left depending on b; i.e., phase shift = $-b/a$. Thus, if $b > 0$, the graph shifts b/a units to the (1)_____; and if $b < 0$, the graph shifts b/a units to the (2)_____.

(1) left   **(2)** right

1296 Fill in the table below for the functions as defined.

	Amplitude	Period	Phase shift
$y = \sin (x + 0.25)$			
$y = -2 \sin (x - 0.25)$			
$y = 3 \sin (-2x)$			

	Amplitude	Period	Phase shift
$y = \sin (x + 0.25)$	1	2π	-0.25 (left $\frac{1}{4}$ unit)
$y = -2 \sin (x - 0.25)$	2 (see Note 1)	2π	0.25 (right $\frac{1}{4}$ unit)
$y = 3 \sin (-2x)$	3	π (see Note 2)	0

Note 1: Maximum and minimum are interchanged but amplitude is $|-2| = 2$.
Note 2: You may have given $(-\pi)$ as the period for $y = 3 \sin (-2x)$. Remember that $\sin (-2x) = -\sin 2x$, so that if we make this change before considering the period, our answer is as stated above.

APPLICATIONS

Comment

In physics we learn that the sound produced by a musical instrument can be represented approximately by an equation consisting of the *sum* of several terms of the type you have been graphing. Graphical representation is very useful in scientific study of functions of this type. We shall start with a simple equation such as $y = \sin x + \cos x$. Briefly stated, the process of sketching the graph of $y = \sin x + \cos x$ can be done as follows:

1. Make two simpler statements of $y = \sin x + \cos x$ thus:
   Let $y_1 = \sin x$, $y_2 = \cos x$, then $y = y_1 + y_2$.
2. Sketch $y_1 = \sin x$ and $y_2 = \cos x$ as two separate graphs (on the same set of axes).
3. Add the ordinates y_1 and y_2 corresponding to selected values of x in order to obtain values for y. Note the computation for $x = 0$. Other points will be explained later.

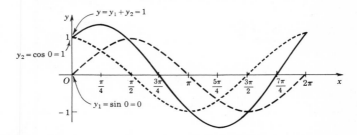

In frames 1297 to 1301 you will find the explanation for constructing the graph of $y = \sin x + \cos x$

1297   Let $y_1 = \sin x$ and $y_2 = \cos x$, then $y = y_1 + y_2$. The first step in graphing the equation $y = \sin x + \cos x$ is to graph the two separate expressions $y_1 = \sin x$ and $y_2 = \cos x$ on the same axes. Do this, graphing one period of each.

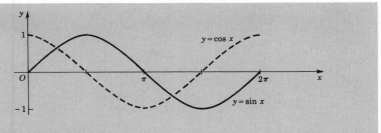

Keep your copy.

1298 The next step in obtaining the graph of $y = \sin x + \cos x$ is to add the ordinates of the two functions $y_1 = \sin x$ and $y_2 = \cos x$ for corresponding values of x since $y = y_1 + y_2$. Complete the table below.

$x =$	0	$\frac{\pi}{4}$	$\frac{\pi}{2}$	$\frac{3\pi}{4}$	π	$\frac{5\pi}{4}$	$\frac{3\pi}{2}$	$\frac{7\pi}{4}$	2π
$y_1 = \sin x =$	0	$\frac{1}{\sqrt{2}}$	1	$\frac{1}{\sqrt{2}}$					
$y_2 = \cos x =$	1	$\frac{1}{\sqrt{2}}$	0	$-\frac{1}{\sqrt{2}}$					
$y = y_1 + y_2 =$	1	$2\frac{1}{\sqrt{2}}$	1	0					
decimal value $y \approx$	1	1.41	1	0					

$x =$	0	$\frac{\pi}{4}$	$\frac{\pi}{2}$	$\frac{3\pi}{4}$	π	$\frac{5\pi}{4}$	$\frac{3\pi}{2}$	$\frac{7\pi}{4}$	2π
$y_1 = \sin x =$	0	$\frac{1}{\sqrt{2}}$	1	$\frac{1}{\sqrt{2}}$	0	$-\frac{1}{\sqrt{2}}$	-1	$-\frac{1}{\sqrt{2}}$	0
$y_2 = \cos x =$	1	$\frac{1}{\sqrt{2}}$	0	$-\frac{1}{\sqrt{2}}$	-1	$-\frac{1}{\sqrt{2}}$	0	$\frac{1}{\sqrt{2}}$	1
$y = \sin x + \cos x =$	1	$2\frac{1}{\sqrt{2}}$	1	0	-1	$-2\frac{1}{\sqrt{2}}$	-1	0	1
decimal value $y \approx$	1	1.41	1	0	-1	-1.41	-1	0	1

1299 To be sure that you sketch correctly the graph of $y = \sin x + \cos$ you should compute some additional values for y. Complete the table below.

$x =$	0	$\frac{\pi}{6}$	$\frac{\pi}{4}$	$\frac{\pi}{3}$	$\frac{\pi}{2}$	$\frac{2\pi}{3}$	$\frac{3\pi}{4}$	$\frac{5\pi}{6}$	π
$y_1 = \sin x =$	0		$\frac{1}{\sqrt{2}}$		1		$\frac{1}{\sqrt{2}}$		0
$y_2 = \cos x =$	1		$\frac{1}{\sqrt{2}}$		0		$-\frac{1}{\sqrt{2}}$		-1
$y = y_1 + y_2 =$	1		$2\frac{1}{\sqrt{2}}$		1		0		-1
decimal value $y \approx$	1		1.4		1		0		-1

continued →

$x =$	$\frac{7\pi}{6}$	$\frac{5\pi}{4}$	$\frac{4\pi}{3}$	$\frac{3\pi}{2}$	$\frac{5\pi}{3}$	$\frac{7\pi}{4}$	$\frac{11\pi}{6}$	2π
$y_1 = \sin x =$		$-\frac{1}{\sqrt{2}}$		-1		$-\frac{1}{\sqrt{2}}$		0
$y_2 = \cos x =$		$-\frac{1}{\sqrt{2}}$		0		$\frac{1}{\sqrt{2}}$		1
$y = y_1 + y_2 =$		$-2\frac{1}{\sqrt{2}}$		-1		0		1
decimal value $y \approx$		-1.4		-1		0		1

$x =$	0	$\frac{\pi}{6}$	$\frac{\pi}{4}$	$\frac{\pi}{3}$	$\frac{\pi}{2}$	$\frac{2\pi}{3}$	$\frac{3\pi}{4}$	$\frac{5\pi}{6}$	π
$y_1 = \sin x =$	0	$\frac{1}{2}$	$\frac{1}{\sqrt{2}}$	$\frac{\sqrt{3}}{2}$	1	$\frac{\sqrt{3}}{2}$	$\frac{1}{\sqrt{2}}$	$\frac{1}{2}$	0
$y_2 = \cos x =$	1	$\frac{\sqrt{3}}{2}$	$\frac{1}{\sqrt{2}}$	$\frac{1}{2}$	0	$-\frac{1}{2}$	$-\frac{1}{\sqrt{2}}$	$\frac{-\sqrt{3}}{2}$	-1
$y = \sin x + \cos x =$	1	$\frac{1+\sqrt{3}}{2}$	$2\frac{1}{\sqrt{2}}$	$\frac{1+\sqrt{3}}{2}$	1	$\frac{\sqrt{3}-1}{2}$	0	$\frac{-\sqrt{3}+1}{2}$	-1
decimal value $y \approx$	1	1.37	1.4	1.37	1	0.37	0	-0.37	-1

$x =$	$\frac{7\pi}{6}$	$\frac{5\pi}{4}$	$\frac{4\pi}{3}$	$\frac{3\pi}{2}$	$\frac{5\pi}{3}$	$\frac{7\pi}{4}$	$\frac{11\pi}{6}$	2
$y_1 = \sin x =$	$-\frac{1}{2}$	$-\frac{1}{\sqrt{2}}$	$-\frac{\sqrt{3}}{2}$	-1	$-\frac{\sqrt{3}}{2}$	$-\frac{1}{\sqrt{2}}$	$-\frac{1}{2}$	0
$y_2 = \cos x =$	$\frac{-\sqrt{3}}{2}$	$-\frac{1}{\sqrt{2}}$	$-\frac{1}{2}$	0	$\frac{1}{2}$	$\frac{1}{\sqrt{2}}$	$\frac{\sqrt{3}}{2}$	1
$y = \sin x + \cos x =$	$\frac{-1-\sqrt{3}}{2}$	$-2\frac{1}{\sqrt{2}}$	$\frac{-\sqrt{3}-1}{2}$	-1	$\frac{-\sqrt{3}+1}{2}$	0	$\frac{\sqrt{3}-1}{2}$	1
decimal value $y \approx$	-1.37	-1.4	-1.37	-1	-0.37	0	0.37	1

1300 Locate the points for $y = \sin x + \cos x$ on the axes with the graphs of $y_1 = \sin x$ and $y_2 = \cos x$. Sketch the graph of $y = \sin x$ $+ \cos x$ by drawing a smooth line through these points. The choice

continued →

of points for sketching the sum is arbitrary. Enough points should
be used, however, so that you have a true picture of the function.

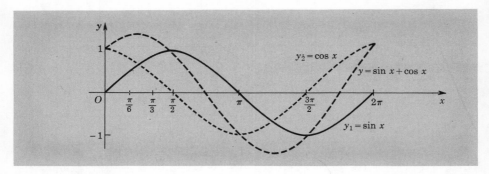

1301   Recall earlier in the discussion of functions in general that we
stated: "If two periodic functions f and g have period a, then the
function $f + g$ also has period a." The functions defined by
$y_1 = \sin x$ and $y_2 = \cos x$ each has period (1)_____. Therefore,
$y = \sin x + \cos x$ has period (2)_____. (3) Your sketch then
should represent how many periods of the function $y = \sin x +
\cos x$?

   (1) 2π **(2)** 2π **(3)** one

1302   The method of sketching used for the function $y = \sin x + \cos x$ is
known as *composition of ordinates*. As another example consider
$y = \sin x + \sin 2x$. The first step in sketching this function is to
sketch, on the same axes, the graphs of the two separate functions:
$y_1 = \sin x$ and $y_2 = \sin 2x$. Do this over the interval $0 \le x \le 2\pi$.

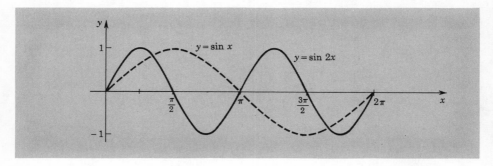

1303   The sum $y_1 + y_2$ at any point x can be obtained directly from the
graph in the following manner:

   1. Select a point x_2 (we have chosen $x_2 = \pi/4$); erect a perpendicular to the x axis at this point.

continued ➔

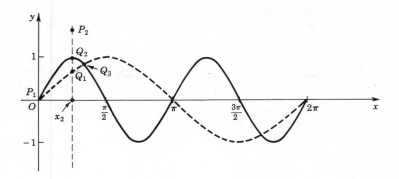

2. The segment x_2Q_1 represents the ordinate y_1. The segment x_2Q_2 represents the ordinate y_2.

3. Using a compass, you can represent the sum of $y_1 + y_2$ by placing the segment x_2Q_2 in the new position Q_1P_2.
   a. Follow these steps and locate on your graph the point P_2.
   b. Then through Q_3 draw a perpendicular to the x axis and find a point P_3 which is the sum of the ordinates for this value of x. (Note that $y_1 = y_2$ at this point.)

see frame 1304 for the location of P_3

1304 The graphical sum $y_1 + y_2$ for any designated x can be found as we have shown. Notice that P_3 is located by "adding" the lengths of the equal ordinates y_1 and y_2 on the perpendicular erected at x_3.

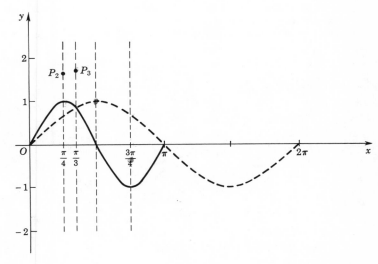

continued ➤

On your graph draw perpendiculars at the two additional points $\pi/2$ and $3\pi/4$ as shown above. On each perpendicular locate a point which represents $y_1 + y_2$.

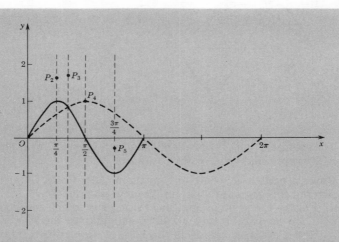

To locate P_4, note that $y_1 = 1$ and $y_2 = 0$. To locate P_5, we must note that y_1 is positive and y_2 is negative

1305 As indicated in frame 1304, the second step in obtaining the graph of $y = \sin x + \sin 2x$ is to add the ordinates of the two functions $y_1 = \sin x$ and $y_2 = \sin 2x$ for corresponding values of x. Some things to remember when graphing are: Care must be taken when y_1 or y_2 is negative. Sufficient points should be checked to give a true representation of the function $y = \sin x + \sin 2x$. Points to consider are maximum and minimum points, points of intersection of two graphs, etc. Complete the graph of $y = \sin x + \sin 2x$.

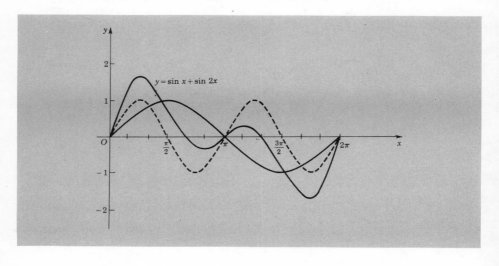

$y = \sin x + \sin 2x$

1306 The period for $y_1 = \sin x$ is **(1)**_____. The period for $y_2 = \sin 2x$ is **(2)**_____. The period for $y = \sin x + \sin 2x$ is **(3)**_____. (Look at your graph for the third answer.)

(1) 2π **(2)** π **(3)** 2π
Note: We have defined two functions having different periods.

1307 In order to graph the function defined by $y = \sin x - \sin 3x$
1. Let $y_1 = \sin x$ and $y_2 = \sin 3x$, and sketch each of these functions on the same set of axes.
2. Select appropriate points along the x axis, and subtract graphically the ordinates $(y_1 - y_2)$ at these points.
3. Sketch the curve suggested by these points. This is the graph of $y_1 - y_2$ or $y = \sin x - \sin 3x$. First answer these questions: **(1)** The function $y = \sin x$ has period = **(a)**_____ and amplitude **(b)**_____. **(2)** The function $y_2 = \sin 3x$ has period = **(a)**_____ and amplitude **(b)**_____.

(1)(a) 2π, **(b)** 1, **(2)(a)** $\dfrac{2\pi}{3}$, **(b)** 1

1308 Sketch, on the same set of axes, the graphs of the functions $y_1 = \sin x$ and $y_2 = \sin 3x$.

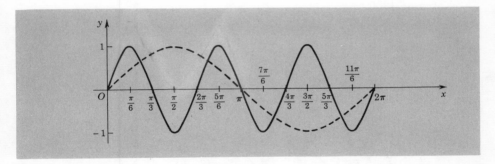

1309 Construct (draw) perpendiculars to the x axis at points

$$0, \ \frac{\pi}{6}, \ \frac{\pi}{3}, \ \frac{\pi}{2}, \ \frac{2\pi}{3}, \ \frac{5\pi}{6}, \ \pi, \ldots \text{ (intervals of } \frac{\pi}{6})$$

and mark on each the point representing $y = y_1 - y_2$.

continued →

Note: In some instances the perpendiculars should extend below the axis in order to show the graphical sum (or difference).

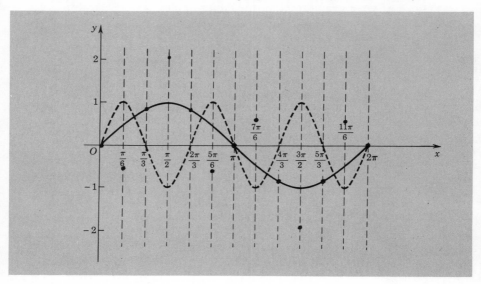

1310 Complete the graph of the function determined by $y = \sin x - \sin 3x$ by drawing a smooth curve through the points you located in frame 1309.

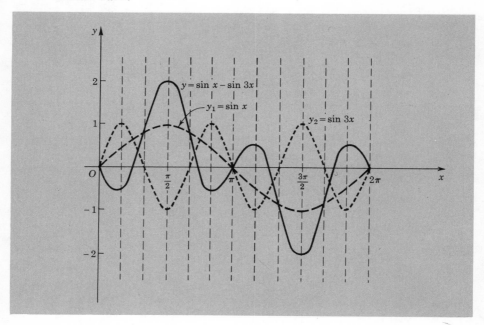

1311 In the problem $y = \sin x - \sin 3x$, we let $y_1 = \sin x$ and $y_2 = \sin 3x$, then $y = y_1 - y_2$. The process of "adding" the ordinates y_1 and y_2 in order to determine the ordinate y is called the *composition of ordinates*. We shall use this method to sketch the graph of the function defined by $y = 3 \sin x + \cos 2x$. Answer these questions before you start the actual graphing. **(1)** The function defined by $y_1 = 3 \sin x$ has amplitude $A = $ **(a)**_____ and period = **(b)**_____. **(2)** The function defined by $y_2 = \cos 2x$ has amplitude $A = $ **(a)**_____ and period = **(b)**_____.

(1)(a) 3, (b) 2π (2)(a) 1, (b) π

▽ **1312** Sketch, on the same axes, the graphs for $y_1 = 3 \sin x$ and $y_2 = \cos 2x$. The final step in the composition of ordinates will be delayed until frame 1313.

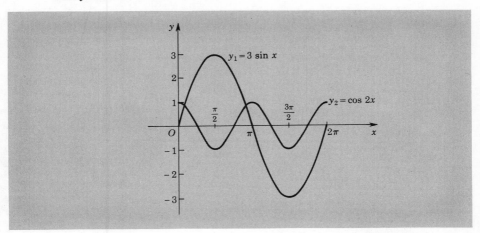

▽ **1313** Use care in selecting and adding ordinates so that you have a good graphical representation of the function. Some key points are shown here where we have located vertical lines. Continue the process for the remainder of the graph. Sketch the graph of $y = 3 \sin x + \cos 2x$.

continued ➝

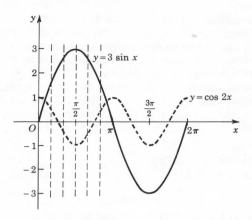

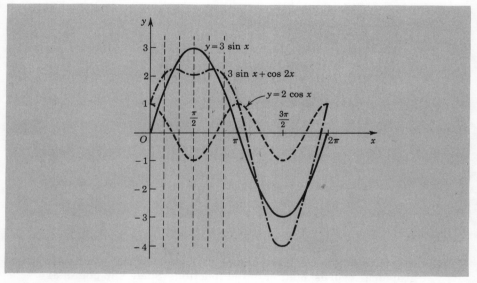

Frames 1314 to 1364 are applications. They may be omitted for a brief course.

1314   As we have mentioned previously, the scientist applies the knowledge of circular functions in his study of periodic phenomena. A simple harmonic motion, which he observes, for example, in the motion of the tip of a swinging pendulum, has a pattern which can be described and analyzed by means of the circular functions with which you are now familiar. Imagine a pendulum swinging from a

continued →

fixed point with a recording device
attached to its tip. As it is swinging,
a sheet of paper moving at a constant
velocity, as shown in the sketch, is
recording an impression of the movement of the tip. The tracing on the
paper gives a graphic idea of the

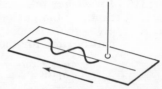

simple harmonic motion of the swinging pendulum. You would say,
no doubt, that this sketch resembles the graph of the_____
_____ function which also has this "wave-
like" pattern. *Note:* You may have more than one correct answer.

sine, or cosine, function or a circular function or y = sin x, etc.

1315 Frames 1315 to 1320 contain general statements related to simple
harmonic motion (or uniform circular motion).
Simple harmonic motion is oscillatory in character, repeating
itself in definite units of time. This repetitive feature, which
is a characteristic of the circular functions, is noted when we
speak of the_____ of the function.
Note: The characteristics we considered were the amplitude, the
period, and the phase shift in our discussions of the circular
functions.

period

1316 In simple harmonic motion the time required for one complete
oscillation (vibration) is also called the period. In working with
circular functions defined by y = A sin ax and y = A cos ax, what
"formula" is used for finding the period?

period $= \dfrac{2\pi}{a}$

1317 For the function y = A sin ax we noted that $2\pi/a$ tells us the
(1)_____, or time required for **(2)**_____.

(1) period   **(2)** one complete cycle or vibration

1318   *Frequency* tells us how many complete cycles occur in one unit of time. If the period for a function is $2\pi/a$, then $\frac{1}{2}\pi/a$ or $a/2\pi$ gives the frequency. Give the **(1)** *period* and **(2)** the *frequency* per unit of time for the function $y = 4 \sin 6\pi x$.

---

(1) period $= \dfrac{1}{3}$ *Solution:* $\dfrac{2\pi}{6\pi} = \dfrac{1}{3}$

(2) frequency $= 3$ cycles per unit of time   *Solution:* $\dfrac{1}{1/3} = 3$

1319   **(1)** In terms of an electrical current we may give a frequency as 60 cps (cycles per second). What does this mean?

(2) Find the period (the length of time required for one cycle) for the example above.

(3) Can you find the numerical value for a from the above information for the function $y = \sin ax$.

---

(1) There are 60 complete cycles per second.

(2) The period is $\frac{1}{60}$ (sec).

(3) $a = 120\pi$ *Solution:* period $= \dfrac{2\pi}{a}$

Therefore, $\dfrac{1}{60} = \dfrac{2\pi}{a}$

$a = 120\pi$

1320   There is a maximum displacement from the central point of the motion in simple harmonic motion. We identify displacement with _____ as it relates to the circular functions $A \sin ax$ or $A \cos ax$.

---

amplitude, A

1321   The term *phase shift* also applies to simple harmonic motion and has the same effect as we have seen on the circular functions, i.e., to shift the curve to the right or left along the x axis. As we consider simple harmonic motion, this shift could be produced by a change in time; e.g., if you think of the sketch of the swinging pendulum, you could designate any point as the beginning

continued →

of a unit of time. Recall how we find the phase shift. Find it for
$y = 3 \sin (3x - \pi)$.

Given $y = A \sin (ax + b)$ or $y = A \cos (ax + b)$

  phase shift $= -\dfrac{b}{a}$ $-\dfrac{-\pi}{3} = \dfrac{\pi}{3}$

1322   For a more thorough discussion,
we shall take as our model the
motion of a point P around a
circle of radius r, and suppose
that P moves at a constant speed
of s units/sec. If P_0 is the initial
position of P, then at the end of
1 sec, P will be at the point
marked P_1, an arc distance s
from $P(r, 0)$. At the end of 2
sec, P will be at the position
marked **(1)**_____ on the circle,
which is a distance $2s$ from P_0.

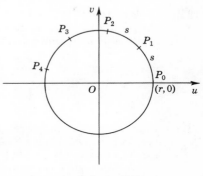

At the end of 3 sec, the point will be at P_3, which is a distance
(2)_____ from P_0.

(1) P_2 **(2)** $3s$

1323   Refer to Panel 13. If we continue the uniform circular motion of
point P, then after t sec, the point P would be a distance ts from
P_0 if it is moving at a speed of s units/sec.
If the uniform speed is 4 units/sec, then
    after 1 sec, P will be $4 \cdot 1 = 4$ units from P_0,
    after 2 sec, P will be **(1)**_____ units from P_0,
    after 3 sec, P will be **(2)**_____ units from P_0,
    after t sec, P will be **(3)**_____ units from P_0.

(1) $4 \cdot 2 = 8$ **(2)** $4 \cdot 3 = 12$ **(3)** $4 \cdot t = 4t$

1324   Refer to Panel 13. Now let each of the points $P_1, P_2, P_3, \ldots$, be
connected with point O. Then the central angles $P_0 O P_1, P_1 O P_2, \ldots$,
are equal since from geometry we know that equal arcs subtend
equal central angles. To find the radian measure of each of these
angles, the formula is $\omega =$ _____. (Give the answer in terms of s
and r.) *Note:* Instead of using θ, we are using the Greek letter ω

continued →

(omega) to represent the central angle, because this symbol is frequently used to describe uniform motion.

$\dfrac{s}{r}$

Recall the formula: angle in radians = $\dfrac{\text{arc}}{\text{radius}}$, i.e., $\omega = \dfrac{s}{r}$

1325 Look at Panel 13. A point moves with a constant speed of 2 ft/sec along the circumference of a circle of radius 3 ft. Find the central angle ω through which OP_0 has rotated in 1 sec.

$\omega = \dfrac{s}{r} = \dfrac{2}{3}$ radian

1326 Since $\omega = s/r$ then ω radians/sec represents the *angular* speed corresponding to the *linear* speed s ft/sec. *Example:* A point moves along a circle with a constant linear speed of 6 ft/sec. Find the angular speed in radians per second if the radius of the circle is **(1)** 2 ft **(2)** 3 ft.

(1) 3 radians/sec   **(2)** 2 radians/sec

1327 When the point P moves around a *unit* circle with a constant speed of s units/sec, then $\omega = s/1 = s$. (Recall that this observation was made when we first defined radians.) However, keep in mind that you can always transfer from a linear speed of s units/sec and to an angular speed of ω units/sec if you know r, and conversely,

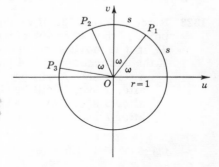

If $s = 12$ units/sec and $r = 4$ units then $\omega =$ **(1)**_____ radians/sec.

If $\omega = 3\pi/4$ radians and $r = 2$ units then $s =$ **(2)**_____ units/sec.

(1) 3   **(2)** $\dfrac{3\pi}{2}$

1328 Refer to Panel 13. If the point P is moving around the circle at a constant speed of s units/sec, then in 1 sec, OP_0 will have rotated

continued →

through an angle of ω radians; in 2 sec, through an angle of 2ω; in 3 sec, through an angle of **(1)** _____; in t sec, through an angle of **(2)** _____.

(1) 3ω or $\omega \cdot 3$ **(2)** $t\omega$ or $\omega \cdot t$

1329 Refer to Panel 13. Thus, we can say that after t sec, point P has moved from its original position P_0 through an arc length $t \cdot s$ to the position P_t and that $P_0 O$ has rotated through an angle $t \cdot \omega$ from its initial position to the position $P_t O$. $t \cdot s$ is the measure of the arc. $t \cdot \omega$ is the measure of the _____.

central angle

1330 Refer to Panel 13, figure b. Notice that we have labeled the axes ω and v; therefore, the point P_t has coordinates (ω, v). In the circle with radius r we can state the sine and cosine of the angle $t\omega$ thus: $\sin t\omega = v/r$ and $\cos t\omega =$ _____.

$\dfrac{\omega}{r}$ $\dfrac{u}{r}$

1331 We have the statements

$\sin t\omega = v/r$; therefore, $v =$ **(1)**_____ (solve for v)

$\cos t\omega = u/r$; therefore, $u =$ **(2)**_____ (solve for u)

(1) $r \sin t\omega$ **(2)** $r \cos t\omega$

1332 Suppose we wish to represent the statements from the frame 1331 graphically. Consider first $v = r \sin t\omega$. If we let $t = x$ and $v = y$, the statement above is written **(1)**_____, and we could sketch the graph as before. Suppose $r = 3$ and $\omega = 2$. **(2)** Sketch two periods (cycles) of the motion thus described.

continued →

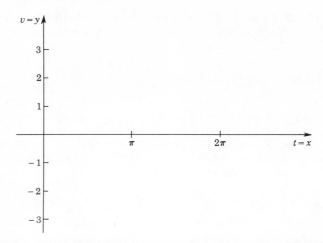

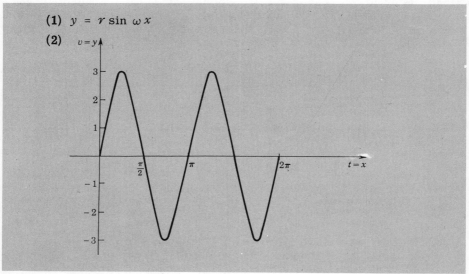

(1) $y = r \sin \omega x$

(2)

1333 If we wish to represent the second statement in frame 1331, $u = r \cos t$, graphically on an xy axis, we let $x = t$ as before and now let $y = u$. Then $u = r \cos t\omega$ takes the form **(1)**_____.

continued →

Here again we have identified uniform circular motion with one of the circular functions. Let $r = 3$ and $\omega = 2$. (2) Sketch two periods of this motion.

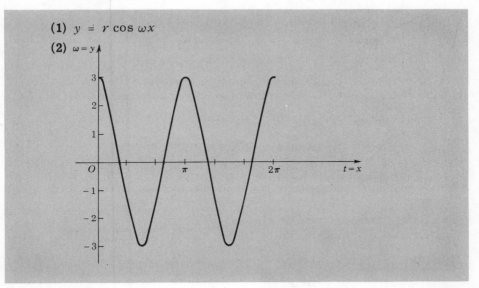

(1) $y = r \cos \omega x$

(2) $\omega = y$

1334 Now recall that on a previous occasion we saw that the curves representing $y = \cos x$ and $y = \sin x$ differ from each other only in phase shift; i.e., if the graph of $y = \cos x$ is shifted $\pi/2$ units to the right, it will coincide with the graph of $y = \sin x$. (Look at the graphs in frames 1332 and 1333 to verify this.) This means that either $u = r \cos t\omega$ or $v = r \sin t\omega$ can be used to give a graphical representation of simple harmonic motion where ω expresses angular velocity in radians per unit of time t. The two graphs will differ from each other only in _____ (amplitude, period, phase shift).

phase shift

1335 Examine the statements $v = r \sin \omega t$ and $y = r \sin \omega x$. The amplitude of these functions is (1)_____. The period is (2)_____.

(1) r (2) $\dfrac{2\pi}{\omega}$

1336   State (1) the amplitude and (2) the period $u = r \cos \omega t$ and $y = r \cos \omega x$.

---

(1) amplitude is r (2) period is $\dfrac{2\pi}{\omega}$.

1337   Thus, if we wish to picture the motion of a point P as it moves around the circumference of a circle of radius r at a constant angular speed of ω radians/sec, we can sketch on a set of axes the graph of
1. $v = r \sin \omega t$, letting $y = v$ and $x = t$.
or
2. $u = r \cos \omega t$, letting $y = u$ and $x = t$.
Suppose P is a point on the rim of a wheel rotating at an angular speed of π radians/sec. The wheel has a radius of 2 in. Represent graphically the motion of the point during 2 sec, using statement 1 above.

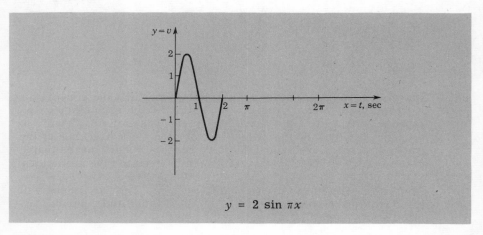

$$y = 2 \sin \pi x$$

1338   We mentioned that one complete cycle occurs during one period $(2\pi/\omega)$ in the function defined by $y = r \sin \omega x$. And that the *frequency* is the number of cycles occurring per unit of time $1/(2\pi/\omega)$. [Note that $1/(2\pi/\omega) = \omega/2\pi$.] So we say that the frequency is the reciprocal of the period, namely, $\omega/2\pi$. Check your previous problem $2\pi/\pi$ represents one period the frequency then is (1)_____. This tells us the number of cycles per time unit is (2)_____ _____.

---

(1) $\dfrac{\pi}{2\pi} = \dfrac{1}{2}$ (2) $\frac{1}{2}$ cycle completed in 1 sec

1339 Consider the problem in frame 1337 again: *P* is a point on the rim of a wheel rotating at an angular speed of π radians/sec. The wheel has a radius of 2 units. Represent graphically the motion of the point during 4 sec, using the function defined by $u = r \cos \omega t$ (let $y = \omega$, $x = t$). *Note:* The graph is to cover 4 sec of time, and you are asked to use the cosine function instead of the sine.

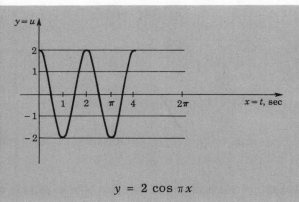

$$y = 2 \cos \pi x$$

1340 The wavelike pattern exhibited in the graphs of the sine and cosine functions is common in many motions. Take the example of the electric current (alternating). Starting at 0, the current builds up to a maximum at *A* then returns to 0 at *B*, builds up to a maximum in the other direction at *C*, then returns to 0 at *D*. For a 100-cycle current, the pattern is repeated 100 times a second; that is, _____ of these patterns would be "squeezed in" from 0 to 1 on the *x* axis.

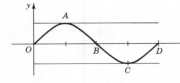

100

1341 We shall continue discussing the graph of the 100-cycle electric current in frame 1340. The *frequency*, recall, is the reciprocal of the period; therefore, we know that the period in this case is **(1)**_____. This means that one complete cycle occurs during **(2)**_____ of a second. **(3)** Does the function $y = A \cos 200 \pi x$ have this period?

(1) $\frac{1}{100}$ **(2)** $\frac{1}{100}$ **(3)** yes, $\frac{2\pi}{200\pi} = \frac{1}{100}$

1342   The following equation represents simple harmonic motion: $y = 6 \sin 3x$. Give the **(1)** amplitude, **(2)** period, and **(3)** frequency. *Note:* You will note that x and t have been used interchangeably in these frames. The choice of t might emphasize that we are speaking of units of time.

> **(1)** amplitude is 6   **(2)** period is $\dfrac{2\pi}{3}$
>
> **(3)** frequency is $\dfrac{1}{2\pi/3} = \dfrac{3}{2\pi}$

1343   Let $y = \frac{1}{4} \sin 5t$ represent a uniform circular motion. State its **(1)** amplitude, **(2)** period, and **(3)** frequency.

> **(1)** amplitude is $\frac{1}{4}$ **(2)** period is $\dfrac{2\pi}{5}$ **(3)** frequency is $\dfrac{5}{2\pi}$

1344   What do we mean when we say that the amplitude of the motion represented by $y = \frac{1}{4} \sin 5t$ is $\frac{1}{4}$?

> The maximum (or minimum) displacement from the x axis is $\frac{1}{4}$. (If this equation represents the simple uniform motion of a point around a circle, then the circle has a radius of $\frac{1}{4}$ unit.)

1345   What do we mean when we say that the period of the function represented by $y = \frac{1}{4} \sin 5t$ is $2\pi/5$?

> $2\pi/5$ represents the number of units of time t which are required for one complete cycle of the motion (for a point to move completely around the circle in simple harmonic motion).

1346   What do we mean when we say that the frequency for the motion represented by $y = \frac{1}{4} \sin 5t$ is $5/2\pi$?

> It indicates how many cycles (or part of one cycle) are completed in one unit of time. In one unit of time a point has completed this part ($5/2\pi$) of a cycle.

1347 Suppose a simple harmonic motion has an amplitude of 4 units and a frequency of $\frac{1}{2}$ cps. Write the equation expressing this motion in the form $y = r \sin \omega t$ using correct numerical values for r and ω.

$y = 4 \sin \pi t$ *Solution for* ω: frequency $= \dfrac{1}{\text{period}} = \dfrac{1}{2\pi/\omega}$

$$\frac{1}{2} = \frac{1}{2\pi/\omega}$$

$$\frac{1}{2} = \frac{\omega}{2\pi}$$

$$\omega = \pi$$

1348 Suppose a simple harmonic motion has an amplitude of $\frac{1}{2}$ and a frequency of 10 cps. Express this motion in the form $y = r \sin \omega t$ by supplying correct numerical values for r and ω.

$y = \frac{1}{2} \sin 20\pi t$ *Solution for* ω: frequency $= \dfrac{1}{\text{period}}$, $10 = \dfrac{1}{2\pi/\omega}$

$$10 = \frac{\omega}{2\pi} , \quad 20\pi = \omega$$

1349 In a previous example we said that the sound produced by a musical instrument could be represented approximately by an expression consisting of the sum of several terms of the type $A \sin (ax + b)$. Without attempting to discuss the theory of sound we shall make one or two more comments.

A *pure musical tone* is produced by any pressure wave which can be described by a circular function such as $y = A \sin \omega x$. (A sound wave is produced by a rapid alternation, rise and fall, of pressure in a medium such as air).

Considering $y = A \sin \omega x$ as a description of a musical tone, we identify the *pitch* of the tone with the frequency. The pitch therefore depends on (1)_____ in the statement above. The loudness depends on the *amplitude* which is (2)_____ in the equation above.

(1) ω (2) A

1350 When two musical instruments are tuned to the same note, we say that they produce a "pleasing" sound when played together. If two pure tones are produced by individual pressure waves of the same frequency (i.e., they have a common period), then combined they have the same frequency. *Recall:* if function f has period a and

continued ➔

and function g has period a, then $f + g$ has period a. This is one of
the basic principles of harmony. If we represent two pure tones by
$\omega = A \cos \omega t$ and $v = B \sin \omega t$, where A, B, and ω are positive, then
$u + v = A \cos \omega t + B \sin \omega t$. Can we identify the period for
$\omega + v$? If so, what is it?

yes, $\dfrac{2\pi}{\omega}$

1351   Here is another application from physics. Suppose a weight is
suspended from a spring and is vibrating in a vertical direction.

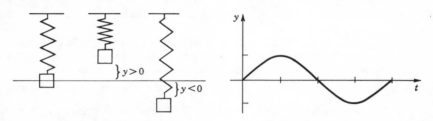

Scientists have found that the distance y of the weight at a particular
time t above or below the "rest" position can be plotted on a t, y
coordinate system and the graph can be described by an equation of
the form $y = A \sin (ax + b)$ or $y = A \cos (ax + b)$. If a very
strong "pull" is made on the spring to set it in motion, this will
affect the displacement above or below the t axis and will be reflected in the value of **(1)**_____ in the formula. A very
strong spring will vibrate more rapidly than a weak one, the number of vibrations will be reflected in the value of **(2)**_____
in the formula. The particular moment at which observations are
made will be evidenced in the phase shift.

(1) A or amplitude   **(2)** a, period or frequency

▽ **1352**   Now that you have an idea of a few of the scientific applications of
the sine and cosine function of real numbers, we shall ask you to
sketch several, or to answer questions relating to them. The
problems will include graphing fundamental wave patterns such as
$y = A \sin ax$ and harmonic wave patterns obtained by the composition of ordinates such as $y = A \sin ax + B \cos bx$.

Problem 1. State **(1)** the period and **(2)** the range [(a) maximum
and (b) minimum values] for the function defined by $y = 2 \sin 3t$.

(1) period $= \dfrac{2\pi}{3}$ **(2)(a)** maximum 2, **(b)** minimum − 2;
or − 2 ≤ y ≤ 2

▽ 1353   Problem 1 *(continued)*. What is **(1)** the frequency and **(2)** the amplitude for the function defined by $y = 2 \sin 3t$.

(1) frequency $= \dfrac{3}{2\pi}$, i.e., the reciprocal of the period

(2) amplitude $= 2$, i.e., the $|A|$ in $y = A \sin at$

▽ 1354   Problem 1 *(continued)*. Sketch the graph of three periods of the function defined by $y = 2 \sin 3t$. Represent t on the x axis. A scale for sketching is indicated below; it is suitable for the period $2\pi/3$.

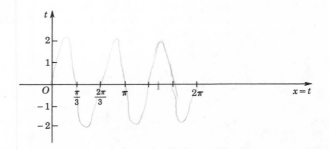

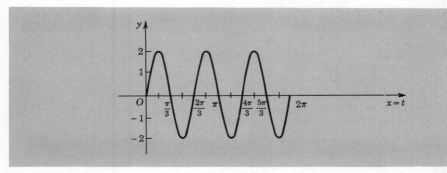

▽ 1355   Problem 2. State the **(1)** amplitude, **(2)** period, and **(3)** phase shift for the function defined by $y = \frac{1}{2} \cos (x - \pi/4)$.

(1) amplitude $= \frac{1}{2}$ **(2)** period $= 2\pi$ **(3)** phase shift $= \dfrac{\pi}{4}$

Keep this information.

▽ **1356**   Problem 2 *(continued)*. To sketch quickly one period of $y = \frac{1}{2} \cos (x - \pi/4)$, mark the points on the x axis where the period begins and where it ends,

and divide the space between in four equal parts. Do this on an axis similar to the one here. Also indicate the amplitude on the y axis. Keep your work.

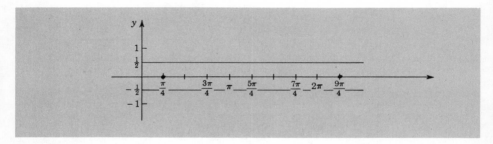

▽ **1357**   Problem 2 *(continued)*. Sketch one period of the function defined by $y = \frac{1}{2} \cos (x - \pi/4)$.

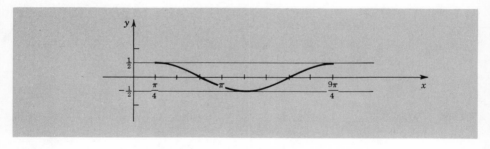

▽ **1358**   Problem 3. A function is defined by $y = \sin x + \frac{1}{3} \sin 3x$. If we graph this function by the method called *composition of ordinates*, we must sketch the graphs of two separate functions $y_1 =$ **(1)**_____ and $y_2 =$ **(2)**_____. Then by adding the ordinates, we have $y = y_1 + y_2 =$ **(3)**_____ .

(1) $\sin x$ **(2)** $\frac{1}{2} \sin 3x$ **(3)** $\sin x + \frac{1}{3} \sin 3x$

1359   Problem 3 *(continued)*. Sketch the graphs of $y_1 = \sin x$ and $y_2 = \frac{1}{3} \sin 3x$ on the same axes. Since you will be asked in frame 1360 to sketch the graph of one cycle of $y = \sin x + \frac{1}{3} \sin 3x$ try to decide over how many periods to extend the graphs of y_1 and y_2 as you sketch them.

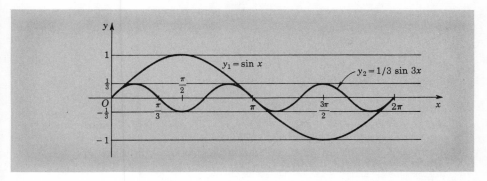

1360   Problem 3 *(continued)*. Sketch the graph of $y = \sin x + \frac{1}{3} \sin 3x$ by the addition of ordinates. Make the sketch on the same axes as y_1 and y_2. Show one complete wave pattern of the graph.

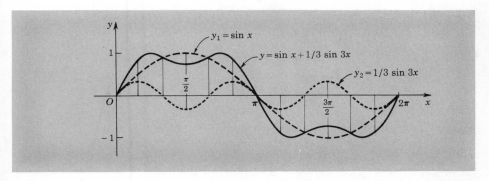

1361   Problem 4. To sketch the graph of $y = x + \cos 2x$ by the composition of ordinates, we first sketch the graphs of $y_1 = $ **(1)**_____ and $y_2 = $ **(2)**_____ on the same set of axes.

(1) x **(2)** $\cos 2x$

1362   Problem 4 *(continued)*. Sketch the graph of $y = x + \cos 2x$ by the addition of ordinates.

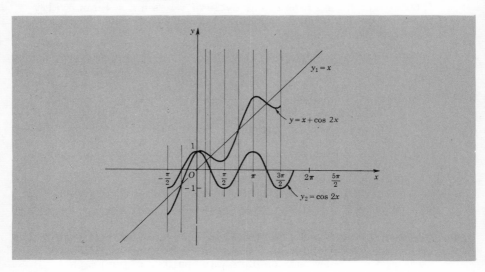

1363   Problem 4 *(continued)*. *Optional*. Continue the graph of $y = x + \cos 2x$ over the interval $-3\pi/2 \le x \le 3\pi$.

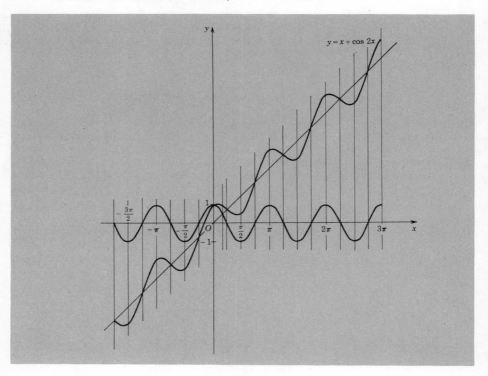

1364 *Optional*. Sketch the graph of $y = \cos^2 x + \sin^2 x$.

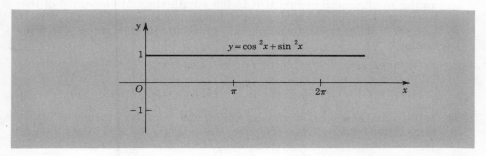

▽1365 We shall conclude this section on circular functions with a short discussion on tan x, cot x, sec x, and csc x and their graphs where x represents a real number. Recall the definition, tan x = **(1)**_____/_____. tan x is undefined when x = **(2)**_____ in the interval $0 \leq \theta < 2\pi$. Since tan x is undefined for certain values of x, there are "gaps" in the graph of the function. We say that the function is *discontinuous* at these points.

(1) $\dfrac{\sin x}{\cos x}$ **(2)** $\dfrac{\pi}{2}$ or $90°$, $\dfrac{3\pi}{2}$ or $270°$

1366 Recall from the graphs you sketched earlier that the tangent function has a pattern which repeats every π radians. We can *prove* that the tangent is periodic with period π if we can prove that $\tan(x + \pi) = \tan x$.

$$\tan(x + \pi) = \frac{\sin(x + \pi)}{\cos(x + \pi)} \qquad \text{by definition}$$

$$= \frac{\sin x \cos \pi + \cos x \sin \pi}{\cos x \cos \pi - \sin x \sin \pi} \qquad \begin{array}{l}\text{applying formula} \\ \text{for } \sin(\alpha + \beta) \\ \text{and } \cos(\alpha + \beta)\end{array}$$

$$= \textbf{(1)}\text{_____} \qquad \text{simplifying}$$

$$= \textbf{(2)}\text{_____} \qquad \begin{array}{l}\text{by definition} \\ \text{of tangent}\end{array}$$

(1) $\dfrac{-\sin x}{-\cos x}$ **(2)** tan x

1367 Since $\tan(x + \pi) = \tan x$ for all values of x for which the tangent is defined, we know that the tangent function is periodic and that the period is π, by definition of periodicity. (A function F is periodic

continued →

with period a if $F(x + a) = f(x)$ for all x.) We refer to a period as the *fundamental* period if it is the smallest positive period of the function. Can we say that π is the fundamental period for **(1)** the tangent? What is the fundamental period for **(2)** the sine? **(3)** The cosine?

(1) yes **(2)** 2π **(3)** 2π

1368 Make a statement about the maximum and minimum values of the tangent function.

there is no maximum value nor minimum value for the tangent function

1369 Complete the table below. Do not use Panel 1. This is review material which you will need for sketching the graph of $y = \tan x$. Refer to the sketches if necessary.

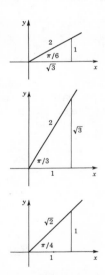

x	$\tan x$
0	
$\pi/6$	
$\pi/4$	
$\pi/3$	
$\pi/2$	
$2\pi/3$	
$3\pi/4$	
$5\pi/6$	
π	
$-\pi/2$	
$-\pi/3$	
$-\pi/4$	
$-\pi/6$	

x	$\tan x$
0	0
$\pi/6$	$1/\sqrt{3} = \sqrt{3}/3 = 0.58$
$\pi/4$	1
$\pi/3$	$\sqrt{3} = 1.7$
$\pi/2$	undefined

continued →

x	$\tan x$
$2\pi/3$	$-\sqrt{3} = -1.7$
$3\pi/4$	-1
$5\pi/6$	$-1/\sqrt{3} = -0.58$
π	0
$-\pi/2$	undefined
$-\pi/3$	-1.7
$-\pi/4$	-1
$-\pi/6$	-0.58

1370 Sketch the graph of the function defined by $y = \tan x$ over the interval $-\pi/2 < x < 3\pi/2$. Use the table in frame 1369, but extend the graph over the interval required. Do not refer to Panel 7 or to previous graphs you may have drawn. Label the axes as indicated below. At the points $-\pi/2$, $\pi/2$, $3\pi/2$, the vertical broken lines called *vertical asymptotes* indicate the points where the function is undefined.

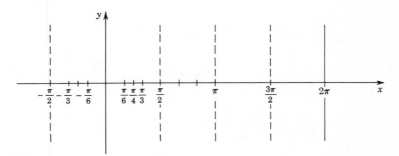

see Panel 7 for the answer

1371 By definition $\cot x =$ **(1)**_____; $\cot x$ is undefined when $x =$ **(2)**_____ and $x =$ **(3)**_____ in the interval $0 \leq x < 2\pi$. Therefore, the graph of $y = \cot x$ is discontinuous at the points $x =$ **(4)**_____ and $x =$ **(5)**_____.

(1) $\dfrac{\cos x}{\sin x}$ **(2)** 0 **(3)** π **(4)** 0 **(5)** π

1372   Is the cotangent a periodic function? If so, what is its fundamental period? *Optional:* Construct a proof as we did for the tangent function.

yes, π

Proof:

$$\cot (x + \pi) = \frac{\cos (x + \pi)}{\sin (x + \pi)} \qquad \text{by definition}$$

$$= \frac{\cos x \cos \pi - \sin x \sin \pi}{\sin x \cos \pi + \cos x \sin \pi} \qquad \begin{array}{l}\text{applying}\\ \cos (\alpha + \beta) \text{ and}\\ \sin (\alpha + \beta)\end{array}$$

$$= \frac{- \cos x}{- \sin x} \qquad \text{simplifying}$$

$$= \cot x \qquad \text{by definition}$$

1373   Complete the table below to which you may refer when you graph the function $y = \cot x$. Recall that $\cot x = 1/\tan x$.

x	$\cot x$
0	
$\pi/6$	
$\pi/4$	
$\pi/3$	
$\pi/2$	
$2\pi/3$	
$3\pi/4$	
$5\pi/6$	
π	

x	$\cot x$
0	undefined
$\pi/6$	$\sqrt{3} = 1.7$
$\pi/4$	1
$\pi/3$	$1/\sqrt{3} = 0.58$
$\pi/2$	0
$2\pi/3$	−0.58
$3\pi/4$	−1
$5\pi/6$	−1.7
π	undefined

1374 On axes labeled as shown below sketch the graph of the function defined by $y = \cot x$ over the interval $0 < x < 2\pi$.

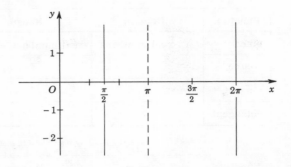

Note: The broken lines (vertical asymptotes) at π and 2π indicate points of discontinuity, as on the graph of the tangent function. The graph is also discontinuous at $x = 0$.

see Panel 14 for the answer

1375 The graph of the cotangent function indicates that we do not consider the amplitude, since there are no maximum nor minimum points. If we wish to state the domain and range of the cotangent function, we say that

1. The *domain* is all *real numbers except* $\pm\, n\pi$, since the function is defined for all real numbers x except $x =$ _____, _____, _____(list at least three values).

2. The *range* is *all real numbers*, since the cotangent increases (numerically) without limit as x approaches the points mentioned in statement 1 above.

0, π, 2π... (or $-\pi$, -2π,...)

1376 Complete the table summarizing the information we have regarding the domain and range of the functions listed.

Function	Domain	Range
sine	all real numbers	real numbers –1 to 1
cosine		
tangent		
cotangent		

Function	Domain	Range
sine	all real numbers	real numbers –1 to 1
cosine	all real numbers	real numbers –1 to 1
tangent	all real numbers except $\pm\pi/2 \pm n\pi$	all real numbers
cotangent	all real numbers except $\pm n\pi$	all real numbers

1377 We could consider tangent and cotangent functions of the form $y = A \tan(ax + b)$ and $y = A \cot(ax + b)$, but they have no great importance. Roughly speaking we can identify A, a, and b with the same constants in the sine and cosine functions.
1. A is *not* the amplitude, but it has the effect of multiplying the value of each ordinate by A.
2. π/a represents the **(1)**_____. The constant a has the effect of "compressing" or "stretching" the graph along the x axis.
3. $-b/a$ represents the **(2)**_____. This has the effect of **(3)**____(explain)____.

(1) period   (2) phase shift
(3) shifting (translating) the graph to the right or left along the x axis

1378 To conclude the section on the graphs of the circular or trigonometric functions, we shall consider the graphs of $y = \sec x$ and $y = \csc x$. First complete the table of values and then in frame 1379 plot the points and draw the graph for $y = \sec x$. Recall that $\sec x = 1/\cos x$.

continued →

x	sec x	x	sec x	x	sec x
0	1	$3\pi/4$		$3\pi/2$	
$\pi/6$		$5\pi/6$		$5\pi/3$	
$\pi/4$		π		$7\pi/4$	
$\pi/3$		$7\pi/6$		$11\pi/6$	
$\pi/2$		$5\pi/4$		2π	
$2\pi/3$		$4\pi/3$			

x	sec x	x	sec x	x	sec x
0	1	$3\pi/4$	$-\sqrt{2} \approx 1.4$	$3\pi/2$	not defined
$\pi/6$	$\dfrac{1}{\sqrt{3}/2} \approx 1.2$	$5\pi/6$	$-2/\sqrt{3} \approx -1.2$	$5\pi/3$	2
$\pi/4$	$\dfrac{1}{1/\sqrt{2}} \approx \sqrt{2} \approx 1.4$	π	-1	$7\pi/4$	1.4
$\pi/3$	$\dfrac{1}{1/2} = 2$	$7\pi/6$	-1.2	$11\pi/6$	1.2
$\pi/2$	not defined	$5\pi/4$	-1.4	2π	1.0
$2\pi/3$	-2	$4\pi/3$	-2		

1379 Draw the graph of $y = \sec x$ on a set of axes as shown here. Referring to the table in frame 1378, plot the points and draw a smooth curve through them.

continued →

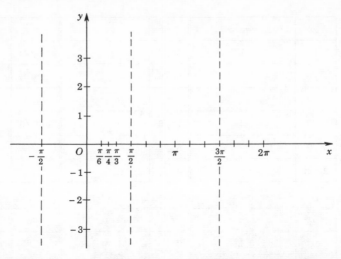

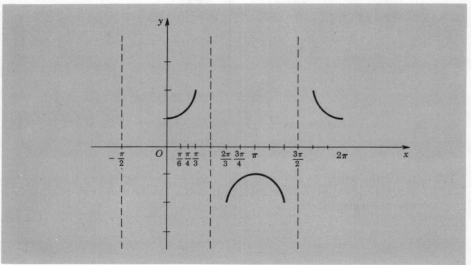

1380 In order to get a more complete picture of the graph of $y = \sec x$:
1. Find several more values of y for x near $\pi/2$ and $3\pi/2$.
2. Extend the graph to the left and right so that the interval for x is $-\pi/2 \le x \le 5\pi/2$.
Consult Panel 1 and use the fact that $\sec x = 1/\cos x$ to compute the additional numerical values you need. *Examples:* $4\pi/9$ $(75°)$ and $7\pi/9$ $(105°)$.

see Panel 15 for the answer

1381 Complete the table below which will be used in frame 1382 in plotting the graph of $y = \csc x$.

x	$\csc x$	x	$\csc x$	x	$\csc x$
0		$3\pi/6$		$3\pi/2$	
$\pi/6$		$5\pi/6$		$5\pi/3$	
$\pi/4$		π		$7\pi/4$	
$\pi/3$		$7\pi/6$		$11\pi/6$	
$\pi/2$		$5\pi/4$		2π	
$2\pi/3$		$4\pi/3$			

x	$\csc x$	x	$\csc x$	x	$\csc x$
0	undefined	$3\pi/4$	1.4	$3\pi/2$	-1
$\pi/6$	2	$5\pi/6$	2	$5\pi/3$	-1.2
$\pi/4$	1.4	π	undefined	$7\pi/4$	-1.4
$\pi/3$	1.2	$7\pi/6$	-2	$11\pi/6$	-2
$\pi/2$	1	$5\pi/4$	-1.4	2π	undefined
$2\pi/3$	1.2	$4\pi/3$	-1.2		

1382 On a set of axes similar to the one shown below plot the points of the table in frame 1381. Then draw a smooth curve through these points and extend it as before to show the graph of $y = \csc x$ over the interval $-\pi/2 \leq x \leq 2\pi$.

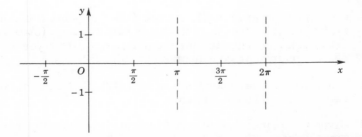

see Panel 16 for the answer

1383   Find the **(1)** amplitude **(2)** period, **(3)** frequency, and **(4)** phase shift for the motion described thus: $y = 25 \cos (3t + \pi/2)$.

(1) amplitude = 25   **(2)** period = $\dfrac{2\pi}{3}$

(3) frequency = $\dfrac{3}{2\pi}$ **(4)** phase shift = $\dfrac{-\pi/2}{3} = -\dfrac{\pi}{6}$

Note: phase shift = $-\dfrac{b}{a}$ where $y = A \sin (ax + b)$

1384   State the **(1)** amplitude, **(2)** period, **(3)** frequency, and **(4)** phase shift for the motion described thus: $y = 400 \cos (2x - \pi/6)$.

(1) amplitude = 400   **(3)** frequency = $\dfrac{2\pi}{2} = \pi$

(3) frequency = $\dfrac{1}{\pi}$ **(4)** phase shift = $\dfrac{-(-\pi/6)}{2} = \dfrac{\pi}{12}$

SELF-TEST 5

1   **(a)** A force of 400 lb is acting east, and another force of 300 lb is acting north; make a sketch showing the magnitude and direction of the resultant. **(b)** Find the magnitude of the resultant and the direction the resultant takes with respect to the eastward force.

2   Find the x and y components of a vector which represents a force of 12 lb and which makes an angle of $60°$ with the positive x axis. Make a sketch.

3   Two forces, $F_1 = 8$ and $F_2 = 10$, act at an angle of $45°$ with respect to each other. Find the magnitude and direction of the resultant.

4   **(a)** Represent graphically a point P having polar coordinates $(4, 5\pi/6)$. **(b)** Find its rectangular coordinates. **(c)** Give another set of polar coordinates for the point P. **(d)** Can you give another set of rectangular coordinates for point P?

5   P has rectangular coordinates $(-5, -12)$, find a set of polar coordinates for P. Make a sketch.

6   Given two points $P(4, 6)$ and $R(9, -5)$. Find the distance between these points.

7 Let $A = 4 - 3i$ and $B = 1 + 2i$. **(a)** Find $A + B$. **(b)** Find $A - B$. **(c)** Represent graphically $A = 4 - 3i$, $B = 1 + 2i$, and the sum $A + B$.

8 Find the product of $(4 - 3i) \cdot (1 + 2i)$. Express the answer in $a + bi$ form.

9 Find the quotient of $(4 - 3i)/(1 + 2i)$. Express the answer in $a + bi$ form.

10 Write the conjugate of $4 - 3i$. Plot $4 - 3i$ and its conjugate on the complex plane. Find the sum of $4 - 3i$ and its conjugate. Indicate this sum on the graph.

11 Simplify **(a)** i^2, **(b)** i^3, **(c)** i^4, **(d)** i^{15}, and **(e)** i^{78}.

12 Find the values for x and y for which the following are true statements: **(a)** $3x - 14i = 12 - 2yi$ and **(b)** $2x + y + 5i = 5 + (3x - y)i$.

13 Simplify **(a)** $\dfrac{i - 3}{3 + i}$ and **(b)** $\dfrac{3i(-1 + i)}{(1 + i)(2 - i)}$.

14 Find a complex number z such that $2(3i + z) + 15 = (3i + 2)z$.

15 Write the polar form for the following complex numbers: **(a)** $3 + 4i$ and **(b)** $-1 - 2i$. Make a sketch of each.

16 **(a)** Change $4(\cos 30° + i \sin 30°)$ to rectangular form.
(b) Change $5(\cos 90° + i \sin 90°)$ to rectangular form.

17 **(a)** The complex number whose polar coordinates are $(\sqrt{2}, 5\pi/4)$ is written _____ (in complex polar form). **(b)** Represent the number graphically.

18 Carry out the computation $[3(\cos 20° + i \sin 20°)]^3$.

19 Find the quotient

$12(\cos 190° + i \sin 190°) \div 3(\cos 70° + i \sin 70°)$

Change the answer to rectangular form.

20 Express each of the numbers in polar form and then perform the indicated operation. Leave the answer in polar form.

$$\frac{(1 - \sqrt{3}i)^2}{(1 + i)}$$

21 Use De Moivre's theorem to calculate $(\sqrt{3} + i)^8$.

22 Find the three cube roots of $27(\cos 240° + i \sin 240°)$.

23 Find the two square roots of i. Write the answers in both polar and rectangular form.

24 Find all the roots of the equation $x^5 - 1 = 0$. You may leave your answer in polar form.

25 Select the correct words, "pure imaginary" or "real number," for the following: **(a)** The product of a complex number and its conjugate is_____. **(b)** The sum of a complex number and its conjugate is _____. **(c)** The difference of a complex number and its conjugate is _____.

PART THREE

UNIT 6 ▌Vectors

Comment

Sometimes in mathematics, science, or industry we are interested only in the magnitude of a quantity: the length of a line segment, the weight of an object, the population of a city, the speed of a plane.

The magnitude can be represented by merely applying a numerical unit (measure). It can be represented by the distance between two points on a line and may be referred to as a *scalar* quantity. At other times we want to know not only the magnitude of a quantity but the direction as well: a man walks across the street to the bank, a baseball player throws a ball to first base, a plane travels south for one hour. When we need to specify (1) distance (using a suitable unit) and (2) direction from one point to another to identify quantities, we may refer to them as *vector quantities*. Forces, velocities, and accelerations are examples of vector quantities studied in physics.

1385 *Vector quantities* may be represented geometrically by directed line segments which we call vectors. The magnitude is represented by the length of the line segment, the direction is indicated by the angle which this line makes with a given line, and an arrow shows the direction (sense) along the line.
For example, a force of 10 lb acting at an angle of 60° with the horizontal might be shown as indicated in the sketch. Use directed line segments to represent the following vector quantities. (1) A

continued →

velocity of 200 mph (miles per hour) in a northwest direction. (Let
1 in. = 200 miles.) **(2)** A displacement in position of 12 ft to the
right. (Use a suitable scale.)

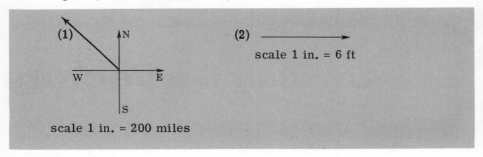

scale 1 in. = 200 miles

1386 In this sketch you see vectors which appear to be equivalent since they are represented by directed line segments of *equal
length* and are drawn *parallel* to each
other. (They make equal angles with the
horizontal.) Also, the arrows indicate an
agreement in sense (direction along the
lines). **(1)** Indicate on a parallelogram
two sets of equivalent vectors, e.g., **AB**
is equivalent to **(2)**___ and **AD** is
equivalent to **(3)**___. Use arrows to
show sense (direction along the segments). *Note:* Assume the usual properties of a parallelogram.

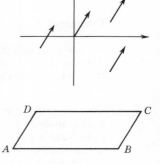

(1)   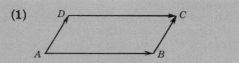   **(2) DC**

(3) BC

Note: **AB** is a symbol used to denote a vector from A to B

1387 When we discussed *equivalent* directed line segments in frame
1386, we specified (1) length, (2) direction, and (3) sense (direction along the line). Unless we specify an initial point, there are
many directed segments which represent equally well the same

continued →

vector quantity. From three points, A, B, and C, using a scale of 1 in. = 45 miles, show three vectors which may represent "a train travels east at 45 mph for one hour." *Note:* The customary arrangement for geographical directions on a map is shown here.

1388 There are various notations for vectors in common use. One we shall use is shown in this example. If we think of a vector as the displacement of a point P to the point Q on a plane, we write **PQ** where P represents the initial point and Q the terminal point. Then **-PQ** indicates that the sense is opposite (direction along the line is opposite), but the distance is the same. **(1)** Represent a vector **OA** whose initial point is at the origin of a rectangular coordinate system and which makes a 30° angle with the horizontal and represents a distance equal to **PQ** shown in the sketch above. **(2)** Is vector **OA** equivalent to **PQ**? **(3)** Explain what we would mean by **-OA**.

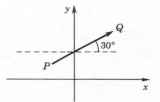

(1)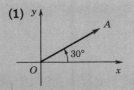

(2) yes

(3) sense is opposite to **OA**, (or the direction is from A to O.)

1389 Which of the following would you classify as *(A)* scalars (quantities which can be represented by a unit of measure and a number without specified direction) and *(B)* as vectors (*directed* line segments):
1. a person's age
2. the velocity of a motor boat
3. the number of pages in a book
4. the acceleration of gravity

: 1, 3 (age and pages in a book are magnitudes only)
: 2, 4 (velocity and acceleration involve both direction and magnitude; hence they are termed vectors)

1390 A vector gives us three characteristics of a force or motion, the
(1)_____ represented by the length of the segment, the
(2)_____ represented by the angle which the segment makes
with a given line, and the **(3)**_____ represented by the arrow.

> **(1)** magnitude   **(2)** direction   **(3)** sense

1391 In a sketch of a parallelogram labeled
as this one, **(1)** place arrows properly
and name the following: **(2)** a vector
equal to **BC**, **(3)** a vector equal to **-AB**,
(4) a vector equal to **-ED**, and **(5)** a
vector equal to **-AE**. Assume the usual properties of
parallelograms.

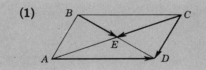

> **(1)**
>
>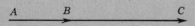
>
> **(2)** AD
> **(3)** CD or BA or -DC
> **(4)** -BE or EB or DE
> **(5)** CE or EA or -EC

1392 If we think of **AB** as a displacement from A to B,
and then follow this with a displacement from B to
C, continuing in the direction from A to B, so that
$BC = AB$, we say that **AC** = 2**AB**. The new vector
is twice as long as the original (you may think of
this as a stretch or dilation). We say that **AC** is the
product of the scalar 2 and the vector **AB**. Make a
sketch that represents a vector **AC** which is the
product of the scalar 3 and a vector **AB** where **AB**
represents a displacement of 1 in. to the right.

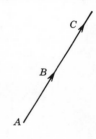

> A B C

1393 We could just as well represent a contraction of a vector **AB**
by taking the product of a scalar, such as $\frac{1}{2}$, and the vector
AB. For example, let **AB** represent a displacement from A
to B in a vertical direction. Indicate on your sketch the vector **AC** that represents $\frac{1}{2}$**AB**.

1394 If **AB** represents a horizontal displacement to the right from A to B, then the product of the scalar (-2) and the vector **AB** would *reverse* the direction and "stretch" the vector so that the horizontal displacement is twice the original and to the left of A. Given vector **AB** shown here , indicate a vector

equivalent to -2**AB**.

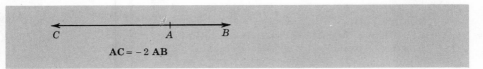

$$AC = -2 \, \mathbf{AB}$$

1395 Thus, we say that $\kappa \cdot \mathbf{AB}$, where κ is a scalar and **AB** is a vector, is the product of the scalar κ and the vector **AB**. If $\kappa > 1$, then $\kappa \cdot \mathbf{AB}$ (multiplication by the scalar κ) produces an extension or expansion of **AB**. If $0 < \kappa < 1$, then $\kappa \cdot \mathbf{AB}$ produces a contraction of **AB**. If $\kappa < 0$, then $\kappa \cdot \mathbf{AB}$ produces a reversal of direction and (depending on κ) either an expansion or contraction of **AB**. If $\kappa = 0$, then $0 \cdot \mathbf{AB}$ is a vector of zero length. We refer to a vector of zero length as the *zero vector*. Let **AB** represent a displacement of 16 ft downward (use a suitable scale). Make sketches showing the product of **AB** and the scalar κ when $\kappa = 1, 1\frac{1}{2}, \frac{1}{4}, -1, 0$.

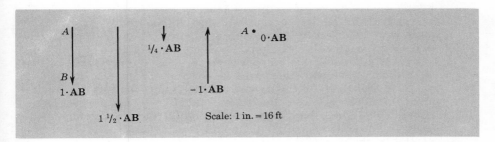

∇**1396** (1) Let **AB** represent a speed 16 mph eastward across a lake in a motor boat. (Use a scale of 1 in. = 16 miles.) (2) Represent a speed twice as fast and in the opposite direction by vector **CD**. (3) Represent a speed three-fourths as fast as **AB** and in the same direction. Label the vector **EF**. (4) Let **GH** represent a speed equal to **AB** + **EF**.

(1) $A \longrightarrow B$

(2) $D \longleftarrow C$

(3) $E \longrightarrow F$

(4) $G \longrightarrow H$

1397 We want to consider next the addition of vectors. A motorist looks at a map showing
towns A, B, and C with connecting roads as   (1)
shown in sketch 1. If he wants to go from A
to C, he has the choice of going by way of B
(AB followed by BC) or of going directly from
A to C (AC). Since the end result is the same
we say that AB + BC = AC (this does not
mean addition in the usual sense). *Note:* We
are considering the displacement (distance   (2)
and direction) A to B followed by displacement B to C. In a sketch similar to sketch 2,
identify the two displacements which have the same end result as
displacement x to y. Write the answer as a vector sum.

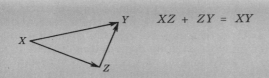

$$XZ + ZY = XY$$

1398 If a boy who can row a boat at the rate of
5 mph in still water tries to row across
a broad stream whose current is 2 mph,
he is propelled by two forces: F_1 dis-
places him across the stream and F_2 dis-
places him downstream. From physics
we learn that the end effect can be shown
by the diagonal AC of the parallelogram having the two forces as
adjacent sides. AC is called the resultant of the two forces. Assume that B (or D) is a right angle, find (1) the displacement AC
after one hr of time and (2) the angle BAC which indicates the direction of the vector AC.

(1) $\sqrt{5^2 + 2^2} = \sqrt{29}$ (2) $\tan < BAC = \frac{2}{5} = 0.4, < BAC \approx 22°$
This problem is continued in frame 1399.

1399 Now, go back to the vector notation. Recall that we can represent
AC as the vector sum of AB + BC, i.e., AC = AB + BC. Is this
equivalent to saying that, speaking of lengths of line segments,
$AC = AB + BC$? Explain your answer.

no   The sum of the lengths of two sides of a triangle is always
greater than the length of the third side, in this case
$(5 + 2) > \sqrt{29}$

1400 Two forces act on a body located at point O. F_1 is a force of 36 lb exerted in a horizontal direction toward the right. F_2 is a force of 24 lb exerted in a vertical direction upward. Using a scale of 1 in. = 12 lb, make a sketch in which you show as a vector the displacement produced by F_1 and F_2 acting on the body (resultant of F_1 and F_2). *Note:* This problem will be continued in frame 1401.

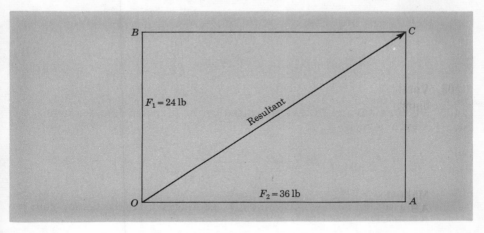

1401 Find the resultant of the two forces given in frame 1400 and the direction of the resultant with respect to the larger force; i.e., find (1) the vector **OC** and (2) the angle AOC. Leave the answer in radical form.

(1) $OC = \sqrt{36^2 + 24^2} = \sqrt{1,872}$
(2) $\tan \angle AOC = \frac{24}{36} = \frac{1}{3}, \quad \angle AOC \approx 34°$

1402 Given two vectors **AB** and **CD** as shown in sketch a. To represent the vector sum of **AB** and **CD** geometrically, we proceed in the following manner: See sketch b. First, draw a vector equivalent to **AB**. Second, at B, construct a vector **BE** equivalent to **CD**. Then the displacement from A to E represents the same final displacement as the displacement from A to B *followed*

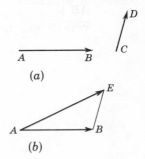

(a)

(b)

continued →

by the displacement from B to E, or as a vector sum we write **AB** + **BC** = **AE**. Given the
vectors **MN** and **RS** as shown in sketch 3, represent geometrically their vector sum.

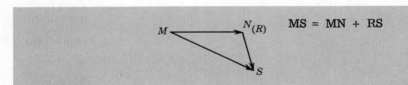

(c)

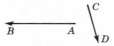

MS = MN + RS

1403   Vectors **AB** and **CD** are indicated by the directed line segments
shown here.

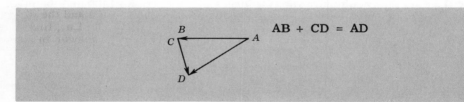

Make a sketch in which you show, geometrically, the vector sum
AB + **CD**.

AB + CD = AD

▽**1404**   In general the *vector* sum **AB** + **BC** is not equivalent to the length
AB plus the length BC.   Vectors represent direction as well as
magnitude.   Given vectors **AB**, **CD**, and **EF** as shown below.

continued ➝

Make three sketches showing the following additions: **(1) AB + CD,** **(2) AB + EF,** and **(3) CD + EF.** **(4)** In which of your sketches is the *magnitude* of the vector sum equal to the sum of the lengths of its two component vectors?

(1)

AD represents
the vector sum

(2)

(3)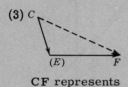

CF represents
the vector sum

(4) the second sketch,

1405 Find the vector sum geometrically for the vectors shown below.

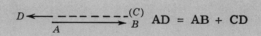

Note the direction (or sense) along the directed segment *CD*.

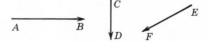   AD = AB + CD

1406 You can show geometrically the sum of three vectors **AB, CD,** and **EF** as follows:
  1. Add vectors **AB** and **CD** as we have done.
  2. Consider the sum **AB + CD** as a vector **AD.**
  3. Represent the vector sum **AD + EF.**
Carry out the steps outlined above to find the vector sum of the three vectors shown here.

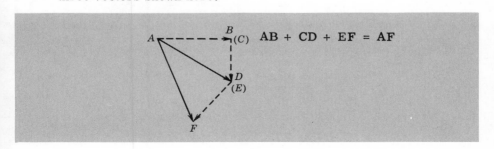

AB + CD + EF = AF

1407 Show geometrically the sum of three vectors **AB, CD,** and **EF** as represented here.

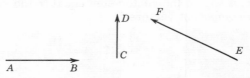

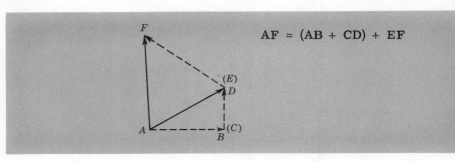

$$AF = (AB + CD) + EF$$

1408 Find the vector sum **AB + CD + EF** geometrically for the vectors shown below

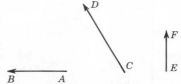

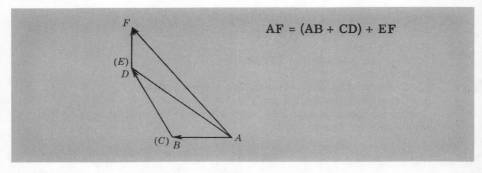

$$AF = (AB + CD) + EF$$

1409 Vectors **AB** and **CD** are represented in this sketch.

continued →

Indicate geometrically the following: **(1)** AB + CD, **(2)** AB - CD, and **(3)** CD - AB. *Note:* AB - CD = AB + (-CD).

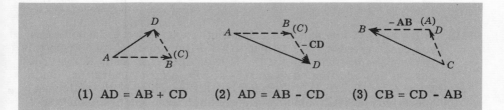

(1) AD = AB + CD   **(2)** AD = AB - CD   **(3)** CB = CD - AB

1410 Given vectors **AB** and **CD**. **(1)** Find the vector sum geometrically of **AB + CD**. **(2)** Find the vector sum geometrically of **CD + AB**. **(3)** Does it appear that **AB + CD = CD + AB**? (*m* and *n* call attention to the numerical measures of the lengths of segments *AB* and *CD*. θ indicates the angle that *CD* makes with a horizontal line.)

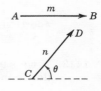

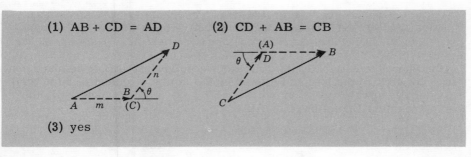

(1) AB + CD = AD   **(2)** CD + AB = CB

(3) yes

1411 Given vector **AB** of length *m* which makes an angle of α degree with a horizontal line, and vector **CD** of length *n* which makes an angle of β degrees with a horizontal line as shown in the accompanying sketch. Represent geometrically **(1)** AB + CD and **(2)** CD + AB. **(3)** Indicate on your triangles from questions (1) and (2) the parts which are equal by construction. **(4)** Does this guarantee congruent $\triangle s$?

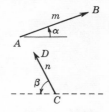

(1) AD = AC + CD   **(2)** CB = CD + AB

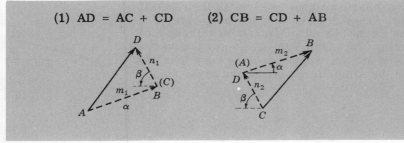

continued →

(3) $m_1 = m_2$ **(4)** yes, two sides and the included
            $n_1 = n_2$ angle are equal, respectively
            $\angle ABD = \angle CDB$

1412   In frame 1411 you saw that congruent triangles were formed when
         you constructed **AB + CD** and **CD + AB** geometrically. From this
         you can deduce that **AB + CD = CD + AB**. This leads to the con-
         clusion that addition of vectors is a *commutative* operation, i.e.,
         $\mathbf{V}_1 + \mathbf{V}_2 = \mathbf{V}_2 + \mathbf{V}_1$. In elementary algebra which of the following
         operations on real numbers are commutative: addition, subtrac-
         tion, multiplication, division?

         addition, $a + b = b + a$; and multiplication, $a \cdot b = b \cdot a$

1413   If we say that addition of vectors is a *commutative* operation, what
         do we mean?

         when we say that vector addition is commutative, we mean that
         AB + CD = CD + AB for all vectors **AB** and **CD**.

▽1414   Show geometrically the result of the following: **AB**, a displacement
         of 40 ft to the left, is followed by **CD**, a displacement of 50 ft verti-
         cally upward (use a suitable scale).   **(2)** Show geometrically the
         result of **CD** followed by **AB**.

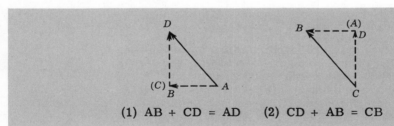

         (1) AB + CD = AD   **(2) CD + AB = CB**

1415   To simplify our discussions of vectors, we shall
         assume that the vectors have the origin of a
         rectangular coordinate system as their initial
         point. (They are called *centered vectors*.)
         Thus, in the sketch, *PQ* above would take the
         position *OQ*, shown below. We say that vectors
         OQ and **PQ** are equivalent if we know that they
         have the same *direction* and are *equal* in

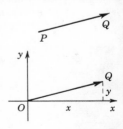

                                                    continued →

length. If you now imagine a perpendicular from point Q to the horizontal axis, you see that point Q can be expressed in terms of its x and y components. Conversely, if you know the x and y co-ordinates of a point Q, you can represent the vector OQ on a plane. Represent a vector OA on a coordinate system such that the co-ordinates of a point A are (3, 4).

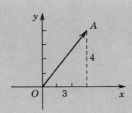

1416 Notice in connection with the problem in frame 1415 that if you are given the coordinates of the terminal point A of the vector OA, you can find the length r and the direction θ of OA. (By direction we mean the angle θ which OA makes with the horizontal axis.) Thus

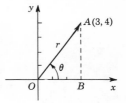

$\tan \theta = \frac{4}{3}$

$\theta \approx$ (1)_____ $^\circ$

$r^2 = 4^2 + 3^2$

$r =$ (2)_____

(1) 53   (2) 5

1417 Using the same example again, we say that the two *components* of OA are the x component, 3, and the y component, 4, and that OA is the result of two dis-placements O to B followed by B to A. We refer to OA as the sum of OB + BA. This is a *vector sum*, or the *resultant*, of the two components x and y. Suppose you know that $r = 8$ and that $\theta = 30°$, what is (1) the y component of OA? (2) The x component of OA?

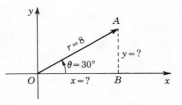

(1) $y = 4$ *Solution:* $\sin \theta = \frac{y}{r}$, $y = 8(\frac{1}{2}) = 4$

(2) $x \approx 6.9$ *Solution:* $\cos 30° = \frac{x}{r}$, $x = 8\left(\frac{\sqrt{3}}{2}\right) \approx 6.928 \approx 6.9$

1418 To find the length of the centered vector OA, given the x and y components, we use the distance formula, i.e., $r =$ _____. The *length* of the vector OA is sometimes indicated by using the symbol $|OA|$. The absolute-value sign emphasizes the fact that the *length* (without regard to direction) is a nonnegative quantity.

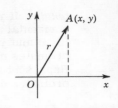

$$\sqrt{x^2 + y^2}$$

1419 Given a centered vector OA as indicated in the sketch. **(1)** What is meant by the symbol $|OA|$? **(2)** Find $|OA|$. **(3)** Find θ (the angle which vector OA makes with the negative x axis.)

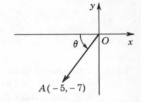

(1) $|OA|$ is the symbol indicating the length of the vector.

(2) $|OA| = \sqrt{(-5)^2 + (-7)^2} = \sqrt{74}$

(3) $\tan \theta = \dfrac{-7}{-5} = 1.400, \ \theta \approx 54.5°$

1420 The x and y components of a centered vector OA are 6 and -3 respectively. Find **(1)** $|OA|$ and **(2)** the angle θ which the vector OA makes with the positive x axis.

(1) $|OA| = 3\sqrt{5}$
Solution:
$|OA| = \sqrt{6^2 + (-3)^2}$
$= \sqrt{45} = 3\sqrt{5}$

(2) $\theta \approx 26.50$
Solution:
$\tan \theta = -\frac{3}{6} = -\frac{1}{2} = -0.5$
$\theta \approx 26.50$

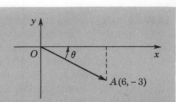

1421   Given centered vectors OB and OC as represented in the sketch. Make a similar sketch
in which you indicate geometrically the vector sum OB + OC. Also indicate on your
sketch the sum OC + OB.

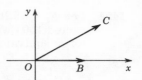

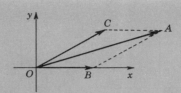

Note: The resulting figure is a parallelogram with the
diagonal representing the sum of the two vectors.

∇1422   OX represents a force of 35 lb along the positive x axis. OY represents a force of 50 lb along the positive y axis. (1) Make a sketch
showing the vector sum. Compute (2) the resultant of these two
forces and (3) its direction with respect to the x axis.

(1)

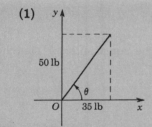

(2) $r \approx 61$ lb
Solution:
$$r = \sqrt{35^2 + 50^2}$$
$$= \sqrt{3,725}$$
$$\approx 61 \text{ lb}$$
(3) $\theta \approx 55°$
Solution:
$$\tan \theta = \tfrac{50}{35} \approx 1.430$$
$$\theta \approx 55°$$

1423   The single directed force which has the
same effect as two forces F_1 and F_2 acting together on a body is called the
(1)_____ of the two forces. If we
represent F_1 and F_2 as vectors, then the
vector sum also represents the (2)_____
of F_1 and F_2 combined. When the given forces are *not parallel* to
each other, we can represent the vector sum by constructing a parallelogram whose sides are the original forces centered at A. Then
the diagonal (3)_____ represents the (4)_____ of the two
forces.

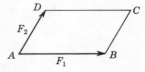

(1) resultant   (2) resultant   (3) AC **(4) resultant**

1424   Let $F_1 = 15$ lb directed $40°$ with the horizontal and $F_2 = 24$ lb directed $150°$ with the horizontal. Make a sketch showing the single force equivalent to the vector sum of F_1 and F_2.

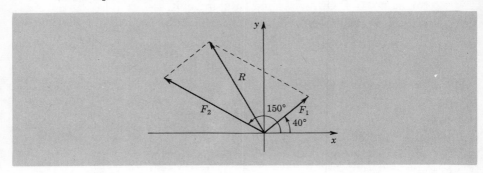

▽1425

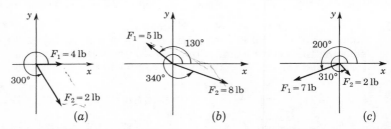

Make sketches showing geometrically the resultants for sketches a, b, and c.

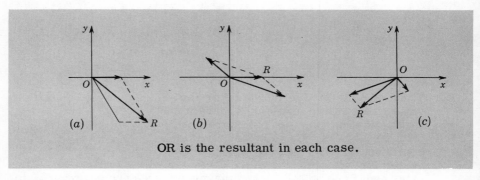

OR is the resultant in each case.

▽1426   Compute the (1) magnitude and (2) direction of two forces F_1 and F_2 if F_1 acts horizontally toward the right with a force of 62 lb and

continued ➤

F_2 acts vertically downward with a force of 40 lb.   (3) Make a sketch showing the forces and their resultant vector. (Let the direction be indicated by the angle between the resultant and the positive x axis.)

(1) $r = \sqrt{62^2 + 40^2}$
≈ 74

(2) $\tan \theta = \frac{40}{62}$
$\theta = 33°$

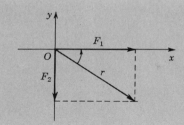

▽1427 Find the **(1)** x and **(2)** y components of the vector whose magnitude is 300 and whose direction with the positive x axis is 40°.

(1) $x \approx 230$
Solution:
$$\cos 40° = \frac{x}{300}$$
$$300(0.766) = x$$
$$230 \approx x$$

(2) $y \approx 193$
Solution:
$$\sin 40° = \frac{y}{300}$$
$$300(0.643) = y$$
$$193 \approx y$$

1428 The resultant of two forces, one horizontal and one vertical, is a single force of 220 lb which makes an angle of 63° with the horizontal. Find the **(1)** horizontal and **(2)** vertical components.

(1) $x \approx 100$
Solution:
$$\cos 63° = \frac{x}{220}$$
$$220(0.454) = x$$
$$100 \approx x$$

(2) $y \approx 196$
Solution:
$$\sin 63° = \frac{y}{220}$$
$$220(0.891) = y$$
$$196 \approx y$$

1429   The point (-3, 8) represents the terminal point of a vector OR on a
       rectangular coordinate system. (1) Represent this vector graphi-
       cally. -3 is the (2)_____ component of this vector, and 8 is
       the (3)_____ component of OR.

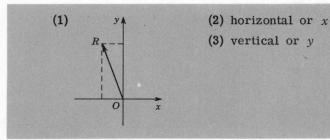

(1)   (2) horizontal or x

                           (3) vertical or y

1430   Refer to the problem in frame 1429. (1) Find the length of OR (the
       magnitude). (2) Find the angle OR makes with the positive x axis
       (the direction).

(1) $|OR| = \sqrt{73}$ Solution: $|OR| = \sqrt{(-3)^2 + 8^2} = \sqrt{73}$

(2) $\theta \approx 111°$ Solution: $\tan \theta = \frac{8}{3} = -2.667$
                                      $\theta \approx 180 - 69° \approx 111°$

1431   When a boy pulls a wagon along the side-
       walk with a force of 50 lb and the angle at
       which he is pulling is 25°, part of his ef-
       fort is moving the wagon forward and the
       other part is an upward pull. Find the force exerted in the forward
       motion.

$x = 45.3$ lb

Solution: $\cos 25° = \dfrac{x}{50}$, $x = 50(0.906) = 45.3$ lb

1432   Suppose a pilot is heading a plane due north at
       a speed of 200 mph (air speed). Also there is
       a wind blowing directly east at 40 mph. What
       will be the actual direction of the plane, and
       what will be the distance covered in an hour (the
       ground speed)? You can represent the velocity
       of the plane by the vector OA and the velocity
       of the wind by the vector OC; the sum (or re-
       sultant) of these two vectors is represented by
       the vector OB. (The speed of the plane takes it
       north, and the wind blows it toward the east.)

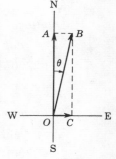

continued →

This is an application of the parallelogram law of velocities studied in physics. You are asked to find (1) r and (2) θ. (θ represents the angle between OA and OB.)

(1) $r \approx 204$ (2) $\theta \approx 11°$
Solution: $40^2 + 200^2 = r^2$, $204 \approx r$
    $\tan \theta = \frac{40}{200} = \frac{1}{5} = 0.200$
        $\theta \approx 11°$ (This direction might be reported thus N 11° E)
Note: OB = OC + CB (vector sum)
or OB = OA + AB (vector sum).

1433 If two forces, one of 60 lb and one of 80 lb, act at right angles to each other, what is the resultant? Find the magnitude R and the direction θ, where θ is the angle between the resultant R and the 80-lb force.

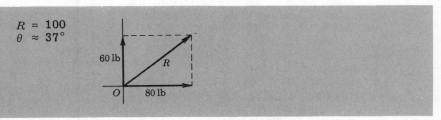

$R = 100$
$\theta \approx 37°$

1434 Consider the two forces F_1 and F_2 in frame 1433 acting so that they form an angle of 60° with respect to each other. We can find R, the resultant of these two forces, thus: In parallelogram OACB, OB = AC, angle CAO = 120°, OA + OB = OA + AC = OC. The law of cosines can be used to find R, and the law of sines for θ. Complete the solution.

$R^2 = 80^2 + 60^2 - 2(80)(60) \cos 120°$

   $= 10,000 - 2(4,800)(-\frac{1}{2})$ *Note:* $\cos 120° = (-\frac{1}{2})$

   $= 10,000 + 4,800 = 14,800$ $R \approx 121.6 \approx 122$

$\dfrac{\sin \theta}{60} = \dfrac{\sin 120°}{121.6}$, $\sin \theta \approx 0.427$, $\theta \approx 25°$

1435 A force F_1 of 10 lb and another force F_2 of 15 lb act at an angle of 45° with respect to each other. Find the resultant R of these two forces and the direction the resultant takes with respect to the larger force.

$R^2 = 10^2 + 15^2$
$\quad\quad - 2(10)(15) \cos 135°$
$\quad R \approx 23$

$\dfrac{\sin \theta}{10} = \dfrac{\sin 135°}{23}$

$\sin \theta \approx 0.307$
$\quad \theta \approx 18°$

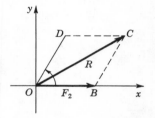

1436 Notice in frame 1435 that in finding R and θ, we considered F_1 as represented by its equivalent **BC** and made the computations from triangle OBC. The single force R (displacement from O to C) is equal to F_2 (displacement from O to B) followed by F_1 (displacement from B to C). So that we sometimes refer to this as the *triangle law* for combining directed-line segments, instead of the parallelogram law. From your knowledge of geometry and trigonometry, would you say that given the directed segments **OB** and **BC** above, there is a *unique* resultant **OC**?

yes   Recall that $OBCD$ is a parallelogram with **OB**, **OD**, and angle BOD specified.

1437 A plane is heading due west with an air speed of 300 mph; a wind of 25 mph is blowing from due south. What will be the actual speed of the plane (ground speed) and its direction? (In reporting the direction for this problem, give the reading of the angle indicated as θ in the sketch. It is the angle sometimes used in navigation, and is measured from the north in a clockwise direction.)

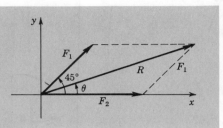

$r = \sqrt{(25)^2 + (300)^2}$ 301 mph

$\tan \theta_1 = \frac{25}{300}, \ \theta_1 \approx 5°, \ \theta \approx 270° + 5° \approx 275°$

1438 An airplane is headed due north at a speed of 400 mph. A 30-mph wind has its direction indicated as 300°. Make a sketch in which the speed due north is represented as a vector which is followed by a vector representing the wind speed with direction 300°. Draw the vector that is the resultant of these two vectors.

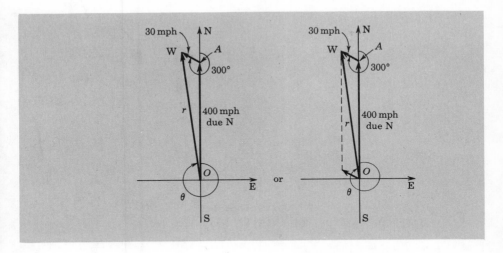

1439 To find the numerical values for r and θ in frame 1438, you should note that
1. The number of degrees in angle WAO is (1) _____.
2. The law of (2) _____ can be used to find r.
3. Then the law of (3) _____ can be used to find angle AOW.

(1) 120°   (2) cosines   (3) sines

1440 Find (1) r and (2) θ in frame 1439.

(1) $r \approx 416$ (2) $\theta = 356.5°$

Solution: $r^2 = 30^2 + (400)^2 - 2(30)(400) \cos 120°$

$r = \sqrt{172,900} \approx 416$

$\dfrac{\sin AOW}{30} = \dfrac{\sin 120°}{416}, \quad \sin AOW = \dfrac{30\sqrt{3}/2}{416} = \dfrac{15\sqrt{3}}{416}$

$AOW \approx 3.5°$

$\theta \approx 360° - 3.5° = 356.5°$

1441 A plane is heading in a direction of 200°, as indicated in the sketch, at an air speed of 360 mph.
A wind directly from the east is blowing with a
force of 30 mph. Make a sketch showing the resultant of these two forces.

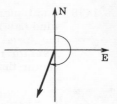

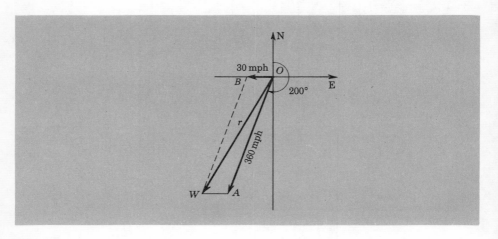

1442 Refer to frame 1441. (1) How many degrees are in angle WAO ?
(2) Find r.

(1) angle WAO = 110°
Note: angle BOA = 70°; angle WAO is a supplement
of angle BOA.
(2) $r \approx 371$
Solution: $r^2 = 30^2 + 360^2 - 2(30)(360) \cos 110°$, $r \approx 371$

1443 In frame 1441 find the direction the plane actually is taking.

$$\frac{\sin AOW}{30} = \frac{\sin 110°}{360}, \quad \sin AOW = \frac{(30(0.940))}{360} = 0.078,$$

angle $AOW \approx 4.5°$

direction of plane 200° + 4.5° ≈ 204.5°

▽1444 A plane is headed due west with a speed of 300 mph. The wind blows from the northwest at 30 mph. Make a sketch showing the resultant path of the plane.

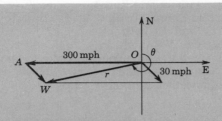

Note: Angle θ represents the direction; r represents the speed.

▽1445 Find the ground speed of the plane in frame 1444. *Note:* Angle $OAW = 45°$ when the wind is from the northwest.

$r = 280$ mph   *Solution:* $r = 30^2 + 300^2 - 2(30)(300) \cos 45°$
≈ 280 mph

▽1446 Find the direction the plane takes for the problem in frames 1444 and 1445.

$\dfrac{\sin AOW}{30} = \dfrac{\sin 45°}{280}$, $\sin AOW = \dfrac{(30(0.707))}{280} \approx 0.076$,

angle $AOW \approx 4°$

Direction of plane $270° - 4° \approx 266°$

▽1447 It is known that the resultant of two forces, one acting due east and another due north, is a force of 18 lb in a direction 20° east of north; find the north and east components.

$F_1 \approx 17$, $F_2 \approx 6.2$
In triangle OAB

$\sin 70° = \dfrac{F_1}{18}$

$F \approx 18(0.940)$
≈ 17

$\cos 70° = \dfrac{F_2}{18}$

$F \approx 18(0.342)$
≈ 6.2

1448 We point out that a single vector has many pairs of components. Here we have indicated the answer to a previous exercise. You could not, without additional information, find the particular components F_1 and F_2 with which you started. We might,

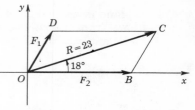

however, ask for the x component or the y component of vector **OC**. Write a statement indicating how you would find each. You need not complete the solution.

$$\sin 18° = \frac{y}{23}$$

$$\cos 18° = \frac{x}{23}$$

1449 A force of 50 lb is acting in a direction which makes an angle of 35° with the level ground. Find the horizontal and vertical components.

$x \approx 41$

$y \approx 29$

1450 The angle between two forces, $F_1 = 30$ lb and $F_2 = 60$ lb, is 144°. Find the **(1)** resultant R of the two forces and the **(2)** direction θ with respect to F_1.

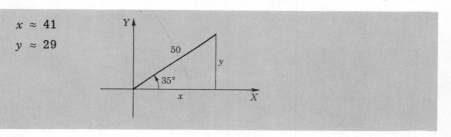

(1) $R \approx 40$
Solution:
$$R^2 = 30^2 + 60^2$$
$$- 2(30)(60)\cos 36°$$
$$\approx 2,912.4$$
$$R \approx 39.8 \approx 40$$
(2) $\theta \approx 62°$ or $118°$
Solution:
$$\frac{60}{\sin \theta} \approx \frac{39.8}{\sin 36°}$$

$$\sin \theta \approx 0.886$$
$$\theta \approx 62° \text{ or } 118°$$

continued →

In this case $\theta = 118°$ since angle $A = 36°$; angle $OBA < 36°$ would require that θ be $118°$ for the third angle of triangle OAB.

1451 Two forces are represented as in the accompanying sketch. F_1 is a force of 50 lb
which acts at an angle of 30° with the positive x axis, and F_2 is a force of 30 lb
which acts at an angle of 90° with the x
axis. Show geometrically the resultant of
these two forces.

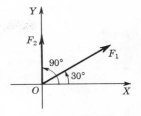

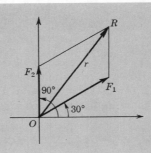

1452 Refer to the problem in frame 1451.   angle $F_2OF_1 = $ **(1)**_____° and
angle $OF_1R = $ **(2)**_____°.

(1) 60   **(2)** 120

1453 Refer to the problem in frame 1452.   **(1)** By means of the law of
cosines find the resultant force.   **(2)** Find the direction of the resultant with respect to F_1.   **(3)** Find the angle the resultant makes
with the positive x axis.

(1) $r \approx 70$
Solution: In triangle OF_1R, angle $F_1 = 120°$, $F_1 = 50$, $F_2 = 30$

$$r^2 = 50^2 + 30^2 - 2(50)(30)\cos 120° = 4,900, \quad r \approx 70$$

(2) $\theta \approx 22°$
Solution: $\dfrac{\sin \theta}{30} = \dfrac{\sin 120°}{70}$, $\sin \theta = \dfrac{(30(0.866))}{70} \approx 0.371$, $\theta \approx 22°$

(3) $30° + 22° = 52°$

1454 A ball is thrown due east at 12 yards/sec from a car that is travel-
ing due north at the rate of 24 yards/sec. Represent by vectors the
velocity of the ball and the direction of its path with respect to the
moving car.

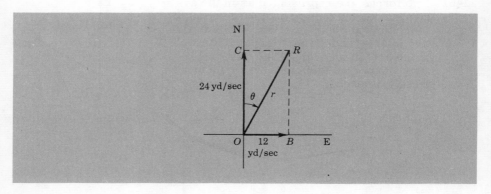

1455 Refer to frame 1454. Find the velocity of the ball and its direction
with respect to the highway (angle *COR*).

$$r = \sqrt{12^2 + 24^2} \approx 27 \text{ yd/sec}$$

$$\tan \theta = \tfrac{12}{24} = \tfrac{1}{2}, \quad \theta \approx 26.5°$$

UNIT 7 | Polar Coordinates

1456 In the graphical work thus far in this program most of the plotting of points has been done on a rectangular coordinate system. Another system called the polar coordinate system is convenient for some applications of mathematics. As you have seen in the section on vectors, you can locate a point P on a coordinate plane by means of an ordered pair (r, θ) where r represents the distance of P from the origin and θ represents the angle between the positive x axis and the line OP as shown in the sketch.
(1) Locate a point $P_1(r, \theta)$ on a rectangular coordinate system if $r = 2$ in. and $\theta = \pi/4$.
(2) Locate a point $P_2(r, \theta)$ if $r = 1$ in. and $\theta = 5\pi/6$.

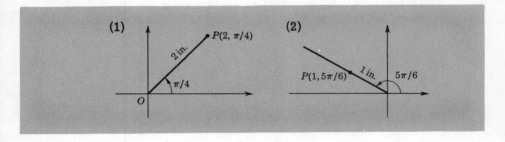

1457 In the polar coordinate system the basis is a fixed point O and a fixed half-line (or ray) OA. A point P whose coordinates are (r, θ)

continued →

475

is located by assuming the fixed point O as the vertex for angle θ, OA as the initial side, and OP as the terminal side and finally locating point P on the terminal side at a distance r from O. Locate a point $P(3,\ \pi/2)$ with reference to a fixed point O and a horizontal line OA extending in a positive direction.

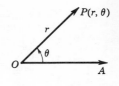

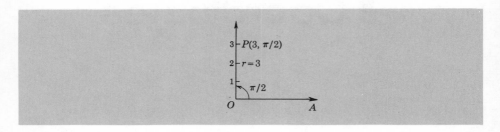

1458 In the polar coordinate system we refer to the point O as the *pole* and the horizontal line OX as the *polar* axis. Make a sketch locating a point $P(1,\ 3\pi/4)$ in the polar coordinate system. Label the *pole* and the *polar axis* by writing these words at the proper places on your sketch.

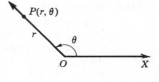

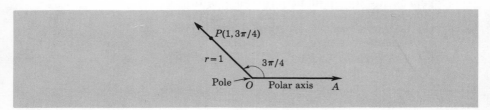

1459 We refer to the directed segment **OP** as the *radius vector* in the polar coordinate system. The polar coordinates $(r,\ \theta)$ of point P give us the length and direction of the radius vector. *Length* is indicated by **(1)**____. *Direction* is indicated by **(2)**____. *Note:* The arrowhead on OX or OP indicates the *sense* along the line, i.e., to the right or left, up or down, etc.

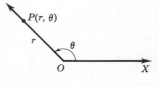

(1) r **(2)** θ

▽1460 You should have the following terms clearly
        identified: The ordered pair (r, θ) locates the
        point P in the *polar coordinate* system. The
        point O is the **(1)**_____.   The horizontal ray
        OX is the **(2)**_____.   The directed seg-
        ment **OP** is the **(3)**_____ .

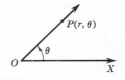

(1) pole   **(2)** polar axis   **(3)** radius vector

▽1461 Since r denotes the *length* of the radius vector, we have agreed that
        the sign of this quantity shall be _____.

positive

▽1462 **(1)** Can you locate a point P if θ is a negative angle ?   **(2)** If your
        answer to **(1)** is "yes," then locate P when θ = -30° and r = 2
        with reference to a given pole O and polar axis OX.

(1) yes   **(2)**
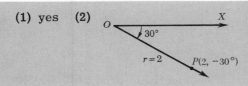

1463 Given the polar coordinates (r, θ) of point P. r is **(1)**_____
       (positive, negative), and θ is a directed angle; hence, it may be
       (2)_____ (positive, negative).

(1) positive   **(2)** positive or negative

1464 With reference to the polar axis OX and the pole O
       shown here, **(1)** how many points can be located such
       that r = $\frac{1}{2}$ in. and θ = 80° ?   **(2)** Make a sketch locating the
       point(s) (r, θ) with the given coordinates.   **(3)** Any pair of polar co-
       ordinates r and θ, which we write as an ordered pair (r, θ), deter-
       mines how many points with reference to a given pole and polar
       axis ?

(1) one   **(2)**   **(3)** one

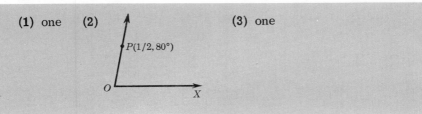

1465 (1) Select a convenient unit of measure for the representation of r; locate a point O as the pole, and draw the polar axis OX. Then locate a point $P(4, 5\pi/4)$ on your sketch.   (2) If the pole O and the polar axis OX are stationary, can another distinct point be found on this coordinate system having coordinates $(4, 5\pi/4)$?

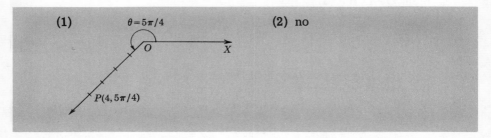

(1) $\theta = 5\pi/4$ (2) no

$P(4, 5\pi/4)$

1466 Since there is only one point corresponding to the ordered pair $(4, 5\pi/4)$ in the polar coordinate system, we say that $(4, 5\pi/4)$ determines a unique point. Make a sketch locating $P(3, 3\pi/2)$ on a polar coordinate system. Locate the point $(3, 7\pi/2)$ on the same coordinate system.

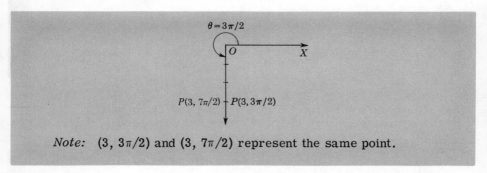

$\theta = 3\pi/2$

$P(3, 7\pi/2) \dashv P(3, 3\pi/2)$

Note: $(3, 3\pi/2)$ and $(3, 7\pi/2)$ represent the same point.

1467 With reference to the same pole O and polar axis OX used for $P(3, 3\pi/2)$, locate the point $P(3, -\pi/2)$.

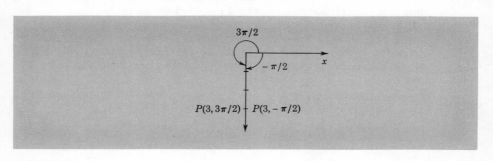

$3\pi/2$

$-\pi/2$

$P(3, 3\pi/2) \dashv P(3, -\pi/2)$

1468 You observed in frame 1467 that corresponding to a point P, there might be more than one pair of polar coordinates. Which of the following ordered pairs represent the same point?

1. $\left(2, \dfrac{5\pi}{8}\right)$ 2. $\left(3, \dfrac{5\pi}{8}\right)$ 3. $\left(\dfrac{-11\pi}{8}\right)$ 4. $\left(2, \dfrac{21\pi}{8}\right)$

1. $\left(2, \dfrac{5\pi}{8}\right)$ 3. $\left(\dfrac{-11\pi}{8}\right)$ 4. $\left(2, \dfrac{21\pi}{8}\right)$

▽1469 Decide which of the following statements is true with reference to a given pole and polar axis:
(1) Any pair of polar coordinates determines a unique point P. (true, false)
(2) A unique pair of coordinates (r, θ) is associated with a given point P. (true, false)

(1) true

(2) false

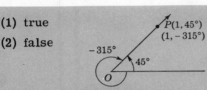

(see sketch, P has coordinates $(1, 45°)$, $(1, -315°)$, etc.)

1470 Make a sketch similar to the one to the right and indicate with curved arrows at least two angles which we might designate as θ with the position of point P unchanged.

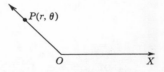

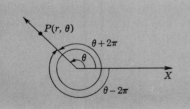

The polar coordinates for P could be (r, θ) or $(r, (\theta - 2\pi n))$ where n is an integer.

1471 When we identify a point P on a plane with reference to a pole O and a polar axis OX, the ordered pair (r, θ) represents the

continued →

(1) _____ coordinates of point P. When we identify a point P on a plane with reference to a pair of perpendicular lines (x, y axes), the ordered pair (x, y) represents the **(2)** _____ coordinates of point P.

(1) polar   (2) rectangular or (abscissa, ordinate)

1472   Make a sketch locating the point $P(a, 270°)$ with reference to a given pole and polar axis. (Select a convenient unit of measurement for the length of a.)

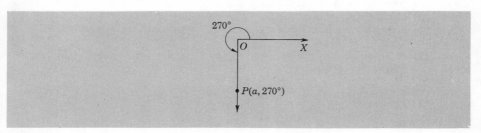

1473   Recall the comment in frame 1464 that a pair of polar coordinates $(a, 270°)$ determines **(1)** _____ point(s). However, there are many sets of polar coordinates associated with point P. Two other ordered pairs $(r, \ )$ for the point P, as shown in the sketch, are **(2)** $(a, $ _____$)$ and **(3)** $(a, $ _____$)$.

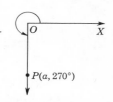

(1) one or a unique   (2) $(a, -90°)$ **(3)** $(a, 630°)$
or any pair $(a, 270° + n(360°))$ where n is an integer

▽1474   Make a sketch locating the following points from a common pole and polar axis: **(1)** $P_1(2, \pi/8)$, **(2)** $P_2(5, \pi/8)$, and **(3)** $P_3(2, 9\pi/8)$.

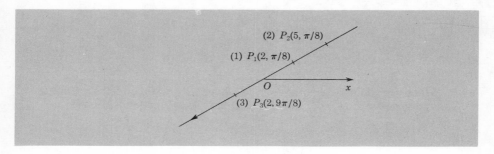

1475 There are three important notions to be
pointed out at this time: The point P has
rectangular coordinates, namely, (1)_____.
The point P has *polar coordinates*, namely,
(2)_____. The directed line segment **OP**
has magnitude (3)____ and direction angle
(4)____. We refer to it as the *radius
vector* or more simply the vector **OP** which has rectangular components (5)_____.

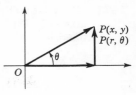

(1) (x, y) **(2)** (r, θ) **(3)** r **(4)** θ **(5)** (x, y)

1476 Recall our previous discussion of vectors.
We identified a vector by giving an ordered
pair (a, b). They are the (1)_____
coordinates of a point P with reference to
the usual x, y axes. Furthermore either
the directed segment **OP** or the ordered
pair (a, b) is called a vector. The radius
vector **OP** in the *polar* coordinate system is shown graphically as
the same line but is identified by the ordered pair (2) (__, __).

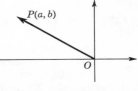

(1) rectangular or (x, y) **(2)** (r, θ)

1477 You need to review now how to transfer from the rectangular coordinate system $P(x, y)$ to the polar coordinate system $P(r, \theta)$ and
vice versa. Given the x, y coordinates, is it always possible to
compute r and θ?

yes

1478 **(1)** What is the equation used to find r given x
and y? **(2)** What trigonometric function may be
used to find θ, given x and y?

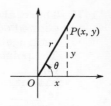

(1) $r^2 = x^2 + y^2$, or $r = \sqrt{x^2 + y^2}$ recall that r is positive
(2) tangent function or $\tan \theta = \dfrac{y}{x}$

1479 This comment should be made regarding the choice of solutions for
numerical problems: For the student who uses logarithms, a slide
rule, or a desk calculator for computations, the method suggested
in a particular problem may not be the most advantageous. For example, look at the problem in frame 1478: given $P(x, y)$, find
(r, θ). With mechanical aids to calculation, find θ as before; $\tan \theta =$
(1)___/___. Then find r using $\sin \theta = y/r$, i.e., $r =$ **(2)**___/___,
instead of using $r = \sqrt{x^2 + y^2}$. In the problems which follow only
one method may be outlined, but bear in mind that it may not be the
only one.

(1) $\dfrac{y}{x}$ **(2)** $\dfrac{y}{\sin \theta}$

1480 Given point P having rectangular coordinates
$(1, \sqrt{3})$, find the polar coordinates (r, θ).
(1) $r =$ _____
(2) $\theta =$ _____
(3) $(r, \theta) =$ _____

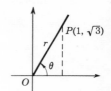

(1) 2   **(2)** 60° or $\dfrac{\pi}{3}$ radians   **(3)** $(2, 60°)$ or $\left(2, \dfrac{\pi}{3}\right)$

▽**1481** Point P has rectangular coordinates (-1, 2). (1) Make a sketch showing radius vector **OP**. (2) Find the polar coordinates r and θ.

(1)

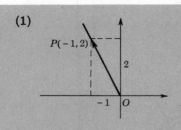

$P(-1, 2)$

(2) $P(\sqrt{5}, 116.5°)$
Solution:
$$r = \sqrt{(-1)^2 + 2^2} = \sqrt{5}$$
$$\tan \theta = \frac{2}{-1} = -2$$
$$\theta \approx 180° - 63.5° \approx 116.5°$$
$$P(-1, 2) = P(\sqrt{5}, 116.5°)$$

1482 Find the polar coordinates of the point P whose rectangular co-ordinates are (-3, -4). Make a sketch.

$P(5, 233°)$
Solution:
$$r = \sqrt{(-3)^2 + (-4)^2} = 5$$
$$\tan \theta = \frac{-4}{-3} = 1.333$$
$$\theta \approx 180° + 53° \approx 233°$$
$$P(-3, -4) = P(5, 233°)$$

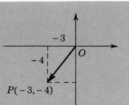

$P(-3, -4)$

1483 In order to find the rectangular coordinates (x, y) of P given the polar coordinates (r, θ), we recall that $\sin \theta = $ **(1)**_____$/r$ and $\cos \theta = $ **(2)**___$/r$.

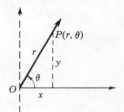

$P(r, \theta)$

(1) $\frac{y}{r}$ **(2)** $\frac{x}{r}$

1484 In frame 1483 we have: $\sin \theta = y/r$ and therefore $y = $ **(1)**_____; and $\cos \theta = x/r$, and therefore $x = $ **(2)**_____.

(1) $r \sin \theta$ **(2)** $r \cos \theta$

1485 Using the facts in frame 1484, i.e., $x = r \sin \theta$ and $x = r \cos \theta$, we can substitute these values for x and y and write $P(x, y)$ as
$$P(\underline{\hspace{1.5cm}}, \underline{\hspace{1.5cm}}).$$

$P(r \cos \theta, r \sin \theta)$

▽1486 Given the point P with *polar* coordinates $(2, \pi/3)$, find the *rectangular* coordinates (x, y).

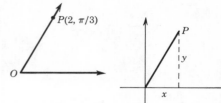

$$x = (1)\underline{\hspace{3cm}}$$
$$y = (2)\underline{\hspace{3cm}}$$
$$(x, y) = (3)\underline{\hspace{3cm}}$$

(1) 1   *Solution:* $x = r \cos \theta = 2(\frac{1}{2}) = 1$

(2) $\sqrt{3}$ *Solution:* $y = r \sin \theta = 2\left(\dfrac{\sqrt{3}}{2}\right) = \sqrt{3}$

(3) $(1, \sqrt{3})$

▽1487 Given point P having polar coordinates $(2, 3\pi/4)$, find the rectangular coordinates.

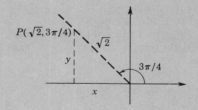

$P(-1, 1)$
Solution:
$$x = r \cos \frac{3\pi}{4}$$
$$= \left(\frac{\sqrt{2}}{1}\right)\left(\frac{-1}{\sqrt{2}}\right)$$
$$= -1$$
$$y = r \sin \frac{3\pi}{4}$$
$$= \left(\frac{\sqrt{2}}{1}\right)\left(\frac{1}{\sqrt{2}}\right)$$
$$= 1$$
$$P(x, y) = P(-1, 1)$$

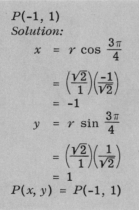

1488 Point P in the figure is identified as $P(3, 11\pi/6)$. We have given this reading in (1) _____ coordinate form. (2) Using the same coordinate system, give another ordered pair (r, θ) identifying the same point.

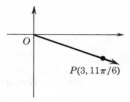

$P(3, 11\pi/6)$

---

(1) polar
(2) Three possible answers are given:

$P\ 3,\left(\dfrac{-\pi}{6}\right)$, $P\ 3,\left(\dfrac{23\pi}{6}\right)$, $P\ 3,\left(\dfrac{-13\pi}{6}\right)$. There are others

---

1489 Occasionally a point P is identified by an ordered pair (r, θ) where r is negative, for example, $P(-3, \pi/6)$. We define *negative r* as the distance measured *along the extension of the terminal side* *of θ through the pole.* The point $P(-3, \pi/6)$ mentioned above would be

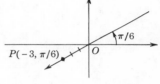

$P(-3, \pi/6)$ $\pi/6$

represented as in the sketch. Make a sketch locating a point $P(-4, 5\pi/6)$.

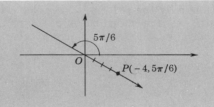

$5\pi/6$

O $P(-4, 5\pi/6)$

1490 Change $P(-4, 5\pi/6)$ to rectangular coordinate form, i.e., $P(x, y)$.

$P(2\sqrt{3}, -2)$
One solution is shown here: $P(-4, 5\pi/6)$ may be written as $P(4, -\pi/6)$, then

$$x = r\ \cos\ \theta \qquad y = r\ \sin\ \theta$$

$$= 4\ \cos\ \frac{-\pi}{6} \qquad\quad = 4\ \sin\ \frac{-\pi}{6}$$

$$= 4\left(\frac{\sqrt{3}}{2}\right) = 2\sqrt{3} \qquad = 4\left(\frac{-1}{2}\right) = -2$$

$-\pi/6$

x

O y

4 $P(4, -\pi/6)$

$P(x, y) = P(2\sqrt{3}, -2)$

Comment

Since polar coordinates having r represented as a negative number can be changed to an equivalent form where r is positive, we shall not take further time with the negative values of r. In some textbooks, brackets are used to enclose the polar coordinates thus $[r, \theta]$, while parentheses (x, y) are used for rectangular coordinates. In this program we do not make this distinction.

1491   (1) Plot the following point, and (2) give the corresponding rectangular coordinates (10, 60°).

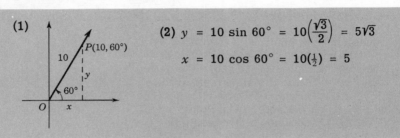

(1)

(2) $y = 10 \sin 60° = 10\left(\dfrac{\sqrt{3}}{2}\right) = 5\sqrt{3}$

$x = 10 \cos 60° = 10(\tfrac{1}{2}) = 5$

1492   Suppose $r = 0$, then regardless of the choice of θ, a unique point is determined, namely the pole 0. *Examples:* $P(0, 0°)$, $P(0, \pi/4)$, $P(0, \pi/6)$, etc., all are coordinates of the same point. How would you identify this point using rectangular coordinates?

$P(x, y) = P(0, 0)$
Note: Both x and y are 0 when the rectangular coordinates are given.

1493   (1) Where do all the points (r, θ) lie for which $r = 3$?   (2) Make a sketch. *Note:* This is equivalent to a locus problem of geometry.

(1) Any point having the radius vector $r = 3$ would lie on a *circle* having O as its center and 3 as a radius.

(2)

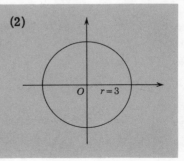

1494 **(1)** Where do all the points (r, θ) lie for which $\theta = 30°$?   **(2)** Make a sketch.

(1) All the points $P(r, 30°)$ lie on   **(2)**
the terminal side of the 30° angle
in standard position.

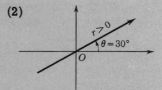

Note: For negative values of r as discussed in frame 1489, the terminal side would also be extended in the other direction through O.

1495 Locate the three points whose polar coordinates are as follows: $B(2, \pi/2)$, $C(4, \pi/6)$, and $A(0, 0)$. Sketch the triangle ABC determined by these three points. Keep this sketch for frame 1496.

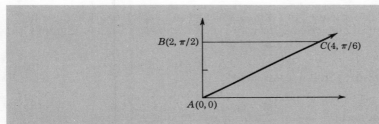

1496 Refer to the information in frame 1495.   **(1)** What is the length of **(a)** AC?   **(b)** of AB?   **(2)** What is the measure of angle BAC (in radians)?   **(3)** Use the law of cosines to find the length of BC.

(1) (a) $AC = 4$, **(b)** $AB = 2$ **(2)** $BAC = \dfrac{\pi}{3}$ radians

(3) $(BC) = 2\sqrt{3}$ *Solution:* $BC = \sqrt{2^2 + 4^2 - 2 \cdot 2 \cdot 4 \cos \dfrac{\pi}{3}}$

$$= \sqrt{4 + 16 - 16(\tfrac{1}{2})}$$

$$= \sqrt{12} = 2\sqrt{3}$$

1497 Change from polar coordinates
to rectangular coordinates
the three points (1) (0, 0),
(2) $(2, \pi/2)$, and (3) $(4, \pi/6)$
shown in the sketch.

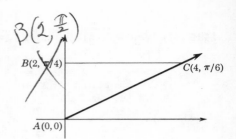

---

	polar	*rectangular*
(1)	(0, 0)	(0, 0)
(2)	$\left(2, \dfrac{\pi}{2}\right)$	(0, 2)
(3)	$\left(4, \dfrac{\pi}{6}\right)$	$(2\sqrt{3}, 2)$

1498 Use the coordinates in frame 1497 and the knowledge you have of
rectangular coordinates to confirm your answer for the distance d
(the length of BC) in frame 1496.

One solution: distance formula
$$d^2 = (x_2 - x_1)^2 + (y_2 - y_1)^2; \text{ therefore, } d = 2\sqrt{3}$$
Second solution: Observe that points B and C are on the same
horizontal line. Therefore,
$$d = x_2 - x_1 = 2\sqrt{3} - 0 = 2\sqrt{3}$$

1499 Two points $P_1(r, \theta)$ and $P_2(R, \phi)$
together with the origin $P_3(0, 0)$
determine a triangle $P_1 P_2 P_3$.
Express P_1 and P_2 in rectangular
coordinate form. This problem
will be continued in frames 1500
and 1501. *Note:* If $\phi - \theta = 0$
or $n\pi$, then $P_2 P_3 P_1$ becomes a
straight line rather than a triangle.

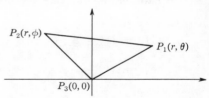

$P_1(r \cos \theta,\ r \sin \theta)$, $P_2(R \cos \phi,\ R \sin \phi)$

1500 Recall that the distance between two points can be expressed by the relationship $d^2 = (x_2 - x_1)^2 + (y_2 - y_1)^2$. Rewrite this formula substituting the values shown above. Keep your answer for frame 1501.

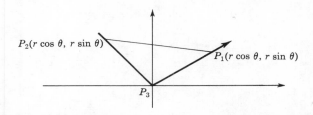

$P_2(r \cos \theta, r \sin \theta)$

$P_1(r \cos \theta, r \sin \theta)$

P_3

$$d^2 = (R \cos \phi - r \cos \theta)^2 + (R \sin \phi - r \sin \theta)^2$$

1501 Expand the right member of the equation below and rearrange and simplify the terms as shown to obtain a formula which you should recognize.

$d^2 = (R \cos \phi - r \cos \theta)^2 + (R \sin \phi - r \sin \theta)^2$

$\quad = R^2 \cos^2 \phi - 2Rr \cos \phi \cos \theta + r^2 \cos^2 \theta$

$\quad \quad \quad + \underline{\hspace{5cm}}$

$\quad = R^2 (\cos^2 \phi + \sin^2 \phi) + r^2(\underline{\hspace{3cm}})$

$\quad \quad \quad \quad \quad -2Rr (\underline{\hspace{4cm}})$

$\quad = \underline{\hspace{1.5cm}} + \underline{\hspace{1.5cm}} - \underline{\hspace{3cm}}$

$d^2 = (R \cos \phi - r \cos \theta)^2 + (R \sin \phi - r \sin \theta)^2$

$\quad = R^2 \cos^2 \phi - 2Rr \cos \phi \cos \theta + r^2 \cos^2 \theta$

$\quad \quad \quad \quad + R^2 \sin^2 \phi - 2Rr \sin \phi \sin \theta + r^2 \sin^2 \theta$

$\quad = R^2(\cos^2 \phi + \sin^2 \phi) + r^2(\cos^2 \theta + \sin^2 \theta)$

$\quad \quad \quad \quad \quad -2Rr(\cos \phi \cos \theta + \sin \phi \sin \theta)$

$\quad = R^2 + r^2 - 2Rr \cos (\phi - \theta)$

Note: This is essentially the law of cosines.

1502 Find the distance between the points $P_1(5, \pi/6)$ and $P_2(3, -\pi/3)$.

$\sqrt{34}$

One solution:

$$d = \sqrt{5^2 + 3^2 - 2(5)(3)\cos\left(\frac{\pi}{6} - \frac{-\pi}{3}\right)}$$

$$= \sqrt{25 + 9 - 30\cos\frac{\pi}{2}} = \sqrt{34}$$

Note: Since angle $P_1OP_2 = \pi/2$, $d = \sqrt{5 + 3}$.

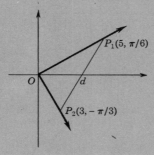

1503 In Panel 9 there are formulas for finding areas of triangles. Refer to this panel, if necessary, to find the area of the triangle determined by the points $(0, 0)$, $P_1(3, -\pi/3)$, and $P_2(5, \pi/6)$.

area $= 7\frac{1}{2}$

area $= \frac{1}{2}ab \sin C$, given two sides and the included angle

area $= \frac{1}{2}(5 \cdot 3) \sin\left[\frac{\pi}{6} - \left(\frac{-\pi}{3}\right)\right]$

$$= \frac{1}{2} \cdot 15 \cdot \sin\frac{\pi}{2}$$

$$= \frac{1}{2} \cdot 15 \cdot 1 = 7\frac{1}{2}$$

Note: Since $P_1OP_2 = \pi/2$, the simpler formula $A = \frac{1}{2}bh$ could be used.

1504 Find the area of the triangle determined by the points $(0, 0)$, $P_1(8, \pi/4)$, and $P_2(0, 2\pi/3)$.

area ≈ 34.8

Solution: area $= \frac{1}{2} \cdot 8 \cdot 9 \sin\left(\frac{2\pi}{3} - \frac{\pi}{4}\right) = 36 \sin \frac{5\pi}{12} \approx 34.8$

1505 Find the distance between the points $P_1(8, \pi/4)$ and $P_2(9, 2\pi/3)$ of the triangle in frame 1504.

$d \approx \sqrt{108}$

One solution: $d = \sqrt{8^2 + 9^2 - 2 \cdot 8 \cdot 9 \cos\left(\frac{2\pi}{3} - \frac{\pi}{4}\right)}$

$= \sqrt{64 + 81 - 144 \cos \frac{5\pi}{12}} = \sqrt{107.7}$

▽1506 Change the rectangular coordinates $x = -4$ and $y = 4$ to polar form: $r =$ (1)_____ and $\theta =$ (2)_____. Let have a positive value.

(1) $4\sqrt{2}$ (2) $\frac{3\pi}{4}$

▽1507 Change to rectangular form the polar coordinates $r = 100$, $\theta = -750°$. Make a sketch.

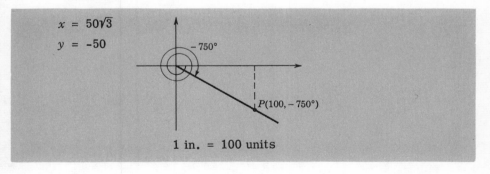

$x = 50\sqrt{3}$

$y = -50$

$-750°$

$P(100, -750°)$

1 in. = 100 units

1508   The resultant of two vectors OA_1 and OA_2 is unique.   Explain what
       this means.

there is exactly one vector which represents the sum of OA_1
plus OA_2.

1509   Assume that **OR** is the resultant of two vectors
       OA_1 and OA_2.   Can you reconstruct the problem
       and find a unique set of components OA_1 and OA_2
       for **OR**?   If your answer is "yes," make a sketch
       showing the two vectors.   If your answer is "no,"
       make at least two sketches showing components
       OA_1 and OA_2.

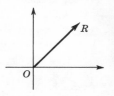

no

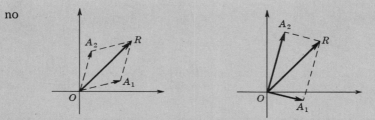

The two sketches above are examples to show that **OR** represents the vector sum of more than one pair of components.

1510   Given A_1 with polar coordinates $(2, \pi/6)$ and A_2 with polar coordi-
       nates $(4, \pi/3)$.   Make a sketch of vectors OA_1 and OA_2 and their
       resultant **OR**.   Keep this sketch for frame 1511.

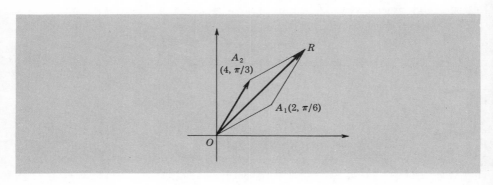

1511 Find the polar coordinates of R shown in the sketch from frame 1510. Do not refer to the suggestions in this frame unless you cannot solve the problem. The answer appears in frame 1512. In order to find the polar coordinates of R, we need the following information: $(OA_1) = $ **(1)**_____ , $(A_1R) = $ **(2)**_____ , and angle $OA_1R = $ **(3)**_____ . Keep this information for frame 1512.

---

(1) 2   **(2)** 4   **(3)** $\dfrac{5\pi}{6}$

Note: angle $A_1OA_2 = \dfrac{\pi}{3} - \dfrac{\pi}{6} = \dfrac{\pi}{6}$ and angle $OA_1R = \pi - \dfrac{\pi}{6} = \dfrac{5\pi}{6}$

1512 **(1)** Find (OR) using the law of cosines on triangle OA_1R. **(2)** Find angle A_1OR using the law of sines. **(3)** Find angle XOR. **(4)** Write the polar coordinates of R. Keep this information for frame 1513.

---

(1) $(OR) = \sqrt{2^2 + 4^2 - 2(2)(4)\cos\dfrac{5\pi}{6}} = \sqrt{4 + 16 - 16 - \dfrac{\sqrt{3}}{2}} \approx 5.8$

(2) $\dfrac{\sin A_1OR}{4} = \dfrac{\sin(5\pi/6)}{5.8}$, angle $A_1OR \approx 20°$ or $\dfrac{\pi}{9}$

(3) angle $XOR \approx \dfrac{\pi}{6} + \dfrac{\pi}{9} = \dfrac{5\pi}{18}$

(4) R has polar coordinates $\left(5.8, \dfrac{5\pi}{18}\right)$

1513 You can resolve the vector **OR** into the components **OA** and **OB** shown here. What are the *polar coordinates* of **(1)** A? **(2)** B?

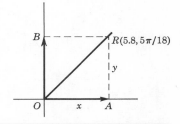

---

(1) $(3.7, 0)$ **(2)** $\left(4.4, \dfrac{\pi}{2}\right)$

Solution: $\sin\dfrac{5\pi}{18} = \dfrac{y}{5.8}$, $y \approx 4.4$

$\cos\dfrac{5\pi}{18} = \dfrac{x}{5.8}$, $x \approx 3.7$

1514 Find the rectangular (x, y) coordinates
associated with polar coordinates
(1) $A_1(2, \pi/6)$ and **(2)** $A_2(4, \pi/3)$.

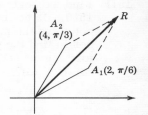

(1) $A_1(\sqrt{3}, 1)$
Solution:

$$\sin \frac{\pi}{6} = \frac{y_1}{2}$$

$$2(\tfrac{1}{2}) = y_1$$

$$1 = y_1$$

$$\cos \frac{\pi}{6} = \frac{x_1}{2}$$

$$2\left(\frac{\sqrt{3}}{2}\right) = x_1$$

$$\sqrt{3} = x_1$$

$A_1(\sqrt{3}, 1)$

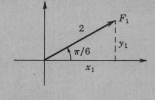

(2) $A_2(2, 2\sqrt{3})$
Solution:

$$\sin \frac{\pi}{3} = \frac{y_2}{4}$$

$$4\left(\frac{\sqrt{3}}{2}\right) = y_2$$

$$2\sqrt{3} = y_2$$

$$\cos \frac{\pi}{3} = \frac{x_2}{4}$$

$$4(\tfrac{1}{2}) = x_2$$

$$2 = x_2$$

$A_2(2, 2\sqrt{3})$

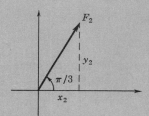

1515   What are the rectangular coordinates
       of R?

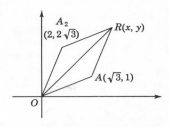

$R(\sqrt{3} + 2,\ 1 + 2\sqrt{3})$ or $R(3.732,\ 4.464)$

Solution: Horizontal component $x_1 + x_2 = \sqrt{3} + 2$ or 3.732

Vertical component $y_1 + y_2 = 1 + 2\sqrt{3}$ or 4.464

1516   Refer to frame 1515. R has rectangular coordinates $(\sqrt{3} + 2,\ 1 + 2\sqrt{3})$. R has polar coordinates $(5.8,\ 5\pi/18)$. To see that these two are equivalent, change $R(\sqrt{3} + 2,\ 1 + 2\sqrt{3})$ to polar form by first finding θ, i.e., $\tan\theta = (1 + 2\sqrt{3})/(\sqrt{3} + 2)$ and $\theta = $ _____. Compare your answer with value of θ indicated in the polar coordinate form.

$50°$ or $\dfrac{5\pi}{18}$

Solution: $\tan\theta = \dfrac{1 + 2\sqrt{3}}{2 + \sqrt{3}} \cdot \dfrac{2 - \sqrt{3}}{2 - \sqrt{3}} \approx 1.196$

$\theta \approx 50°$ or $\dfrac{5\pi}{18}$

1517   Find the radius vector r, to complete the check which was proposed in frame 1516. Use either $r = \sqrt{x^2 + y^2}$ or $\sin\theta = y/r$.

$r \approx 5.8$

Solution: $\sin\dfrac{5}{18} = \dfrac{4.5}{r}$

$r \approx \dfrac{4.5}{0.766} \approx 5.89$

or $r = \sqrt{(1 + 2\sqrt{3})^2 + (2 + \sqrt{3})^2} \approx 5.8$

1518   The advantages of having several ways of representing line segments and points will become apparent as you study the next topic, complex numbers. The coordinates of two points A and B are $(-3, 7)$ and $(-6, -4)$, respectively. Find the resultant of the two vectors **OA** and **OB**; report the answer in (1) rectangular form and in (2) polar form.

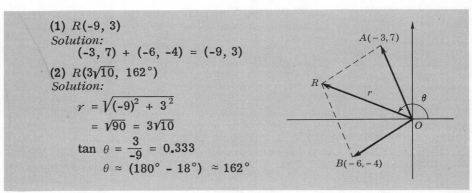

(1) $R(-9, 3)$
Solution:
   $(-3, 7) + (-6, -4) = (-9, 3)$

(2) $R(3\sqrt{10}, \ 162°)$
Solution:

$$r = \sqrt{(-9)^2 + 3^2}$$

$$= \sqrt{90} = 3\sqrt{10}$$

$$\tan \theta = \frac{3}{-9} = 0.333$$

$$\theta \approx (180° - 18°) \approx 162°$$

1519   Given the point P with polar coordinates $(3, \pi/2)$, find the rectangular coordinates (x, y).

$P(0, 3)$

1520   Given the point P having rectangular coordinates $(\sqrt{3}, 1)$, find the polar coordinates.

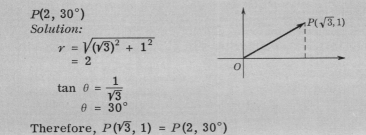

$P(2, 30°)$
Solution:

$$r = \sqrt{(\sqrt{3})^2 + 1^2}$$

$$= 2$$

$$\tan \theta = \frac{1}{\sqrt{3}}$$

$$\theta = 30°$$

Therefore, $P(\sqrt{3}, 1) = P(2, 30°)$

1521   Change $P(-4, 0)$ to polar form. Make a sketch.

$P(4, \pi)$
Solution:

$r = \sqrt{(4)^2 + 0^2} = 4$

It is evident from the sketch that
$\theta = 180°$ or π
Therefore, $P(-4, 0) = P(4, \pi)$

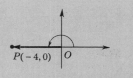

1522   Change $P(5, \pi/2)$ to rectangular form.

$P(0, 5)$
The answer can be obtained from the sketch
by inspection, or from the solution.
Solution:

$\sin \dfrac{\pi}{2} = \dfrac{y}{5}$

$5(1) = y$

$\cos \dfrac{\pi}{2} = \dfrac{x}{5}$

$5(0) = x$

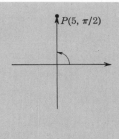

1523   (1) Change $P(2, \pi)$ to rectangular form.
        (2) Change $P(0, -5)$ to polar form.

The answers can be obtained from the sketches
by inspection or from the solutions which follow.
(1) $P(-2, 0)$
Solution:

$\sin \pi = \dfrac{y}{2}$ $\cos \pi = \dfrac{x}{2}$

$2(0) = y$ $2(-1) = x$

$0 = y$ $-2 = x$

Therefore, $(-2, 0)$

(2) $P\left(5, \dfrac{3\pi}{2}\right)$ or $P(5, 270°)$

Solution:

$r = \sqrt{0 + (-5)^2}$

$= \sqrt{25} = 5$

The sketch indicates that θ is 270° or $3\pi/2$.

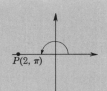

1524 Plot the following: **(1)** $(3, -3\pi/4)$, **(2)** $(5, 0°)$, and **(3)** $(2, \pi)$.

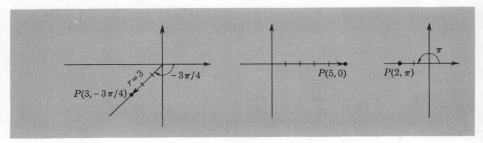

1525 **(1)** Locate on a polar coordinate system the point $P(6, 11\pi/3)$.
(2) Find the rectangular coordinates for point P. **(3)** Suggest a "simpler" form for $P(6, 11\pi/3)$ but keep the polar form.

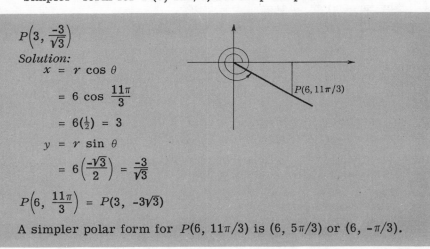

$P\left(3, \dfrac{-3}{\sqrt{3}}\right)$

Solution:

$\quad x = r \cos \theta$

$\quad\quad = 6 \cos \dfrac{11\pi}{3}$

$\quad\quad = 6(\tfrac{1}{2}) = 3$

$\quad y = r \sin \theta$

$\quad\quad = 6\left(\dfrac{-\sqrt{3}}{2}\right) = \dfrac{-3}{\sqrt{3}}$

$P\left(6, \dfrac{11\pi}{3}\right) = P(3, -3\sqrt{3})$

A simpler polar form for $P(6, 11\pi/3)$ is $(6, 5\pi/3)$ or $(6, -\pi/3)$.

1526 Find the distance between the points $(2, 225°)$ and $(4, -270°)$.

$d = \sqrt{26}$
Solution 1:
$d^2 = 4^2 + (\sqrt{2})^2 - 2 \cdot 4 \cdot \sqrt{2} \cos (-270 - 225)$
$\quad = 26$
$d = \sqrt{26}$
Solution 2:

Polar	Rectangular
$(\sqrt{2}, 225°)$	$(-1, -1)$
$(4, -270°)$	$(0, 4)$

$d^2 = (4 - (-1))^2 + (0 - (-1))^2 = 26$

$d = \sqrt{26}$

1527 You are given the magnitude and direction of
the vector **OP**, i.e., **OP** represents a force of
80 lb acting in a direction which makes a 45°
angle with OX. The polar coordinates of P
are (1) (____, ____). The rectangular coordinates of P are (2) (_____, _____).

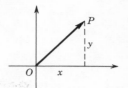

(1) $(80, 45°)$ (2) $(40\sqrt{2}, 40\sqrt{2})$

1528 Show how to find graphically the resultant
(vector sum) of the vectors $\mathbf{OA_1}$ and $\mathbf{OA_2}$.

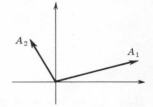

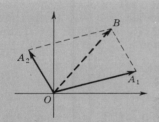

OB (the diagonal of the parallelogram OA_1BA_2) represents the
vector sum ($\mathbf{OA_1} + \mathbf{OA_2}$).

UNIT **8** | Complex Numbers

1529 Up to this point in our study of trigonometry we have considered *real numbers* only. Problems occur in physics and engineering as well as in pure mathematics where the real number system is inadequate. Take a simple equation such as $x^2 = -1$. (1) Is there any *real* number x such that $x^2 = -1$? Recall that if $x = 1$, then $x^2 = (1)^2 = (2)$____, and if $x = -1$, then $x^2 = (-1)^2 = (3)$____.

---

(1) no **(2)** 1 **(3)** 1

1530 Let x have the values indicated below, 0, -2, 2, etc.; find x^2 in each case.

$0^2 = (1)$____	$(-2)^2 = (2)$____	$(2)^2 = (3)$____
$(-0.5)^2 = (4)$____	$(\frac{1}{2})^2 = (5)$____	$(-\sqrt{3})^2 = (6)$____
$(-\sqrt{7})^2 = (7)$____	$(\frac{8}{7})^2 = (8)$____	$(-\frac{9}{4})^2 = (9)$____

(10) Are there any negative numbers as answers? It appears from these examples that if x is a *real* number, then $x^2 \geq (11)$_____?

---

(1) 0   **(2)** 4   **(3)** 4   **(4)** 0.25   **(5)** $\frac{1}{4}$ **(6)** 3
(2) 7   **(8)** $\frac{64}{49}$ **(9)** $\frac{81}{16}$ **(10)** no   **(11)** 0

1531 The attempt by early mathematicians to find a solution to an equation of the type $x^2 + 1 = $ (i.e., $x^2 = -1$) led to the extension of the number system to include numbers of the form $\sqrt{-1}$ and $-\sqrt{-1}$. Since these units did not appear among the *real numbers,* they were called *imaginary* numbers when they were first introduced. (Although this is not an appropriate title in the light of present knowledge,

continued →

it continues to be used.) In general, given $x^2 + N = 0$, where N is positive, the solution can be indicated in the following steps:

If $x^2 + N = 0$		hypothesis
then $x^2 = $ (1)_____		adding $-N$ to both members
and $\pm x = $ (2)_____		taking the square root of
or $x = \pm$ (3)_____		both members

To check your answers substitute in the original equation thus (copy the entire equation as you answer):

(4) (_____)$^2 + N = 0,$ _____ $+ N = 0$
(5) (_____)$^2 + N = 0,$ _____ $+ N = 0$

(1) $-N$ **(2)** $\sqrt{-N}$ **(3)** $\sqrt{-N}$ **(4)** $(\sqrt{-N})^2 + N = 0, -N + N = 0$
(5) $(-\sqrt{-N})^2 + N = 0, -N + N = 0$

1532   Before we continue the study of the *complex-number system*, it is important that you understand the terminology used to describe different kinds of numbers in our number system. First of all we have the whole numbers or *positive integers*. (These are also called the natural numbers or the counting numbers.) When we include the number zero, we call the set composed of the positive integers and zero the *nonnegative* integers. If we enlarge this set to include negative integers also, we obtain the set of *all integers*. (1) Which of the sets listed below is the set of nonnegative integers? (2) Which set is the set of natural numbers? (3) What other names could you give for this set?
    $A = (\ldots -3, -2, -1, 0, 1, 2, 3 \ldots)$
    $B = (0, 1, 2, 3 \ldots)$
    $C = (1, 2, 3, 4, 5 \ldots)$

(1) B **(2)** C
(3) whole numbers or counting numbers or positive integers

1533   Notice that if you were limited to integers alone, you could not solve a simple equation such as $3x = 7$. The solution of this equation would require a number system which included _____ in addition to the integers.

Acceptable answers are: fractions, rational numbers, numbers which are not whole numbers

1534   Given a pair of integers a and b ($b \neq 0$), we can form another number called a *fraction* (or rational number) which is written
    a/b or $\frac{a}{b}$. (The name *rational* number suggests that a/b is a

"ratio-like" number, the ratio of a to b.) Write the rational number which is determined when: (1) $a = 3, b = 7$; (2) $a = 7, b = 3$; (3) $a = -6, b = 4$; (4) $a = -10, b = 5$; and (5) $a = 9, b = 1$.

(1) $\dfrac{3}{7}$ (2) $\dfrac{7}{3}$ (3) $\dfrac{-6}{4}$ or $\dfrac{-3}{2}$ (4) $\dfrac{-10}{-5}$ or $\dfrac{2}{1}$ (5) $\dfrac{9}{1}$

1535 Since the *order*, a/b or b/a) in which we write the two integers that make up a fraction is important, we might define a fraction as an *ordered pair* of integers. Then the fraction could be written (a, b); however, this form has not come into common usage. If it is agreed that 6 is to be the first integer and 7 the second, then the fraction formed from this pair of integers could be written as (1) (__, __) or (2) ___ / ___.

(1) (6, 7)   (2) $\dfrac{6}{7}$

Comment

According to our definition of a fraction or a rational number, any integer a may be written in a fractional form by assigning to b the value 1: thus, $4 = 4/1, 9 = 9/1$, etc. Many rational numbers may be equivalent in value. *Example:* $\dfrac{3}{2} = \dfrac{-9}{-6} = \dfrac{12}{8} = \dfrac{300}{200} = \dfrac{42}{28}$, etc.

1536 Write two equivalent fractional forms for each of the following: (1) $\dfrac{36}{48}$, (2) $\dfrac{8}{7}$, and (3) 19.

(1) $\dfrac{3}{4}$, $\dfrac{6}{8}$, $\dfrac{9}{12}$, $\dfrac{72}{96}$, etc.   (2) $\dfrac{8}{7}$, $\dfrac{16}{14}$, $\dfrac{24}{21}$, $\dfrac{64}{56}$, etc.

(3) $\dfrac{19}{1}$, $\dfrac{38}{2}$, $\dfrac{57}{3}$, $\dfrac{-19}{-1}$, etc.

1537 According to your knowledge of rational numbers, which of the following sets of numbers are sets of rational numbers (or could be written as equivalent numbers in rational form)?
A. The set of nonnegative integers.
B. The set of ordered pairs of integers (a, b) with $b < 0$.
C. The set of numbers a/b where a is any integer and $b = 1$.
D. The set of natural numbers.

They are all sets of rational numbers.
Note: A rational number is any number which can be expressed as the quotient of two integers a and b, $b \neq 0$.

1538 Which numbers of the set below are: (1) Natural numbers? (2) Integers? (3) Rational numbers?

$$\{6, \tfrac{2}{3}, -0.5, -9, 15\tfrac{1}{8}, 436, 0\}$$

Note: Some of the numbers may be labeled in more than one way.

(1) 6, 436   (2) 6, -9, 436, 0

(3) 6, $\tfrac{2}{3}$, -0.5, -9, 15$\tfrac{1}{8}$, 436, 0

Note: $-0.5 = \tfrac{-1}{2}$ and $15\tfrac{1}{8} = \tfrac{121}{8}$

1539 Does the equation $x^2 = 2$ have a solution if we are limited to the two number systems listed below?

1. Integers
   negative integers
   zero
   positive integers or natural numbers
2. Rational numbers

Explain your answer.

no
Explanation: If $x^2 = 2$, then $x = +\sqrt{2}$ or $-\sqrt{2}$. These numbers cannot be expressed as integers or as the quotient of two integers. See frame 1540 for further discussion on this kind of number.

1540 About the sixth century B.C. Pythagoras and his students discovered that there were simple problems in geometry which required numbers for their solution which were not in the system of rational numbers. You are familiar with one of the problems which they encountered: "What is the length of the hypotenuse of a right triangle whose legs are each 1 *unit long*? Since there was no rational number to represent this length, it was necessary to extend the number system to include solutions to problems of this kind. If a number is not rational, an appropriate name for it is *irrational;* hence, our number system contains both rational and (1)   numbers. (2) If the legs of a right triangle are 3 and 4 units long, is the hypotenuse represented by a rational or an irrational number? (3) What is the number? (4) If the legs of a right triangle are 2 and 3 units long, is the hypotenuse represented by a rational or an irrational number?

(1) irrational   (2) rational   (3) 5   (4) irrational

1541 We define an *irrational* number as a number which cannot be expressed as the quotient of two integers. Sometimes a number is written in decimal form, and we would like to know whether this number is a rational number. Look at the decimal 0.5. You know that $\frac{1}{2}$ = 0.5; therefore, 0.5 is a rational number; i.e., we can express it as a quotient of the two integers 1 and 2. Likewise, 0.75 = (1)_____, and 0.62 = (2)_____, and 0.333 ··· = (3)_____. Hence, these are classified as (4)_____?

(1) $\frac{3}{4}$ (2) $\frac{62}{100}$ or $\frac{31}{50}$ (3) $\frac{1}{3}$ (4) rational numbers

1542 Look at the following examples:

1. $\frac{5}{8}$ = 0.625

2. $\dfrac{852}{2,500}$ = 0.3412

3. $\frac{1}{9}$ = 0.111 ···

4. $\frac{5}{7}$ = 0.714285714285 ···

The first two are examples of what are usually called *terminating* decimals; the last two are *repeating* decimals. Notice that all examples are expressions of quotients of two integers; therefore, they are _____ (rational, irrational) numbers.

rational

1543 If you are given a *rational* number, you can write it as a decimal. The decimal will be one of two types, a *repeating* decimal or a *terminating* decimal. Conversely, it can be shown that every *repeating* or *terminating* decimal can be expressed as a *rational* number. Frame 1544 will show how to change a repeating decimal to its fractional form.) *Nonterminating* (nonrepeating) decimals are called *irrational* numbers. From your previous knowledge of mathematics select the *irrational* numbers in this list: $\sqrt{3}, 3, \frac{7}{9}, \pi, 0.48$.

$\sqrt{3}$ and π

Note: The numbers $\frac{22}{7}$, 3.14, 3.1416, 3.14159, etc., are *approximations* commonly used for the irrational number π, but extensive studies have shown that π cannot be written as the quotient of two integers. Consult a good geometry textbook for a discussion on π. We use 1.732 as an approximation for $\sqrt{3}$, but here again there are no two integers whose quotient is exactly $\sqrt{3}$.

1544 The *repeating* decimal $0.222 \cdots$ can be changed to a fractional form as follows:

1. Let $x = 0.222 \cdots$

2. then $10x = 2.222 \cdots$ multiply both members of the equation by 10

3. $10x - x = 2.000 \cdots$ subtract the equation in step 1 from that in step 2.

4. $\qquad 9x = 2.000 \cdots$

5. $\qquad x = \frac{2}{9}$

Change the repeating decimal $0.777 \cdots$ to its fractional form.

Let $x = 0.777 \cdots$, then
$10x = 7.777 \cdots$, $9x = 7.000 \cdots$, $x = \frac{7}{9}$

1545 Change the repeating decimal $0.878787 \cdots$ so that it is written as the quotient of two integers.

Let $x = 0.878787 \cdots$, then
$100x = 87.878787 \cdots$, $99x = 87.000 \cdots$, $x = \frac{87}{99} = \frac{29}{33}$

1546 Change $0.121121121 \cdots$ to fractional form.

Let $x = 0.121121 \cdots$, then
$1,000x = 121.121121 \cdots$, $999x = 121.000 \cdots$, $x = \frac{121}{999}$

1547 To change a number such as $29.48181 \cdots$ to its fractional form, first let $x = 29.48181 \cdots$, then $100x = 2948.181 \cdots$. Complete the problem.

$\dfrac{3,243}{100}$

$$99x = 2,918.7, \quad x = \frac{2,918.7}{99}, \ = \frac{29,187}{990} = \frac{3,243}{100}$$

1548 Any repeating or terminating decimal can be expressed as the quotient of two integers. Such numbers are called (1)_____ numbers. Nonrepeating, nonterminating decimals cannot be expressed as the quotient of two integers. Such numbers are called (1)_____ numbers.

(1) rational   (2) irrational

1549 If possible change the following to fractional form: **(1)** $0.351351 \cdots$ and **(2)** $\sqrt{10}$.

> **(1)** $\frac{13}{37}$ **(2)** $\sqrt{10}$ is irrational

Comment

The set of numbers which includes *all* of the rational numbers and the irrational numbers is called the set of *real numbers*. This is the set which enables you to solve most of the problems of elementary algebra and geometry. One of the significant facts about the real-number system is that these numbers may be put into a one-to-one correspondence with the points of a line. As we have pointed out, irrational numbers were necessary so that we would have a representation for the hypotenuse of any right triangle, i.e., $\sqrt{a^2 + b^2}$, where a and b are the lengths of the sides forming the right angle. The ratio of the circumference C of a circle to its diameter required another irrational number, i.e., $C/d = \pi$. There was a time when the rational and irrational numbers appeared to be sufficient for all *real* mathematical problems; hence, it seemed quite natural then to refer to this set of numbers as the set of *real numbers*. Later, of course, it became necessary to extend the number system again, and the result is the complex-number system which is the topic of our discussion here.

1550 Make a list showing (historically) the order in which our number system might have developed.

> natural numbers (counting numbers)
> integers (positive, negative)
> real:
>   rational numbers
>   irrational numbers
> complex:
>   real numbers
>   imaginary numbers
>
> *Note:* Historically there is some uncertainty regarding the time of the introduction of 0, and whether or not rational numbers might have preceded the negative integers.

1551 A complex number is a number of the form $a + bi$ where a and b are real numbers and $i = \sqrt{-1}$. Thus $4 + 3i$ is a **(1)**_____ number, a = **(2)**_____, b = **(3)**_____. Look again at the solution for the equation $x^2 = -1$. *Note:* We have $\pm x = \sqrt{-1}$ which is the number i as defined above. This equation then has a solution in the

continued →

form of a complex number, although its solution did not appear among the rational or irrational numbers.

(1) complex **(2)** 4 **(3)** 3

1552 Recall the statement: "Each real number may be made to corre-spond to a point on a number line, and conversely." (1) Draw a straight line and locate approximately the points corresponding to the following real numbers: $-4, -3, -2, -1, 0, 1, 2, 3, 4, \frac{2}{3}, \sqrt{3},$ $\frac{-9}{2}, \pi, \frac{-5}{4}, 0.5, \frac{-31}{10}, \sqrt{18}, -\sqrt{2}, -2.6$. (Choose a convenient unit of measurement.) (2) Do the complex numbers each have a place on this number line?

(1)

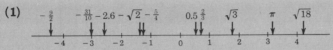

(2) no (Later we shall discuss a way of representing complex numbers on a number plane.)

1553 Which of the following names could be associated with the numbers below: complex number, real number, irrational number, rational number, integer, natural number? **(1)** $-4i$ **(2)** 8 **(3)** $2.353535\cdots$ **(4)** $\sqrt{2}$

(1) complex number
(2) natural number, integer, rational number, real number, com-plex number (8 can be written as $8 + 0i$)
(3) rational number, real number, complex number
(4) irrational number, real number, complex number

Comment

Before we come back to the study of complex numbers in particu-lar, one further remark is in order. You might wonder how much further the number system will need to be extended for this pro-gram. The answer is "no further." It has been proved that with imaginary numbers available, *every algebraic equation* has a solution; that is, there is no algebraic equation whose solution will require the invention of any new numbers. From a practical point of view and for our purposes here the number system is now com-plete. The statement about the extension of our number system beyond the complex numbers may be misleading. Although all *algebraic* (polynomial) equations with complex coefficients have complex roots, the reader should know that even larger number systems do exist. The set of complex numbers is a subset of a mathematical system called *quaternions*. An application of this system is found in quantum mechanics. The quaternions, in turn, form a subset of another system, a system of matrices. Although neither the quaternions nor the system of matrices will be a part of this program, it is well to know that they exist and that in more advanced courses you may learn about them.

1554   Arrange the following in order of comprehensiveness starting with most comprehensive: natural numbers, complex numbers, real numbers, integers, rational numbers.

complex numbers, real numbers, rational numbers, integers, natural numbers

1555   In the solution of the equation $x^2 + N = 0$ by the usual techniques, we find that $x = \pm\sqrt{-N}$. The special symbol i has been assigned to the imaginary unit $\sqrt{-1}$. Hence, if N itself is a positive number, then $\sqrt{-N}$ may be written thus: $\sqrt{-N} = \sqrt{-1}\,\sqrt{N} = i\sqrt{N}$. Let $N = 16$, then $\sqrt{-16} = \sqrt{-1} \cdot \sqrt{16} = i\sqrt{16} = i4$ or $4i$. Express each of the following in terms of i: (1) $\sqrt{-25}$, (2) $\sqrt{-64}$, (3) $\sqrt{-\frac{1}{4}}$, and (4) $\sqrt{-a^2}$.

(1) $5i$ (2) $8i$ (3) $\frac{1}{2}i$ (4) ai

1556   In the following two examples notice how the imaginary number $-\sqrt{-N}$ is written in terms of i:

$-\sqrt{-N} = -\sqrt{-1} \cdot \sqrt{N} = -i\sqrt{N}$

$-\sqrt{-4} = -\sqrt{-1} \cdot \sqrt{4} = -i \cdot 2$ or $-2i$

Express each of the following in terms of i: (1) $-\sqrt{-36}$, (2) $-\sqrt{-\frac{4}{9}}$, (3) $\sqrt{-0.81}$, and (4) $-\sqrt{-5}$.

(1) $-6i$ (2) $-\frac{2}{3}i$ (3) $0.9i$ (4) $-i\sqrt{5}$ or $-2.236i$

1557   In mathematics i is a symbol which represents (1)_____. It is called a(n) (2)_____unit or number.

(1) $\sqrt{-1}$ (2) imaginary

1558   We are ready now to consider the properties of the so-called "imaginary" numbers. By definition $i^2 = -1$ and $i = \sqrt{-1}$. If the symbol i is to obey the ordinary laws of exponents, we can write (using the definition above)

continued →

$$i^3 = i^2 \cdot i = (-1) \cdot i = -i$$
$$i^4 = i^2 \cdot i^2 = \underline{\hspace{1cm}} \cdot \underline{\hspace{1cm}} = \underline{\hspace{1cm}}$$

$(-1) \cdot (-1) = 1$

1559 You must remember that by definition i^2 = (1)_____ and i (2)_____.

(1) -1 (2) $\sqrt{-1}$

1560 To find i^3 in terms of a real number and i, we indicated that $i^3 = i^2 \cdot i$ = (1)_____ · ____ = ____. In a similar manner we found that i^4 = (2)_____ · ____ = _____. Now find (3) i^5 and (4) i^6.

(1) $(-1) \cdot i = -1 = -i$ (2) $(-1) \cdot (-1) = 1$
(3) $i^5 = i^4 \cdot i = 1 \cdot i = i$ (4) $i^6 = i^4 \cdot i^2 = 1 \cdot (-1) = -1$

1561 If we make a list of several powers of i, you should see a "pattern":

$$\sqrt{-1} = i^1 = i, \; i^2 = -1, \; i^3 = -i, \; i^4 = 1,$$
$$i^5 = (1)\underline{\hspace{1cm}}, \; i^6 = (2)\underline{\hspace{1cm}}, \; i^7 = (3)\underline{\hspace{1cm}},$$
$$i^8 = (4)\underline{\hspace{1cm}} \quad i^9 = (5)\underline{\hspace{1cm}}$$

(6) What do you observe as a recurring sequence?

(1) i (2) -1 (3) $-i$ (4) 1 (5) i
(6) any positive integral power of i can be reduced to one of the four quantities $i, -1, -i, 1$.

1562 Make use of the observation in frame 1561 to find (1) i^{13}, (2) i^{14}, (3) i^{15}, and (4) i^{16}.

(1) $i^{13} = (i^4)^3 \cdot i = 1 \cdot i = i$
(2) $i^{14} = (i^4)^3 \cdot i^2 = 1 \cdot (-1) = -1$
(3) $i^{15} = (i^4)^3 \cdot i^3 = 1 \cdot (-i) = -i$
(4) $i^{16} = (i^4)^4 = 1$

1563 What is (1) i^{29}, (2) i^{42}, and (3) i^{100} ?

(1) $i^{29} = (i^4)^7 i = 1 \cdot i = i$

(2) $i^{42} = (i^4)^{10} i^2 = 1 \cdot (-1) = -1$

(3) $i^{100} = (i^4)^{25} = 1$

1564 What is (1) i^0 and (2) i^{-1} ? *Note:* Recall that by definition $a^{-1} = 1/a$ for any a except $a = 0$; therefore, $a^{-2} = 1/a^2$, $a^{-3} = 1/a^3$, etc.

(1) $i^0 = 1$ (2) $i^{-1} = \dfrac{1}{i} = \dfrac{1}{i} \cdot \dfrac{i}{i} = \dfrac{i}{-1} = -i$

1565 Find (1) i^{-2} and (2) i^{-3}.

(1) $i^{-2} = \dfrac{1}{i^2} = \dfrac{1}{-1} = -1$

(2) $i^{-3} = \dfrac{1}{i^3} = \dfrac{1}{-i} \cdot \dfrac{i}{i} = \dfrac{i}{1} = i$ or $i^{-3} = \dfrac{1}{i^3} \cdot \dfrac{i}{i} = \dfrac{i}{1} = i$

1566 Here is a summary of a statement from a previous frame. If N is any positive quantity, then $\sqrt{-N}$ can be written $\sqrt{(-1) \cdot N}$ and this, in turn, by definition is written in the form $\sqrt{-1} \cdot \sqrt{N} = i\sqrt{N}$. Thus, we can express the square root of *any* negative number $-N$ in terms of real numbers and the symbol i. After this change in the form of the imaginary number has been made, the operations of addition, multiplication, etc., can be defined. Change (1) $\sqrt{-5}$ and (2) $\sqrt{-3}$ to the form involving i, then (3) find the product of $\sqrt{-5} \cdot \sqrt{-3}$.

(1) $\sqrt{-5} = i\sqrt{5}$ (2) $\sqrt{-3} = i\sqrt{3}$

(3) $\sqrt{-5} \cdot \sqrt{-3} = i\sqrt{5} \cdot i\sqrt{3} = i^2\sqrt{15} = -\sqrt{15}$

1567 Mistakes are often made in attempting to multiply imaginary numbers which are not expressed in terms of i. For example, $\sqrt{-5} \cdot \sqrt{-3} \neq \sqrt{(-5) \cdot (-3)} \neq \sqrt{15}$. The identity $\sqrt{a} \cdot \sqrt{b} = \sqrt{ab}$ applies only when $\sqrt{a}$ and $\sqrt{b}$ represent real numbers. To find the product $\sqrt{-7} \cdot \sqrt{-2}$, we first express each factor in terms of i. Thus $\sqrt{-7} =$ (1)_____ and $\sqrt{-2} =$ (2)_____; then $\sqrt{-7} \cdot \sqrt{-2} =$ (3)_____ = _____.

(1) $i\sqrt{7}$ (2) $i\sqrt{2}$ (3) $i\sqrt{7} \cdot i\sqrt{2} = i^2\sqrt{14} = -\sqrt{14}$

1568 Find the following products: $\sqrt{-10} \cdot \sqrt{-3} = $ (1)_____ and
$-\sqrt{10} \cdot -\sqrt{3} = $ (2)_____.

(1) $-\sqrt{30}$ (2) $\sqrt{30}$

1569 Simplify the following: (1) $\sqrt{-28}$, (2) $\sqrt{3} \cdot i\sqrt{27}$, and (3) $\sqrt{-6} \cdot \sqrt{-6}$.

(1) $\sqrt{-28} = i\sqrt{28} = i\sqrt{4 \cdot 7} = 2i\sqrt{7}$

(2) $i\sqrt{3} \cdot i\sqrt{27} = i^2\sqrt{81} = -9$

(3) $\sqrt{-6} \cdot \sqrt{-6} = i\sqrt{6} \cdot i\sqrt{6} = i^2\sqrt{36} = -6$

1570 In the study of the complex-number system, you must keep in mind
that i is the symbol used for (1)_____, and that by definition $i^2 = $
(2)_____.

(1) $\sqrt{-1}$ (2) -1

1571 A complex number is identified in the following manner: If a and b
are real numbers and $i = \sqrt{-1}$, a number of the form $a + bi$ is
called a *complex* number. The real number a is called the *real
part* (or real component) of the complex number, and the real number b is called the *imaginary part* (or imaginary component) of the
complex number. If $b = 0$, then $a + 0i = a$, and we have a *pure
real number*. If $a = 0$ and $b \neq 0$, then $0 + bi = bi$, and we have a
pure imaginary number. Give the appropriate names for (1) $2 + 3i$
(2) 2, and (3) $3i$.

(1) complex number   (2) pure real number   (3) pure imaginary
number

1572 (1) Given the complex numbers $3 + 4i$ and $a + bi$, what values
would you assign to a and b respectively if $a + bi = 3 + 4i$?
(2) If $x = 7$ and $y = 2$, is $x + yi = 7 + 2i$ a true statement?
(3) If $m = 9$ and $n = 6$, is $m + ni = 8 + 5i$ a true statement?

(1) $a = 3, b = 4$ (2) yes   (3) no
(See frame 1573 for a definition of equality of the complex
numbers.)

1573 Two complex numbers $a + bi$ and $c + di$ are equal if and only if
their real parts are equal *and* their imaginary parts are equal.

continued →

This definition may be stated briefly as follows: $a + bi = c + di$ if and only if $a = $ (1)_____ and $b = $ (2)_____.

---

(1) c (2) d

1574 (1) What is the real part of the complex number $4 - 3i$?
   (2) What is the imaginary part of the complex number $-a - 2bi$?
   (3) The complex number $6 + 0i$ is usually written in the simpler form (a)_____ and is called a(n) (b) _____.
   (4) The complex number $0 + 4i$ is usually written in the simpler form (a)_____ and is called a(n) (b) _____.

---

(1) 4   (2) $-2b$ (the negative sign is part of the coefficient of i)
(3) (a) 6,   (b) pure real number or real number
(4) (a) $4i$ (b) pure imaginary number or imaginary number

1575 If the complex numbers $a + 7i$ and $-4 + 7i$ are equal, then $a = $ (1)_____.   (2) Find the product of $\sqrt{-6} \cdot \sqrt{5} \cdot \sqrt{-2} \cdot \sqrt{-5}$.

---

(1) -4 (2) $\sqrt{-6} \cdot \sqrt{5} \cdot \sqrt{-2} \cdot \sqrt{-5} = -10i\sqrt{3}$

1576 If $x + 4i = \sqrt{3} - yi$, what are the numerical values for (1) x and (2) y ?

---

(1) $x = \sqrt{3}$ (2) $y = -4$

1577 If $(x - 4) + 3i = 6 + (yi + 5i)$, find values for (1) x and (2) y.
   Suggestion: Make use of the fact that two complex numbers $a + bi$ and $c + di$ are equal if and only if $a = c$ and $b = d$.

---

(1) $x = 10$ (2) $y = -2$

Solution: $\overset{a}{\overbrace{(x - 4)}} + \overset{b}{\overbrace{3i}} = \overset{c}{\overbrace{6}} + \overset{d}{\overbrace{(y + 5)i}}$

   $x - 4 = 6,\ x = 10$ $y + 5 = 3,\ y = -2$

1578 You know that the negative of 2 is -2; the negative of -2 is 2. What would you expect to be the negative of the complex number $5 + 6i$?

$-(5 + 6i)$ or $-5 - 6i$

1579 The negative of the complex number $a + bi$ is $-(a + bi)$ or $-a - bi$. What is the negative of (1) $2 - 3i$, (2) $4 - 0i$, and (3) $-2 - \overline{3}i$?

(1) $-(2 - 3i)$ or $-2 + 3i$ (2) $-4 + 0i$ or -4
(3) $-(-2 - 3i)$ or $2 + 3i$

1580 If two complex numbers differ only in the sign of their *imaginary parts*, either is said to be the *conjugate* of the other. *Examples:* $2 + 3i$ and $2 - 3i$, $-2 + 3i$ and $-2 - 3i$, and $a - bi$ and $a + bi$. What is the conjugate of (1) $6 + 5i$, (2) $7 - 2i$, (3) $-1 + 3i$, and (4) $-\sqrt{3} - i$?

(1) $6 - 5i$ (2) $7 + 2i$ (3) $-1 - 3i$ (4) $-\sqrt{3} + i$

1581 (1) What is the conjugate of (a) $\sqrt{2} - \sqrt{3i}$ and (b) $-(4 + i)$?
(2) What is the negative of (a) $\sqrt{2} - \sqrt{3i}$ and (b) $-(4 + i)$?

(1)(a) $\sqrt{2} + \sqrt{3i}$, (b) $-4 + i$ (2)(a) $-\sqrt{2} + \sqrt{3i}$, (b) $4 + i$

1582 Explain how to obtain the conjugate of a given complex number.

The conjugate of a complex number is obtained by changing the sign of the imaginary part. Thus the conjugate of $a + bi$ is $a - bi$.

1583 Give the conjugate of each of the following: (1) $4 + 5i$, (2) $2 - i$, (3) $0 + 3i$, (4) $5 + 0i$, (5) bi, and (6) a.

(1) $4 - 5i$ (2) $2 + i$ (3) $0 - 3i = -3i$
(4) $5 - 0i = 5$ (5) $-bi$ (6) a
Note: 5 (in part (4)) and a (in part (6)) are their own conjugates)

1584 In the complex-number system (1) $\sqrt{-1}$ has the symbol ___; (2) $i^2 = $ ___; (3) the *real component* of the complex number $-i + 3$ is ___; (4) the *imaginary component* of the complex number $-3i - 2$ is ___; (5) $i^4 = $ ___; (6) the negative of $-2 + 3i$ is (a) ___ and the conjugate of $-2 + 3i$ is (b) ___ .

(1) i (2) -1 (3) 3   (4) -3 (5) 1   (6)(a) $2 - 3i$ (b) $-2 - 3i$

1585 Sometimes it is convenient to think of a complex number, $a + bi$, as an ordered pair (a, b). Here it is understood that the first component of the ordered pair corresponds to the *real* part of the complex number and the second component corresponds to the *imaginary* part. How would you write (1) $(m + ni)$ as an ordered pair? (2) $(-2 + 3i)$? (3) $(6i + 7)$?

(1) (m, n) (2) $(-2, 3)$ (3) $(7, 6)$

1586 Now we need a definition for *addition* of complex numbers.

$$(a + bi) + (c + di) = (a + c) + (b + d)i$$

Notice that the sum is given as the sum of the *real* parts $(a + c)$ plus the sum of the *imaginary* parts $(b + d)i$. If we had written our complex numbers as ordered pairs (a, b) and (c, d), their sum might be written $(a + c, b + d)$. Find the sum of (1) $(6 + 2i) + (3 - 4i)$ and (2) $(-2 - 5i) + (3i - 1)$.

(1) $(6 + 2i) + (3 - 4i) = 9 - 2i$ or $(6, 2) + (3, -4) = (9, -2)$
(2) $(-2 - 5i) + (3i - 1) = (-2 - 5i) + (-1 + 3i) = (-3 - 2i)$
    or $(-2, -5) + (-1, +3) = (-3, -2)$

1587 Find the sum of
(1) $(1 + i) + (1 - i)$ (2) $(\sqrt{2} + \sqrt{3}i) + (3\sqrt{2} - 4\sqrt{3}i)$
(3) $(1 + \sqrt{5} + 4i) + (2 + \sqrt{5} + 6i)$ (4) $(x + i) + (3x + 4i)$

(1) $2 + 0i = 2$ (2) $4\sqrt{2} - 3\sqrt{3}i$
(3) $3 + 2\sqrt{5} + 10i$ (4) $4x + 5i$

1588 Write the following complex numbers in the ordered-pair notation: (1) $A = (1 + i)$ and (2) $B = (-1 + i)$. Find the sum $A + B$. Write the answer (3) first as an ordered pair, (4) then in the $a + bi$ form.

(1) $A = (1, 1)$ (2) $B = (-1, 1)$
(3) $A + B = (0, 2)$ (4) $A + B = (0 + 2i)$

1589 In a similar manner subtraction of complex numbers is defined:

$$(a + bi) - (c + di) = (a - c) + (b - d)i$$

or

$$(a, b) - (c, d) = (a - c, b - d)$$

continued →

Notice the similarity to subtraction of two algebraic quantities.

$$(a + bi) - (c + di) = a + bi - c - di = a - c + bi - di \quad \longleftarrow$$
$$= (a - c) + (b - d)i$$

Find the sums (or differences) as indicated in the following problems.

$$(7 - 3i) + (-4 + 4i) + 6 = (1)\underline{\hspace{1cm}}$$
$$(8 + 7i) - (8i) = (2)\underline{\hspace{1cm}}$$
$$[(x + yi) + (a - yi)] - (x + bi) = (3)\underline{\hspace{1cm}}$$

(1) $9 + i$ (2) $8 - i$ (3) $a - bi$

1590 Perform the indicated operations

(1) $(-6 + 3i) - (7 - i)$ (2) $(1 + i) - (1 - i)$

(3) $(\sqrt{2} - 3i) - (3 + 2i)$ (4) $(a - 2i) - [(2a + 3i) + (5a - i)]$

(1) $-13 + 4i$ (2) $2i$ (3) $\sqrt{2} - 3 - 5i$ (4) $-6a - 4i$

1591 Write the following complex numbers in the ordered-pair notation:
(1) $A = 2i$ and (2) $B = 3 - i$. Write the difference $A - B$ (3) as an ordered pair, (4) then in the $a + bi$ form.

(1) $A = (0, 2)$ (2) $B = (3, -1)$
(3) $A - B = (-3, 3)$ (4) $A - B = -3 + 3i$

1592 Multiplication of complex numbers in the $a + bi$ form is defined thus:

$\quad \longleftarrow$

$$(a + bi)(c + di) = (ac - bd) + (bc + ad)i$$

As an aid to remembering this definition, think of multiplying the two binomials $(a + bi)$ and $(c + di)$, but at the final stage reduce the answer to standard complex form $a + bi$ by replacing i^2 with -1 and collecting terms:

$$(a + bi) \cdot (c + di) = ac + bci + adi + bdi^2$$
$$= ac + (bc + ad)i + bd(-1)$$
$$= (ac - bd) + (bc + ad)i$$

Find the product of $(2 + 3i) \cdot (4 + 8i)$

$$(2 + 3i) \cdot (4 + 8i) = 8 + 12i + 16i + 24i^2$$
$$= (8 - 24) + (12 + 16)i = -16 + 28i$$

1593   If we think of the complex number $a + bi$ as the ordered pair (a, b) and $c + di$ as the ordered pair (c, d), then multiplication is defined thus:

$$(a, b) \cdot (c, d) = (ac - bd, bc + ad)$$

(1) Find the product $(2 + 3i)(4 + 8i)$ by first changing to ordered pair notation. (2) Change the answer to standard complex form and compare the result with the answer shown above.

(1) $(2, 3)(4, 8) = (8 - 24, 12 + 16) = (-16, 28)$
(2) $-16 + 28i$

1594   Change the complex numbers $2 + 3i$ and $5 + 4i$ to the "ordered-pair form and compute the produt. Check by multiplication in the usual manner; express your answer in standard complex form.

$(2, 3) \cdot (5, 4) = (10 - 12, 15 + 8) = (-2, 23)$
$(2 + 3i)(5 + 4i) = 10 + 15i + 8i + 12i^2$
$\qquad\qquad = (10 - 12) + (15 + 8)i = -2 + 23i$

Note: In both results the *real* component is -2, and the *imaginary* component is 23.

1595   Find the products (1) $(-3 + 2i)(7 - 4i)$ and (2) $(6 - 4i)(2 - i)$. Perform the multiplications in either of the forms shown in frame 1594 but express your answer in $a + bi$ form.

(1) $-13 + 26i$ (2) $8 - 14i$

1596   Find the products (1) $(0 - 3i) \cdot (1 - 0i)$, (2) $(-3 + 2i) \cdot (2 + 0i)$, and (3) $4i \cdot (3i - 5)$.

(1) $(-3i) \cdot (1) = -3i$ or $0 - 3i - 0i + 0i = -3i$
(2) $-6 + 4i$ (3) $12i^2 - 20i = -12 - 20i$

1597   Find the products. Remember to change $\sqrt{-6}$ and $\sqrt{-2}$ to the i form before multiplying.
(1) $(3 - \sqrt{-6}) \cdot (4 + \sqrt{-2})$ (2) $(2 - i) \cdot (1 + 4i) \cdot (1 + i)$

(1) $(12 + 2\sqrt{3}) + (3\sqrt{2} - 4\sqrt{6})i$ (2) $-1 + 13i$

1598 (1) Expand $(5 - 2i)^2$. (2) Expand $(1 - i)^3$.

(1) 21 - 20i (2) -2 - 2i

1599 Let $A = 3 - i$, $B = 4 + 2i$. Find (1) $A + B$ (2) $A - B$ (3) $A \cdot B$
(4) $B + A$ (5) $B - A$, and (6) $B \cdot A$.

(1) $A + B = 7 + i$ (2) $A - B = -1 - 3i$ (3) $A \cdot B = 14 + 2i$
(4) $B + A = 7 + i$ (5) $B - A = 1 + 3i$ (6) $B \cdot A = 14 + 2i$

1600 (1) Expand $(a + bi)^2$. (2) Expand $(a - bi)^2$. (3) Find the product
$(a + bi) \cdot (a - bi)$.

(1) $a^2 - b^2 + 2abi$ (2) $a^2 - b^2 - 2abi$ (3) $a^2 + b^2$

1601 Find the products indicated: (1) $(2 + 0i)(5 - 3i)$, (2) $(2)(5 - 3i)$,
(3) $(a + 0i)(b + ci)$, and (4) $(a)(b + ci)$.

(1) 10 - 6i (2) 10 - 6i (3) $ab + aci$ (4) $ab + aci$

1602 Let $R = a + bi$ and $S = c + di$. (1) Find $R + S$. (2) Find $S + R$.
(3) Compare $(R + S)$ with $(S + R)$. Recall that an operation (such
as addition of real numbers) is a *commutative* operation if $a + b =
b + a$ for any choice of a and b. (4) Does your answer to question
(3) above indicate that addition of *complex* numbers is a *commutative* operation?

(1) $(a + c) + (b + d)i$ (2) $(c + a) + (d + b)i$
(3) $(R + S) = (S + R)$ (a, b, c, d represent real numbers; therefore, $a + c = c + a$, $b + d = d + b$.)
(4) yes   When R and S are written as ordered pairs $R = (a, b)$
and $S = (c, d)$, then $R + S = (a + c, b + d)$ and $S + R =
(c + a, d + b)$. It is evident again that $R + S = S + R$.

1603 Let $R = a + bi$ and $S = c + di$. (1) Find $R - S$. (2) Find $S - R$.
(3) Does $R - S = S - R$? (4) Is subtraction of complex numbers
a commutative operation?

(1) $(a - c) + (b - d)i$ (2) $(c - a) + (d - b)i$
(3) no   In general, if a, b, c, and d represent real numbers
$(a - c) \neq (c - a), (b - d) \neq (d - b)$
(4) no

1604 Let $R = a + bi$ and $S = c + di$. **(1)** Find $R \cdot S$ **(2)** Find $S \cdot R$.
(3) Does $R \cdot S = S \cdot R$? **(4)** Is multiplication of complex numbers a commutative operation?

(1) $(ac - bd) + (bc + ad)i$ **(2)** $(ca - db) + (da + cb)i$
(3) yes, If a, b, c, and d represent real numbers $ac = ca$,
$db = bd$, etc.
(4) yes

1605 Given $A = 1 - i$. **(1)** Write the negative of A(label it N). **(2)** Find the product of A and N. **(3)** Find the sum of A and N.

(1) $N = -(1 - i) = -1 + i$ **(2)** $A \cdot N = (1 - i)(-1 + i) = 2i$
(3) $A + N = (1 - i) + (-1 + i) = 0$

1606 Given $A = 1 - i$. **(1)** Write the conjugate of A (label it C). **(2)** Find the product of A and C. **(3)** Find the sum of A and C.

(1) $C = 1 + i$ **(2)** $A \cdot C = (1 - i)(1 + i) = 2$
(3) $A + C = (1 - i) + (1 + i) = 2$

1607 Is the product of a complex number and its conjugate a real number, a pure imaginary number, or a number having both a real and an imaginary part?

a real number

1608 Is the sum of a complex number and its conjugate a real number, a pure imaginary number, or a complex number having a real part and an imaginary part?

a real number

1609 Given $A = a + bi$. **(1)** Write the conjugate of A (label it C).
(2) Find the product of A and C. **(3)** Find the sum of A and C.
(4) Find the difference $A - C$.

(1) $C = a - bi$
(2) $A \cdot C = a^2 + b^2$ (This product is a *pure real* number.)
(3) $A + C = 2a$ (This sum is also a real number.)
(4) $A - C = 2bi$

1610 For the following questions identify your answer as a real, pure
imaginary, or complex number of the form $a + bi$ with $a \neq 0$ and
$b \neq 0$: (1) The difference of a complex number, $x + yi$, and its
conjugate. (2) The sum of $x + yi$ and its negative.

(1) pure imaginary   (2) real $[x + yi + (-x - yi) = 0]$

1611 *Division* of complex numbers is accomplished by writing the
indicated quotient as a fraction and then multiplying numerator and
denominator by the conjugate of the denominator. Thus $(a + bi) \div$
$(c + di)$ becomes

$$\frac{(a + bi)}{(c + di)} \cdot \frac{(c - di)}{(c - di)} = \frac{ac + bci - adi - bdi^2}{c^2 - d^2 i^2}$$

$$= \frac{(ac + bd) + (bc - ad)i}{c^2 + d^2}$$

When this answer is written in standard form we have

$$\frac{ac + bd}{c^2 + d^2} + \left(\frac{bc - ad}{c^2 + d^2}\right)i$$

Find the quotient $(4 + i) \div (4 + 3i)$

$\frac{19}{25} - \frac{8i}{25}$

Solution:

$$\frac{(4 + i)}{(4 + 3i)} \cdot \frac{4 - 3i}{4 - 3i} = \frac{16 + 4i - 12i - 3i^2}{16 - 9i^2}$$

$$= \frac{16 + 3 - 8i}{16 + 9} = \frac{19 - 8i}{25} = \frac{19}{25} - \frac{8i}{25}$$

1612 The following steps review the procedure for division of complex
numbers.
(1) Write the indicated division in fractional form.
(2) Multiply both numerator and denominator by the conjugate of
the denominator.
(3) Write the answer in $a + bi$ form.
Find the quotient of $3 + 2i$ divided by $1 - 3i$.

(1) $\frac{3 + 2i}{1 - 3i}$ (2) $\frac{3 + 2i}{1 - 3i} \cdot \frac{1 + 3i}{1 + 3i} = \frac{(3 - 6) + (2 + 9)i}{1 + 9} = \frac{-3 + 11i}{10}$

(3) $\frac{-3}{10} + \frac{11i}{10}$

1613   Find the quotient of $3 + 2i$ divided by $1 + 3i$.

$$\frac{3 + 2i}{1 + 3i} \cdot \frac{1 - 3i}{1 - 3i} = \frac{(3 + 6) + (2 - 9)i}{1 + 9} = \frac{9 - 7i}{10} = \frac{9}{10} - \frac{7i}{10}$$

1614   Find the quotient $\dfrac{1 + 2i}{3 - 4i}$

$$\frac{1 + 2i}{3 - 4i} \cdot \frac{3 + 4i}{3 + 4i} = \frac{(3 - 8) + (6 + 4)i}{9 + 16} = \frac{-5 + 10i}{25} = -\frac{1}{5} + \frac{2i}{25}$$

1615   Why is the conjugate of the denominator chosen as the multiplier in the division of complex numbers?

The product of a complex number and its conjugate is a real number. This enables us to express the denominator as a real number, and thus to report the quotient as a complex number in the $a + bi$ form.

1616   Perform the indicated division and write your answer in standard form.

$$\frac{2 - 3i}{4 + i}$$

$$\frac{2 - 3i}{4 + i} \cdot \frac{4 - i}{4 - i} = \frac{(8 - 3) + (-12 - 2)i}{16 + 1} = \frac{5 - 14i}{17} = \frac{5}{17} - \frac{14i}{17}$$

1617   Perform the indicated operation on the following problem and write your result in standard complex form.

$$\frac{1 - i}{1 + i}$$

$$\frac{1 - i}{1 + i} \cdot \frac{1 - i}{1 - i} = \frac{1 - 1 + (-1 - 1)i}{1 + 1} = \frac{0 - 2i}{2} = 0 - i = -i$$

1618   Reduce the following expression to standard complex form:

$$\frac{1}{(1 - i)^2}$$

$$\frac{1}{(1 - i)^2} = \frac{1}{-2i} = \frac{1 \cdot i}{-2i \cdot i} = \frac{i}{-2i^2} = \frac{i}{2}$$

1619   Find the quotient $(2 + i) \div (-1 + i)$

$$\frac{2 + i}{-1 + i} \cdot \frac{-1 - i}{-1 - i} = \frac{(-2 + 1) + (-1 - 2)i}{1 + 1} = \frac{-1 - 3i}{2} = \frac{-1}{2} - \frac{3}{2} i$$

Note: The conjugate of $-1 + i$ is $-1 - i$

1620   Simplify $\dfrac{(2 + i) \cdot (3 - 4i)}{(2 - i)}$

5

1621   If $x = (1 + i\sqrt{3})/2$, show that $x^3 + 1 = 0$

$$\left(\frac{1 + i\sqrt{3}}{2}\right)^3 = \left(\frac{1 + i\sqrt{3}}{2}\right)^2 \left(\frac{1 + i\sqrt{3}}{2}\right)$$

$$= \left(\frac{-1 + i\sqrt{3}}{2}\right)\left(\frac{1 + i\sqrt{3}}{2}\right) = -1$$

Therefore, $x^3 + 1 = (-1) + 1 = 0$

1622   Find the sum $(3 + 4i) + (-2 + i) + (6 + 0i) - (0 - 2i)$

$7 + 7i$

1623   Let $m = -\frac{1}{2} + i\frac{\sqrt{3}}{2}$ and $n = -\frac{1}{2} - i\sqrt{3}/2$. Show that $m \cdot n = 1$

$$\left(-\frac{1}{2} + i\frac{\sqrt{3}}{2}\right) \cdot \left(-\frac{1}{2} - \frac{i\sqrt{3}}{2}\right) = \left(\frac{1}{4} + \frac{3}{4}\right) + \left(\frac{-\sqrt{3}}{4} + \frac{\sqrt{3}}{4}\right)i = \frac{4}{4} = 1$$

1624   Let $m = -\frac{1}{2} + i\sqrt{3}/2$ and $n = -\frac{1}{2} - i\sqrt{3}/2$. Does $m^2 = n$?

yes
Solution:
$$m^2 = \left(-\frac{1}{2} + \frac{i\sqrt{3}}{2}\right)\left(-\frac{1}{2} + \frac{i\sqrt{3}}{2}\right) = \left(\frac{1}{4} - \frac{3}{4}\right) + \left(\frac{-\sqrt{3}}{4} - \frac{\sqrt{3}}{4}\right)i$$

$$= -\frac{1}{2} - \frac{\sqrt{3}}{2} i = -\frac{1}{2} - \frac{\sqrt{3}}{2} i$$

Therefore $m^2 = n$

1625   Let $m = -\frac{1}{2} + i\sqrt{3}/2$ and $n = -\frac{1}{2} - i\sqrt{3}/2$. Does $n^2 = m$?

> yes
>
> *Solution:*
>
> $$n = \left(-\frac{1}{2} - \frac{\sqrt{3}\,i}{2}\right) \cdot \left(-\frac{1}{2} - \frac{\sqrt{3}\,i}{2}\right) = \left(\frac{1}{4} - \frac{3}{4}\right) + \left(\frac{\sqrt{3}}{4} + \frac{\sqrt{3}}{4}\right)i$$
>
> $$= -\frac{1}{2} + \frac{\sqrt{3}}{2}\,i$$
>
> $$m = -\frac{1}{2} + \frac{\sqrt{3}}{2}\,i$$
>
> Therefore, $n^2 = m$

▽ **1626**   Find i when $n = 1, 2, 3, 4, \ldots, 12$.

> $i^1 = i$ (or $\sqrt{-1}$) $i^2 = -1$ $i^3 = -i$ $i^4 = 1$
>
> $i^5 = i$ $i^6 = -1$ $i^7 = -i$ $i^8 = 1$
>
> $i^9 = i$ $i^{10} = -1$ $i^{11} = -i$ $i^{12} = 1$

1627   Find the products **(1)** $(\sqrt{-6}) \cdot (\sqrt{-3})$ and **(2)** $(3i) \cdot (-4i) \cdot (2i) \cdot (-i)$.

> **(1)** $-\sqrt{18}$ or $-3\sqrt{2}$ **(2)** 24

1628   *Geometric representation of complex numbers.* If we return to the
idea of a complex number as an *ordered pair* of real numbers, we
can find a method of representing complex
numbers graphically. Recall that the complex
number $a + bi$ is written as the ordered pair
(a, b). We simply represent this number by
the point whose rectangular coordinates are
(a, b). $P(2, 3)$ represents the complex number $2 + 3i$. Write the following complex numbers as ordered pairs and locate the points
corresponding to them on a complex plane: $A = (4 + 7i)$, $B =$
$-2 + 3i$, and $C = -4 - 2$

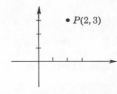

> $A = (4, 7)$ $B = (-2, 3)$ $C = (-4, -2)$

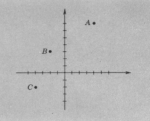

Comment

When the points of a plane are used to represent *complex* numbers, the plane is referred to as the *complex plane* [or the Argand plane in honor of the Swiss mathematician J. R. Argand (1768–1822)]. The horizontal (or x) axis is called the *real* axis, and the vertical (or y) axis is called the *imaginary* axis.

1629   Find the points corresponding to the following complex numbers on a complex plane: $A = 1 + 3i$, $B = -3 - i$, $C = 0 + 3i$, and $D = -4 + 0i$

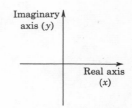

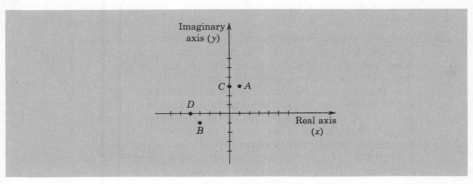

1630   1. You should notice that points representing numbers, $a + 0i$, all lie on the real axis. Locate the following: $A = 2 + 0i$, $B = -2 + 0i$, $C = 6 + 0i$, and $D = -5$.
        2. Notice also that points representing numbers, $0 + bi$, all lie on the imaginary (or y) axis. Locate the following: $E = 0 + 3i$, $F = -4i$, and $G = 6i$.

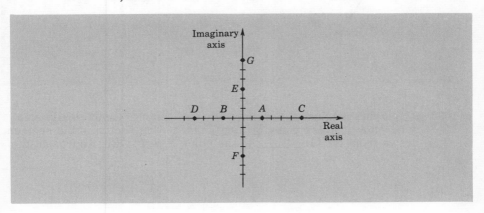

1631 An interesting exercise is to locate the points corresponding to i, $-i$, i^2, and $-i^2$ on a complex plane. First write these complex numbers in the $a + bi$ form (or in the ordered-pair form) and then plot them.

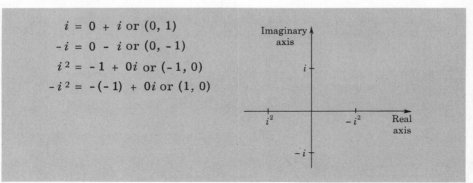

$$i = 0 + i \text{ or } (0, 1)$$
$$-i = 0 - i \text{ or } (0, -1)$$
$$i^2 = -1 + 0i \text{ or } (-1, 0)$$
$$-i^2 = -(-1) + 0i \text{ or } (1, 0)$$

1632 Let $P(a, b)$ represent the complex number $a + bi$. If we think of the segment drawn from the origin O to the point $P(a, b)$ as the *directed* line segment OP, then we say that the complex number $a + bi$ determines a *vector* **OP**. In fact, it is usually not the point $P(a, b)$ which we take as the geometric representation of the complex number but rather the directed segment OP, or vector **OP**, which joints the origin to the point P. Represent the complex number $-3 + 5i$ as a vector.

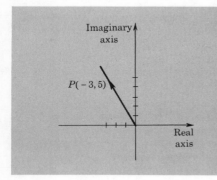

Recall that the symbol **OP** indicates that we are considering both the magnitude and direction of the segment OP.

1633 A complex number $a + bi$ may be represented geometrically as a point on a complex plane or as a *vector*. The vector is the segment drawn from the **(1)**_____ to the point $P(a, b)$. **(2)** Represent the

continued →

following complex numbers as vectors; show with arrowheads the direction of each vector: $A = 5 - i$, $B = -7 - 2i$, and $C = 3i$.

(1) origin (2)

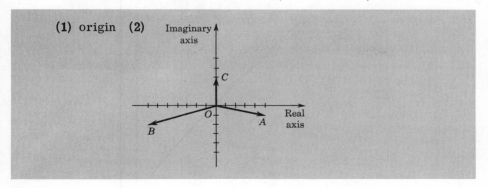

▽**1634** Complex numbers may be represented geometrically either as **(1)_____** or as **(2)_____** on a complex plane. The context of the problem will indicate which form to use. Represent the following complex numbers geometrically: $A = 1$, $B = -2 + i$, $C = -i$, and $D = 1 - 2i$. Make two sketches showing the two representations which you listed above.

(1) vectors   **(2) points**

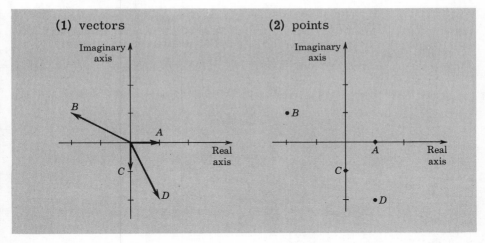

1635 Since complex numbers may be represented as vectors, addition of complex numbers has a simple geometric interpretation. Let $a + bi$ and $c + di$ be two complex numbers. We want to show how to represent their sum. Make a drawing similar to this one in the following way:

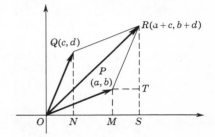

continued →

1. Draw the vectors **OP** and **OQ** representing $a + bi$ and $c + di$, respectively. *Note:* This is a general sketch. We have not assigned special values to a, b, c, and d.
2. From point P draw the vector **PR** having length and direction equal to **OQ**.
3. Draw vector **OR** and segment QR.

Our problem will be to prove that the vector **OR** represents the sum of vectors **OP** and **OQ**. The proof will be given in frames 1636 and 1639.

Your answer is a properly labeled drawing similar to the one in the problem.

1636 Add these lines to your drawing of frame 1635.
1. Draw perpendiculars from Q, P, and R to the x axis. Call them QN, PM, and RS, respectively.
2. Draw PT perpendicular to RS.

your answer is the drawing with the lines correctly drawn and labeled. Refer to the original drawing in frame 1635.

1637 Look at your drawing from frame 1636. In terms of a, b, c, and d indicate on your drawing the lengths of the following segments: $ON =$ **(1)**_____ , $QN =$ **(2)**_____ , $OM =$ **(3)**_____ , and $PM =$ **(4)**_____ .

(1) c
(2) d
(3) a
(4) b

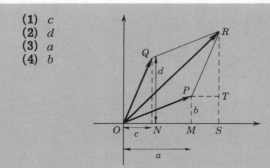

1638 Look at your drawing from frame 1637. In terms of a, b, c, and d, indicate the lengths of the following segments: $PT =$ **(1)**_____ , $MS =$ **(2)**_____ , $RT =$ **(3)**_____ , and $ST =$ **(4)**_____ . *Note:* We constructed the vector **PR** so that it was equivalent in length and direction to **OQ**.

(1) c **(2)** c **(3)** d **(4)** b

1639 Look at your drawing again. We want to show that vector **OR** represents the sum of the vectors **OP** and **OQ**. We must show that the vector **OR** has coordinates representing the sum of the complex numbers $(a + bi)$ and $(c + di)$, i.e., $(a + c) + (b + d)i$. **(1)** What are the lengths (in terms of a, b, c, and d) of **(a)** OS and **(b)** SR ? **(2)** What are the coordinates of point R ?

(1)(a) $OS = a + c$, **(b)** $SR = b + d$ **(2)** $(a + c, b + d)$

Summary: This answer verifies that we have represented geometrically the sum of the complex numbers $a + bi$ and $c + di$ when both vectors lie in quadrant I. (You might like to generalize the proof for vectors lying in any of the four quadrants.)

1640 We shall review the method used to find the sum of two complex numbers geometrically. (Refer to your drawing.)
1. The complex numbers are represented as vectors **OP** and **OQ**.
2. A vector **PR** is drawn at P which is equivalent to **OQ**.
3. A parallelogram is then formed by drawing a segment from Q to R.
4. Finally the vector **OR**, which is the diagonal of the parallelogram $OPQR$, is drawn. This we verified to be the sum of **OP** and **OQ**.

Find the sum of $3 + 2i$ and $-5 + 4i$ geometrically.

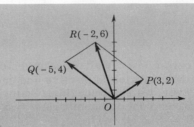

Note: $(3 + 2i) + (-5 + 5i) = (-2 + 6i)$ as shown in the diagram.

1641 The method used in frames 1635 to 1640 to find the sum of two complex numbers geometrically is often referred to as the

continued →

parallelogram law for addition. Find the sum geometrically of the complex numbers $(-6 + 2i)$ and $(-3 - 5i)$.

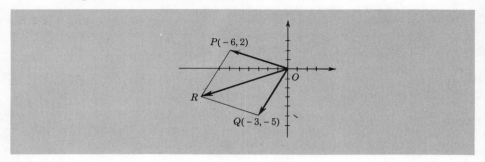

▽1642   Find the sum geometrically of $P + Q$ if $P = 3 + i$ and $Q = -1 - 5i$. Check by finding the algebraic sum S and locating this number on the complex plane.

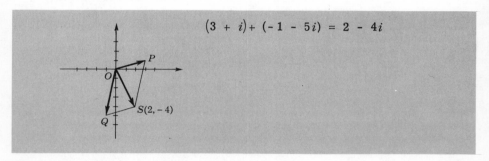

$$(3 + i) + (-1 - 5i) = 2 - 4i$$

▽1643   The parallelogram law for addition of vectors is important in working with vector quantities in physics and engineering. For the present, however, we shall consider examples without relating them to science. Given complex numbers $P = 5 + i$ and $Q = -3 + 2i$. Their sum $R = P + Q = $ (1)_____. (2) On a complex plane represent P, Q, and R as vectors.

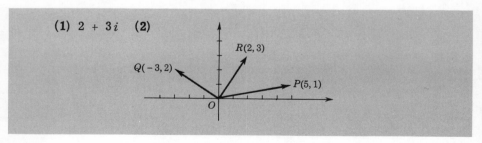

(1) $2 + 3i$ (2)

1644   (1) On your sketch from frame 1643, draw segments PR and RQ. In frames 1644 and 1648 we shall attempt to show that points O,

continued ➔

P, R, Q determine a parallelogram having segment OR as a diagonal. Use the distance formula to find the lengths of (2) OP and (3) RQ.

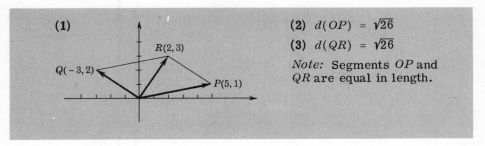

(1)

$R(2, 3)$

$Q(-3, 2)$

$P(5, 1)$

(2) $d(OP) = \sqrt{26}$

(3) $d(QR) = \sqrt{26}$

Note: Segments OP and QR are equal in length.

1645 Use the distance formula to obtain the lengths of (1) OQ and (2) PR in frame 1644.

(1) $d(OQ) = \sqrt{13}$ (2) $d(PR) = \sqrt{13}$

1646 Look at the drawing in frame 1643 (answer). Give a reason, based on the results of frames 1644 and 1645, telling how you know that $OPRQ$ is a parallelogram. *Note:* This concludes a demonstration that in this particular example, when the complex numbers P and Q and their algebraic sum R are represented geometrically as vectors, the vector **OR** is the diagonal of a parallelogram having vectors **OP** and **OQ** as two adjacent sides.

If the opposite sides of a quadrilateral are equal, the figure is a parallelogram.

1647 We can generalize the information regarding addition of complex numbers thus: let $P = a + bi$, $Q = c + di$, and $R = (a + c) + (b + d)i$, then

1. The vector representing the sum of the two complex numbers P and Q is the diagonal of a parallelogram whose adjacent sides are vectors representing the two numbers.
2. Conversely, the diagonal of a parallelogram whose sides represent the two complex numbers is the vector sum of the complex numbers.

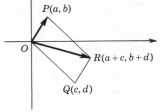

$P(a, b)$

O

$R(a + c, b + d)$

$Q(c, d)$

We have given a proof for statement 2 above. Now we shall construct a proof for statement 1.

continued →

Step 1. Make a sketch similar to the one in this frame in which vectors represent the complex numbers P, Q, and R.

Your sketch is the answer for this frame. The proof will continue in frame 1648.

1648 Look again at statement 1 in frame 1647.
Step 2. The theorem states that if $\mathbf{OP} + \mathbf{OQ} = \mathbf{OR}$, then
_____.

$OQRP$ is a parallelogram or OR is the diagonal of parallelogram $OQRP$

1649 Refer to your sketch from frame 1647.
Step 3. $OQRP$ is a parallelogram if what pairs of segments are equal?

$OP = QR, \quad OQ = PR$

1650 Take the coordinates of Q and R as given on your sketch; use the distance formula to **(1)** find the length of QR. **(2)** Compare the length of QR with the length of OP.

(1) length of $QR = \sqrt{(a + c - c)^2 + (b + d - d)^2} = \sqrt{a^2 + b^2}$

(2) length of $OP = \sqrt{a^2 + b^2}$; therefore, $OP = QR$

1651 In a similar manner **(1)** find the length of PR and **(2)** compare this length with the length of OQ.

(1) length of $PR = \sqrt{[(a + c) - a]^2 + [(b + d) - b]^2} = \sqrt{c^2 + d^2}$

(2) length of $OQ = \sqrt{c^2 + d^2}$; therefore, $OQ = PR$

1652 Look at frames 1647 to 1651.
Step 4. Quadrilateral $OQRP$ is a parallelogram. **(1)** Why?
Step 5. **(2)** Restate the theorem which you have proved.

(1) If a quadrilateral has its opposite sides equal, the figure is a parallelogram.
(2) The vector representing the sum of two complex numbers is the diagonal of a parallelogram whose adjacent sides are vectors representing the two numbers.

▽**1653**   **(1)** Find the sum geometrically of $P = 4 + 0i$ and $Q = 0 - 3i$; label it **OR**.   **(2)** Report the vector **OR** as a complex number in $a + bi$ form.

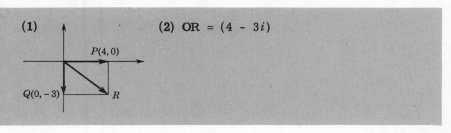

(1)   **(2) OR** = $(4 - 3i)$

1654   **(1)** Find the sum geometrically of $P + Q + S$ given $P = 3 + 5i$, $Q = -4 + 3i$, and $S = 6 - i$.   **(2)** Check by first finding the sum of $P + Q + S$ algebraically and then plotting this complex number as a vector.

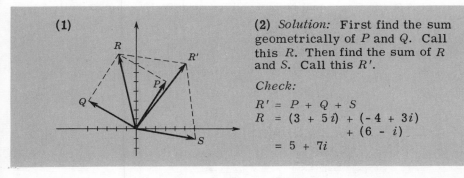

(1)

(2) *Solution:* First find the sum geometrically of P and Q. Call this R. Then find the sum of R and S. Call this R'.

Check:

$R' = P + Q + S$
$R = (3 + 5i) + (-4 + 3i)$
$\qquad\qquad + (6 - i)$
$\quad = 5 + 7i$

1655   Given $P = -5 + 0i$, $Q = 2 - 2i$.   **(1)** Find $R = P + Q$ algebraically.   **(2)** Represent P, Q, and R as vectors. Sketch the parallelogram of which **OR** is the diagonal.

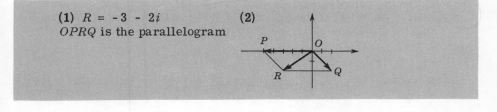

(1) $R = -3 - 2i$ **(2)**
$OPRQ$ is the parallelogram

1656 (1) What is the conjugate of the complex number $4 + 5i$? **(2)** Represent both $4 + 5i$ and its conjugate geometrically as vectors.

(1) conjugate $= 4 - 5i$ **(2)**

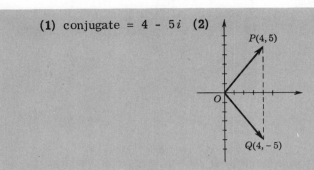

$P(4, 5)$

O

$Q(4, -5)$

1657 Given the complex number $A = 4 + 6i$. **(1)** What is the negative of A? **(2)** Represent both A and the negative N geometrically as vectors.

(1) $N = (4 + 6i) = -4 - 6i$ **(2)**

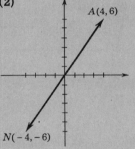

$A(4, 6)$

$N(-4, -6)$

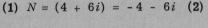

$A = 3 - i$

1658 Given the complex number $A = 3 + i$ **(1)** What is the conjugate of A? **(2)** What is the negative of A? **(3)** Represent A, the conjugate, and the negative geometrically.

(1) $C = 3 + i$ **(2)** $N = -3 + i$ **(3)**

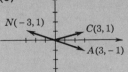

$N(-3, 1)$

$C(3, 1)$

$A(3, -1)$

▽**1659** Given the complex number $A = -3i$. **(1)** What is the negative of A ? **(2)** What is the conjugate of A ? Represent all three geometrically.

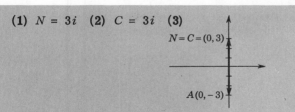

(1) $N = 3i$ **(2)** $C = 3i$ **(3)**

$N = C = (0, 3)$

$A(0, -3)$

1660 **(1)** Find the algebraic sum S of the complex numbers $P = (7 - 3i)$ and $Q = (2 + 3i)$. **(2)** Show P, Q, and S as vectors. Complete the parallelogram which these three vectors determine.

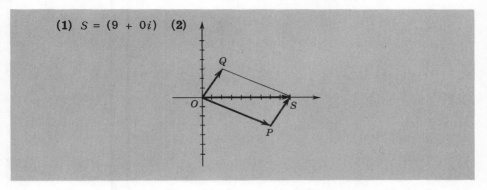

(1) $S = (9 + 0i)$ **(2)**

Q

O S

P

1661 Given vectors P and Q as in frame 1660. Represent P, $-Q$, and $S' = P + (-Q)$ as vectors. Complete the parallelogram which these vectors determine.

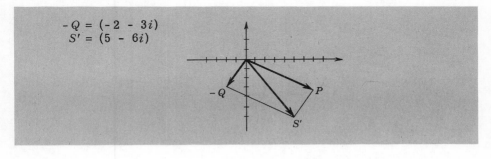

$-Q = (-2 - 3i)$
$S' = (5 - 6i)$

$-Q$ P

S'

1662 Find the sum geometrically of $(7 - 8i)$ and $(2 + 4i)$ in the following manner: .
   (1) Represent $(7 - 8i)$ as a vector **OP**. Represent $(2 + 4i)$ as a vector **PR** *starting at P*.
   (2) Indicate the vector which represents their sum.

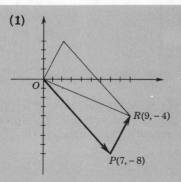

(1)   **(2) OR** is the sum

$R(9, -4)$

$P(7, -8)$

▽**1663** Find the value of x and of y for which the following statement is true: $(x + iy) \cdot (3 - 2i) = 8 - i$. Recall that two complex numbers $a + bi$ and $c + di$ are equal if and only if $a = c$ and $b = d$.

$x = 2, \quad y = 1$

Solution: *Check:*

Given $(x + iy) \cdot (3 - 2i) = 8 - i$ $(2 + i) \cdot (3 - 2i) = 8 - i$
          $a \quad + \quad bi \qquad\quad c + di$ $8 - i = 8 - i$

$\overbrace{3x + 2y} + \overbrace{(3y - 2x)i} = \overbrace{8 - i}$

Therefore, $a = c \leftrightarrow 3x + 2y = 8$
                 $b = d \leftrightarrow -2x + 3y = -1$
                                      $x = 2$
                                      $y = 1$

▽**1664** Find the value of x and of y for which the following statement is true: $(x + 11i)/(3 - 2i) = 2 + iy$

$x = 16, \quad y = 5$

Solution: Given $\dfrac{x + 11i}{3 - 2i} = 2 + iy$

$x + 11i = 6 + 2y - 4i + 3iy$ Multiply both members of
         $= 6 + 2y + (3y - 4)i$ the equation by $3 - 2i$

continued →

$$a = c \leftrightarrow x = 6 + 2y, \quad b = d \leftrightarrow 11 = 3y - 4, 5 = y, 16 = x$$

Check: $\dfrac{16 + 11i}{3 - 2i} = 2 + 5i$

$$\dfrac{16 + 11i}{3 - 2i} \cdot \dfrac{3 + 2i}{3 + 2i} = 2 + 5i$$

1665 Find a complex number z in the $a + bi$ form such that $3 - i + 3z = 18$. *Suggestion:* Solve the equation for z.

$z = 5 + \frac{1}{3}i$

Solution: $3 - i + 3z = 18, 3z = 15 + i, z = 5 + \frac{1}{3}i$

▽**1666** Find a complex number z in the $a + bi$ form such that $8i - z + 5 = (2i - 1)z$.

$z = 4 - \frac{5}{2}i$

Solution: $8i - z + 5 = (2i - 1)z = 2iz - z, 8i + 5 = 2iz,$

$$\dfrac{8i + 5}{2i} = z, \dfrac{8i + 5}{2i} \cdot \dfrac{i}{i} = \dfrac{-8 + 5i}{-2} = z, 4 - \frac{5}{2}i = z$$

1667 Perform the indicated operation algebraically in the following problem. Express your answer in $a + bi$ form.

$$\dfrac{2 + 7i}{1 + i}$$

$$\dfrac{2 + 7i}{1 + i} \cdot \dfrac{1 - i}{1 - i} = \dfrac{(2 + 7) + (7 - 2)i}{1 + 1} = \dfrac{9 + 5i}{2} = \dfrac{9}{2} + \dfrac{5i}{2}$$

1668 If $x + 2i = 3 + iy$, what are the values of x and y?

$x = 3, \quad y = 2$

1669 If $3 + 2iy = 3x - 4i$, what are the values of x and y?

$x = 1, \quad y = -2$

1670 If $2x + y + 5i = 5 + (3x - y)i$, what are the values of x and y?

> $x = 2, \quad y = 1$
>
> *Solution:* The definition for equality of complex numbers gives a pair of equations in x and y.
>
> $$a \quad + \; bi = c + \quad di$$
>
> Given $\overbrace{2x + y} + \overbrace{5i} = \overbrace{5} + \overbrace{(3x - y)i}$
>
> Therefore, $a = c \leftrightarrow 2x + y = 5$, $b = d \leftrightarrow 3x - y = 5$
>
> $\quad 5x = 10, x = 2$ and $4 + y = 5, y = 1$
>
> *Check:* $4 + 1 + 5i = 5 + (6 - 1)i$
> $\qquad\qquad 5 + 5i = 5 + 5i$

1671 Find the **(1)** sum $A + B$, **(2)** difference $A - B$, **(3)** product $A \cdot B$, and **(4)** quotient A/B of the complex numbers $A = 1 + i$ and $B = 1 - i$.

> **(1)** $A + B = 2$ **(2)** $A - B = 2i$ **(3)** $A \cdot B = 2$ **(4)** $\dfrac{A}{B} = i$

1672 Express the quotient of the following problems in standard form:

$$\frac{3 - 2i}{2 - i} = \textbf{(1)} \underline{\hspace{3cm}}$$

$$\frac{3 - 2i}{2} = \textbf{(2)} \underline{\hspace{3cm}}$$

$$\frac{3 - 2i}{i} = \textbf{(3)} \underline{\hspace{3cm}}$$

> **(1)** $\frac{8}{5} - \frac{1}{5}i$ **(2)** $\frac{3}{2} - i$ **(3)** $-2 - 3i$

1673 If we want to multiply, divide, raise to powers, or find roots of complex numbers, there is another form of representation which makes these computations easier. This is the *trigonometric* or *polar* form. Recall that a point P on a plane can be labeled in rectangular form as
(1) $P(\underline{\hspace{1cm}}, \underline{\hspace{1cm}})$ or in polar form as
(2) $P(\underline{\hspace{1cm}}, \underline{\hspace{1cm}})$.

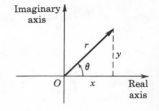

> **(1)** $P(x, y)$ **(2)** $P(r, \theta)$

1674 Given the complex number $A = (5 + 2i)$. **(1)** Make a sketch in which this complex number is represented as a vector. The rectangular co-ordinates of A are **(2)** (____, ____). **(3)** Find the numerical values for r and θ which indicate the polar components of point A.

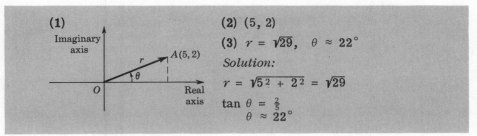

(1)

Imaginary axis

r $A(5,2)$

θ

O Real axis

(2) (5, 2)

(3) $r = \sqrt{29}$, $\theta \approx 22°$

Solution:

$r = \sqrt{5^2 + 2^2} = \sqrt{29}$

$\tan \theta = \frac{2}{5}$

$\theta \approx 22°$

1675 The polar form of a complex number $a + bi$ involves the polar coordinates corresponding to the rectangular coordinates (a, b). If we want to express a and b in terms of r and θ, we may apply the definitions of the sine and cosine of an angle thus: $\sin \theta = b/r$ and $\cos \theta = a/r$. Therefore, $b = $ **(1)**_____, and $a = $ **(2)**_____. Now when we substitute these values for a and b, we can see that $a + bi = $ **(3)**_____ + _____.

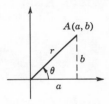

$A(a,b)$

r b

θ

a

(1) $r \sin \theta$ **(2)** $r \cos \theta$ **(3)** $r \cos \theta + ir \sin \theta$

1676 In frame 1675 we found that $r \cos \theta + ir \sin \theta$ was the polar form of a *complex number*, $a + bi$. If you are given the complex number $3 + 2i$ and you want to represent it in its polar form, you must first compute **(1)**____ and **(2)**____. **(3)** Do this. **(4)** Then write the complex number $3 + 2i$ in polar form.

(1) r **(2)** θ **(3)** $r = \sqrt{13}$, $\theta \approx 34°$

(4) $3 + 2i = \sqrt{13} \cos 34° + i\sqrt{13} \sin 34°$

or $= \sqrt{13} (\cos 34° + i \sin 34°)$

1677 Any complex number $(a + bi)$ may be changed
to the polar form. There are two steps
necessary:
1. Find a substitution for a in terms of r
   and θ.
2. Find a substitution for b in terms of r
   and θ.
(1) What are these substitutions? **(2)** Write
the polar form of a complex number.

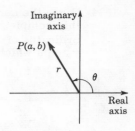

(1) $a = r\cos\theta,\ b = r\sin\theta$
(2) $r\cos\theta + ir\sin\theta$ or $r(\cos\theta + i\sin\theta)$

1678 Refer to frame 1677. **(1)** How do you find r when a and b are known?
(2) How do you find θ when a and b are known?

(1) $r = \sqrt{a^2 + b^2}$ **(2)** $\tan\theta = \dfrac{b}{a}$

▽**1679** Complete the steps necessary to express
$P(1 + \sqrt{3}i)$ in the form $r\cos\theta + ir\sin\theta$.

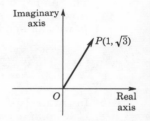

$r = \sqrt{1 + (\sqrt{3})^2} = 2,\quad \tan\theta = \dfrac{\sqrt{3}}{1},\ \theta = 60°$

$(1 + \sqrt{3}i) = 2\cos 60 + 2i\sin 60°$ or $= 2(\cos 60 + i\sin 60°)$

1680 Sometimes we refer to r as the *absolute
value* (or the modulus) of the complex number $r(\cos\theta + i\sin\theta)$. *Note: Absolute
value* is an appropriate name since r represents the *length* of the segment OP, and we
have agreed that length shall be a nonnegative
quantity. **(1)** What is the absolute value of
the complex number $3(\cos 30° + i\sin 30°)$?
(2) What information does the absolute value
give you regarding point P?

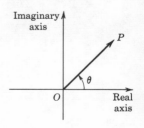

(1) 3   **(2)** P is 3 units from O or the length of OP is 3

1681 *Modulus* (or **(1)**_____) is the name for the component r of a complex number in polar form. Identify the modulus for each of the following complex numbers: **(2)** $6 \cos (\pi/2) + 6i \sin (\pi/2)$, **(3)** $a(\cos \theta + i \sin \theta)$, and **(4)** $\cos 40° + i \sin 40°$.

> **(1)** absolute value   **(2)** 6   **(3)** a **(4)** 1

1682 Component r of a complex number may be called either the **(1)**_____ or the **(2)**_____ of the number. **(3)** Write a complex number in polar form in which the modulus is 5 and θ is $45°$.

> **(1)** absolute value   **(2)** modulus
> **(3)** $5 \cos 45° + 5i \sin 45°$ or $5(\cos 45° + i \sin 45°)$

1683 In this sketch the **(1)**_____ _____ of the complex number is 2. **(2)** Write the complex number in polar form.

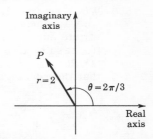

> **(1)** modulus or absolute value   **(2)** $2(\cos \dfrac{2\pi}{3} + i \sin \dfrac{2\pi}{3})$

1684 The angle θ which the radius vector **OP** makes with the positive x axis is called the *amplitude* (or argument) of the complex number $r(\cos \theta + i \sin \theta)$. **(1)** Indicate the complex number which is represented in the sketch in its polar form. $50°$ is the **(2)**_____ of this complex number. 4 is the **(3)**_____ _____ of this complex number.

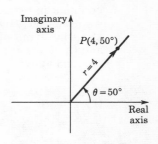

> **(1)** $4(\cos 50° + i \sin 50°)$ **(2)** amplitude or argument
> **(3)** absolute value or modulus

▽1685   A complex number in its polar form has argument $5\pi/6$ and
modulus 2. **(1)** Write this number in its polar form. **(2)** Make a
sketch representing the number graphically.

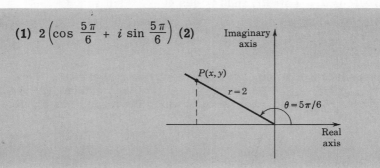

(1) $2\left(\cos \dfrac{5\pi}{6} + i \sin \dfrac{5\pi}{6}\right)$ **(2)**

1686   When we are given the polar form $2[\cos (5\pi/6) + i\sin (5\pi/6)]$ and
we want the rectangular form of a complex number, we may substitute numerical values for $\cos (5\pi/6)$ and $\sin (5\pi/6)$ and simplify
the result. Copy the entire equation as you answer. Thus
(1) $2(\_\_\_ + i\_\_\_) = _____$. From your answer you can see
that the rectangular components are $x =$ **(2)** _____ and $y =$
(3) _____ .

(1) $2 \cdot \dfrac{-\sqrt{3}}{2} + i \cdot \dfrac{1}{2} = -\sqrt{3} + i$ **(2)** $-\sqrt{3}$ **(3)** 1

1687   If we are given the modulus and argument
as 2 and $3\pi/4$, respectively, we may find
x directly by using the definition of
cosine θ in terms of x and r; similarly
we may find y by using the definition of
$\sin \theta$ in terms of y and r. Find **(1)** x
and **(2)** y for the complex number described above.

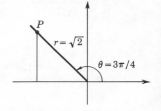

(1) $x = -1$
Solution: $\cos \theta = \dfrac{x}{r}$, $\cos \dfrac{3\pi}{4} = \dfrac{x}{\sqrt{2}}$, $\sqrt{2}\,\dfrac{-1}{\sqrt{2}} = x$, $-1 = x$

(2) $y = 1$
Solution: $\sin \theta = \dfrac{y}{r}$, $\sin \dfrac{3\pi}{4} = \dfrac{y}{\sqrt{2}}$, $\sqrt{2}\,\dfrac{1}{\sqrt{2}} = y$, $1 = y$

▽**1688** If a complex number has $r = \sqrt{2}$ and $\theta = 5\pi/4$, we say that its
(1)_____ is $\sqrt{2}$ and that its **(2)** _____
_____ is $5\pi/4$. The complex number whose polar coordinates are ($\sqrt{2}$, $5\pi/4$) is written **(3)**_____
in polar form.

---

(1) absolute value or modulus   **(2)** amplitude or argument

(3) $\sqrt{2}\left(\cos \frac{5\pi}{4} + i \sin \frac{5\pi}{4}\right)$

1689 Represent this complex number graphically: $\sqrt{2}\,[\cos(5\pi/4) + i \sin(5\pi/4)]$.

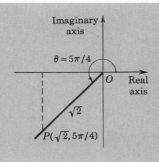

▽**1690** Change this complex number to rectangular form: $\sqrt{2}\,[\cos(5\pi/4) + i \sin(5\pi/4)]$.

$-1 - i$

Solution:

$$\cos \theta = \frac{a}{r} \qquad \cos \frac{5\pi}{4} = \frac{a}{\sqrt{2}} \qquad a = \sqrt{2}\cdot\frac{-1}{\sqrt{2}} = -1$$

$$\sin \theta = \frac{b}{r} \qquad \sin \frac{5\pi}{4} = \frac{b}{\sqrt{2}} \qquad b = \sqrt{2}\cdot\frac{-1}{\sqrt{2}} = -1$$

Therefore, $a + bi = -1 + (-1)i = -1 - i$

1691 Check the problem in frame 1690 by starting with the rectangular
form $a + bi = -1 - i$ and finding the polar form. $r = $ **(1)**_____
and $\theta = $ **(2)**_____. Therefore, **(3)** $a + bi = $ _____(cos _____ +
i sin _____)(copy the entire equation as you answer).

---

(1) $\sqrt{2}$ **(2)** $\dfrac{5\pi}{4}$ **(3)** $a + bi = \sqrt{2}\left(\cos \frac{5\pi}{4} + i \sin \frac{5\pi}{4}\right)$

continued →

Solution:
$$r = \sqrt{(-1)^2 + (-1)^2} = \sqrt{2}$$
$$\tan x = \frac{-1}{-1} = 1, \ x = 45° \text{ or } \frac{\pi}{4}, \ \theta = \pi + \frac{\pi}{4} = \frac{5\pi}{4}$$
Therefore, $-1 - i = \sqrt{2}\left(\cos \frac{5\pi}{4} + i \sin \frac{5\pi}{4}\right)$

1692 Find the **(1)** absolute value and the **(2)** argument for the complex number $15 - 8i$. **(3)** Write the number in polar form.

(1) $r = 17$ **(2)** $\theta \approx 332°$ **(3)** $17(\cos 332° + i \sin 332°)$

▽**1693** You should remember how to derive the polar form of a complex number from the $a + bi$ form. Let a and b represent the rectangular components of a complex number and r and θ represent the polar components. Using the sketch shown here, complete the statement below to show that $a + bi = r \cos \theta + ir \sin \theta$.

$\cos \theta = $ **(1)**_____ $/r$
Therefore, $r \cos \theta = $ **(2)**_____

$\sin \theta = $ **(3)**_____ $/r$
Therefore, $r \sin \theta = $ **(4)**_____

$ir \sin \theta = $ **(5)**_____

Add Steps **(2)** and **(5)**, **(6)**_____ = _____

(1) a **(2)** a **(3)** b **(4)** b **(5)** bi

(6) $r \cos \theta + ir \sin \theta = a + bi$

▽**1694** If you start with the polar form $r(\cos \theta + i \sin \theta)$, you should be able to show how to "get back" to the rectangular form $a + bi$ for any complex number. Make a sketch and show how you would do this.

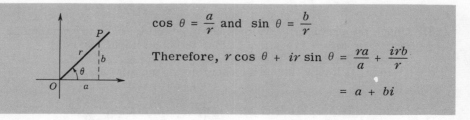

$\cos \theta = \dfrac{a}{r}$ and $\sin \theta = \dfrac{b}{r}$

Therefore, $r \cos \theta + ir \sin \theta = \dfrac{ra}{a} + \dfrac{irb}{r}$

$= a + bi$

1695 Caution must be taken in deciding the particular value of θ to use when transforming a complex number from rectangular to polar form. If tan θ is positive, then θ may be an angle terminating in either quadrant **(1)**_____ or **(2)**_____. For example, given the complex number $-4 - 3i$, we can find the amplitude thus: tan $\theta = -3/-4 = 0.750$. **(3)** Is the amplitude $37°$ or $217°$?

(1) I **(2)** III

(3) If the rectangular coordinates are $(-4, -3)$, then θ terminates in quadrant III.

$$\theta \approx 180° + 37° \approx 217°$$

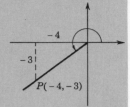

1696 The signs on the (x, y) coordinates of a point P determine the quadrant in which the point lies when you represent P graphically. To be sure that the amplitude of a complex number is correct when you are transferring from rectangular to polar form, you must note in which quadrant the radius vector will lie. Sketch the two complex numbers **(1)** $10 + 9i$ and **(2)** $-10 - 9i$ and give the amplitude for each.

(1)

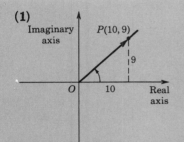

$$\tan \theta = \tfrac{9}{10} = 0.900$$
$$\theta \approx 42°$$

(2)

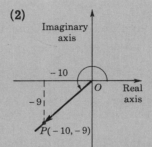

$$\tan \theta = \frac{-9}{-10} = 0.900$$
$$\theta \approx 42° + 180$$
$$\theta \approx 222°$$

1697 If tan θ is negative, then θ may be an angle terminating in quadrant
(1)_____ or (2)_____. Sketch the two complex numbers (3)_____
$(-10 + 9i)$ and (4) $(10 - 9i)$.

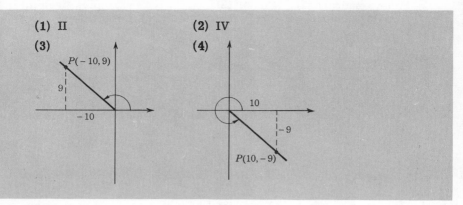

(1) II   (2) IV
(3)   (4)

1698 Find the amplitude for the complex number $(-10 + 9i)$.

$\theta \approx 138°$

Solution: $\tan \theta = \dfrac{9}{-10} = -0.900, \theta \approx 180° - 42° \approx 138°$

1699 Find the amplitude for the complex number $(10 - 9i)$.

$\theta \approx 318°$

Solution: $\tan \theta = -\frac{9}{10} = -0.900$

$\theta \approx 138° + 180° \approx 318°$ or $\theta \approx 360° - 42° \approx 318°$

1700 You know that $(10 - 9i)$ has amplitude $\theta = 318°$. Now (1) find the absolute value of $10 - 9i$ and (2) write this complex number in polar form.

(1) $r = \sqrt{a^2 + b^2} = \sqrt{10^2 + (-9)^2} = \sqrt{181}$

(2) $10 - 9i = \sqrt{181} (\cos 318° + i \sin 318°)$

1701   Take the four complex numbers $P_1 = 10 + 9i$, $P_2 = -10 + 9i$, $P_3 = -10 - 9i$, and $P_4 = 10 - 9i$. Each has absolute value $r =$ **(1)**_____. The amplitude of $P_1 = $ **(2)**_____, $P_2 = $ **(3)**_____, $P_3 = $ **(4)**_____, and $P_4 = $ **(5)**_____.

(1) $r = \sqrt{181}$ **(2)** $42°$ **(3)** $138°$ **(4)** $222°$ **(5)** $318°$
Note: There is an angle terminating in each quadrant.

1702   Write each of the complex numbers in frame 1701 in polar form. On one coordinate system represent these four numbers.

$P_1 = \sqrt{181} (\cos 42° + i \sin 42°)$
$P_2 = \sqrt{181} (\cos 138° + i \sin 138°)$
$P_3 = \sqrt{181} (\cos 220° + i \sin 222°)$
$P_4 = \sqrt{181} (\cos 318° + i \sin 318°)$

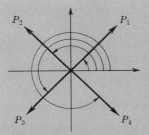

1703   Find the **(1)** absolute value and **(2)** argument of the complex number $1 - i\sqrt{3}$.

(1) 2   **(2)** $300°$ or $\dfrac{5\pi}{3}$

1704   Find the **(1)** modulus and **(2)** argument for the complex number $-7 + 24i$, and **(3)** write the number in polar form.

(1) 25   **(2)** $106°$ **(3)** $25 (\cos 106° + i \sin 106°)$

Solution: modulus $= r = \sqrt{(-7)^2 + 24^2} = 25$

argument $= \theta$,

$$\tan \theta = \frac{24}{-7} = -3.43$$

$$\theta \approx 180 - 74° = 106°$$

$-7 + 24i = 25 (\cos 106° + i \sin 106°)$

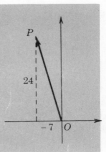

1705   Given the complex number $-4 - 4i$, find its polar form.

$4\sqrt{2}\left(\cos\dfrac{5\pi}{4} + i\sin\dfrac{5\pi}{4}\right)$

Solution: $r = \sqrt{(-4)^2 + (-4)^2} = \sqrt{32} = 4\sqrt{2}$

$\tan\theta = \dfrac{-4}{-4} = 1, \theta = 180° + 45° = 225°$ or $\dfrac{5\pi}{4}$

$-4 - 4i = 4\sqrt{2}\left(\cos\dfrac{5\pi}{4} + i\sin\dfrac{5\pi}{4}\right)$

1706   Change $\sqrt{3}[\cos(5\pi/6) + i\sin(5\pi/6)]$ to rectangular form.

$\sqrt{3}\left(-\dfrac{\sqrt{3}}{2} + \dfrac{1}{2}i\right)$ Therefore, $a + bi = \dfrac{-3}{2} + \dfrac{\sqrt{3}}{2}i$

1707   Given $r = 5, \theta = \pi$, write the complex number in **(1)** the polar form which this information determines. Then write its **(2)** $a + bi$ **form.**

(1) $5(\cos\pi + i\sin\pi)$ **(2)** $-5 + 0i$ or -5

1708   **(1)** Change this complex number to rectangular form: $\sqrt{3}[\cos(11\pi/6) + i\sin(11\pi/6)]$. **(2)** Make a sketch.

(1) $\dfrac{3}{2} - \dfrac{\sqrt{3}}{2}i$ **(2)**

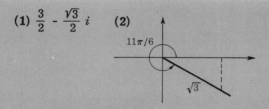

1709   Find the **(1)** absolute value and **(2)** amplitude for the complex number $3/2 - (\sqrt{3}/2)i$ **(3)** Write the number in polar form.

(1) $\sqrt{3}$ **(2)** $330°$ or $\dfrac{11\pi}{6}$

(3) $r(\cos\theta + i\sin\theta) = \sqrt{3}\left(\cos\dfrac{11\pi}{6} + i\sin\dfrac{11\pi}{6}\right)$

1710 Change the complex number $-3/2 - (\sqrt{3}/2)i$ to polar form.

$$r(\cos\theta + i\sin\theta) = \sqrt{3}\left(\cos\frac{7\pi}{6} + i\sin\frac{7\pi}{6}\right)$$

Solution: $r = \sqrt{\left(\frac{-3}{2}\right)^2 + \left(\frac{-\sqrt{3}}{2}\right)^2} = \sqrt{\frac{9}{4} + \frac{3}{4}} = \sqrt{3}$

$\tan\theta = \frac{-\sqrt{3}/2}{3/-2} = \frac{\sqrt{3}}{3}$, $\theta = 180° + 30 = 210°$ or $\frac{7\pi}{6}$

$r(\cos\theta + i\sin\theta) = \sqrt{3}\left(\cos\frac{7\pi}{6} + i\sin\frac{7\pi}{6}\right)$

1711 Change $\sqrt{3}[\cos(\pi/6) + i\sin(\pi/6)]$ to rectangular form.

$\frac{3}{2} + \frac{\sqrt{3}}{2}i$

1712 Refer to the graph of:

$P_1 = \sqrt{3}\left(\cos\frac{\pi}{6} + i\sin\frac{\pi}{6}\right)$

$P_2 = \sqrt{3}\left(\cos\frac{5\pi}{6} + i\sin\frac{5\pi}{6}\right)$

$P_3 = \sqrt{3}\left(\cos\frac{7\pi}{6} + i\sin\frac{7\pi}{6}\right)$

$P_4 = \sqrt{3}\left(\cos\frac{11\pi}{6} + i\sin\frac{11\pi}{6}\right)$

Describe in words how two conjugate complex numbers are located with respect to each other.

Two conjugate complex numbers are reflections of each other with respect to the real axis. (They are located symmetrically with respect to the real axis.) P_1 and P_4 are conjugates; also P_2 and P_3.

1713 Refer to the graph of P_1, P_2, P_3, and P_4 in frame 1712. Describe in words how a complex number and its negative are located with respect to each other.

The vector representing the negative of a complex number is the extension of the segment OP in the opposite direction through the origin a length equal to OP_1. (The point P_1 representing the negative of the complex number P_1 is diametrically opposite the point P_1 which represents the number P_1.)

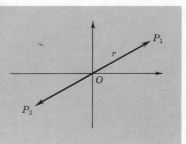

1714 One last remark about the complex numbers P_1, P_2, P_3, and P_4. When these numbers are represented in polar form,

$$P_1 = \sqrt{3}\left(\cos\frac{\pi}{6} + i\sin\frac{\pi}{6}\right)$$

$$P_2 = \sqrt{3}\left(\cos\frac{5\pi}{6} + i\sin\frac{5\pi}{6}\right) \quad \text{etc.}$$

You can see that the points P_1, P_2, P_3, and P_4 all lie on a circle whose radius is **(1)**_____. Or, thinking of the complex numbers as vectors, each vector represents a radius of the circle with center at the origin and radius equal to **(2)**_____.

(1) $\sqrt{3}$ **(2)** $\sqrt{3}$

1715 Write the polar form for the complex number $2i$.

$$2i = 2\left(\cos\frac{\pi}{2} + i\sin\frac{\pi}{2}\right)$$

Solution:

$a = 0$, $b = 2$

$r = \sqrt{0 + 2^2} = 2$

$\sin\theta = \dfrac{2}{2} = 1$ (see note)

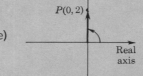

$\theta = \dfrac{\pi}{2}$ or $90°$

$$2i = 2\left(\cos\frac{\pi}{2} + i\sin\frac{\pi}{2}\right)$$

Note: $\theta = \pi/2$ is an angle whose tangent is undefined; i.e., $\tan(\pi/2) = 2/0$ undefined.

1716   Find the polar form for the complex number 4. Make a sketch.

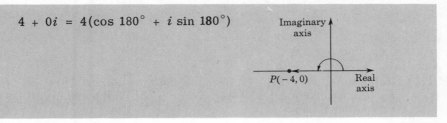

$$4 + 0i = 4(\cos 0° + i \sin 0°)$$

1717   Write the polar form for the complex number - 4. Make a sketch.

$$4 + 0i = 4(\cos 180° + i \sin 180°)$$

1718   If you know the rectangular coordinates a and b of a complex number $a + bi$, how do you find the absolute value of the complex number?

$$r = \text{absolute value of } a + bi = \sqrt{a^2 + b^2}$$

1719   If you know the rectangular coordinates a and b of a complex number $a + bi$, how do you find the amplitude of the complex number?

θ = amplitude of the complex number $a + bi$
 = the angle whose tangent is b/a.

1720   Write the polar form of the complex number $1 - i\sqrt{3}$.

$$1 - i\sqrt{3} = 2\left(\cos \frac{5\pi}{3} + i \sin \frac{5\pi}{3}\right)$$

or

$$1 - i\sqrt{3} = 2(\cos 300° + i \sin 300°)$$

1721 Plot the following four complex numbers on one rectangular co-ordinate system: $P_1 = \frac{3}{2} + (\sqrt{3}/2)i$, $P_2 = -\frac{3}{2} + (\sqrt{3}/2)i$, $P_3 = -\frac{3}{2} - (\sqrt{3}/2)i$, and $P_4 = \frac{3}{2} - (\sqrt{3}/2)i$.

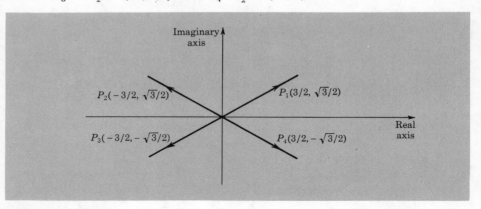

1722 Refer to frame 1721. **(1)** Which of the complex numbers, P_1, P_2, P_3, P_4, are conjugates of each other? **(2)** Which are negatives of each other?

(1) P_1 and P_4, P_2 and P_3 **(2)** P_1 and P_3, P_2 and P_4

1723 Given $A = 3 + 2i$, let $B =$ the conjugate of A. Find **(1)** $A + B$, **(2)** $A - B$, **(3)** $A \cdot B$, and **(4)** $A \div B$.

(1) $A + B = 6$ **(2)** $A - B = 4i$ **(3)** $A \cdot B = 13$

(4) $A \div B = \dfrac{5 + 12i}{13}$

1724 We mentioned earlier that the polar form is better for certain operations with complex numbers; multiplication is one such operation. Your work in frames 1724 to 1726 will be to derive a formula for multiplication of complex numbers in polar form. Let $A = r(\cos \alpha + i \sin \beta)$ and $B = r_1(\cos \alpha + i \sin \beta)$, then

$$A \cdot B = r \cdot r_1 (\cos \alpha + i \sin \beta)(\cos \alpha + i \sin \beta)$$

Carry out the multiplication indicated above and simplify your result.

$A \cdot B = r \cdot r_1 [(\cos \alpha \cos \beta + i^2 \sin \alpha \sin \beta)$
$\quad\quad + i(\sin \alpha \cos \beta + \cos \alpha \sin \beta)]$

$\quad\quad = r \cdot r_1 [(\cos \alpha \cos \beta - \sin \alpha \sin \beta)$
$\quad\quad\quad + i(\sin \alpha \cos \beta + \cos \alpha \sin \beta)]$

See frame 1725 for further simplification.

1725 Examine the expressions enclosed within parentheses in the answer for frame 1724. Refer to Panel 8 if necessary to find simplifications. Write the new form for $A \cdot B$.

$$A \cdot B = r \cdot r_1[\cos(\alpha + \beta) + i \sin(\alpha + \beta)]$$

1726 Let us see now what we know about finding the product of two complex numbers when they are written in polar form. If $A = r(\cos \alpha + i \sin \alpha)$ and $B = r_1(\cos \beta + i \sin \beta)$, then $A \cdot B = r \cdot r_1[\cos(\alpha + \beta) + i \sin(\alpha + \beta)]$.

Note 1: We find the modulus of the product of A and B by
(1)_____ the two moduli r and r_1.
Note 2: We find the amplitude of the product of A and B by
(2)_____ the two amplitudes α and β.

(1) multiplying   **(2)** adding

1727 Let $A = 5(\cos 40° + i \sin 40°)$ and $B = 3(\cos 70° + i \sin 70°)$. To find the product $A \cdot B$, the moduli 5 and 3 are **(1)**_____ and the amplitudes 40° and 70° are **(2)**_____ . Therefore, **(3)** $A \cdot B =$ _____ (cos _____ + i sin _____)(copy the entire equation as you answer).

(1) multiplied   **(2)** added   **(3)** $A \cdot B = 15 (\cos 110° + i \sin 110°)$

1728 Let $A = 3[\cos(\pi/6) + i \sin(\pi/6)]$ and $B = 4[\cos(\pi/4) + i \sin(\pi/4)$. Find the product $A \cdot B$.

$$A \cdot B = 3 \cdot 4\left[\cos\left(\frac{\pi}{6} + \frac{\pi}{4}\right) + i \sin\left(\frac{\pi}{6} + \frac{\pi}{4}\right)\right]$$
$$= 12\left(\cos \frac{5\pi}{12} + i \sin \frac{5\pi}{12}\right)$$

1729 Let $A = \sqrt{2}[\cos(3\pi/4) + i \sin(3\pi/4)]$ and $B = \sqrt{3}[\cos(\pi/2) + i \sin(\pi/2)]$. Find the product of A and B.

$$A \cdot B = \sqrt{6}\left(\cos \frac{5\pi}{4} + i \sin \frac{5\pi}{4}\right)$$

1730 Let $A = \sqrt{2}[\cos(\pi/4) + i\sin(\pi/4)]$ and $B = \sqrt{2}[\cos(\pi/3) + i\sin(\pi/3)]$. Find $A \cdot B$.

$$A \cdot B = 2\left(\cos \frac{7\pi}{12} + i\sin \frac{7\pi}{12}\right)$$

1731 As a review, write out the steps by which we *derived* the formula for the product of two numbers in polar form given the complex number $A = r(\cos \alpha + i\sin \beta)$ and $B = r_1(\cos \alpha + i\sin \beta)$.

$$\begin{aligned} A \cdot B &= r \cdot r_1[(\cos \alpha \cos \beta + i^2 \sin \alpha \sin \beta) \\ &\quad + i(\sin \alpha \cos \beta + \cos \alpha \sin \beta)] \\ &= r \cdot r_1[(\cos \alpha \cos \beta - \sin \alpha \sin \beta) \\ &\quad + i(\sin \alpha \cos \beta + \cos \alpha \sin \beta)] \\ &= r \cdot r_1[\cos(\alpha + \beta) + i\sin(\alpha + \beta)] \end{aligned}$$

1732 Briefly stated this formula tells us that when two complex numbers are given in polar form, we can find their product by **(1)**_____ the absolute values of the two complex numbers and **(2)**_____ the amplitudes of the two complex numbers.

(1) multiplying **(2)** adding

▽**1733** Let $A = 1[\cos(\pi/2) + i\sin(\pi/2)]$ and $B = 3(\cos \pi + i\sin \pi)$. Find $A \cdot B$.

$$A \cdot B = 3\left(\cos \frac{3\pi}{2} + i\sin \frac{3\pi}{2}\right)$$

▽**1734** Let $A = m(\cos \theta + i\sin \theta)$ and $B = n(\cos V + i\sin V)$. Find $A \cdot B$.

$$A \cdot B = m \cdot n[\cos(\theta + V) + i\sin(\theta + V)]$$

1735 The polar form of a number is $2(\cos 90° + i\sin 90°)$. Change this to the $a + bi$ form.

Recall $\cos 90° = 0$ and $\sin 90° = 1$; hence, $2(0 + i \cdot 1) = 0 + 2i = 2i$

1736 Since the product of two complex numbers is a complex number, it is possible to obtain the product of any finite number of complex numbers by a repeated use of the product formula. Try it for the product of $A \cdot B \cdot C$. Given $A = \sqrt{3}(\cos 70° + i \sin 70°)$, $B = \sqrt{4}(\cos 30° + i \sin 30°)$, and $C = \sqrt{3}(\cos 80° + i \sin 80°)$.

$$A \cdot B \cdot C = [\sqrt{3}(\cos 70° + i \sin 70) \cdot \sqrt{4}(\cos 30° + i \sin 30°)]$$
$$\cdot [\sqrt{3}(\cos 80° + i \sin 80°)]$$
$$= [\sqrt{12}(\cos 100° + i \sin 100)][\sqrt{3}(\cos 80 + i \sin 80°]$$
$$= 6(\cos 180° + i \sin 180°)$$

▽**1737** Find the product of the following two numbers without changing them to polar form: $(1 + i) \cdot (1 - i\sqrt{3})$.

$$(1 + i) \cdot (1 - i\sqrt{3}) = (1 + \sqrt{3}) + i(1 - \sqrt{3}) \text{ or } = 2.732 - 0.732i$$

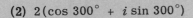

Keep this answer for a check in frame 1739.

1738 **(1)** Change $(1 + i)$ to polar form. **(2)** Change $(1 - i\sqrt{3})$ to polar form.

(1) $\sqrt{2}(\cos 45° + i \sin 45°)$

Solution:

$$r = \sqrt{1 + 1} = \sqrt{2}$$

$$\tan \theta = \frac{1}{1}$$

$$\theta = 45°$$

Therefore, $1 + i = \sqrt{2}(\cos 45° + i \sin 45°)$

(2) $2(\cos 300° + i \sin 300°)$

Solution:

$$r = \sqrt{1 + (-\sqrt{3})^2} = 2$$

$$\tan \theta = \frac{-\sqrt{3}}{1}$$

$$\theta = (360° - 60°) = 300°$$

Therefore, $1 - i\sqrt{3} = 2(\cos 300° + i \sin 300°)$

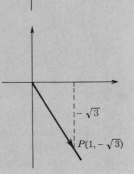

1739 Find the product

$$[\sqrt{2}(\cos 45° + i \sin 45°)] \cdot [2(\cos 300° + i \sin 300°)]$$

Change the answer to rectangular form.

$2\sqrt{2}(\cos 345° + i \sin 345°)$

$2.828(0.966 - 0.259i)$ or $2.732 - 0.732i$

Check frame 1737 to see that answers agree.

1740 First **(1)** change the complex numbers $(-1 + i\sqrt{3})$ and $(\sqrt{3} + i)$ to polar form and **(2)** then multiply. Leave your answer in polar form.

(1) $[2(\cos 120° + i \sin 120°)][2(\cos 30° + i \sin 30)]$

(2) $4(\cos 150° + i \sin 150°)$

1741 Without changing to polar form, find the product of the following two complex numbers: $(-1 + i\sqrt{3}) \cdot (\sqrt{3} + i)$.

$-2\sqrt{3} + 2i$

Solution: $-\sqrt{3} + 3i - i + i^2\sqrt{3}, (-\sqrt{3} - \sqrt{3}) + i(3 - 1),$

$-2\sqrt{3} + 2i$

1742 Show the following two complex numbers geometrically: **(1)** $A = 4(\cos 150° + i \sin 150°)$ and **(2)** $A_1 = -2\sqrt{3} + 2i$.

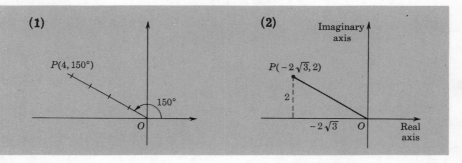

1743 Find the product $[\sqrt{2}(\cos 30° + i \sin 30°)] \cdot [\sqrt{2}(\cos 60° + i \sin 60°)]$.

$2(\cos 90° + i \sin 90°)$

1744 Change $6(\cos 270° + i \sin 270°)$ to rectangular form.

$$6[0 + i(-1)] = -6i$$

1745 Recall that we obtained the quotient of two complex numbers by multiplying both numerator and denominator by the *conjugate* of the denominator. The first step in finding a formula for division of complex numbers in polar form is indicated below. Carry out the indicated operations and simplify the result.

$$\frac{r_1(\cos \alpha + i \sin \alpha)}{r_2(\cos B + i \sin B)} = \frac{r_1(\cos \alpha + i \sin \alpha)}{r_2(\cos B + i \sin B)} \cdot \frac{r_2(\cos B - i \sin B)}{r_2(\cos B - i \sin B)}$$

Consult Panel 8 if necessary to simplify your work.

$$\frac{r_1(\cos \alpha + i \sin \alpha)}{r_2(\cos B + i \sin B)} = \frac{r_1(\cos \alpha + i \sin \alpha)}{r_2(\cos B + i \sin B)} \cdot \frac{r_2(\cos B - i \sin B)}{r_2(\cos B - i \sin B)}$$

$$= \frac{r_1 r_2(\cos \alpha \cos B + \sin \alpha \sin B) + i(\sin \alpha \cos B - \cos \alpha \sin B)}{r_2^2(\cos B \cdot \cos B + \sin B \sin B) + i(\sin B \cos B - \sin B \cos B)}$$

$$= \frac{r_1[\cos (\alpha - B) + i \sin (\alpha - B)]}{r_2(\cos^2 B + \sin^2 B)} = \frac{r_1}{r_2} \frac{[\cos (\alpha - B) + i \sin (\alpha - B)]}{1}$$

1746 We found that for division of complex numbers in polar form:

$$\frac{r_1(\cos \alpha + i \sin \alpha)}{r_2(\cos B + i \sin B)} = \frac{r_1}{r_2}[\cos (\alpha - B) + i \sin (\alpha - B)]$$

If we restate this formula in words, we say that the *absolute value* of the quotient of two complex numbers is the quotient of their absolute values, i.e., r_1/r_2, and an amplitude of the quotient is the (1)_____ of their amplitudes, i.e., (2) α_____. Copy the entire expression as you answer.

(1) difference   (2) $\alpha - B$

1747 Find the quotient

$$\frac{2\sqrt{6}(\cos 120° + i \sin 120°)}{\sqrt{3}(\cos 90° + i \sin 90°)}$$

$2\sqrt{2}(\cos 30° + i \sin 30°)$

1748   Write the formula for finding the quotient of two complex numbers given in polar form:

$$\frac{r_1(\cos \alpha + i \sin \alpha)}{r_2(\cos B + i \sin B)} = \underline{\hspace{3cm}}$$

$$\frac{r_1}{r_2}[(\cos (\alpha - B) + i \sin (\alpha - B)]$$

▽**1749**   See whether you can reconstruct a proof for the following:

$$\frac{r_1(\cos \alpha + i \sin \alpha)}{r_2(\cos B + i \sin B)} = \frac{r_1}{r_2}[\cos (\alpha - B) + i \sin (\alpha - B)]$$

Refer to the proof in frame 1745 if you were not able to complete the proof

▽**1750**   Find the quotient

$$\frac{8(\cos 240° + i \sin 240°)}{2(\cos 210° + i \sin 210°)}$$

$$4(\cos 30° + i \sin 30°)$$

1751   Perform the indicated operations by first changing the complex numbers to polar form. After you have completed the multiplications and divisions, change the result back to rectangular form.

$$\frac{-1 - i}{-1 + i\sqrt{3}}$$

$$\frac{-1 - i}{-1 + i\sqrt{3}} = \frac{\sqrt{2}(\cos 225° + i \sin 225°)}{2(\cos 120° + i \sin 120°)} = \frac{\sqrt{2}}{2}(\cos 105° + i \sin 105°)$$

$$\frac{\sqrt{2}}{2}(-0.259) + i\frac{\sqrt{2}}{2}(0.966) \approx -0.183 + 0.683i$$

1752   Change to polar form and perform the indicated operations:

$$\frac{(1 - i)(-1 + i\sqrt{3})}{\sqrt{3} + i}$$

$$\frac{[\sqrt{2}(\cos 315° + i \sin 315°)][2(\cos 120° + i \sin 120°)]}{2(\cos 30° + i \sin 30°)}$$

$$= \frac{2\sqrt{2}(\cos 435° + i \sin 435°)}{2(\cos 30° + i \sin 30°)},$$

$$= \sqrt{2}(\cos 405° + i \sin 405°) \text{ or } = \sqrt{2}(\cos 45° + i \sin 45°)$$

1753 Change to polar form to compute the following:

$$\frac{3 + i\sqrt{3}}{(2 - 2i)(\sqrt{3} - i)}$$

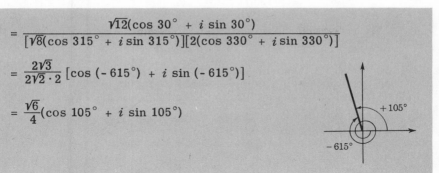

$$= \frac{\sqrt{12}(\cos 30° + i \sin 30°)}{[\sqrt{8}(\cos 315° + i \sin 315°)][2(\cos 330° + i \sin 330°)]}$$

$$= \frac{2\sqrt{3}}{2\sqrt{2} \cdot 2} [\cos (-615°) + i \sin (-615°)]$$

$$= \frac{\sqrt{6}}{4}(\cos 105° + i \sin 105°)$$

$+105°$

$-615°$

1754 Find $(1 + i)^4$ by first changing to polar form and then carrying out the multiplication. *Note:* You can make successive multiplications. If $A = 1 + i$, first you have $A \cdot A = A^2$, then $A^2 \cdot A = A^3$, finally, $A^3 \cdot A$.

$(1 + i)^4 = 4(\cos 180° + i \sin 180°)$

Solution: $(1 + i) = \sqrt{2}(\cos 45° + i \sin 45°)$

$(1 + i)^2 = \sqrt{2} \cdot \sqrt{2} [\cos (45° + 45°) + i \sin (45° + 45°)]$

$= 2(\cos 90° + i \sin 90°)$

etc.

1755 In carrying out the multiplications in frame 1754 the following formula for squaring a complex number might have suggested itself to you: If $C = r(\cos \theta + i \sin \theta)$, then

$$C^2 = r \cdot r[\cos (\theta + \theta) + i \sin (\theta + \theta)]$$

$$= r^2 (\cos 2\theta + i \sin 2\theta)$$

Extend this idea to get a formula for **(1)** C^3 and **(2)** C^4.

(1) $C^3 = C \cdot C \cdot C = r^3(\cos 3\theta + i \sin 3\theta)$

(2) $C^4 = C \cdot C \cdot C \cdot C = r^4(\cos 4\theta + i \sin 4\theta)$

1756 If we continue the process indicated in frame 1755 to any desired positive integral power n, then we have

$$C^n = [r \cdot (\cos \theta + i \sin \theta)]^n = r^n(\cos n\theta + i \sin n\theta)$$

continued ➔

This theorem can be proved by mathematical induction, and is known as De Moivre's theorem (named for the French mathematician Abraham De Moivre, 1667-1754.) Find C^6 if $C = \sqrt{2}(\cos 45° + i \sin 45°)$.

$(\sqrt{2})^6(\cos 6 \cdot 45° + i \sin 6 \cdot 45°)$ or $8(\cos 270° + i \sin 270°)$

1757 De Moivre's theorem tells us how to raise a complex number to an integral power n. Complete the following statement of the theorem: $C^n = [r(\cos \theta + i \sin \theta)]^n =$ _____ .

$r^n(\cos n\theta + i \sin n\theta)$

1758 Use De Moivre's theorem to find C^n when $C = \sqrt{3}(\cos 60° + i \sin 60°)$ and $n = 3$.

$(\sqrt{3})^3(\cos 3 \cdot 60° + i \sin 3 \cdot 60°) = 3\sqrt{3}(\cos 180° + i \sin 180°)$

1759 Change $(1 - i\sqrt{3})/2$ to polar form, then use De Moivre's theorem to find $[(1 - i\sqrt{3})/2]^3$. Change your answer to rectangular form.

Solution 1:

$$\left(\frac{1 - i\sqrt{3}}{2}\right)^3 = \left(\tfrac{1}{2} - \tfrac{1}{2}i\sqrt{3}\right)^3 = 1[(\cos 300° + i \sin 300°)]^3$$
$$= 1(\cos 900° + i \sin 900°) = -1$$

Solution 2:

$$\left(\frac{1 - i\sqrt{3}}{2}\right)^3 = \frac{(1 - i\sqrt{3})^3}{2} = \frac{[2(\cos 300° + i \sin 300°)]^3}{2}$$

etc.

1760 As a check on the solution of the problem in frame 1759, calculate $[(1 - i\sqrt{3})/2]^3$ without changing to polar form.

$$\left(\frac{1 - i\sqrt{3}}{2}\right)^3 = \frac{(1 - 2i\sqrt{3} + 3i^2)(1 - i\sqrt{3})}{8}$$
$$= \frac{-2(1 + i\sqrt{3})(1 - i\sqrt{3})}{8}$$
$$= \frac{-2(1 - 3i^2)}{8} = \frac{-2(4)}{8} = -1$$

1761 Perform the indicated operation. (Change to polar form before making the calculation.) $[(-1 - i\sqrt{3})/2]^6$

$$\left(\frac{-1 - i\sqrt{3}}{2}\right)^6 = \left(-\frac{1}{2} - \frac{i\sqrt{3}}{2}\right)^6 = [1(\cos 240° + i \sin 240°)]^6$$

$$= 1(\cos 1{,}440° + i \sin 1{,}440°)$$

$$= 1(\cos 0° + i \sin 0°) = 1 \cdot 1 + i \cdot 0 = 1$$

1762 Express the following problem in polar form, then perform the indicated operations:

$$\frac{2i(\sqrt{3} - i)}{(1 + i) \cdot (-\sqrt{3} - i)}$$

$$\frac{[2(\cos 90° + i \sin 90°)][2(\cos 330° + i \sin 330°)]}{[\sqrt{2}(\cos 45° + i \sin 45°)][2(\cos 210° + i \sin 210°)]}$$

$$= \frac{4(\cos 420° + i \sin 420°)}{2 \cdot \sqrt{2}(\cos 255° + i \sin 255°)} = \sqrt{2}(\cos 165° + i \sin 165°)$$

▽**1763** Perform the indicated operations

$$7[1 \cdot (\cos 51° + i \sin 51°)]^{10} \cdot 4[1 \cdot (\cos 6° + i \sin 6°)]^5$$

$$[7(\cos 10 \cdot 51° + i \sin 10 \cdot 51)][4(\cos 5 \cdot 6° + i \sin 6 \cdot 5°)]$$

$$= [7(\cos 510° + i \sin 510°)][4(\cos 30° + i \sin 30)]$$

$$= 28(\cos 540° + i \sin 540°) =$$

$$= 28(\cos 180° + i \sin 180°) = -28$$

1764 We can show that De Moivre's theorem holds for n a negative integer thus:

$$[r(\cos \theta + i \sin \theta)]^{-n} = \frac{1}{[r(\cos \theta + i \sin \theta)]^n}$$

Applying De Moivre's theorem, we may write the denominator of the right member of this equation as $[r(\cos \theta + i \sin \theta)]^{-n} = 1/\underline{\hspace{3cm}}$.

$$r^n(\cos n\theta + i \sin n\theta)$$

1765 Multiply both numerator and denominator of the fraction in the right member of the previous equation by $\cos(-n\theta) + i\sin(-n\theta)$:

$$[r(\cos\theta + i\sin)]^{-n}$$

$$= \frac{1}{r^n(\cos n\theta + i\sin n\theta)} \cdot \frac{\cos(-n\theta) + i\sin(-n\theta)}{\cos(-n\theta) + i\sin(-n\theta)}$$

$$= \frac{\cos(-n\theta) + i\sin(-n\theta)}{r^n[\cos n\theta + i\sin n\theta][\cos n\theta - i\sin n\theta]}$$

$$= \frac{\cos(-n\theta) + i\sin(-n\theta)}{?}$$

$$[r(\cos\theta + i\sin\theta)]^{-n} = \frac{\cos(-n\theta) + i\sin(-n\theta)}{r^n(\cos^2 n\theta + \sin^2 n\theta)}$$

1766 The denominator of the right member may now be simplified to

$$[r(\cos\theta + i\sin\theta)]^{-n} = \frac{\cos(-n\theta) + i\sin(-n\theta)}{r^n(\quad ? \quad)}$$

Note: Now this may be written as

$$[r(\cos\theta + i\sin\theta)]^{-n} = r^{-n}[\cos(-n\theta) + i\sin(-n\theta)]$$

which is what we wanted to show.

1

1767 Complete the two formulas: $[r(\cos\theta + i\sin\theta)]^n = \textbf{(1)}\underline{\hspace{3cm}}$ and $[r(\cos\theta + i\sin\theta)]^{-n} = \textbf{(2)}\underline{\hspace{3cm}}.$

(1) $r^n(\cos n\theta + i\sin n\theta)$ **(2)** $r^{-n}[\cos(-n\theta) + i\sin(-n\theta)]$

1768 Perform the indicated operation $(\frac{1}{4})[1(\cos 36° + i\sin 36°)]^{-5}$ and report your final answer in rectangular form.

$$\tfrac{1}{4} \cdot 1^{-5}[\cos(-180°) + i\sin(-180°)] = \tfrac{1}{4}(-1 + 0i) = -\tfrac{1}{4}$$

1769 Perform the indicated operation and simplify the result: $(7 - 7\sqrt{3}\,i)^{-3}$

$$(7 - 7\sqrt{3}\,i)^{-3} = [14(\cos 300° + i\sin 300°)]^{-3}$$

$$= \frac{1}{14^3}[\cos(-900°) + i\sin(-900°)]$$

$$= \frac{1}{14^3}[\cos(-180°) + i\sin(-180°)] = \frac{-1}{14^3}$$

1770 Let $n = 0$; apply De Moivre's theorem to perform the indicated operation and simplify the result: $[r(\cos \theta + i \sin \theta)]^n$. Recall from previous work with exponents that any number other than 0 raised to the 0 power is 1. Compare your answer above with this statement.

$$[r(\cos \theta + i \sin \theta)]^0 = r^0[\cos (0 \cdot \theta) + i \sin (0 \cdot \theta)]$$
$$= 1(\cos 0 + i \sin 0) = 1(1 + 0i) = 1$$

This answer indicates that De Moivre's theorem holds for $n = 0$

1771 $[\sqrt{3}(\cos 140° + i \sin 140°)]^3 = \underline{\hspace{5cm}}$.
Change the answer to rectangular form.

$$[\sqrt{3}(\cos 140° + i \sin 140°)]^3 = 3\sqrt{3}(\cos 420° + i \sin 420°)$$
$$= 3\sqrt{3}(\cos 60° + i \sin 60°)$$
$$= 3\sqrt{3}\left(\frac{1}{2} + \frac{i\sqrt{3}}{2}\right) = \frac{3\sqrt{3}}{2} + \frac{9}{2}i$$

1772 Find the **(1)** absolute value and the **(2)** amplitude of $5 + 12i$.

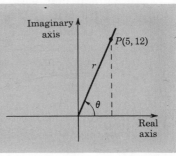

(1) 13   **(2)** 67.4°

Solution:
$$r = \sqrt{5^2 + 12^2} = 13$$
$$\tan \theta = \tfrac{12}{5} = 2.400$$
$$\theta \approx 67.4°$$

1773 Represent graphically and find the polar form for each of the following: **(1)** $A = 5$, **(2)** $B = 5i$, **(3)** $C = -5$, and **(4)** $D = -5i$.

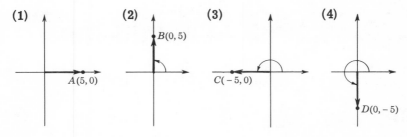

(1)   **(2)**   **(3)**   **(4)**

$A(5, 0)$ $B(0, 5)$ $C(-5, 0)$ $D(0, -5)$

continued →

(1) $5 = 5 + 0i = 5(\cos 0° + i \sin 0°)$
(2) $5i = 0 + 5i = 5(\cos 90° + i \sin 90°)$
(3) $-5 = -5 + 0i = 5(\cos 180° + i \sin 180°)$
(4) $-5 = 0 - 5i = 5(\cos 270° + i \sin 270°)$

▽1774 $[2(\cos 15° + i \sin 15°)]^9 = $ _____. Give the
answer in both (1) polar and (2) rectangular form.

(1) $512(\cos 135° + i \sin 135°)$ (2) $-256\sqrt{2} + 256i\sqrt{2}$

▽1775 Carry out the indicated operations:

$$\frac{(\cos 345° + i \sin 345°)^2 \cdot [7(\cos 10° + i \sin 10°)]}{[2(\cos 130° + i \sin 130°)]^3}$$

Leave the answer in polar form.

$\frac{7}{8}(\cos 310° + i \sin 310°)$

1776 (1) Change the following complex numbers to polar form, (2) then
find their quotient:

$$\frac{1 - i}{1 + i\sqrt{3}}$$

(1) $\frac{\sqrt{2}(\cos 315° + i \sin 315°)}{2(\cos 60° + i \sin 60°)}$ (2) $\frac{\sqrt{2}}{2}(\cos 255° + i \sin 255°)$

1777 In the field of *real* numbers, we have no square root of -4, no fourth
root of -16, and in general no *even* root of a negative number. Also
we can find only one cube root of 27 and only one fifth root of -32.
However if we are working in the field of complex numbers, we can,
by using De Moivre's theorem, obtain n n^{th} *roots* of any number.
Recall our original statement of the theorem: If n is a positive
integer, then $[r(\cos \theta + i \sin \theta)]^n = $ _____.

$r^n(\cos n\theta + i \sin n\theta)$

1778 De Moivre's theorem also holds for all *rational powers* of *n*. We shall not attempt a proof of this part of the theorem but shall examine its usefulness. First, how would you state the theorem for $n = 1/m$? $[r(\cos \theta + i \sin \theta)]^{1/m}$ = _____.

$$r^{1/m}\left(\cos\frac{\theta}{m} + i \sin\frac{\theta}{m}\right)$$

1779 Frames 1779 to 1785 will show you how to apply De Moivre's theorem to find *n* *n*th roots of any number. (*Examples:* three cube roots of 27 and four fourth roots of - 16.) Recall first that $\cos(\theta + k \cdot 360°) = \cos \theta$ and that $\sin(\theta + k \cdot 360°) = \sin \theta$ for any integer *k*. When we make this substitution, we may write

$$[r(\cos \theta + i \sin \theta)]^{1/m} = \{r[\cos(\theta + k\cdot360°) + i\sin(\theta + k\cdot360°)]\}^{1/m}$$

(where *m* is a positive integer). Rewrite the right member of the above equation applying De Moivre's theorem.

$$r^{1/m}\left(\cos\frac{\theta + 360°k}{m} + i\sin\frac{\theta + 360°k}{m}\right)$$
$$\text{or } r^{1/m}\left\{\cos\left[\frac{1}{m}(\theta + 360°k)\right] + i\sin\left[\frac{1}{m}(\theta + 360°k)\right]\right\}$$

1780 The problem below illustrates the extension of De Moivre's theorem to obtain the *n* *n*th roots of a given number. Let $n = 1/m$.
Theorem:

$$[r(\cos \theta + i \sin \theta)]^{1/m} = r^{1/m}\left(\cos\frac{\theta + 360°k}{m} + i\sin\frac{\theta + 360°k}{m}\right)$$

Example: Find the three cube roots of 27.
Step 1. $27 = (27 + 0i)$ in rectangular form
= _____ in polar form

This problem will be continued in frame 1781.

$27(\cos 0° + i \sin 0°)$

1781   Step 1. $\begin{cases} 27 = 27(\cos 0° + i \sin 0°) \\ \quad = 27[(\cos (0° + 360° k) + i \sin (0° + 360° k)] \end{cases}$

Step 2. $27^{1/3} = \{27[\cos (0°, + 360° k) + i \sin (0° + 360° k)]\}^{1/3}$

$$= 27^{1/3} \left(\cos \frac{0° + 360° k}{3} + i \sin \frac{0° + 360° k}{3} \right)$$

Step 3. Simplify the result in Step 2 with $k = 1$.

This problem will be continued in frames 1782 and 1783.

$$= 3 \left(\cos \frac{0° + 360° \cdot 1}{3} + i \sin \frac{0° + 360° \cdot 1}{3} \right) \quad \text{when } k = 1$$

$$= 3(\cos 120° + i \sin 120°)$$

$$= 3 \left(\frac{-1}{2} + i \frac{\sqrt{3}}{2} \right) = \frac{-3}{2} + \frac{3\sqrt{3}i}{2}$$

(This is one cube root of 27, it will be checked later.)

1782   Step 4. Find the value of

$$27^{1/3} = 3 \left(\cos \frac{0° + 360° k}{3} + i \sin \frac{0 + 360° k}{3} \right)$$

when $k = 2$

$$3 \left(\cos \frac{360° \cdot 2}{3} + i \sin \frac{360° \cdot 2}{3} \right) = 3(\cos 240° + i \sin 240°)$$

$$= 3 \left(\frac{-1}{2} + i \frac{-\sqrt{3}}{2} \right)$$

$$= \frac{-3}{2} - i \frac{3\sqrt{3}}{2}$$

(This is the second cube root of 27.)

1783   Step 5. Find the value of

$$27^{1/3} = 3 \left(\cos \frac{0° + 360° k}{3} + i \sin \frac{0° + 360° k}{3} \right)$$

when $k = 3$

$$3 \left(\cos \frac{360° \cdot 3}{3} + i \sin \frac{360 \cdot 3}{3} \right) = 3(\cos 360° + i \sin 360°$$

$$= 3(1 + 0i) = 3$$

(This is the third cube root of 27.)

1784 The work of frames 1779 to 1783 gave you this information: Three cube roots of 27 are $(-3/2 + 3\sqrt{3}i/2)$, $(-3/2 - 3\sqrt{3}i/2)$, 3. Two questions might arise in your mind.
1. Are there more cube roots of 27 ?
2. Are we sure that each of the numbers listed above is a cube root of 27 ?
Try $k = 4, 5,$ or 6 to find an answer to question 1.

If $k = 4$, the result is the same as when $k = 1$:

$$3\left(\cos\frac{360\cdot 4}{3} + i\sin\frac{360\cdot 4}{3}\right) = 3(\cos 480 + i\sin 480)$$
$$= 3(\cos 120 + i\sin 120)$$

If $k = 5$, the result is the same as when $k + 2$. If $k = 6$, the result is the same as when $k = 3$. In fact any integral value of k will reduce to one of the three roots already found.

1785 Prove that $(-3/2 + 3\sqrt{3}\,i/2)$ is a cube root of 27 by showing that $(-3/2 +\sqrt{3}\ 3i/2)^3 = 27$. Perform this multiplication keeping the number in rectangular form.

$$\left(\frac{-3}{2} + \frac{3\sqrt{3}i}{2}\right)^3 = \left(\frac{-3}{2} + \frac{3\sqrt{3}i}{2}\right)^2\left(\frac{-3}{2} + \frac{3\sqrt{3}i}{2}\right)$$
$$= \left[\left(\frac{9}{4} - \frac{27}{4}\right) + \left(\frac{-9\sqrt{3}}{4} - \frac{9\sqrt{3}}{4}\right)i\right]\left(\frac{-3}{2} + \frac{3\sqrt{3}}{2}\right)i$$
$$= \left(\frac{-9}{2} - \frac{9\sqrt{3}}{2}i\right)\cdot\left(\frac{-3}{2} + \frac{3\sqrt{3}}{2}i\right)$$
$$= \left(\frac{27}{4} + \frac{81}{4}\right) + \left(\frac{27\sqrt{3}}{4} - \frac{27\sqrt{3}}{4}\right)i = \frac{108}{4} + 0i = 27$$

1786 Prove that $[-3/2 - (-3\sqrt{3}i/2)]^3 = 27$. To do this multiplication, change the complex number to polar form first.

$$\left(\frac{-3}{2} - \frac{-3\sqrt{3}i}{2}\right)^3 = [3(\cos 240° + i\sin 240°)]^3$$
$$= 27(\cos 720° + i\sin 720°)$$
$$= 27(1 + 0i) = 27$$

1787 As another example we shall work out, in frames 1787 to 1792 the fourth roots of - 16. In polar form $- 16 = $ **(1)** _____.
Therefore, we begin our problem by stating that $(-16)^{1/4} = $ _____
_____.

(1) $16(\cos 180° + i\sin 180°)$ **(2)** $[16(\cos 180° + i\sin 180°)]^{1/4}$

1788 Recall that cos (180°) = cos (180° + 360°k) and sin 180° = sin (180° + 360°k). Therefore,

$$(-16)^{1/4} = [16(\cos 180° + 360°k) + i \sin (180° + 360°k)]^{1/4}$$

Now we find the fourth roots of (- 16) by letting k = 1, 2, 3, 4. If k = 1, find the value of the above expression.

$$16^{1/4}\left(\cos \frac{180° + 360°}{4} + i \sin \frac{180° + 360°}{4}\right)$$

$$= 2(\cos 135° + i \sin 135°) = 2\,\frac{-\sqrt{2}}{2} + \frac{i\sqrt{2}}{2} = -\sqrt{2} + i\sqrt{2}$$

Record this answer.

1789 If k = 2, find the value of

$$\{16[\cos (180 + 360k) + i \sin (180 + 360k)]\}^{1/4}$$

$$2\left(\cos \frac{180 + 720}{4} + i \sin \frac{180 + 720}{4}\right) = 2(\cos 225° + i \sin 225°)$$

$$= 2\left[\frac{-\sqrt{2}}{2} + i\left(\frac{-\sqrt{2}}{2}\right)\right]$$

$$= -\sqrt{2} - i\sqrt{2}$$

Record this answer.

1790 If k = 3, find the value of

$$\{16[\cos (180° + 360°k) + i \sin (180° + 360°k)]\}^{1/4}$$

$$2(\cos 315° + i \sin 315°) = 2\left[\frac{\sqrt{2}}{2} + i\left(\frac{-\sqrt{2}}{2}\right)\right] = \sqrt{2} - i\sqrt{2}$$

Record this answer

1791 Finally, if k = 4, find the value of

$$\{16[\cos (180° + 360°k) + i \sin (180 + 360k))]\}^{1/4}$$

$$2(\cos 405° + i \sin 405°) = 2(\cos 45° + i \sin 45°)$$

$$= 2\left(\frac{\sqrt{2}}{2} + i\,\frac{\sqrt{2}}{2}\right) = \sqrt{2} + i\sqrt{2}$$

Record this answer.

1792 Look back over the answers in frames 1788 to 1791. **(1)** What are the fourth roots of -16? **(2)** Might there be more than those you have listed?

(1) $(-\sqrt{2} + i\sqrt{2})$, $(-\sqrt{2} - i\sqrt{2})$, $(\sqrt{2} - i\sqrt{2})$, $(\sqrt{2} + i\sqrt{2})$

(2) no   Any other integral value assigned to k will yield one of the roots already obtained.

1793 Perform the following operation to show that $(-\sqrt{2} + i\sqrt{2})$ is a fourth root of -16: $(-\sqrt{2} + i\sqrt{2})^4 = $ _____.
Change to polar coordinates to perform the multiplication.

$$(-\sqrt{2} + i\sqrt{2})^4 = [2(\cos 135° + i \sin 135°)]^4$$
$$= 16(\cos 540° + i \sin 540°)$$
$$= 16(\cos 180° + i \sin 180) = 16(-1 + \cdot 0i) = -16$$

1794 To find n nth roots of a given number using De Moivre's theorem, the following steps are suggested:

Step 1. Change the given number to polar form if it is not already in that form.

Step 2. Recall that $\cos \theta = \cos (\theta + 360°k)$ and that $\sin \theta = \sin (\theta + 360°k)$
Make these substitutions in De Moivre's theorem.

Step 3. Let $k = 1, 2, 3, \ldots, n$ successively and simplify the resulting expression.

Carry out Steps 1 and 2 above for obtaining three cube roots of 1.

$$1^{1/3} = (1 + 0i)^{1/3} = [1(\cos 0° + i \sin 0°)]^{1/3}$$
$$= \{1[\cos (0° + 360°k) + i \sin (0° + 360°k)]\}^{1/3}$$
$$\text{or} \quad \cos\left(\frac{0° + 360°k}{3}\right) + i \sin\left(\frac{0° + 360°k}{3}\right)$$

Keep your answer for frame 1795.

1795   Complete the operations to find three cube roots of 1.

$\left(\dfrac{-1}{2} + \dfrac{i\sqrt{3}}{2}\right)$, $\left(\dfrac{-1}{2} - \dfrac{i\sqrt{3}}{2}\right)$,   1

Step 3 Solution:

$$\text{If } k = 1, \ 1^{1/3} = \left(\cos \frac{360°}{3} + i \sin \frac{360°}{3}\right)$$

$$= (\cos 120° + i \sin 120°)$$

$$= \frac{-1}{2} + \frac{i\sqrt{3}}{2}$$

$$\text{If } k = 2, \ 1^{1/3} = 1\left(\cos \frac{720}{3} + i \sin \frac{720}{3}\right)$$

$$= 1(\cos 240° + i \sin 240°)$$

$$= \frac{-1}{2} - \frac{i\sqrt{3}}{2}$$

$$\text{If } k = 3, \ 1^{1/3} = 1(\cos 0° + i \sin 0°) = 1$$

1796   What check can you use to prove that $(-\frac{1}{2} + i\sqrt{3}/2)$ is a cube root of 1?

If $(-\frac{1}{2} + i\sqrt{3}/2)^3 = 1$, then you know that you have one of the cube roots of 1.

1797   To find the cube roots of -8, we would proceed as follows:

Step 1. -8 should be written in polar form. **(1)** Do this.
Step 2. Remember that $\cos \theta$ and $\sin \theta$ must be replaced by
          (2) _____ and **(3)** _____,
          respectively, in the complex number form. Do this also.

(1) $-8 = 8(\cos 180° + i \sin 180°)$ **(2)** $\cos (180° + 360°k)$
(3) $\sin (180° + 360°k)$

1798 Complete the steps necessary to obtain the three cube roots of -8.

$-2, \quad (1 - i\sqrt{3}), \quad (1 + i\sqrt{3})$

$$(-8)^{1/3} = 8^{1/3}\left(\cos\frac{180 + 360k}{3} + i\sin\frac{180 + 360k}{3}\right) \qquad \text{if } k = 1$$

$$= 2\left(\cos\frac{540}{3} + i\sin\frac{540}{3}\right)$$

$$= 2(\cos 180° + i\sin 180°)$$

$$= 2(-1) = -2$$

$$= 2\left(\cos\frac{180° + 720°}{3} + i\sin\frac{180° + 720°}{3}\right) \qquad \text{if } k = 2$$

$$= 2(\cos 300° + i\sin 300°)$$

$$= 2\left(\frac{1}{2} - \frac{\sqrt{3}}{2}\right) = 1 - i\sqrt{3}$$

$$= 2\left(\cos\frac{180° + 1{,}080°}{3} + i\sin\frac{180° + 1{,}080°}{3}\right) \quad \text{if } k = 3$$

$$= 2(\cos 420° + i\sin 420°)$$

$$= 2(\cos 60° + i\sin 60°)$$

$$= 2\left(\frac{1}{2} + \frac{i\sqrt{3}}{2}\right) = (1 + i\sqrt{3})$$

1799 You might recall from algebra a method of finding the cube roots of -8. To do this, you assumed that x is a number such that $x^3 = -8$ or that $x^3 + 8 = 0$. Then you solved the equation for x, thus obtaining the cube roots of -8. The algebraic solution depends upon your skill in factoring $x^3 + 8$ and in obtaining the roots from this form. Try it.

$x = -2, \quad x = 1 + i\sqrt{3}, \quad x = 1 - i\sqrt{3}$

Solution: $x^3 + 8 = 0$

$\quad (x + 2)(x^2 - 2x + 4) = 0 \qquad$ factoring

Then $x + 2 = 0$ or $x^2 - 2x + 4 = 0$ and $x = -2$ or, using the quadratic formula,

$$x = \frac{-2 \pm\sqrt{4 - 16}}{2}, \quad = \frac{2 \pm i2\sqrt{3}}{2}, \quad = 1 \pm i\sqrt{3}$$

1800   The algebraic method of obtaining the n nth roots of a number depends upon the solution of an equation of the nth degree. For this reason the algebraic method is limited in its application, and in general the nth roots of a complex number can be found more easily by using De Moivre's theorem. Find three cube roots of i.

$$\frac{-\sqrt{3}}{2} + \frac{1}{2}\, i, \quad i, \quad \frac{\sqrt{3}}{2} + \frac{1}{2}\, i$$

Solution:

$$(i)^{1/3} = (0 + i)^{1/3} = [1(\cos 90° + i \sin 90°)]^{1/3}$$

$$= 1\left(\cos \frac{90°}{3} + \frac{360k}{3} + i \sin \frac{90}{3} + \frac{360k}{3}\right)$$

$$= 1(\cos 150° + i \sin 150°) \qquad\qquad \text{if } k = 1$$

$$= \frac{-\sqrt{3}}{2} + \frac{i}{2}$$

$$= 1(\cos 270° + i \sin 270°) \qquad\qquad \text{if } k = 2$$

$$= 0 - i$$

$$= 1(\cos 390° + i \sin 390°) \qquad\qquad \text{if } k = 3$$

$$= \cos 30° + i \sin 30°$$

$$= \frac{\sqrt{3}}{2} + \frac{i}{2}$$

1801   Observe the three cube roots of i in frame 1800 in their polar form: $R_1 = 1(\cos 150° + i \sin 150°)$, $R_2 = 1(\cos 270° + i \sin 270°)$, and $R_3 = 1(\cos 30° + i \sin 30°)$. In each the absolute value (or modulus) is **(1)**_____. This suggests that if these numbers were represented graphically, the end points of the vectors would all lie on a circle whose radius is **(2)**_____.

(1) 1   (2) 1

1802 Look again at the roots in frame 1800. The amplitude (or argument) of 1(cos 150° + i sin 150°) is **(1)**_____. **(2)** Draw a circle with radius 1 unit and indicate with a vector this complex number.

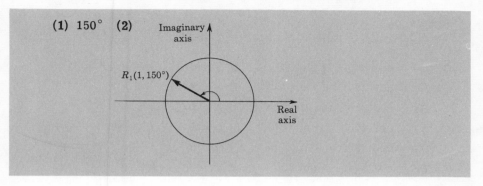

(1) 150°   **(2)**

1803 On the same graph with R_1, represent as vectors the complex numbers R_2 and R_3 in frame 1801 (these are the other cube roots of i).

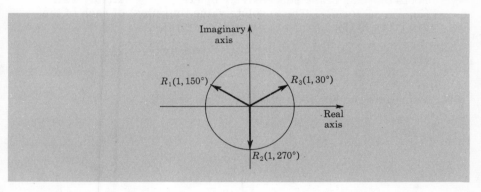

1804 What do you notice about the spacing of the vectors representing R_1, R_2, and R_3 in the graph in frame 1803 ?

The vectors representing the nth roots of i are equally spaced at regular intervals of 120°. This will be discussed in more detail in frame 1805.

1805   Show how you would proceed to find the six sixth roots of -1. You need not change the answers to rectangular form at this time.

$$(-1)^{1/6} = (-1 + 0i)^{1/6} = [1(\cos 180° + i \sin 180°)]^{1/6}$$
$$= \cos\left(\frac{180°}{6} + \frac{360k}{6}\right) + i \sin\left(\frac{180}{6} + \frac{360k}{6}\right)$$

$R_1 = \cos 90° + i \sin 90°$ if $k = 1$

$R_2 = \cos 150° + i \sin 150°$ if $k = 2$

$R_3 = \cos 210° + i \sin 210°$ if $k = 3$

$R_4 = \cos 270° + i \sin 270°$ if $k = 4$

$R_5 = \cos 330° + i \sin 330°$ if $k = 5$

$R_6 = \cos 30° + i \sin 30°$ if $k = 6$

1806   The *arguments* of the complex numbers representing the six sixth roots of -1 increase successively by **(1)**_____° starting with **(2)**_____° for R_1. The absolute value (modulus) of each of the six roots is **(3)**_____.

(1) 60°   **(2)** 90°   **(3)** 1

1807   Represent the six sixth roots of -1 graphically.

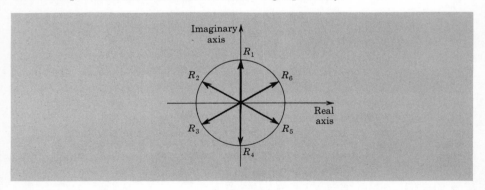

1808   Look at the list of complex numbers representing the six sixth roots of -1 in frame 1805. Change these to rectangular form.

$R_1 = 0 + i$ $R_2 = \dfrac{-\sqrt{3}}{2} + \dfrac{1}{2}i$ $R_3 = \dfrac{-\sqrt{3}}{2} - \dfrac{1}{2}i$

$R_4 = 0 - i$ $R_5 = \dfrac{\sqrt{3}}{2} - \dfrac{1}{2}i$ $R_6 = \dfrac{\sqrt{3}}{2} + \dfrac{1}{2}i$

1809 Look at the list in frame 1808 and the graph of the six sixth roots of -1 in frame 1807. Which of these complex numbers are conjugates? List them by pairs.

R_1 and R_4, R_2 and R_3, R_5 and R_6

1810 Find the four fourth roots of $1 + i$. Leave your answers in polar form.

$$(1 + i) \quad = \sqrt{2}(\cos 45° + i \sin 45°)$$

$$(1 + i)^{1/4} = \left\{ \sqrt{2}[\cos (45° + 360k) + i \sin (45° + 360k)] \right\}^{1/4}$$

$$= \sqrt{2}^{1/4} \left(\cos \frac{45° + 360k}{4} + i \sin \frac{45° + 360k}{4} \right)$$

$$= 2^{1/8} (\cos 101\tfrac{1}{4}° + i \sin 101\tfrac{1}{4}°) \qquad \text{if } k = 1$$

$$= 2^{1/8} (\cos 191\tfrac{1}{4}° + i \sin 191\tfrac{1}{4}°) \qquad \text{if } k = 2$$

$$= 2^{1/8} (\cos 281\tfrac{1}{4}° + i \sin 281\tfrac{1}{4}°) \qquad \text{if } k = 3$$

$$= 2^{1/8} (\cos 371\tfrac{1}{4}° + i \sin 371\tfrac{1}{4}°) \qquad \text{if } k = 4$$

$$\text{or} \quad 2^{1/8} (\cos 11\tfrac{1}{4}° + i \sin 11\tfrac{1}{4}°)$$

1811 Let us see whether we can develop a technique for finding the roots of a complex number which will eliminate some of the tedious computation. In frame 1810 when $k = 1$, we wrote

$$(1 + i)^{1/4} = 2^{1/8} \left(\cos \frac{45 + 360 \cdot 1}{4} + i \sin \frac{45 + 360 \cdot 1}{4} \right)$$

When $k = 2$, we wrote

$$(1 + i)^{1/4} = 2^{1/8} \left(\cos \frac{45 + 360 \cdot 2}{4} + i \sin \frac{45 + 360 \cdot 2}{4} \right)$$

etc.

When $k = 1$, note that

$$\frac{45° + 360° \cdot 1}{4} = \frac{45°}{4} + \frac{360°}{4} \cdot 1 = 11\tfrac{1}{4}° + 90° = 101\tfrac{1}{4}°$$

When $k = 2$, note that

$$\frac{45° + 360° \cdot 2}{4} = \frac{45°}{4} + \frac{360°}{4} \cdot 2 = 11\tfrac{1}{4}° + 180° = 191\tfrac{1}{4}°$$

What is the argument for $k = 3$ and $k = 4$?

$11\tfrac{1}{4}°$ $270° = 281\tfrac{1}{4}°$ and $11\tfrac{1}{4}° + 360° = 371\tfrac{1}{4}°$

1812 Summarizing: We have the information from 1811 about the arguments of the four fourth roots of $1 + i$. **(1)** Make a complete table for $k = 1$ to $k = 4$.

When $k = 1$, $\dfrac{45°}{4} + \dfrac{360°}{4} \cdot 1 = 11\frac{1}{4} + 90°$

$k = 2$, $\dfrac{45}{4} + \dfrac{360}{4} \cdot 2 = 11\frac{1}{4} +$ _____

$k = 3$, $\dfrac{45}{4} +$ _____ $+$ _____ $+$ _____

$k = 4$, _____ $+$ _____ $=$ _____ $+$ _____

Note:

1. Each argument is the sum $\theta/n + (360°/n) \cdot k$
   For this particular problem $\theta/n =$ **(2)**_____, $360/n =$ **(3)**_____, and **(4)** $k =$ _____, _____, _____, _____.

2. The arguments consist of an initial amount θ/n plus successive additions (four in all for this example) of $360/n$; hence, the arguments are **(5)** $101\frac{1}{4}°$, _____, _____, _____.

(1) $\dfrac{45°}{4} + \dfrac{360°}{4} \cdot 1 = 11\frac{1}{4} + 90°$

$\dfrac{45°}{4} + \dfrac{360°}{4} \cdot 2 = 11\frac{1}{4} + 180°$

$\dfrac{45°}{4} + \dfrac{360}{4} \cdot 3 = 11\frac{1}{4} + 270°$

$\dfrac{45°}{4} + \dfrac{360}{4} \cdot 4 = 11\frac{1}{4} + 360$

(2) $\frac{45}{4}$ **(3)** $\frac{360}{4}$ **(4)** 1, 2, 3, 4

(5) $101\frac{1}{4}°$, $191\frac{1}{4}°$, $281\frac{1}{4}°$, $371\frac{1}{4}°$ (or $11\frac{1}{4}$)

1813 Change $\frac{1}{2}(-1 - i\sqrt{3})$ to polar form.

$r = \sqrt{\frac{1}{4} + \frac{3}{4}} = 1$

$\tan \theta = \dfrac{-\sqrt{3}/2}{-1/2} = \sqrt{3}$

$\theta = 240°$ (a third-quadrant angle)

Therefore, $\dfrac{-1}{2} - \dfrac{\sqrt{3}}{2} i = 1(\cos 240° + i \sin 240°)$

1814 To find the arguments (or amplitudes) for the five fifth roots of
$1(\cos 240° + i \sin 240°)$, we note that $\theta/n =$ **(1)**_____ and $360/n =$
(2)_____. Then when $k = 1$, the argument is **(3)**_____ + _____ =
_____; when $k = 2$, the argument is **(4)**_____; when $k = 3$, the argument is **(5)**_____; when $k = 4$, the argument is **(6)**_____; when $k =$
5, the argument is **(7)**_____.

> **(1)** 48°   **(2)** 72°   **(3)** 48 + 72 = 120°   **(4)** 192°
>
> **(5)** 264°   **(6)** 336°   **(7)** 408° or 48°

1815 Look back now at your work. We want the complex numbers in
polar form which represent the five fifth roots of $\frac{1}{2}(-1 - i\sqrt{3})$.
First we wrote the number in polar form $(-\frac{1}{2} - i\sqrt{3}/2) =$
(1)_____, then $[(-\frac{1}{2} - i/3\sqrt{2})]^{1/5} =$
(2) (_____)   . **(3)** Write the five roots
in polar form.

> **(1)** $1(\cos 240° + i \sin 240°)$ **(2)** $[1(\cos 240° + i \sin 240)]^{1/5}$
>
> **(3)** $R_1 = 1(\cos 120 + i \sin 120°)$
>
> $R_2 = 1(\cos 192° + i \sin 192°)$
>
> $R_3 = 1(\cos 264° + i \sin 264°)$
>
> $R_4 = 1(\cos 336° + i \sin 336°)$
>
> $R_5 = 1(\cos 48° + i \sin 48°)$

1816 Show the fifth roots of $1(\cos 240° + i \sin 240°)$ graphically.

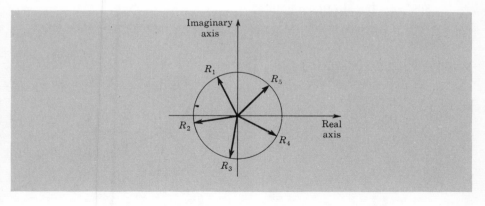

1817 To find the six sixth roots of $1(\cos 240° + i \sin 240°)$, we need to find θ/n and $360/n$. What are they?

$$\frac{\theta}{n} = 40°, \quad \frac{360}{n} = 60°$$

▽**1818** What are the six *arguments* for the sixth roots of $1(\cos 240° + i \sin 240°)$?

$100°, 160°, 220°, 280°, 340°, 400°$ or $40°$

▽**1819** Write in polar form the six sixth roots of $1(\cos 240° + i \sin 240°)$

$R_1 = 1(\cos 100° + i \sin 100°)$

$R_2 = 1(\cos 160° + i \sin 160°)$

$\cdot$
$\cdot$
$\cdot$

$R_6 = 1(\cos 400° + i \sin 400°)$

or $1(\cos 40° + i \sin 40°)$

1820 To find the six sixth roots of $1(\cos 240° + i \sin 240°)$, we first found $240/n$ and $360/n$. If we were showing the roots graphically, we could start with a circle with radius = _____ and find the point corresponding to $240°/n$ and then succeeding points separated by $360°/n$. Locate these points.

$r = 1$

$$\frac{240°}{6} = 40°, \quad \frac{360°}{6} = 60°$$

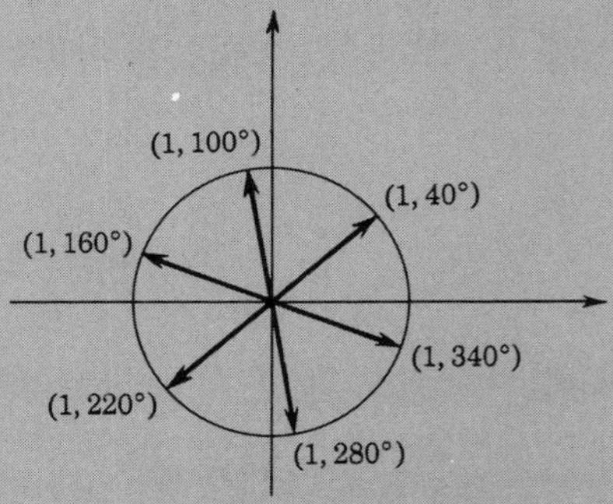

1821 If you start with 40° and successively add 60°, you have the
arguments for the six sixth roots of 1(cos 240° + i sin 240°).
Suggest a short method for finding the *arguments* for the *eight
eighth* roots of this same complex number.

Find 240°/8 and 360°/8. Start with 240°/8 and make eight
additions of 360°/8.

▽**1822** Write the eight eighth roots of 1(cos 240° + i sin 240°).

$\dfrac{240°}{8} = 30°$, $\dfrac{360°}{8} = 45°$

$R_1 = 1(\cos 75° + i \sin 75°)$

$R_2 = 1(\cos 120° + i \sin 120°)$

$R_3 = 1(\cos 165° + i \sin 165°)$

.
.
.

$R_8 = 1(\cos 390° + i \sin 390°)$

or $1(\cos 30° + i \sin 30°)$

1823 Given the complex number $C = 1,024(\cos 30° + i \sin 30°)$. To find
the ten tenth roots of this number, we first indicate this problem as
$C^{1/10} = [2^{10}(\cos 30° + i \sin 30°)]^{1/10}$. Second the right member
is written (copy the entire equation as you answer)
(1) = ___ [cos (_____ + _____ k) + i sin (_____ + _____ k)]
where **(2)** k = _____ , _____ , _____ , . . . , _____

(1) $2\left[\cos\left(\dfrac{30°}{10} + \dfrac{360°}{10} \cdot k\right) + i \sin\left(\dfrac{30°}{10} + \dfrac{360°}{10} \cdot k\right)\right]$

$2[\cos (3° + 36°k) + i \sin (3° + 36°k)]$

(2) $k = 1, 2, 3, \ldots, 10$

1824 What are the amplitudes (or arguments) for the ten tenth roots of
$1,024(\cos 30° + i \sin 30°)$?

39°, 75°, 111°, 147°, 183°, 219°, 255°, 291°, 327°, 363°

1825 If the ten tenth roots of $1,024(\cos 30° + i \sin 30°)$ were represented graphically, they would appear as points (or as vectors

continued →

having their end points) on a circle with a radius of **(1)**_____ units. The points would appear at equal intervals of **(2)**_____°, starting with R_1 at **(3)**_____ when $k = 1$.

(1) 2 **(2)** 36 **(3)** 39

1826 When $k = 1$, the tenth root of $1,024(\cos 30° + i \sin 30°)$ is the complex number _____ (in polar form).

$2(\cos 39° + i \sin 39°)$

1827 Change the complex number $2(\cos 39° + i \sin 39°)$ to rectangular form. Refer to Panel 1.

$a + bi = r(\cos 39° + i \sin 39°) = 2(0.777 + i\,0.629)$
$= 1.554 + 1.258i$

▽1828 Find the cube roots of $8(\cos 84° + i \sin 84°)$. Leave answers in polar form.

$2(\cos 148° + i \sin 148°)$ $2(\cos 268° + i \sin 268°)$
$2(\cos 388° + i \sin 388°)$ or $2(\cos 28° + i \sin 28°)$

▽1829 Find the square roots of $-2 + 2\sqrt{3}i$ by changing the number to its polar form and applying De Moivre's theorem.

$(-2 + 2\sqrt{3}i)^{1/2} = [4(\cos 120° + i \sin 120°)]^{1/2}$
$R_1 = 2(\cos 240° + i \sin 240°)$
$R_2 = 2(\cos 420° + i \sin 420°)$ or $2(\cos 60° + i \sin 60°)$

1830 Refer to the answer in frame 1829. Change **(1)** R_1 and **(2)** R_2 to rectangular form.

(1) $R_1 = 2\left(\dfrac{-1}{2} - \dfrac{i\sqrt{3}}{2}\right) = -1 - i\sqrt{3}$

(2) $R_2 = 2\left(\dfrac{1}{2} + \dfrac{i\sqrt{3}}{2}\right) = 1 + i\sqrt{3}$

1831 If $-1 - i\sqrt{3}$ is a square root of $-2 + 2i\sqrt{3}$, then $(-1 - i\sqrt{3})^2 =$ $-2 + 2i\sqrt{3}$. **(1)** Compute the square of $(-1 - i\sqrt{3})$, keeping the number in rectangular form. **(2)** Is $(-1 - i\sqrt{3})$ one of the square roots of $-2 + 2i\sqrt{3}$?

(1) $(-1 - i\sqrt{3})^2 = (1 - 3) + (\sqrt{3} + \sqrt{3})i = -2 + 2i\sqrt{3}$ **(2)** yes

1832 Is $(-\sqrt{3} - i)$ a root of the equation $x^3 + 8i = 0$? Check by substituting $(-\sqrt{3} - i)$ for x and simplifying the result. Perform the multiplication by first changing $(-\sqrt{3} - i)$ to polar form.

$$(-\sqrt{3} - i)^3 + 8i = [2(\cos 210° + i \sin 210°)]^3 + 8i$$
$$= 2^3[\cos 3(210)° + i \sin 3(210)°] + 8i$$
$$= 8(\cos 630° + i \sin 630°) + 8i$$
$$= 8(\cos 270° + i \sin 270°) + 8i$$
$$= 8 \cdot 0 + 8 (-1i) + 8i = 0$$

Therefore, $(-\sqrt{3} - i)^3 + 8i = 0$ and $-\sqrt{3} - i$ is a root of the equation $x^3 + 8i = 0$

1833 Given the equation $x^3 + 8i = 0$, find the three roots. *Note:* If $x^3 + 8i = 0$, then $x^3 = -8i$ and $x = [-8i]^{1/3}$.

$R_1 = 2(\cos 210° + i \sin 210°)$

$R_2 = 2(\cos 330° + i \sin 300°)$

$R_3 = 2(\cos 90° + i \sin 90°)$

If your answers are all correct, skip to frame 1837.
If your answers are not all correct, go on to frame 1834.

1834 Make a sketch to see how to change $-8i$ to polar form. Write the polar form.

Imaginary axis

Real axis

$P(0, -8i)$

$r = \sqrt{0 + (-8)^2} = 8$

$\theta = 270°$

$-8i = 8(\cos 270° + i \sin 270°)$

1835 $(-8i)^{1/3} = [8(\cos 270° + i \sin 270°)]^{1/3}$. Copy the entire equation as you answer. $8^{1/3}[\cos (\underline{\hspace{1cm}} + \underline{\hspace{1cm}} k) + i \sin (\underline{\hspace{1cm}} + \underline{\hspace{1cm}} k)]$

$$8^{1/3}\left[\cos\left(\frac{270}{3} + \frac{360}{3} k\right) + i \sin\left(\frac{270}{3} + \frac{360}{3} k\right)\right]$$

1836   For each *cube* root of $-8i$, the absolute value is **(1)**_____ and the arguments are **(2)**_____, _____, _____. Therefore, the three cube roots written in polar form are **(3)** $R_1 = $ _____ (cos _____ + $i \sin$ _____) **(4)** $R_2 = $ _____ (cos _____ + $i \sin$ _____) **(5)** $R_3 = $ _____ (cos _____ + $i \sin$ _____) (copy the entire equations as you answer).

(1) 2   **(2)** $210°, 330°, 90°$ **(3)** $R_1 = 2(\cos 210° + i \sin 210°)$

(4) $R_2 = 2(\cos 330° + i \sin 330°)$

(5) $R_3 = 2(\cos 90° + i \sin 90°)$

1837   To find the seven roots of the equation $x^7 + 1 = 0$, first note that $x^7 = $ **(1)**_____ and $x = $ **(2)**_____. (In advanced algebra you learn that the number of roots of an equation of the form $x^n \pm 1 = 0$ is indicated by the exponent n if n is a positive integer.)

(1) -1 **(2)** $(-1)^{1/7}$

1838 $x = (-1)^{1/7} = [\underline{\hspace{5cm}}]^{1/7}$. Fill in the polar form for -1.

$[1(\cos 180° + i \sin 180°)]^{1/7}$

1839 $(-1)^{1/7} = [1(\cos 180° + i \sin 180°)]^{1/7}$. Copy the entire equation as you answer. $[1^{1/7} \cos (\underline{\hspace{1cm}} + \underline{\hspace{1cm}} k) + i \sin (\underline{\hspace{1cm}} + \underline{\hspace{1cm}} k)]$

$$1^{1/7}\left[\cos\left(\frac{180°}{7} + \frac{360°}{7} k\right) + i \sin\left(\frac{180°}{7} + \frac{360°}{7} k\right)\right]$$

or

$1^{1/7}[\cos (25\tfrac{5}{7}° + 51\tfrac{3}{7}°k) + i \sin (25\tfrac{5}{7}° + 51\tfrac{3}{7}°k)]$

Note: The sum of $25\tfrac{5}{7}°$ and $51\tfrac{3}{7}°$ is $77\tfrac{1}{7}°$

1840 For each seventh root of -1, the absolute value is **(1)**_____ and
the arguments are, respectively, **(2)** $77\frac{1}{7}°$, _____, _____, _____,
_____, _____, _____.
(3) Write in polar form the root which has $77\frac{1}{7}°$ as its argument.

(1) 1

(2) $77\frac{1}{7}°$, $128\frac{4}{7}°$, $180°$, $231\frac{3}{7}°$, $282\frac{6}{7}°$, $334\frac{2}{7}°$, $385\frac{5}{7}°$ or $25\frac{5}{7}°$

(3) $1(\cos 77\frac{1}{7}° + i \sin 77\frac{1}{7}°)$ or $(\cos 77\frac{1}{7}° + i \sin 77\frac{1}{7}°)$

1841 If $x^2 = -3 + 4i$, what are the two roots of this equation? *Suggestion:*
1. $x = (-3 + 4i)^{?}$
2. Change $-3 + 4i$ to polar form (use Panel 1 to find the approximate value of the argument).
3. Check this answer before completing the solution.

$x = (-3 + 4i)^{1/2}$ and $-3 + 4i = 5(\cos 127° + i \sin 127°)$

1842 $(-3 + 4i)^{1/2} = [5(\cos 127° + i \sin 127°)]^{1/2}$

$R_1 = $ **(1)**_____

$R_2 = $ **(2)**_____

(1) $\sqrt{5}(\cos 243\frac{1}{2}° + i \sin 243\frac{1}{2}°)$

(2) $\sqrt{5}(\cos 423\frac{1}{2}° + i \sin 423\frac{1}{2}°)$ or $\sqrt{5}(\cos 63\frac{1}{2}° + i \sin 63\frac{1}{2}°)$

1843 **(1)** How many roots has the equation $x^9 - i = 0$? To find the
roots of this equation, we would first write the equation in the form
$x = $ **(2)** (_____$)^{1/9}$

(1) nine   **(2)** i

1844 The next step in finding the roots of the equation $x = (x)^{1/9}$ is to
write the complex number i in its polar form. **(1)** Represent i
graphically and then **(2)** write the polar form.

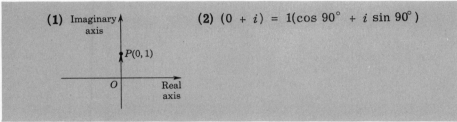

(1) Imaginary axis

$P(0, 1)$

O Real axis

(2) $(0 + i) = 1(\cos 90° + i \sin 90°)$

1845 Copy the entire right side of the equation as you answer.

$$[r(\cos\theta + i\sin\theta)]^{1/n} = [r^? \cos(\underline{\hspace{1cm}} + \underline{\hspace{1cm}}k)$$
$$+ i\sin(\underline{\hspace{1cm}} + \underline{\hspace{1cm}}k)]$$

$$\left[r^{1/n}\cos\left(\frac{\theta}{n} + \frac{360k}{n}\,k\right) + i\sin\left(\frac{\theta}{n} + \frac{360k}{n}\,k\right)\right]$$

1846 Copy the entire right side of the equation as you answer.

$$[1(\cos 90° + i\sin 90°)]^{1/9} = 1[\cos(\underline{\hspace{1cm}} + \underline{\hspace{1cm}}k)$$
$$+ i\sin(\underline{\hspace{1cm}} + \underline{\hspace{1cm}}k)]$$

$$1\left[\cos\left(\frac{90°}{9} + \frac{360°k}{9}\,k\right) + i\sin\left(\frac{90°}{9} + \frac{360°k}{9}\,k\right)\right]$$
or
$$1[\cos(10° + 40°k) + i\sin(10° + 40°k)]$$

1847 Write the nine ninth roots of $x^9 - i = 0$ (in polar form).

$$R_1 = \cos 50° + i\sin 50° \quad R_2 = \cos 90° + i\sin 90°$$
$$R_3 = \cos 130° + i\sin 130° \quad R_4 = \cos 170° + i\sin 170°$$
$$R_5 = \cos 210° + i\sin 210° \quad R_6 = \cos 250° + i\sin 250°$$
$$R_7 = \cos 290° + i\sin 290° \quad R_8 = \cos 330° + i\sin 330°$$
$$R_9 = \cos 10° + i\sin 10°$$

1848 To check that $\cos 10° + i\sin 10°$ is a root of the equation $x^9 =$ we must show that $(\cos 10° + i\sin 10°)^9 = i$. Using De Moivre's theorem, find $(\cos 10° + i\sin 10°)^9$.

$$(\cos 10° + i\sin 10°)^9 = \cos 90° + i\sin 90° = 0 + i = i$$
Therefore, $\cos 10° + i\sin 10°$ is a root of $x^9 = i$ or $x^9 - i = 0$

1849   Refer to the list of the nine roots of the equation $x^9 - i = 0$ in frame 1847. Make a graphical representation of these roots.

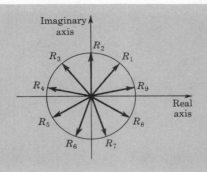

1850   In applying De Moivre's theorem to find the n nth roots of a complex number, there is a comment to be made about the choices of values for k. Our choice is $k = 1, 2, 3, \ldots, n$. We could equally well let $k = 0, 1, 2, \ldots, (n - 1)$. As an example, first find the five fifth roots of $32(\cos 200° + i \sin 200)$ where $k = 1, 2, 3, 4, 5$, respectively.

$R_1 = 2(\cos 112° + i \sin 112°)$ $R_2 = 2(\cos 184° + i \sin 184°)$
$R_3 = 2(\cos 256° + i \sin 256°)$ $R_4 = 2(\cos 328° + i \sin 328°)$
$R_5 = 2(\cos 40° + i \sin 40°)$

1851   Now find the five fifth roots of $32(\cos 200° + i \sin 200°)$ where $k = 0, 1, 2, 3, 4$.

$R_1 = 2(\cos 40° + i \sin 40°)$ $R_2 = 2(\cos 112° + i \sin 112°)$
$R_3 = 2(\cos 184° + i \sin 184°)$ $R_4 = 2(\cos 256° + i \sin 256°)$
$R_5 = 2(\cos 328° + i \sin 328°)$

1852   Addition of complex numbers is more easily performed if the numbers are in _____ (rectangular, polar) form.

rectangular

1853   Find the sum of $a + bi$ and $c + di$.

$(a + c) + (b + d)i$

1854 **(1)** Show graphically the addition of $2 + 3i$ and $7 - 4i$. **(2)** Find the algebraic sum.

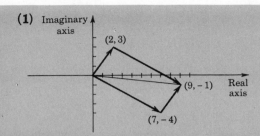

(2) $(2 + 3i) + (7 - 4i) = 9 - i$

1855 **(1)** Show graphically the difference $(3 + 5i) - (3 - 5i)$. **(2)** Find the difference algebraically.

(1)

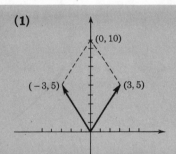

(2) $(3 + 5i) - (3 - 5i) = 0 + 10i$

1856 Find the algebraic sum $(3 + 2i) + (\sqrt{2} + 7i) + \sqrt{3}i$

$(3 + \sqrt{2}) + (9 + \sqrt{3})i$

1857 Find the product, working in rectangular form, for the following: $(a + bi) \cdot (c + di)$.

$(ac - bd) + (bc + ad)i$

1858 Find the product $(8 + \sqrt{2}i) \cdot (1 + \sqrt{3}i)$.

$(8 - \sqrt{6}) + (\sqrt{2} + 8\sqrt{3})i$

1859 Find the product $(3 - \sqrt{-4}) \cdot (7 + \sqrt{-9})$.

$(3 + 2i) \cdot (7 + 3i) = 27 - 5i$

1860 Simplify the following: **(1)** i^4, **(2)** i^{15}, and **(3)** i^{78}.

(1) 1   **(2)** $-i$ **(3)** -1

1861 Perform the indicated operations $i[(3i + 6) - (2i + 7)]$.

$-1 - i$

1862 Find values for **(1)** x and **(2)** y which satisfy the equation $8x + 3yi = 4 - 9i$.

(1) $x = \frac{1}{2}$ **(2)** $y = -3$

Solution: If two complex numbers are equal, then we know that the real components $8x$ and 4 are equal and the imaginary components $-3y$ and -9 are equal.

Therefore, $8x = 4$, $x = \frac{1}{2}$ and $3y = -9$, $y = -3$.

1863 Find values for **(1)** x and **(2)** y which satisfy the equation $2x + 3yi - 4 = 5x - yi + 8i$.

(1) $x = -\frac{4}{3}$ **(2)** $y = 2$

1864 Find the quotient $(a + bi)/(c + di)$.   Write the answer in standard $a + bi$ form.

$$\frac{ac + bd}{c^2 + d^2} + \frac{bc - ad}{c^2 + d^2} i$$

Solution:

$$\frac{a + bi}{c + di} \cdot \frac{c - di}{c - di} = \frac{(ac + bd) + (bc - ad)i}{c^2 + d^2} = \frac{ac + bd}{c^2 + d^2} + \frac{bc - ad}{c^2 + d^2} i$$

1865 Find the quotient $(2 - 3i)/(3 + 2i)$.

> $-i$
>
> *Solution:*
>
> $$\frac{2 - 3i}{3 + 2i} \cdot \frac{3 - 2i}{3 - 2i} = \frac{(6 - 6)}{13} - \frac{(9 + 4)i}{13} = 0 - \frac{13i}{13} = -i$$

1866 Perform the indicated operations $\dfrac{2 + i}{1 + 3i} + \dfrac{2 - i}{1 - 3i}$

> **1**
>
> *Solution:*
>
> $$\frac{(2 + i)(1 - 3i)}{(1 + 3i)(1 - 3i)} + \frac{(2 - i)(1 + 3i)}{(1 - 3i)(1 + 3i)} = \frac{5 - 5i}{10} + \frac{5 + 5i}{10}$$
>
> $$= \frac{10}{10} = 1$$

1867 What is the product of the two complex numbers
$$[r_1(\cos \theta_1 + i \sin \theta_1)] \cdot [r_2(\cos \theta_2 + i \sin \theta_2)]$$

> $r_1 r_2[\cos (\theta_1 + \theta_2) + i \sin (\theta_1 + \theta_2)]$

1868 **(1)** Find the indicated product in polar form.
(2) Express the answer in rectangular form.
$$2\left(\cos \frac{2\pi}{3} + i \sin \frac{2\pi}{3}\right) \cdot 3\left(\cos \frac{\pi}{6} + i \sin \frac{\pi}{6}\right)$$

> **(1)** $6\left(\cos \dfrac{5\pi}{6} + i \sin \dfrac{5\pi}{6}\right)$ **(2)** $-3\sqrt{3} + 3i$

1869 What is the quotient $\dfrac{r_1(\cos \theta_1 + i \sin \theta_1)}{r_2(\cos \theta_2 + i \sin \theta_2)}$?

> $\dfrac{r_1}{r_2}[\cos (\theta_1 - \theta_2) + i \sin (\theta_1 - \theta_2)]$

1870 **(1)** Find the indicated quotient in polar form, **(2)** then express the result in rectangular form.

$$\frac{8(\cos\ 105^\circ\ +\ i\ \sin\ 105^\circ)}{2(\cos\ 15^\circ\ +\ i\ \sin\ 15^\circ)}$$

(1) $4(\cos\ 90^\circ\ +\ i\ \sin\ 90^\circ)$ **(2)** $4i$

1871 r is called the **(1)**_____ of the complex number $r(\cos\ \theta\ +\ i\ \sin\ \theta)$. θ is called the **(2)**_____ of the complex number $r(\cos\ \theta\ +\ i\ \sin\ \theta)$.

(1) absolute value or modulus   **(2)** amplitude or argument

1872 Complete the statement of De Moivre's theorem when n is a positive integer. $[r(\cos\ \theta\ +\ i\ \sin\ \theta)]^n =$ _____.

$r^n(\cos\ n\theta\ +\ i\ \sin\ n\theta)$

1873 Complete the statement below for finding roots of a complex number.

$[r(\cos\ \theta\ +\ i\ \sin\ \theta)]^{1/n} =$ _____.

$$r^{1/n}\left[\cos\left(\frac{\theta}{n}\ +\ \frac{360k}{n}\ k\right)\ +\ i\ \sin\left(\frac{\theta}{n}\ +\ \frac{360k}{n}\ k\right)\right]$$

1874 **(1)** Change $1 + i$ to polar form, **(2)** then find $(1 + i)^5$. **(3)** Change the result back to rectangular form.

(1) $1 + i = \sqrt{2}(\cos\ 45^\circ\ +\ i\ \sin\ 45^\circ)$

(2) $(1 + i)^5 = (\sqrt{2})^5\,(\cos\ 225^\circ\ +\ i\ \sin\ 225^\circ)$

$$= 4\sqrt{2}\left[\frac{-1}{\sqrt{2}}\ +\ i\left(\frac{-1}{\sqrt{2}}\right)\right]$$

(3) $-4 - 4i$

1875 Find four fourth roots of $81[\cos(\pi/3) + i\sin(\pi/3)]$.

$$3\left[\cos\left(\frac{\pi}{12} + \frac{2\pi}{4}k\right) + i\sin\left(\frac{\pi}{12} + \frac{2\pi}{4}k\right)\right]$$

where $k = 1, 2, 3, 4$

$$R_1 = 3\left(\cos\frac{7\pi}{12} + i\sin\frac{7\pi}{12}\right) \qquad R_2 = 3\left(\cos\frac{13\pi}{12} + i\sin\frac{13\pi}{12}\right)$$

$$R_3 = 3\left(\cos\frac{19\pi}{12} + i\sin\frac{19\pi}{12}\right) \qquad R_4 = 3\left(\cos\frac{\pi}{12} + i\sin\frac{\pi}{12}\right)$$

1876 Solve the equation $x^6 - 1 = 0$ (i.e., find the six roots).

$$x^6 = 1, \; x = 1^{1/6}$$
$$1^{1/6} = (1 + 0i)^{1/6} = [1(\cos 0° + i\sin 0°)]^{1/6}$$
$$= \{1[\cos(0° + 60°k) + i\sin(0° + 60°k)]\}$$
$$\text{where } k = 1, 2, \ldots, 6$$

$R_1 = \cos 60° + i\sin 60°$

$R_2 = \cos 120° + i\sin 120°$

$\cdot$
$\cdot$
$\cdot$

$R_6 = \cos 360° + i\sin 360°$

1877 Refer to the answer in frame 1876. Find the sum of the six roots of the equation. *Suggestion:* Change the complex numbers to rectangular form.

0

Solution: In rectangular form

$$R_1 = \frac{1}{2} + \frac{\sqrt{3}}{2}i \qquad R_2 = -\frac{1}{2} + \frac{\sqrt{3}}{2}i$$

$$R_3 = -1 + 0i \qquad R_4 = -\frac{1}{2} - \frac{\sqrt{3}}{2}i$$

$$R_5 = \frac{1}{2} - \frac{\sqrt{3}}{2}i \qquad R_6 = 1 + 0i$$

Sum $= 0 + 0i = 0$

1878 **(1)** Is $-1 + \sqrt{3}i$ a root of the equation $x^3 - 1 = 0$?
(2) Check by substitution.

(1) no **(2)** $(-1 + \sqrt{3}i)^3 - 1 = 8 - 1 \neq 0$

1879 **(1)** Is $(1 + i\sqrt{3}/2)$ a root of the equation $x^3 - 1 = 0$?
(2) Check by substitution.

(1) no **(2)** $\dfrac{(1 + i\sqrt{3})^3}{2} - 1 = \dfrac{-8}{8} - 1 \neq 0$

1880 Find the roots of $x^3 - 1 = 0$

$$\frac{-1}{2} + \frac{\sqrt{3}}{2} i \;, \quad \frac{-1}{2} - \frac{\sqrt{3}}{2} i \;, \; 1$$

Solution: $R_1 = \cos 120° + i \sin 120° = \dfrac{-1}{2} + \dfrac{\sqrt{3}}{2} i$

$R_2 = \cos 240° + i \sin 240° = \dfrac{-1}{2} - \dfrac{\sqrt{3}}{2} i$

$R_3 = \cos 360° + i \sin 360° = 1$

1881 Represent graphically the resultant of two forces: one of 50 lb which makes an angle of 30° with the positive x axis and the other of 80 lb which makes an angle of 120° with the positive x axis.

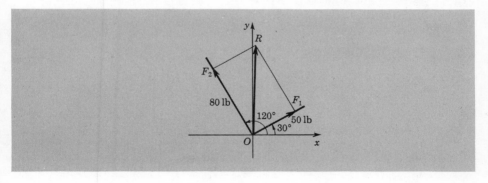

1882 Refer to the problem in frame 1881. Compute the **(1)** magnitude of the resultant and the **(2)** direction it takes with respect to the positive x axis.

> **(1)** 94 approximately   **(2)** $88°$
>
> *Note:* The law of cosines could be used to find the length of OR, and the law of sines for angle ROF_1. However, since angle F_1 is a right angle, you could very well use a simpler formula.

1883 Resolve a vector represented by the complex number $9(\cos 60° + i \sin 60°)$ into its x and y components. Make a sketch.

> $x = 4.5,\quad y \approx 7.8$
>
> *Solution:*
>
> $$\cos 60° = \frac{x}{9}$$
>
> $$x = 9 \cdot \frac{1}{2} = 4.5$$
>
> $$\sin 60° = \frac{y}{9}$$
>
> $$y = 9(0.866) \approx 7.8$$
>
>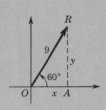

1884 **(1)** Represent graphically as vectors the complex numbers $A = 5 + 3i$ and $B = -2 - 6i$. Find their sum graphically. **(2)** Check your answer algebraically.

> **(1)**
>
>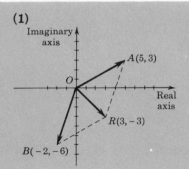
>
> **(2)** $(5 + 3i) + (-2 - 6i) = 3 - 3i$

1885 Show by a vector sketch the speed and direction of a passenger on a ship if he is strolling due south across the deck at the rate of 3 mph while the ship is sailing due east at the rate of 25 mph.

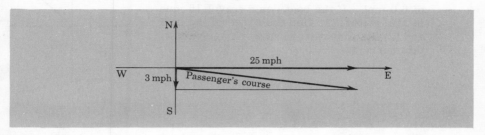

1886 Compute the (1) speed and (2) direction of the passenger in the problem in frame 1885.

(1) $S \approx 25.1$ mph   (2) $x \approx 7°$ ($7°$ south of east)

1887 A plane is flying at an air speed of 360 mph in a wind blowing from the south at 30 mph. Represent by a vector sketch the direction in which the pilot must head the plane in order to fly due east.

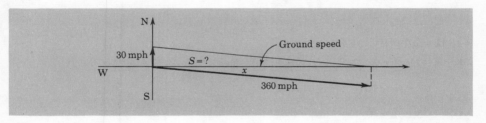

1888 Find the (1) actual speed of the plane in the easterly direction and the (2) angle x, in the problem in frame 1887.

(1) $S \approx 359$ mph   (2) $x \approx 5°$

1889 Two forces of 2.0 lb and 3.0 lb produce a resultant force of 4.0 lb. (1) Represent these forces as vectors and (2) find the angle the resultant makes with the smaller force.

(1)   (2) $x \approx 47°$

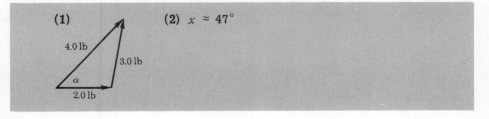

1890 A boat is headed in a direction 48° east of north as indicated in the sketch. The current of the stream is due south at the rate of 6.0 mph. If the boat could travel 16 mph in still water, **(1)** find the speed of the boat and **(2)** its direction when working against this current.

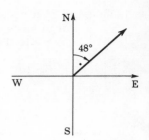

(1) $S \approx 12.8$ mph   **(2)** $x \approx 20°$

Solution: $S^2 = 16^2 + 6^2 - 2 \cdot 6 \cdot 16 \cos 48°$

$$S \approx \sqrt{163.6}$$

$$\approx 12.8$$

$$\sin \frac{x}{6} = \sin \frac{48°}{12.8}$$

$$x \approx 20°$$

1891 Simplify the following:

$$\frac{3(\cos 112° + i \sin 112°) \cdot 4(\cos 216° + i \sin 216°)}{6(\cos 88° + i \sin 88°)}$$

$2(\cos 240° + i \sin 240°)$

1892 Find the fifth roots of $16 - 16i\sqrt{3}$.

$16 - 16i\sqrt{3} = 32(\cos 300° + i \sin 300°)$

$[16 - 16i\ 3]^{1/5} = [32(\cos 300° + i \sin 300°]^{1/5}$

$$= 2\left[\cos\left(\frac{300°}{5} + \frac{360°}{5}k\right) + i \sin\left(\frac{300°}{5} + \frac{360°}{5}k\right)\right]$$

continued →

where $k = 1, 2, 3, 4, 5$

$R_1 = 2(\cos 132° + i \sin 132°)$

$R_2 = 2(\cos 204° + i \sin 204°)$

$R_3 = 2(\cos 276° + i \sin 276°)$

$R_4 = 2(\cos 348° + i \sin 348°)$

$R_5 = 2(\cos 420° + i \sin 420°)$

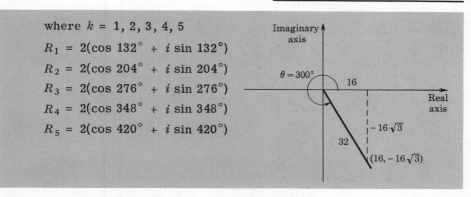

▽**1893** Show the five roots of $16 - 16i\sqrt{3}$ graphically.

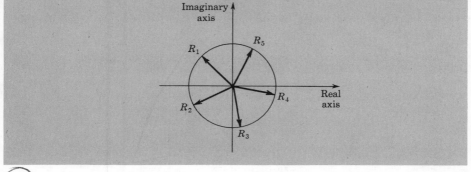

▽**1894** Solve $x^3 + 4i\sqrt{3} = 4$. $x^3 + 4i\sqrt{3} = 4$

$x^3 = 4 - 4i\sqrt{3}$

$x = (4 - 4i\sqrt{3})$

$\quad = [8(\cos 300° + i \sin 300°)]^{1/3}$

$\quad = 2\left[\cos\left(\dfrac{300°}{3} + \dfrac{360°}{3}k\right) - i\sin\left(\dfrac{300°}{3} + \dfrac{360°}{3}k\right)\right]$

where $k = 1, 2, 3$

$x_1 = 2(\cos 220° + i \sin 220°)$

$x_2 = 2(\cos 340° + i \sin 340°)$

$x_3 = 2(\cos 460° + i \sin 460°)$

or $2(\cos 100° + i \sin 100°)$

▽1895 Perform the multiplication and simplification necessary to prove that

$$r(\cos x + i \sin x) \cdot s(\cos B + i \sin B) = rs[\cos(x + B) + i \sin(x + B)]$$

Refer to Panel 8 if necessary when you are simplifying.

$r(\cos x + i \sin x) \cdot s(\cos B + i \sin B)$

$= r \cdot s(\cos x \cos B + i \sin x \cos B$
$\quad + i \cos x \sin B - \sin x \sin B)$ multiplication

$= r \cdot s[(\cos x \cos B - \sin x \sin B)$
$\quad + i \sin x \cos B + \cos x \sin B)]$ rearranging and collecting terms

$= r \cdot s[\cos(x + B) + i \sin(x + B)]$ addition formula, see Panel 8II

▽1896 Change the following complex numbers to polar form and perform the indicated operations:

$$\frac{[1/\sqrt{2} + i(1/\sqrt{2})]^7}{1 - i}$$

Express your answer in $a + bi$ form.

$$\frac{[1/\sqrt{2} + i(1/\sqrt{2})]^7}{1 - i} = \frac{[1(\cos 45° + i \sin 45°)]^7}{\sqrt{2}(\cos 315° + i \sin 315°)}$$

$$= \frac{1(\cos 315° + i \sin 315°)}{\sqrt{2}(\cos 315° + i \sin 315°)}$$

$$= \frac{1}{\sqrt{2}}(\cos 0° + i \sin 0°)$$

$$= \frac{1}{\sqrt{2}}(1 + i0)$$

$$= \frac{1}{\sqrt{2}} \text{ or } \frac{\sqrt{2}}{2}$$

SELF-TEST 6

1 Given the function f such that $y = f(x)$ and $y = \frac{1}{2}x + 5$, find
   (a) $f(0)$, (b) $f(4)$, and (c) $f(-6)$.

2 If $y = f(x) = \frac{1}{2}x + 5$, what is the inverse function $f^{-1}(x)$?

   In Prob. 3, 4, and 5 for the inverse trigonometric functions:
   (a) State the quadrant in which θ may terminate. (b) Give the
   principal value of θ in (b) *degrees* and in (c) *radians*. (d) Make
   a sketch of the angle in standard position representing the
   principal value of θ.

3 $\theta = \arcsin \frac{1}{2}$.

4 $\theta = \arccos (\sqrt{2}/2)$.

5 $\theta = \arctan (-\sqrt{3})$.

6 Sketch the graph of $y = \sin^{-1} x$ on
   a set of axes as labeled here.
   Your graph should indicate the
   principal-value function.

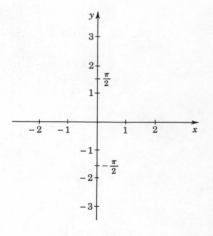

7 Find the value of $\sin (\mathrm{Cos}^{-1} \frac{1}{2})$.

8 Find the value of $\mathrm{Tan}^{-1} (\cos 180°)$.

9 Show that $2 \mathrm{Sin}^{-1} \frac{1}{2} = \mathrm{Cos}^{-1} \frac{1}{2}$.

10 Find the value of $\sin [\mathrm{Tan}^{-1} (-2)]$.

11 Prove that $\mathrm{Tan}^{-1} 1 + \mathrm{Tan}^{-1} \frac{1}{2} = \mathrm{Tan}^{-1} 3$, without using Panel 1.

12 Find $\mathrm{Arccos} [\sin (\pi/2)]$.

13 Find the value of $\sin^{-1} u + \sin^{-1}(-u)$ for $-1 \le u \le 1$.

14 Find the value of $\sin\left[\text{Arcsin } \frac{4}{5} - \text{Arcsin}\left(-\frac{1}{3}\right)\right]$.

Inverse Trigonometric Functions

1897 Given the algebraic equation $y = 3x + 2$, we say that y is a function of x, $y = f(x)$. This statement implies that if we are given a value for x, we can find the corresponding value for y. We also say that x is the independent variable and y is the dependent variable. In the example above, let $x = 2$, then $y = $ **(1)**____. If $x = -2$, then $y = $ **(2)**____. If $x = 0$, then $y = $ **(3)**____. If $x = 0.4$, then $y = $ **(4)**____. **(5)** With each value assigned to x how many values did you find for y?

(1) 8   **(2)** -4   **(3)** 2   **(4)** 3.2   **(5)** one

1898 The notation $y = f(x)$ is read "y is the value of the function f at x" or more briefly "y equals f at x." If $y = f(x)$ when $y = 1 - x^2$, **(1)** find $f(-4)$. (This means find the value of y when $x = -4$.) Find **(2)** $f(-3)$, **(3)** $f(-2)$, **(4)** $f(-1)$, **(5)** $f(-\frac{1}{2})$, **(6)** $f(0)$, **(7)** $f(\frac{1}{2})$, **(8)** $f(1)$, **(9)** $f(2)$, and **(10)** $f(3)$.

(1) -15   **(2)** -8   **(3)** -3   **(4)** 0   **(5)** $\frac{3}{4}$

(6) 1   **(7)** $\frac{3}{4}$ **(8)** 0   **(9)** -3   **(10)** -8

1899 You are given the function f such that $y = f(x)$ is defined by $y = 4x - 3$. Find **(1)** $f(0)$, **(2)** $f(3)$, **(3)** $f(\frac{1}{2})$, and **(4)** $f(-\frac{1}{4})$.

(1) -3   **(2)** 9   **(3)** -1   **(4)** -4

1900   Sometimes we are given a function $y = f(x)$ such as $y = 4x - 3$ and
we want to reverse the point of view and consider an equivalent
form of the function in which y is the independent variable and x is
the dependent variable. In which case, it may be more convenient to
solve the defining equation for x, thus $x = (y + 3)/4$. Now we could
write $x = f(y)$. How would you read this?

x is the value of the function f at y or x equals f at y

1901   We usually refer to $y = f(x)$ as the *direct function*, and we refer to
the result of solving for x in terms of y as the *inverse* function.
An expression commonly used to denote the *inverse* function is
$x = f^{-1}(y)$. If the direction function $y = f(x)$ is defined by $y = \frac{1}{2}x + 6$, then the inverse function is denoted by the expression
(1)_____, and if we solve the equation $y = \frac{1}{2}x + 6$ for x, the
resulting statement is $x = $ (2)_____ .

(1) $x = f^{-1}(y)$ (2) $2y - 12$

1902   (1) Sketch the graphs of (a) $y = f(x)$ where $y = \frac{1}{2}x + 6$ and
(b) $x = f^{-1}(y)$ where $x = 2y - 12$.   (2) Are these two statements
equivalent?

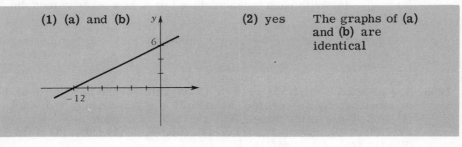

(1) (a) and (b)   (2) yes   The graphs of (a)
and (b) are
identical

1903   The difficulty in using $x = f^{-1}(y)$ as described in frame 1901 is
that we are obliged to think of y as the *independent* variable and
x as the *dependent* variable which is contrary to general usage.
Let us go back to the inverse function $x = f^{-1}(y)$ where $x = 2y - 12$ and interchange the symbols x and y and then study the

continued →

resulting expression $y = f^{-1}(x)$ and $y = 2x - 12$. On the same coordinate system sketch the graphs of $y = f(x)$, where $y = \frac{1}{2}x + 6$, and $y = f^{-1}(x)$, where $y = 2x - 12$.

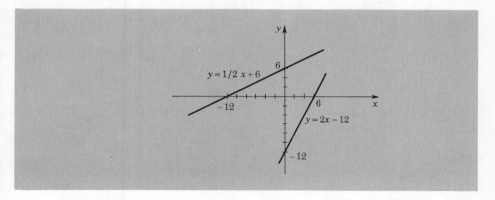

1904 In frame 1903 you sketched the graphs of the functions $y = f(x)$, where $y = \frac{1}{2}x + 6$, and $y = f^{-1}(x)$, where $y = 2x - 12$. You saw that the graphs were not identical. In fact the result of interchanging x and y as we have done, is to reflect the original graph in the line $x = y$ as shown here. As another example, let $y = f(x)$ where $y = 2x + 1$. **(1)** Solve for x, and interchange x and y, then $y = f^{-1}(x) =$ **(2)** _____ .

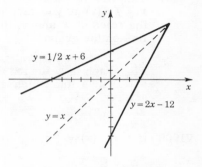

(1) $x = \dfrac{y - 1}{2}$ **(2)** $\dfrac{x - 1}{2}$

1905 Plot $y = f(x)$ and $y = f^{-1}(x)$ on the same set of axes given $y = f(x) = 2x + 1$ and $y = f^{-1}(x) = (x - 1)/2$.

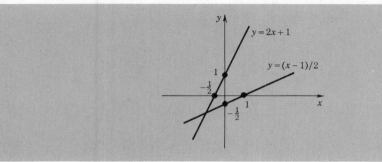

1906 (1) Sketch the line $y = x$ on your graph from frame 1905. (2) Are the lines for $y = f(x)$ and $y = f^{-1}(x)$ reflections of each other across this line $y = x$?

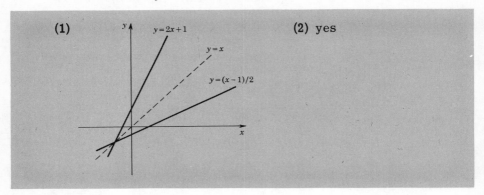

(1)

$y = 2x + 1$

$y = x$

$y = (x-1)/2$

(2) yes

1907 This new function $y = f^{-1}(x)$ is *not* the same as $y = f(x)$ *nor* as $x = f^{-1}(y)$ as you have noted on your graph. When we interchange the roles of x and y, the effect is that of a reflection across what line on the graph?

The graph is reflected across the line representing the equation $y = x$ or a line which makes a 45° angle with the positive x axis.

▽1908 If $y = f(x) = \frac{1}{3}x - 2$ find $y = f^{-1}(x)$.

$y = f^{-1}(x) = 3x + 6$
Solution: If $y = \frac{1}{3}x - 2$, then solving for x, $x = 3y + 6$ and interchanging x and y, $y = 3x + 6$

▽1909 Show graphically that $y = f(x) = \frac{1}{3}x - 2$ and $y = f^{-1}(x) = 3x + 6$ are reflections of each other across the line $y = x$.

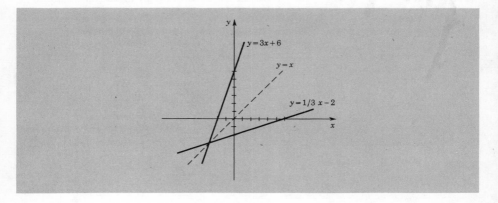

$y = 3x + 6$

$y = x$

$y = 1/3\,x - 2$

1910   Find $y = f^{-1}(x)$, given $y = (2x - 3)/4$.

$$y = f^{-1}(x) = \frac{4x + 3}{2}$$

Solution: If $y = (2x - 3)/4$, then solving for x, $x = (4y + 3)/2$ and interchanging x and y, $y = (4x + 3)/2$.

1911   If $y = x^2$, find $y = f^{-1}(x)$.

$$y = f^{-1}(x) = \pm\sqrt{x}$$

1912   The graph of $y = x^2$ is a parabola as shown in the sketch. With each value of x there is *exactly one* value for y.
For example:

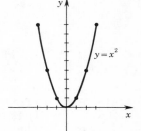

$x =$	2	1	$\frac{1}{2}$	0	$-\frac{1}{2}$	-1	-2
$y =$							

$x =$	2	1	$\frac{1}{2}$	0	$-\frac{1}{2}$	-1	-2
$y =$	4 2	1	$\frac{1}{4}$	0	$\frac{1}{4}$	1	4

1913   If $y = f(x) = x^2$, then $y = f^{-1}(x) = $ **(1)**_____.   Complete the table below for values of y for the inverse function above.

(2)

x	0	$\frac{1}{4}$	1
y			

(1) $\pm\sqrt{x}$ **(2)**

x	0	$\frac{1}{4}$	1
y	0	$\pm\frac{1}{2}$	± 1

1914   The table in frame 1913 indicates that $y = f^{-1}(x)$ is not a *single-valued* function, i.e., for each value of x there are two values of y.

continued →

In order to avoid ambiguity, it is customary to select a portion of the graph having the property that it contains one and only one point for each value of x for which the function is defined. This portion is called the *principal value*, and having it eliminates the confusion which otherwise would result. Refer to the table for the inverse $f^{-1}(x) = \pm\sqrt{x}$ in frame 1913. Let us designate $y = +\sqrt{x}$ as the principal value. Sketch this graph.

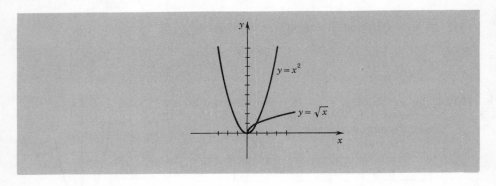

1915 Refer to the table of values for $y = \pm\sqrt{x}$ in frame 1913. Let $y = -\sqrt{x}$. (1) Is this a *single-valued* function? (2) Sketch this graph on the same axes with the $y = +\sqrt{x}$, but use a broken line to show the graph.

(1) yes   (2)

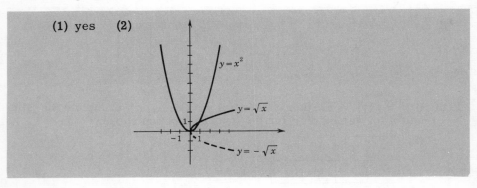

1916 What is the inverse function, $y = f^{-1}(x)$, when $y = f(x)$ is defined by the equation $y = \frac{3}{2}x + 3$?

$$y = f^{-1}(x) = \frac{2x - 6}{3} \quad \text{or} \quad y = \frac{2}{3}x - 2$$

1917   Refer to frame 1916. On the same set of axes, sketch both $y = f(x)$ and $y = f^{-1}(x)$ given $y = \frac{3}{2}x + 3$. Sketch also the reflection line $y = x$.

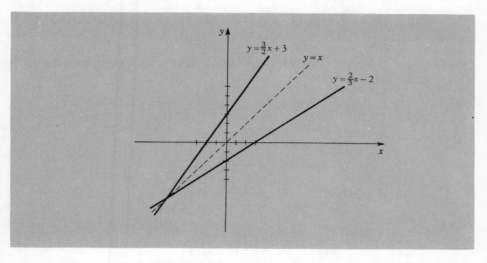

1918   Refer to frame 1917. Is the inverse function a single-valued function? Explain your answer.

yes, with each value of x there is exactly one value of y.

▽**1919**   To sum up what we have said about inverse functions in general, complete the statements below.
   (1) If $y = f(x) = ax + b$, a and b real numbers, then we write the inverse function $f^{-1}(x)$ by interchanging (a)____ and (b)____ and solving the resulting equation for (c)____.
   (2) If the function is such that its inverse is not a single-valued function, for example, $y = ax^2$, then we may restrict the function to certain values and refer to these values as the *principal* values of the function. The principal values have the property that with each x _____.

   (1) (a) x, **(b)** y, **(c)** y **(2)** there corresponds exactly one y

∇1920 If $y = f(x) = -2x + 5$, then $f^{-1}(x) =$

$\dfrac{x - 5}{-2}$ or $\dfrac{-x}{2} + \dfrac{5}{2}$

1921 Graph $y = f(x) = -2x + 5$ and $y = f^{-1}(x) = -x/2 + 5/2$ on the same set of axes.

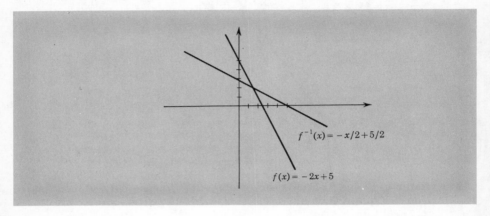

1922 Let us turn now to the trigonometric functions and their inverses. If we consider the relation $y = \sin \theta$, our problem may be to find y when θ is given, or we may be required to find θ, the angle (or real number θ), whose sine y is given.
Examples: If $y = \sin 45°$, then $y = $ **(1)**_____. If $\theta =$ an angle whose sin is 1, then $\theta = $ **(2)**_____.

(1) $\dfrac{\sqrt{2}}{2}$ or $\dfrac{1}{\sqrt{2}}$ **(2)** 90° or 90° + 360°n, where n is an integer.

1923 The following two statements express the same relationship between y and θ: $y = \sin \theta$ and $\theta =$ an angle whose sine is y. The first is called the *direct* form and the second is called the *inverse* form. Write a statement in inverse form which is equivalent to $\frac{1}{2} = \sin 30°$.

30° = an angle whose sine is $\frac{1}{2}$ or $\pi/6$ is an angle whose sin is $\frac{1}{2}$

1924 We speak of $y = \sin \theta$ as the direct form of the sine function. What is the inverse form?

θ = an angle whose sine is y

1925 Expressions or abbreviations for the *inverse* form of $y = \sin \theta$ are $\theta = \arcsin y$ and $\theta = \sin^{-1} y$. Read them as: "θ equals the arc-sine of y" and "θ equals the inverse sine of y." You must remember, however, what they mean: $\theta = \arcsin y$ means $\theta =$ _____ _____.

an angle whose sine is y or a real number whose sine is y

1926 $\theta = \sin^{-1} y$ is read "θ equals the inverse sine of y." It is an abbreviation for what statement?

θ equals an angle whose sine is y or θ is a number whose sine is y

1927 Given $y = \cos \theta$, what are two ways of writing the *inverse* form for this function?

$\theta = \arccos y$, $\theta = \cos^{-1} y$

1928 $\theta = \arccos y$ is the (1)_____ form of the statement whose direct form is (2)_____.   (3) Write a statement giving the meaning of $\theta = \arccos y$.

(1) inverse   (2) $y = \cos \theta$
(3) θ is an angle whose cosine is y or θ is a number whose cosine is y

1929 Given $\sqrt{3}/2 = \cos 30°$.   (1) Write the inverse form (give two).
(2) Make a statement giving the meaning.

(1) $30° = \arccos \dfrac{\sqrt{3}}{2}$, $30° = \cos^{-1} \dfrac{\sqrt{3}}{2}$

(2) $30°$ is an angle whose cosine is $\dfrac{\sqrt{3}}{2}$

1930 Write the following in direct form: **(1)** $330° = \arccos(\sqrt{3}/2)$ and **(2)** $150° = \arccos(\sqrt{3}/2)$. Are the statements true?

(1) $\cos 330° = \dfrac{\sqrt{3}}{2}$, true

(2) $\cos 150° = \dfrac{\sqrt{3}}{2}$, false $\left(\cos 150° = \dfrac{-\sqrt{3}}{2}\right)$

1931 Check the accuracy of **(1)** $90° = \cos^{-1} 1$, **(2)** $180° = \cos^{-1}(-1)$, and **(3)** $270° = \arccos 0$. Write each in direct form.

(1) $\cos 90° = 1$, false   **(2)** $\cos 180° = -1$, true
(3) $\cos 270° = 0$, true

1932 $\pi/4 = \arcsin$ **(1)**_____. This means $\pi/4$ equals an angle whose sine is **(2)**_____.

(1) $\dfrac{1}{\sqrt{2}}$ or $\dfrac{\sqrt{2}}{2}$ or 0.707   **(2)** $\dfrac{1}{\sqrt{2}}$

1933 $\theta = \sin^{-1} y$ is one of the expressions for the **(1)**_____ form of the sine function. Do not confuse this expression with $(\sin y)^{-1}$ which means $1/\sin y$. If we are given $\sin 90° = 1$, we can present the same information in the inverse form by writing **(2)**_____.

(1) inverse   **(2)** $90° = \sin^{-1} 1$

▽1934 Two expressions for the inverse of the function $y = \tan \theta$ are **(1)**_____ and **(2)**_____. **(3)** Make a statement in words interpreting the expressions.

(1) $\theta = \arctan y$ **(2)** $\theta = \tan^{-1} y$
(3) θ is an angle whose tangent is y

1935 **(1)** Is it true that $45° = \arctan 1$?
(2) Is the following statement true? $225° = \arctan 1$

(1) yes   **(2)** yes

∇**1936** Refer to frame 1935. **(1)** Is the inverse function $y = \arctan \theta$ a *single-valued function*? **(2)** Is the direct form $\tan \theta = y$ single-valued?

(1) no. In frame 1935 arctan 1 = 45° and 225° **(2)** yes

1937 $\theta = \arccos (-\frac{1}{2})$. Consider the four quadrants in which an angle may terminate. What values might θ have if θ is an angle between 0 and 360°.

120° and 240°

1938 $\theta = \sin^{-1} 0.588$. Consult Panel 1. What values may θ have if $0 \le \theta \le 2\pi$.

36° and 144°

∇**1939** _____ $= \tan^{-1} 0.325$. Consult Panel 1 to find the answers for this question. Assume that θ is an angle between 0 and 360°.

18° and 198°

1940 You have noted that although the direct forms $\sin \theta = y$, $\cos \theta = y$, $\tan \theta = y$ are single-valued functions, the inverse functions, defined by $\theta = \arcsin y$, $\theta = \arccos y$, and $\theta = \arctan y$ are not. For example, if $\sin 30° = y$, then $y = \frac{1}{2}$ (a single value), but if $\theta = \arcsin \frac{1}{2}$, there are four possibilities for θ as suggested by these sketches. Name them.

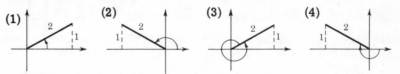

(1) 30°   **(2)** 150°   **(3)** 390°   **(4)** –210°

1941 Refer to frame 1940. If $\theta = \arcsin \frac{1}{2}$, you have many choices of values for θ. $\sin 30° = \sin 150° = \sin (30° + 360°n) = \sin (150° + 360°n) = \frac{1}{2}$, where $n = 0, \pm 1, \pm 2, \ldots$. If $\theta = \arccos \frac{1}{2}$, what are the choices of values for θ?

$\theta = 60°, 300°, (60° + 360°n), (300° + 360°n)$
where $n = 0, \pm 1, \pm 2, \ldots$

1942 In order to simplify the study of the *inverse* trigonometric functions, it is often desirable to restrict the values so that the inverse function is single-valued. The graph of $y = \sin \theta$ will be helpful in selecting the range of θ for the inverse sine function. Sketch the graph of $y = \sin \theta$ where θ has values from -2π to 2π inclusive.

see Panel 3 for the graph of $y = \sin \theta$

1943 Look at the graph of the sine function as shown here. In the interval indicated by the heavy line, we have restricted the values of θ so that we have the set of all angles, from **(1)**_____ to **(2)**_____ inclusive. In this same interval y has values from **(3)**   to **(4)**____ inclusive.

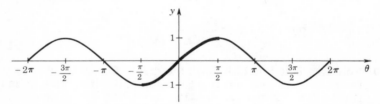

(1) $\dfrac{-\pi}{2}$ or $-90°$ **(2)** $\dfrac{\pi}{2}$ or $90°$ **(3)** -1 **(4)** 1

1944 Look again at the graph in frame 1943. In the interval indicated by the heavy line, namely, **(1)**____ $\le y \le$ ____, there are single values for arcsin y.
(2)

$y =$	1/2	–1/2	$1/\sqrt{2}$	$-1/\sqrt{2}$	0	–1	1
$\theta =$							

(1) $-1 \le y \le 1$
(2)

$y =$	1/2	–1/2	$1/\sqrt{2}$	$-1/\sqrt{2}$	0	–1	1
$\theta =$	30° or $\pi/6$	–30° or $-\pi/6$	45° or $\pi/4$	–45° or $-\pi/4$	0° or 0	–90° or $-\pi/2$	90° or $\pi/2$

1945 When we restrict the values of an inverse trigonometric function so that for each value of the trigonometric function the inverse function has only one value such values are called the *principal values*. The principal values of arcsin y are defined to lie in the interval which we marked on the graph of $\dot{y} = \sin \theta$. According to this definition, the principal value of θ when $\sin \theta = \sqrt{3}/2$ (or $\theta =$ arcsin $\sqrt{3}/2$) is _____ .

60° or $\dfrac{\pi}{3}$

1946 Give the principal value of θ for each of the following statements: **(1)** θ = arcsin 0.375, **(2)** θ = sin⁻¹ 0.500, **(3)** θ = sin⁻¹ 0.866, **(4)** θ = arcsin (-0.906), and **(5)** θ = arcsin (-0.309). Use Panel 1.

(1) 22°   **(2)** 30°   **(3)** 60°   **(4)** -65°   **(5)** -18°

1947 Here are facts to keep in mind: The function $y = \sin \theta$ is *single-valued*; this means that for each value of θ there is **(1)**_____ _____.   The domain of $y = \sin \theta$ is the set of all real numbers; this means that θ may be **(2)**_____.   The range of $y = \sin \theta$ is the set of all real numbers in the interval from   **(3)**_____ to **(4)**____ inclusive.   In frame 1948 we shall review the inverse function.

(1) one value of y **(2)** any real number   **(3)** -1   **(4)** 1

1948 Here are facts to keep in mind regarding the inverse sine function θ = arcsin y. y may be any real number in the interval **(1)**_____ $\leq y \leq$ ____; hence, we say the *domain* of the inverse function is all real numbers from **(2)**____ to **(3)**_____ inclusive.   By restricting the values of θ to the interval **(4)**_____ $\leq \theta \leq$ ___, we define a *single*-valued function for the inverse sine function.   We refer to each value of θ in this interval as the **(5)**_____ value for arcsin y.

(1) $-1 \leq y \leq 1$ **(2)** -1   **(3)** 1

(4) $-90° \leq \theta \leq 90°$ or $\dfrac{-\pi}{2} \leq \theta \leq \dfrac{\pi}{2}$ **(5)** principal

1949 Give the principal value for each of the following: arcsin 0.829 =
(1)_____, arcsin (-0.695) = (2)_____, arcsin (-0.990) = (3)_____,
and sin⁻¹ 0 = (4)_____. Consult Panel 1 when necessary.
Examples: arcsin 0.122 = 7° and arcsin (-0.122) = -7°.

    (1) 56°   (2) -44°   (3) -82°   (4) 0°

1950 (1) Given θ = arcsin 0.743 without the restriction $-\pi/2 \le \theta \le \pi/2$,
find two values of θ which satisfy the equation.   (2) What is the
value of θ called if it must satisfy the condition $-\pi/2 \le \theta \le \pi/2$ and
θ = arcsin y?

    **(1) 48° or (48° + 360°n) n an integer
    132° or (132° + 360°n) n an integer
    (2) principal value**

1951 In constructing the graph of a function, it is customary to represent
the independent variable on the horizontal axis and the dependent
variable on the vertical axis. You are familiar with the graph of
y = sin θ. Values of θ are plotted along the (1)_____ axis
and values of y along the (2)_____ axis. For the inverse
function θ = arcsin y, the independent variable is (3)_____. If we
follow the customary graphing procedure, we would plot (4)_____ on
the horizontal axis and (5)_____ on the vertical.

    (1) horizontal   (2) vertical   (3) y (4) y (5) θ

1952 To graph the inverse function θ = arcsin y,
the horizontal and vertical axes are la-
beled y and θ as shown here. Since y
varies only from (1)_____ to (2)_____ inclusive, the horizontal axis requires no
numbers in absolute value greater than
(3)_____. (4) On the vertical axis, what
is the range of values necessary to show
the *principal* values for θ = arcsin y?
(5) Draw a set of axes. Label the axes y
and θ and mark the points indicating the
largest and smallest values of y and θ.

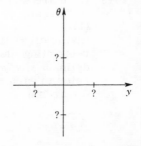

    (1) -1   (2) 1   (3) 1   (4) $\dfrac{-\pi}{2} \le \theta \le \dfrac{\pi}{2}$

continued →

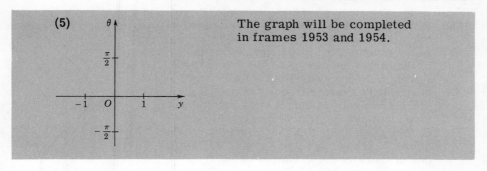

(5)   The graph will be completed
                           in frames 1953 and 1954.

1953 Complete the table below giving the principal values for θ =
arcsin y.   You will use this information for the graph in frame
1954.

y	-1	$-\sqrt{3}/2$	$-\sqrt{2}/2$	$-1/2$	0	$1/2$	$\sqrt{2}/2$	$\sqrt{3}/2$	1
θ	$-\pi/2$								

y	-1	$-\sqrt{3}/2$	$-\sqrt{2}/2$	$-1/2$	0	$1/2$	$-\sqrt{2}/2$	$\sqrt{3}/2$	1
θ	$-\pi/2$	$-\pi/3$	$-\pi/4$	$-\pi/6$	0	$\pi/6$	$\pi/4$	$\pi/3$	$\pi/2$

1954 Locate the points from the table in frame 1953 on the set of axes
from frame 1952.

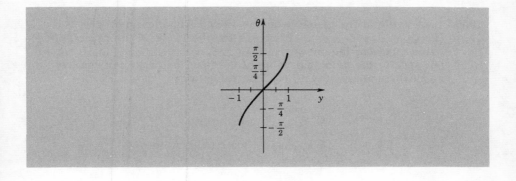

1955 If the graph of $\theta = \arcsin y$ is extended beyond the portion which has been labeled the *principal-value* function, the graph resembles the graph of the direct function $y = \sin \theta$ with the y and θ axes interchanged. Notice that when θ is not restricted to values from $-\pi/2$ to $\pi/2$ inclusive, there are *many* values of θ associated with a given value of y. **(1)** For example, when $y = 0$, this graph indicates that θ may have what values? (There are five shown.) **(2)** Which one of these is the *principal value*?

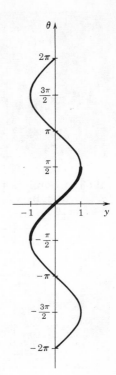

(1) $-2\pi,\ -\pi,\ 0,\ \pi,\ 2\pi$ **(2)** 0

1956 Look again at the graph in frame 1955. The domain of y is **(1)**_____ $\leq y \leq$ _____. If we ask for the range of the principal-value function, the answer is **(2)**_____ $\leq \theta \leq$ _____. **(3)** If we do not specify the principal value of the function, what can you say about the domain of y? **(4)** The range of θ?

(1) $-1 \leq y \leq 1$ **(2)** $\dfrac{-\pi}{2}$ $\dfrac{\pi}{2}$

(3) $-1 \leq y \leq 1$ **(4)** θ may be any real number

1957 We shall return now to the use of x and y as independent and dependent variables, respectively. We shall use:
1. $y = \sin x$ instead of $y = \sin \theta$
2. $x = \arcsin y$ instead of $\theta = \arcsin y$
Be careful in your interpretation of the second statement. Make a statement in words for 2 above.

x is the angle whose sine is y, θ is the angle whose sine is y

1958 The principal value of the inverse sine function is ordinarily indicated by a capital letter for the first letter of either of the usual inverse sine abbreviations, thus: $\text{Sin}^{-1} x$ or $\text{Arcsin } x$. Show that you understand these expressions by completing the following: $\text{Sin}^{-1} \frac{1}{2} = $ **(1)**_____ and $\sin^{-1} \frac{1}{2} = $ **(2)**_____.

(1) $\dfrac{\pi}{6}$

(2) $\ldots, \dfrac{-11\pi}{6}, \dfrac{-7\pi}{6}, \dfrac{\pi}{6}, \dfrac{5\pi}{6}, \ldots$

or $\dfrac{\pi}{6}, \left(\dfrac{\pi}{6} + 2\pi n\right), \dfrac{5\pi}{6}, \left(\dfrac{5\pi}{6} + 2\pi n\right)$ where n is an integer

1959 Recall that we can think of the inverse of a given function graphically as a reflection across the line whose equation is $y = x$. Carefully label a set of axes as indicated here and sketch the graph of $y = \sin x$. Then sketch the graph of $y = \arcsin x$ over the interval from $-\pi$ to π (-3 to 3 approximately).

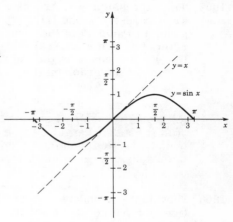

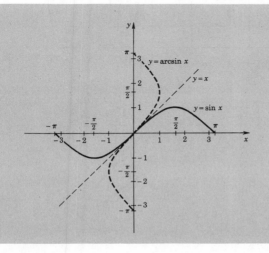

Note: The graphs have been extended here to show more of the reflected pattern.

1960   On your graph from frame 1959 indicate, with a heavy line, the portion of the graph which represents $y = \text{Arcsin } x$.

see Panel 17 for the answer. The heavy line indicates $y = \text{Arcsin } x$.

1961   Supply the correct values for the blanks: (1)_____ = Arcsin 1, (2)_____ = Arcsin (-1), (3)_____ = Sin^{-1} ($\sqrt{2}/2$), and (4)_____ = Sin^{-1} ($-\sqrt{2}/2$).

(1) 90°   (2) -90°   (3) 45°   (4) -45°

1962   The expression $y = \text{Arccos } x$ (or $y = \text{Cos}^{-1} x$) indicates that we are interested in the (1)_____ value of $y = \text{arccos } x$. The graph in Panel 17 of the inverse cosine function shows that the domain of x is the interval (2)_____ $\leq x \leq$ _____. The range of y for $y = \text{Arccos } x$ is the interval (3)_____ $\leq y \leq$ _____. (The portion of the graph marked with the heavy line is, by definition, the graph of $y = \text{Arccos } x$.)

(1) principal   (2) $-1 \leq x \leq 1$ (3) $0 \leq y \leq \pi$
Note: Another range of values might have been defined as the principal-value function. The one indicated here is useful in later applications in mathematics.

1963   Show that you understand the meaning of the *principal-value* function $y = \text{Arccos } x$ by supplying the correct values for the table below.

x	1	$\sqrt{3}/2$	$\sqrt{2}/2$	1/2	0	-1/2	$-\sqrt{2}/2$	$-\sqrt{3}/2$	-1
y									

Fill in the table without referring to Panel 17.

x	1	$\sqrt{3}/2$	$\sqrt{2}/2$	1/2	0	-1/2	$-\sqrt{2}/2$	$-\sqrt{3}/2$	-1
Arccos $x = y$	0	$\pi/6$	$\pi/4$	$\pi/3$	$\pi/2$	$2\pi/3$	$3\pi/4$	$5\pi/6$	π

1964 On a set of axes similar to the one labeled as shown here, sketch the graph of $y =$ Arccos x. Use the table from frame 1963, but do not refer to Panel 17.

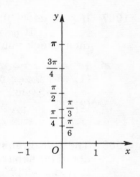

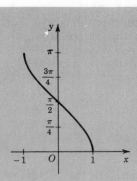

1965 Make a statement showing that you understand the difference in meaning between $y =$ arccos x and $y =$ Arccos x.

Two possible answers are:
1. $y =$ arccos x is a many-valued function.
   $y =$ Arccos x is a single-valued function.
2. y may be any real number in $y =$ arccos x. y is restricted to values in the interval $0 \leq y \leq \pi$ in the function $y =$ Arccos x.

1966 Look at Panel 17. If $y =$ Arccos 0, then $y =$ (1)_____. If $y =$ arccos 0, then three values for y are (2)_____, _____, _____.

(1) $\dfrac{\pi}{2}$

(2) Any three of the following: $\dfrac{-5\pi}{2}, \dfrac{-3\pi}{2}, \dfrac{-\pi}{2}, \dfrac{\pi}{2}, \dfrac{3\pi}{2}, \dfrac{5\pi}{2}$

[general form $(\pi/2 + n\pi)$, where n is an integer]

1967 If $y = \cos^{-1} 0.927$, then three values of y are **(1)**_____, _____,
_____. If $y = \text{Cos}^{-1} 0.927$, then $y =$ **(2)**_____. Consult Panel 1,
then check your answers by referring to the graph in Panel 17.

(1) any three of the following: ..., $-382°$, $-338°$, $-22°$, $22°$
    $338°$, $382°$, ...
(2) $22°$

1968 The list of answers for the problem $y = \cos^{-1} 0.927$ in frame 1967
could be separated into two groups.
1. ..., $-338°$, $22°$, $382°$, ...
2. ..., $-382°$, $-22°$, $338°$, ...
If you represent the first group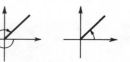
as angles in the standard position,
notice that they are the set of
angles which terminate in quadrant **(1)**_____; the general form for
the first group of angles is $(22° + n \cdot 360°)$ where n is any integer,
i.e., $-338° = (22 + (2)$_____$\cdot 360)$, $22° = (22 + (3)$_____$\cdot 360)$, and
$382° = (22 + (4)$_____$\cdot 360)$.

(1) I   **(2)** -1 **(3)** 0 **(4)** 1

1969 Here is a continuation of the problem in frame 1968. Make sketches
showing the three angles **(1)** $-382°$, **(2)** $-22°$, and **(3)** $338°$ in
standard position.   **(4)** Write a statement for the general form of
these angles.

(1)   **(2)**   **(3)**
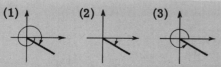

(4) $(-22° + n \cdot 360)$, where n is an integer, or $(-382° + n \cdot 360)$
    or $(338° + n \cdot 360)$

▽**1970** Find y **(1)** if $y = \text{Arccos} (-\sqrt{3}/2)$ or **(2)** if $y = \text{Arcsin} (-\sqrt{3}/2)$.

(1) $y = 150°$ **(2)** $y = -60°$

▽1971   The principal value of y for the inverse sine function is in the interval (1)_____ $\leq y \leq$ _____.   The principal value of y for the
inverse cosine function is in the interval (2)_____ $\leq y \leq$ _____.

(1) $\dfrac{-\pi}{2} \leq y \leq \dfrac{\pi}{2}$ (2) $0 \leq y \leq \pi$

1972   The expressions indicating the principal value of the inverse tangent function are similar to those for the sine or cosine, i.e.,
$y = $ Arctan x or $y = $ Tan^{-1} x. The principal value of y for the inverse tangent function is, by definition, in the same range as the inverse sine function. Therefore, the range of y for $y = $ Arctan x
is _____ $\leq y \leq$ _____.

$\dfrac{-\pi}{2} \leq y \leq \dfrac{\pi}{2}$

1973   If $y = $ Arctan 1, then $y = $ (1)_____ . If $y = $ Arctan (-1), then
$y = $ (2)_____ .

(1) $45°$ (2) $-45°$

▽1974   If $y = $ Sin^{-1} (-1), then $y = $ (1)_____ . If $y = $ Cos^{-1} (-1), then
$y = $ (2)_____ . If $y = $ Tan^{-1} (0), then $y = $ (3)_____ .

(1) $\dfrac{-\pi}{2}$ (2) π (3) 0

1975   If $y = $ Tan^{-1} 1.192, $y = $ (1)_____ .
If $y = $ Tan^{-1} 2.475, $y = $ (2)_____ .
If $y = $ Tan^{-1} 8.144, $y = $ (3)_____ .
If $y = $ Tan^{-1} 57.29, $y = $ (4)_____ .

(1) $50°$ (2) $68°$ (3) $83°$ (4) $89°$

1976   If $y = $ Tan^{-1} (-0.425), $y = $ (1)_____ .
If $y = $ Tan^{-1} (-0.900), $y = $ (2)_____ .
If $y = $ Tan^{-1} (-1.664), $y = $ (3)_____ .
If $y = $ Tan^{-1} (-6.314), $y = $ (4)_____ .
If $y = $ Tan^{-1} (-28.64), $y = $ (5)_____ .

(1) $-23°$ (2) $-42°$ (3) $-59°$ (4) $-81°$ (5) $-88°$

1977 What is the domain of x for the function $y = \text{Tan}^{-1}\, x$?

the set of all real numbers

1978 Fill in the table below for values of y when $y = \text{Arctan}\, x$.

x	undefined	-4.011	$-\sqrt{3}$	-1	$-1/\sqrt{3}$	0	$1/\sqrt{3}$	1	3	4.011	undefined
y	$-\pi/2$										

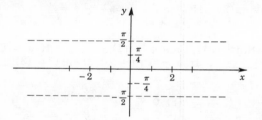

x	undefined	-4.011	$-\sqrt{3}$	-1	$-1/\sqrt{3}$	0	$1/\sqrt{3}$	1	3	4.011	undefined
y	-90°	-76°	-60°	-45°	-30°		30°	45°	60°	76°	90°

Note: 4.011 is obtained from Panel 1.

1979 Refer to the table in frame 1978. Sketch the graph of $y = \text{Arctan}\, x$. Use a set of axes as shown below.

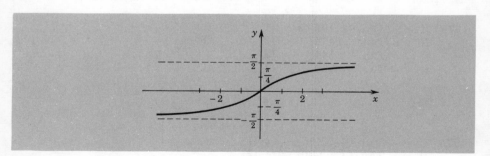

1980 Refer to Panel 18. Here you see the graph of $y = \text{Arctan } x$ shown as a heavy line and other portions of $y = \text{arctan } x$ shown as lighter lines. From this graph you can see that $y = \text{arctan } x$ is not single-valued. For example, if $x = 1$, y may be _____, _____, or _____ .

$\dfrac{\pi}{4}$, $\dfrac{5\pi}{4}$, $\dfrac{-3\pi}{4}$

▽**1981** Evaluate the following: (1) $\text{Sin}^{-1}(\sqrt{3}/2)$, (2) $\text{Sin}^{-1}(-\tfrac{1}{2})$, (3) $\text{Arcsin}(\sqrt{2}/2)$, and (4) $\text{Arcsin}(-1)$.

(1) $60°$ or $\dfrac{\pi}{3}$ (2) -30 or $-\dfrac{\pi}{6}$ (3) $45°$ or $\dfrac{\pi}{4}$ (4) $-90°$ or $\dfrac{-\pi}{2}$

▽**1982** Evaluate the following: (1) $\text{Arccos}(\sqrt{2}/2)$, (2) $\text{Arccos}(-\tfrac{1}{2})$, (3) $\text{Cos}^{-1} 1$, and (4) $\text{Cos}^{-1} 0$.

(1) $45°$ or $\dfrac{\pi}{4}$ (2) $120°$ or $\dfrac{2\pi}{3}$ (3) 0 (4) $90°$ or $\dfrac{\pi}{2}$

▽**1983** Evaluate the following: (1) $\text{Tan}^{-1} \sqrt{3}$, (2) $\text{Arctan}(-\sqrt{3}/3)$, (3) $\text{Arctan}(-1)$, and (4) $\text{Tan}^{-1} 0$.

(1) $60°$ or $\dfrac{\pi}{3}$ (2) $-30°$ or $\dfrac{-\pi}{6}$ (3) -45 or $\dfrac{-\pi}{4}$ (4) 0

1984 A problem may be stated in the following manner: Find the value of $\sin(\text{Arccos } \tfrac{1}{2})$. It means "Find the *sine* of the angle whose cosine is $\tfrac{1}{2}$." What is the answer?

$\dfrac{\sqrt{3}}{2}$ *Solution:* $\text{Arccos } \tfrac{1}{2} = 60°$

Therefore, $\sin(\text{Arccos } \tfrac{1}{2}) = \sin 60° = \dfrac{\sqrt{3}}{2}$

1985 Explain in words what you are to find when a problem is stated in this form: $\cos(\text{Arctan } \tfrac{3}{4})$.

the value of the cosine of the principal value of an angle whose tangent is $\tfrac{3}{4}$.

1986 To find the value of the trigonometric function cos (Arctan $\frac{3}{4}$) without referring to Panel 1, you should proceed as follows:
(1) Make a sketch of the angle in standard position.
(2) Form a right triangle and assign the values 3 and 4 to the proper sides.
(3) Find the third side of the triangle.
(4) Use your definition, cos θ = x/r, to find the required answer.
Complete the steps outlined above.

(1) and (2)

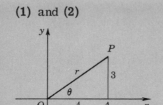

(3) r = 5

(4) cos θ = $\frac{4}{5}$

Note: θ is in quadrant I; therefore, cos θ is positive.

1987 Using the method described in frame 1986, find the value of sin [Arctan $(-\frac{5}{12})$]. Check carefully the sign of your answer.

sin θ = $-\frac{5}{13}$

Solution:
$$r = \sqrt{12^2 + (-5)^2} = 13$$

$$\sin \theta = -\frac{5}{13}$$

Note: θ terminates in quadrant IV; therefore, sin θ is negative.

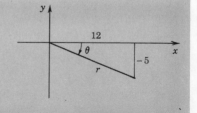

1988 Find the value of sin [Arccos $(-\frac{5}{6})$] using the identity sin θ = $\pm\sqrt{1 - \cos^2 \theta}$.

sin θ = $\dfrac{\sqrt{11}}{6}$

Solution: Let θ = Arccos $(-\frac{5}{6})$, then cos θ = $-\frac{5}{6}$

$$\sin \theta = \pm\sqrt{1 - (-\tfrac{5}{2})^2} = \frac{\pm\sqrt{11}}{6} = \frac{\sqrt{11}}{6}$$

Note: $\frac{\pi}{2} < \theta \le \pi$; therefore, sin θ is positive

1989   Find the value of cos [Arccos $(-\frac{5}{6})$].

$\cos \theta = -\frac{5}{6}$
This question is similar to: What is the name of the man whose name is Smith?

1990   Find the value of tan [Arccos $(-\frac{5}{6})$].

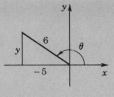

$\tan \theta = \dfrac{-\sqrt{11}}{5}$

Solution 1:

$y = \sqrt{6^2 - (-5)^2} = \sqrt{11}$

$\tan \quad = \dfrac{\sqrt{11}}{-5}$

Solution 2:
Use the results of frames 1988 and 1989.

$\tan \theta = \dfrac{\sin \theta}{\cos \theta} = \dfrac{\sqrt{11}/6}{-5/6} = \dfrac{-\sqrt{11}}{5}$

1991   Find the value of sin (Tan⁻¹ 2).   *Note:* Tan⁻¹ 2 is equivalent to Tan⁻¹ $\frac{2}{1}$.

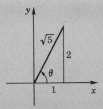

$\sin \theta = \dfrac{2}{\sqrt{5}}$

1992   Find the value of **(1)** cos [Tan⁻¹ (-2)] and **(2)** sin [Tan⁻¹ (-2)].

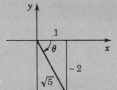

(1) $\cos \theta = \dfrac{1}{\sqrt{5}}$ or $\dfrac{\sqrt{5}}{5}$

(2) $\sin \theta = \dfrac{-2}{\sqrt{5}}$ or $\dfrac{-2\sqrt{5}}{5}$

1993   Find the value of Sin⁻¹ (cos 30°). *Note:* This problem asks you to find the angle whose sine equals the cos 30°.

60°
Solution: cos 30° = $\frac{\sqrt{3}}{2}$, Sin⁻¹ (cos 30°) = sin⁻¹ $\frac{\sqrt{3}}{2}$ = 60°

1994   Find the value of Cos⁻¹ (sin 90°).

0°   *Solution:* sin 90° = 1

Therefore, Cos⁻¹ (sin 90°) = Cos⁻¹ 1 = 0°

1995   Refer to Panel 9F for the definitions of cotangent, secant, and co-secant if necessary for the succeeding problems. Find the value of cot [Cos⁻¹ $(-\frac{3}{8})$].

$\frac{-3}{\sqrt{55}}$ or $\frac{-3\sqrt{55}}{55}$

Solution:

$y = \sqrt{64 - (-3)^2} = \sqrt{55}$

$\cot \theta = \frac{1}{\tan \theta} = \frac{1}{\sqrt{55}/-3} = \frac{-3}{\sqrt{55}}$

▽**1996**   Find the value of sec (sin⁻¹ $\frac{7}{9}$).

$\frac{9}{4\sqrt{2}}$ or $\frac{9\sqrt{2}}{8}$

Solution:

$x = \sqrt{9^2 - 7^2} = 4\sqrt{2}$

$\sec \theta = \frac{1}{\cos \theta} = \frac{1}{4\sqrt{2}/9} = \frac{9}{4\sqrt{2}}$

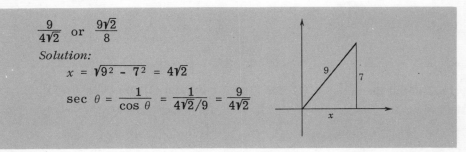

▽**1997**   Find the value of Sin⁻¹ (cos 180°).

$\frac{-\pi}{2}$ or -90°   *Solution:* Cos 180° = -1, Sin⁻¹ (-1) = $\frac{-\pi}{2}$

1998 Consider a to be a positive number in frames 1998 to 2017. Find the value of sin (Arccos a). *Suggestion:* First find the length of AP in terms of a, thus $AP = \sqrt{}$; then find sin θ. Or, use the identity sin $\theta = \pm\sqrt{1 - \cos^2 \theta}$; select the correct sign.

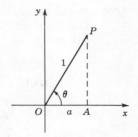

$\sin \theta = \sqrt{1 - a^2}$

Solution 1:

$$AP = \sqrt{1 - a^2}, \quad \sin (\text{Arccos } a) = \sin \theta = \frac{\sqrt{1 - a^2}}{1} = \sqrt{1 - a^2}$$

Solution 2: Let $\theta = $ Arccos a, then cos $\theta = a$

$\sin \theta = +\sqrt{1 - a^2}$

1999 Find the value of tan (Arccos a). (Refer to frame 1998.)

$$\frac{\sqrt{1 - a^2}}{a}$$

2000 Refer to Panel 9F and frames 1998 and 1999. Find the value of (1) cot (Arccos a), (2) sec (Arccos a), and (3) csc (Arccos a).

(1) cot $\theta = \dfrac{a}{\sqrt{1 - a^2}}$ **(2)** sec $\theta = \dfrac{1}{a}$ **(3)** csc $\theta = \dfrac{1}{\sqrt{1 - a^2}}$

▽2001 Find the value of cos (Tan^{-1} a). First make a sketch and label it carefully.

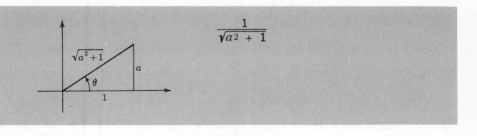

$$\frac{1}{\sqrt{a^2 + 1}}$$

2002 Refer to the sketch in frame 2001 to find the values of:
(1) sin (Tan^{-1}a), (2) tan (Tan^{-1}a), (3) cot (Tan^{-1}a),
(4) sec (Tan^{-1}a), and (5) csc (Tan^{-1}a).

(1) $\sin \theta = \dfrac{a}{\sqrt{a^2+1}}$ (2) $\tan \theta = a$ (3) $\cot \theta = \dfrac{1}{a}$

(4) $\sec \theta = \sqrt{a^2+1}$ (5) $\csc \theta = \dfrac{\sqrt{a^2+1}}{a}$

2003 Find the value of cos (Sin^{-1} $\sqrt{1-a^2}$). First make a sketch and
label the parts carefully.

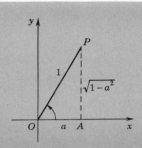

$$\cos \theta = \frac{a}{1} = a$$

2004 Find the value of tan [Arcsin ($w/\sqrt{1+w^2}$)]. First make a sketch
and label the parts carefully.

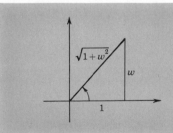

$$\tan \theta = \frac{w}{1} = w$$

2005 Explain in words the following expression tan (2 Arctan a).

tangent of twice the angle whose tan is a

2006 To find the value of tan (2 Arctan a), you should review the formula
for tan 2θ. If you do not remember it, refer to Panel 8III and copy

continued →

it. Your copy of the formula is the answer for this frame. The problem will be completed in frame 2007.

$$\tan 2\theta = \frac{2 \tan \theta}{1 - \tan^2 \theta}$$

2007 Let θ = Arctan a, then tan θ = a. Substitute this value in the formula for tan 2θ and simplify the result.

$$\tan 2\theta = \frac{2a}{1 - a^2}$$

2008 Find the value of cos $(2 \text{ Cos}^{-1} a)$. Refer to Panel 8III for the formula for cos 2θ. You may use any one of the three forms given, but on the basis of what is given above, there is one which is easy to use. Which do you think it is and why? Complete the problem.

$\cos 2\theta = 2 \cos^2 \theta - 1$
We know that the cosine of a certain angle θ is a, i.e.,
$\theta = \cos^{-1} a$ or $\cos \theta = a$.
    $\cos 2\theta = 2a^2 - 1$

2009 Write the formula for sin 2θ.

$\sin 2\theta = 2 \sin \theta \cos \theta$

2010 Find the value of sin $(2 \text{ Cos}^{-1} a)$. *Suggestion:* If we let $\theta = \text{Cos}^{-1} a$, then **(1)** cos θ = _____ and **(2)** sin θ = $\sqrt{\underline{\hspace{1.5cm}}}$. Therefore, sin $(2 \text{ Cos}^{-1} a)$ = **(3)** sin 2θ = _____ · _____ = _____

Solution:
(1) $\cos \theta = a$
(2) $\sin \theta = \sqrt{1 - a^2}$
(3) $\sin 2\theta = 2\sqrt{1 - a^2} \cdot a$
(4) $\qquad 2a\sqrt{1 - a^2}$

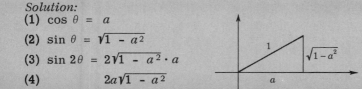

2011   Find the value of sin [2 Arccos (-a)].   *Suggestions:*   Let θ = Arccos (-a). Use the formula for sin 2θ.

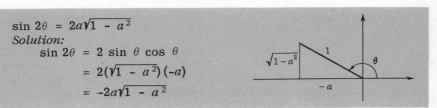

$\sin 2\theta = 2a\sqrt{1 - a^2}$
Solution:
$$\sin 2\theta = 2 \sin \theta \cos \theta$$
$$= 2(\sqrt{1 - a^2})(-a)$$
$$= -2a\sqrt{1 - a^2}$$

2012   Find the value of Cos [2 Arccos (-a)].

$\text{Cos } 2\theta = 2a^2 - 1$
Solution: $\text{Cos } 2\theta = 2 \cos^2 \theta - 1 = 2(-a)^2 - 1 = 2a^2 - 1$

2013   Find the value of tan [2 Arccos (-a)].

$\tan 2\theta = \dfrac{-2a\sqrt{1 - a^2}}{2a^2 - 1}$

Solution: $\dfrac{2 \tan \theta}{1 - \tan^2 \theta} = \dfrac{2\sqrt{1 - a^2}/-a}{1 - [(\sqrt{1 - a^2})/-a]^2}$

$$= \frac{-2\sqrt{1 - a^2}}{a} \cdot \frac{a^2}{2a^2 - 1} = \frac{-2a\sqrt{1 - a^2}}{2a^2 - 1}$$

▽**2014**   Find the value of **(1)** Cos^{-1} (sin 90°) and **(2)** Cos^{-1} [sin (-90°)].

(1) 0°   **(2)** 180°

2015   Find the value of sin ($\frac{1}{2}$ Arccos a). Refer to Panel 8IV for the formula for sin $\frac{1}{2}\theta$.

$\sin \frac{1}{2}\theta = \sqrt{\dfrac{1 - a}{2}}$
Solution:
$$\sin \tfrac{1}{2}\theta = \pm\sqrt{\frac{1 - \cos \theta}{2}}$$
$$= \pm\sqrt{\frac{1 - a}{2}}$$
$$= \sqrt{\frac{1 - a}{2}}$$

continued →

Since the principal value of the inverse-cosine function is between 0 and π then $\frac{1}{2}\theta$ will be between 0 and $\pi/2$. Hence the sign of the answer above is *positive*.

2016 Find the value of $\cos\left(\frac{1}{2}\text{ Arccos } a\right)$.

$$\cos\tfrac{1}{2}\theta = \pm\sqrt{\frac{1 + \cos\theta}{2}} = \pm\sqrt{\frac{1 + a}{2}} = \sqrt{\frac{1 + a}{2}}$$

Note: The positive sign is chosen for this answer.

2017 Find the value of $\tan\left(\frac{1}{2}\text{ Arccos } a\right)$.

$$\tan\tfrac{1}{2}\theta = \pm\sqrt{\frac{1 - \cos\theta}{1 + \cos\theta}} = \sqrt{\frac{1 - a}{1 + a}}$$

2018 Another type of problem involving inverse sine and cosine functions is the following: Evaluate $\cos(\pi + \text{Arcsin } a)$. *Solution:* If we let $\theta = \text{Arcsin } a$, then our problem reduces to the evaluation of $\cos(\pi + \theta)$. Now $\cos(\pi + \theta) = $ _____ (use the addition formula). This problem will be continued in frame 2019.

$-\cos\theta$

2019 We have reduced the problem to the form $\cos(\pi + \text{Arcsin } a) = -\cos\theta$. Now since $\theta = \text{Arcsin } a$, the final step in the evaluation is to find $\cos\theta$ as in previous problems and substitute in the above statement. **(1)** Complete the solution. Be careful in selecting the sign of your answer. If $\theta = \text{Arcsin } a$, then $-\pi/2 \le \theta \le \pi/2$. Therefore $\cos\theta$ will be **(2)**_____ and the final answer will be **(3)**_____ . (Use "positive" or "negative" for the blanks above.)

(1) $-\sqrt{1 - a^2}$

(2) positive

(3) negative

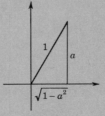

2020 Complete the steps below for the evaluation of sin ($\pi/2$ + Arccos a).
Step 1. Let θ = (1)_____
Step 2. sin ($\pi/2$ + θ) = (2)_____
The problem will be completed in frame 2021.

(1) arccos a **(2)** cos θ

2021 We have reduced the problem to the form sin ($\pi/2$ + Arccos a) =
cos θ. Look back to Step 1 in frame 2020 to help you decide the
final answer, i.e., cos θ = **(1)**_____.   You should check on the signs
in a problem of this kind.
1. If $0 \leq \theta < \pi/2$, then ($\pi/2$ + θ) represents an angle terminating in
    quadrant II and sin ($\pi/2$ + θ) is positive, which agrees in sign
    with cos θ.
2. If $\pi/2 < \theta < \pi$ then ($\pi/2$ + θ) terminates in quadrant **(2)**_____
    and sin ($\pi/2$ + θ) is **(3)**_____.   **(4)** In this case do you have
    an agreement in sign with cos θ?

(1) a **(2)** III   **(3)** negative

(4) yes, cos θ is negative in quadrant III

2022 Evaluate cos (Arcsin a - π).
Step 1. Let θ = **(1)**_____.
Step 2. cos (θ - π) = **(2)**_____.
Check your answers before completing the solution.

(1) Arcsin a **(2)** -cos θ

2023 Refer to frame 2022 and complete the evaluation of
cos (Arcsin a - π).

$- \sqrt{1 - a^2}$

2024 To find cos x when you are given sin $x = \frac{4}{5}$, you may do one of two
things:
1. Sketch the angle and label the known parts, then calculate what
    is required.

continued →

2. Make use of the identity $\sin^2 x + \cos^2 x = 1$ to find what is required, i.e., $\cos x = \pm\sqrt{1 - \sin^2 x} = $ (1) $\pm\sqrt{\underline{\hspace{2cm}}} = \underline{\hspace{2cm}}$.
(2) Which sign is correct, + or - ?

(1) $\sqrt{1 - \left(\frac{4}{5}\right)^2} = \frac{3}{5}$
(2) +   *Note:* x is a first-quadrant angle since $\sin x$ is positive and $-\pi/2 \le x \le \pi/2$.

2025 If $\cos B = \frac{5}{13}$, then using the identity $\sin^2 B + \cos^2 B = 1$, we find that $\sin B = $ (1)_____. (2) Explain the choice of sign on your answer.

(1) $\sqrt{1 - \left(\frac{5}{13}\right)^2} = \frac{12}{13}$

(2) $\sin B$ is positive. We know that if $\cos B = \frac{5}{13}$ and $0 \le B \le \pi$, then B is a first-quadrant angle.

2026 Find $\tan\left[\cos^{-1}\left(-\frac{5}{13}\right)\right]$.

$-\frac{12}{5}$
Solution:
Let $x = \cos^{-1}\left(-\frac{5}{13}\right)$,
then $\cos x = -\frac{5}{13}$

$\sin x = \frac{12}{13}$

$\tan x = -\frac{12}{5}$

Note: $\pi/2 \le x \le \pi$; therefore, $\tan x$ is negative.

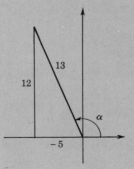

2027 In the problems which follow you may use a method of solution which is different from the one given with the answer. It is important that your answer be numerically correct and that you consider possible variations in signs, the domain of the variable, etc.
Find (1) $\cos\left[\sin^{-1}\left(-\frac{1}{2}\right)\right]$ and (2) $\tan\left[\sin^{-1}\left(-\frac{1}{2}\right)\right]$.

(1) $\cos x = \frac{\sqrt{3}}{2}$ *Solution:* $\cos x = \sqrt{1 - \left(-\frac{1}{2}\right)^2} = \frac{\sqrt{3}}{2}$

(2) $\tan x = \frac{-1}{\sqrt{3}}$ *Solution:* $\tan x = \frac{\sin x}{\cos x} = \frac{-1/2}{\sqrt{3}/2} = \frac{1}{\sqrt{3}}$

2028 Find (1) sin (Cos^{-1} 0) and (2) tan (Cos^{-1} 0).

(1) sin x = 1   *Solution:*   If x = Cos^{-1} 0, then x = 90° and
sin 90° = 1.

(2) tan x is undefined   *Solution:*   tan x = $\dfrac{1}{0}$

2029 In the following problem we are not using principal-value notation.
Find the values of sin (arctan $\frac{3}{4}$).

$\pm\frac{3}{5}$

Solution: Let θ = arctan $\frac{3}{4}$, then tan θ = $\frac{3}{4}$. Since tan θ is
positive, we know that θ terminates in quadrant I or III. sin θ
is positive in quadrant I and negative in quadrant III, hence the
double sign.

2030 Find the values of cos [arcsin ($-\frac{24}{25}$)].

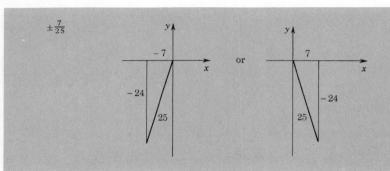

$\pm\frac{7}{25}$

or

2031 Find the values of tan (arccos $\frac{8}{17}$).

$\pm\frac{15}{8}$

2032 Find the values of sin (arccos a).

$\pm\sqrt{1-a^2}$

2033   Find the values of cos [arcsin (-1/a)].

$$\pm\sqrt{1 - \left(\frac{-1}{a}\right)^2} = \pm\sqrt{1 - \frac{1}{a^2}} = \pm\frac{1}{a}\sqrt{a^2 - 1}$$

2034   Find the value of cos [Arcsin ($-\frac{24}{25}$)].

$\frac{7}{25}$ *Note:* This answer is positive. If θ = Arcsin ($-\frac{24}{25}$), then θ terminates in quadrant IV. Therefore, cos θ is positive.

2035   Find the value of Arccos [sin ($\pi/10$)].

$\frac{4\pi}{10}$ or $\frac{2\pi}{5}$

Solution: You are asked to find the principal value of an angle α whose cosine is equal to sin ($\pi/10$). Recall that when cos α = sin β, then $\alpha + \beta = \pi/2$. Let $\pi/10 = B$, then

$$\alpha = \frac{\pi}{2} - B = \frac{\pi}{2} - \frac{\pi}{10} = \frac{2\pi}{5}$$

This could be verified by consulting Panel 1.

2036   (1) Find the value of Arcsin (tan π). This problem requires an angle whose sine is equal to tan π. But tan π is (2)_____. Therefore, the problem reduces to Arcsin (3) _____ = _____.

(1) 0°   (2) 0   (3) 0 = 0°

2037   Find the value of Arctan [sin ($7\pi/2$)].

$-\frac{\pi}{4}$ *Solution:* sin $\frac{7\pi}{2}$ = -1, Arctan (-1) = $\frac{-\pi}{4}$

2038   Verify the following: Sin^{-1} $\frac{1}{2}$ + Sin^{-1} ($\sqrt{3}/2$) = -Sin^{-1} (-1).

$\frac{\pi}{6} + \frac{\pi}{3} = -\left(\frac{-\pi}{2}\right)$, $\frac{\pi}{2} = \frac{\pi}{2}$

2039 Verify the following: $\cos^{-1} x = \tan^{-1} (\sqrt{1 - x^2}/x)$, $0 < x \le 1$.

Let $\theta = \cos^{-1} x$, then $\cos \theta = x$

$\sin \theta = \sqrt{1 - \cos^2 \theta} = \sqrt{1 - x^2}$

$\tan \theta = \dfrac{\sin \theta}{\cos \theta} = \dfrac{\sqrt{1 - x^2}}{x}$

Therefore, $\cos^{-1} x = \tan^{-1} \dfrac{\sqrt{1 - x^2}}{x}$

You may verify the relationships using the values in the sketch.

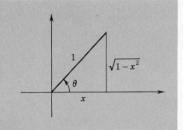

2040 Sketch the graph of $y = \text{Arccos } x$.

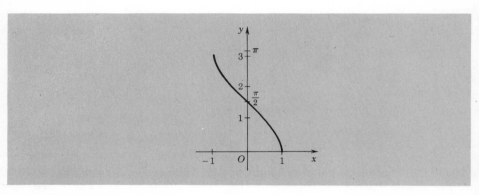

2041 Sketch the graph of $y = \cos x$, $0 \le x \le \pi$.

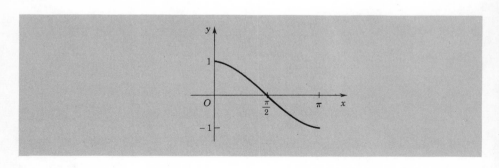

2042 Sketch the graph of $y = \text{Sin}^{-1} x$.

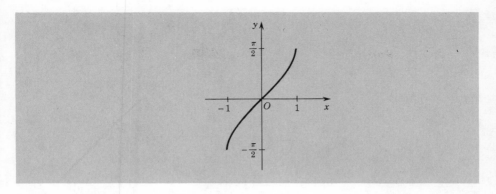

2043 Sketch the graph of $y = \sin x, \ -\pi/2 \le x \le \pi/2$.

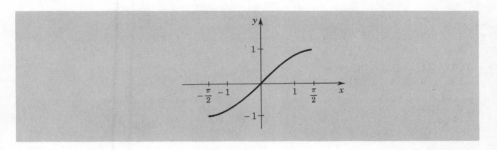

2044 Sketch the graph of $y = \text{Arctan } x$.

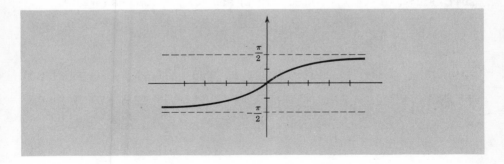

2045 Sketch the graph of $y = \tan x,\ -\pi/2 \le x \le \pi/2$.

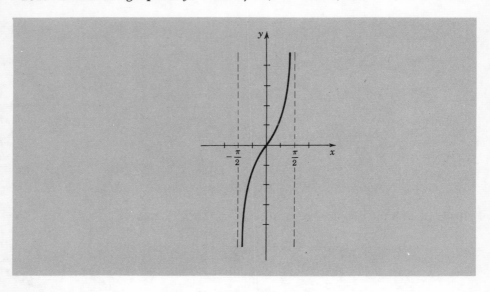

2046 **(1)** Find y if $y = \text{Sin}^{-1}\ (-\sqrt{3}/2)$.
(2) Give another value of y if $y = \sin^{-1}\ (-\sqrt{3}/2)$.

(1) $y = -60°$ **(2)** $y = -120°$

Other answers for $y = \sin^{-1}\ (-\sqrt{3}/2)$ are $y = -120° + 360°n$ and $y = -60° + 360°n$, where n is an integer.

2047 Find y if **(1)** $y = \text{Arccos}\ (\sqrt{2}/2)$ and **(2)** $y = \text{Arccos}\ (-\sqrt{2}/2)$.

(1) $y = 45°$ **(2)** $y = 135°$

2048 Find y if **(1)** $y = \text{Tan}^{-1}\ 0$, **(2)** $y = \text{Tan}^{-1}\ 1$, and **(3)** $y = \text{Tan}^{-1}\ (-1)$.

(1) $y = 0$ **(2)** $y = 45°$ **(3)** $y = -45°$

2049 Without using tables find the value of sin [Arctan (-2)].

$\dfrac{-2}{\sqrt{5}}$

The solution is indicated by the sketch.

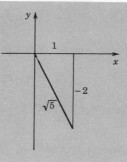

2050 Find the value of **(1)** sin (Arccos $\frac{1}{2}$), **(2)** cos (Arccos $\frac{1}{2}$), and **(3)** tan (Arccos $\frac{1}{2}$).

(1) $\dfrac{\sqrt{3}}{2}$ **(2)** $\frac{1}{2}$ **(3)** $\sqrt{3}$

2051 Find the value of sec [Arccos $(-\frac{12}{13})$].

$-\frac{13}{12}$

2052 Find the value of **(1)** cos [Arcsin $(-\frac{3}{5})$], **(2)** tan [Arcsin $(-\frac{3}{5})$], **(3)** cot [Arcsin $(-\frac{3}{5})$], **(4)** sec [Arcsin $(-\frac{3}{5})$], and **(5)** csc [Arcsin $(-\frac{3}{5})$].

(1) $\frac{4}{5}$ **(2)** $-\frac{3}{4}$ **(3)** $-\frac{4}{3}$ **(4)** $\frac{5}{4}$ **(5)** $-\frac{5}{3}$

2053 Consider a positive, find the value of **(1)** sin (Cos^{-1} a) and **(2)** tan (Cos^{-1} a).

(1) $\sqrt{1 - a^2}$ **(2)** $\dfrac{\sqrt{1 - a^2}}{a}$

2054 Find the value of sin (2 Arccos a). Consider a positive. You may refer to Panel 8III.

$2\sqrt{1 - a^2} \cdot a$

2055   Find the value of cos (2 Arccos $\frac{3}{4}$).

$\frac{1}{8}$ *Solution:* $2(\frac{3}{4})^2 - 1 = \frac{9}{8} - 1 = \frac{1}{8}$

2056   Find the value of Arcsin (cos 180°).

-90°
Solution: cos 180° = -1
Therefore, Arcsin (cos 180°) = Arcsin (-1) = -90°

2057   Show that 2 Sin^{-1} $\frac{1}{3}$ = Cos^{-1} $\frac{7}{9}$. *Suggestions:* Let α = Sin^{-1} $\frac{1}{3}$ and B = Cos^{-1} $\frac{7}{9}$. Now referring to the problem, we must show that 2α = B. This can be done if we can prove that cos 2α = cos B (or sin 2α = sin B).

Given sin α = $\frac{1}{3}$ and cos β = $\frac{7}{9}$. To prove 2α = β, we show
that cos 2α = cos β
Step 1. $1 - 2\sin^2 \alpha$ = Cos β Panel 9III
Step 2. $1 - 2(\frac{1}{9}) = \frac{7}{9}$ substituting
Step 3. $\frac{7}{9} = \frac{7}{9}$ simplifying
Step 4. Therefore, 2α = β and 2 Sin^{-1} $\frac{1}{3}$ = Cos^{-1} $\frac{7}{9}$

2058   Let x represent any real number.   (1) Is tan (Tan^{-1} x) = x true for all values of x?   If your answer is "no," list a value of x for which the statement is false.   (2) Is Tan^{-1}(tan x) = x true for all values of x?

(1) yes

(2) no   Let $x = \frac{5\pi}{4}$, then tan x = 1 and Tan^{-1} 1 = $\frac{\pi}{4}$.

Therefore, Tan^{-1} $\left(\tan \frac{5\pi}{4}\right) \neq \frac{5\pi}{4}$

APPENDIX A ⌷ Interpolation

The method used to find the value of a function of an angle (or real number) between any two consecutive readings in a table is called *interpolation*. Below is an illustrative example of interpolation. Look at Panel 1 as you study this. Find sin 29°18′.

$$1° = 60' \left[18' \left[\begin{matrix} \sin 29°\ 0' = 0.4850 \\ \sin 29°18' = \quad x \\ \sin 30°\ 0' = 0.5000 \end{matrix} \right] x - 0.4850 \right] 0.0150$$

Notice that as the angle increases 1° the value of the sine increases 0.0150. In linear interpolation we assume that if the angle is increased by 18′, then the value of the sine increases by a proportional amount. Therefore, we write

$$\frac{18}{60} = \frac{x - 0.4850}{0.0150}$$

from which we find that

$$x \approx 0.4895$$
$$x \approx 0.490$$

Note: Using a table with three-digit accuracy such as Panel 1 is not recommended for this process. The method is, however, useful when more accurate tables are available. *Problem:* Find an approximate value for tan 29°18′.

$$1° = 60' \left[18' \left[\begin{matrix} \tan 29°\ 0' = 0.554 \\ \tan 29°18' = \quad x \\ \tan 30°\ 0' = 0.577 \end{matrix} \right] x - 0.554 \right] 0.023$$

$$\frac{18}{60} \approx \frac{x - 0.554}{0.023}$$

$$x \approx 0.561$$

Care must be taken in approximating the value of a decreasing function by the interpolation method. *Example:* Find cos 29°18′.

$$60° \left[18' \left[\begin{matrix} \cos 29°\ 0' = 0.875 \\ \cos 29°18' = \quad x \\ \cos 30°\ 0' = 0.866 \end{matrix} \right] x - 0.875 \right] - 0.009$$

$$\frac{18}{60} = \frac{x - 0.875}{-0.009}$$

$$x = 0.872$$

Note that the value of cos 29°18′ must be between 0.875 and 0.866.

Problem: Find cos 53°48′

$$60'\left[48'\begin{bmatrix}\cos 53°\ 0' = 0.602 \\ \cos 53°48' = \quad x \\ \cos 54°\ 0' = 0.588\end{bmatrix} x - 0.602\right] - 0.014$$

$$\frac{48}{60} \approx \frac{x - 0.602}{-0.014}$$

$$x \approx 0.591$$

Equations Involving Radicals

A *radical equation* (sometimes called an irrational equation) is an equation in which the variable appears under a radical sign or with a fractional exponent.

Example 1: $\sqrt{y^2 - 5} + 1 = y$

Example 2: $x^{1/2} + 2 = x$

Such equations may sometimes be transformed into equations not involving radicals by the following procedure:

Step 1. Rewrite the equation so that one member consists of only one radical term. Write example 1 thus:

$$\sqrt{y^2 - 5} = y - 1$$

Step 2. Raise both members of the equation to the power which is equal to the index of the radical:

$$(\sqrt{y^2 - 5})^2 = (y - 1)^2$$

Step 3. Solve the resulting equation

$$y^2 - 5 = y^2 - 2y + 1$$
$$2y = 6$$
$$y = 3$$

Step 4. The process employed in Step 2 *may* introduce solutions for the new (derived) equation which are not roots of the original equation; hence, it is necessary to test the solutions by substitution in the original.

Check: $\sqrt{(3)^2 - 5} + 1 = 3$

$\sqrt{9 - 5} + 1 = 3$

$\sqrt{4} + 1 = 3$ ($\sqrt{4}$ indicates positive square

$2 + 1 = 3$ root only)

$3 = 3$

Therefore, 3 is a solution.

Problem: Use the method outlined above to find the solution to

$$\sqrt{9x^2 + 4} - 3x - 1 = 0$$

Answer: $\frac{1}{2}$

Solution: Given $\sqrt{9x^2 + 4} - 3x - 1 = 0$

Step 1. $\sqrt{9x^2 + 4} = 3x + 1$

Step 2. $(\sqrt{9x^2 + 4})^2 = (3x + 1)^2$

Step 3. $9x^2 + 4 = 9x^2 + 6x + 1$

$$3 = 6x$$
$$\tfrac{1}{2} = x$$

Step 4. *Check:* $\sqrt{9(\tfrac{1}{2})^2 + 4} - 3(\tfrac{1}{2}) - 1 = 0$

$$\sqrt{\tfrac{9}{4} + 4} - \tfrac{3}{2} - 1 = 0$$
$$\sqrt{\tfrac{25}{4}} - \tfrac{3}{2} - 1 = 0$$
$$\tfrac{5}{2} - \tfrac{3}{2} - 1 = 0$$
$$0 = 0$$

Therefore, $\tfrac{1}{2}$ is a solution

Example 3. $x^{1/2} + 2 = x$

Step 1. $x^{1/2} = x - 2$

Step 2. $(x^{1/2})^2 = (x - 2)^2$

Step 3. $x = x^2 - 4x + 4$

$$0 = x^2 - 5x + 4$$
$$0 = (x - 4)(x - 1)$$
$$= 4, 1$$

Step 4. *Check:*

For 4: $(4)^{1/2} + 2 \stackrel{?}{=} 4$

$$2 + 2 \stackrel{?}{=} 4$$
$$4 = 4$$

Therefore, 4 is a solution

For 1: $(1)^{1/2} + 2 \stackrel{?}{=} 1$

$$1 + 2 \neq 1$$

Therefore, 1 is not a solution

Problem: Find the solution for $(y + 2)^{1/2} - 2y = 1$

Answer $\tfrac{1}{4}$

Solution: $(y + 2)^{1/2} - 2y = 1$

Step 1. $(y + 2)^{1/2} = 2y + 1$

Step 2. $(y + 2)^{1/2\,2} = (2y + 1)^2$

Step 3. $y + 2 = 4y^2 + 4y + 1$

$$0 = 4y^2 + 3y - 1$$
$$0 = (4y - 1)(y + 1)$$
$$y = \tfrac{1}{4}, -1$$

Step 4. *Check:*

For $\tfrac{1}{4}$: $(\tfrac{1}{4} + 2)^{1/2} - 2(\tfrac{1}{4}) \stackrel{?}{=} 1$

$$(\tfrac{9}{4})^{1/2} - \tfrac{1}{2} \stackrel{?}{=} 1$$
$$\tfrac{3}{2} - \tfrac{1}{2} = 1$$

Therefore, $\tfrac{1}{4}$ is a solution

For -1: $(-1 + 2)^{1/2} - 2(-1) \overset{?}{=} 1$

$1 + 2 \ne 1$ Therefore, -1 is not a solution

Example 4: $\sqrt{2x + 3} - \sqrt{x + 1} = 1$

This problem will require additional steps to transform it to a form without radicals.

Step 1. Write the equation having only the radical $\sqrt{2x + 3}$ in the left member $\sqrt{2x + 3} = \sqrt{x + 1} + 1$

Step 2. Square both members

$$(\sqrt{2x + 3})^2 = (\sqrt{x + 1} + 1)^2$$

$$2x + 3 = x + 1 + 2\sqrt{x + 1} + 1$$

Step 3. Collect terms, letting the radical term occupy the right member

$$x + 1 = 2\sqrt{x + 1}$$

Step 4. The remainder of the solution follows the pattern of the other problems. Complete the problem.

Answer: 3, -1

$x + 1 = 2\sqrt{x + 1}$

Step 5. $(x + 1)^2 = (2\sqrt{x + 1})^2$

Step 6. $x^2 + 2x + 1 = 4(x + 1)$
$x^2 - 2x - 3 = 0$
$(x - 3)(x + 1) = 0$
$x = 3, -1$

Step 7. *Check:*
For 3: $\sqrt{2(3) + 3} - \sqrt{3 + 1} \overset{?}{=} 1$

$3 - 2 = 1$ Therefore, 3 is a solution

For -1: $\sqrt{2(-1) + 3} - \sqrt{-1 + 1} \overset{?}{=} 1$

$1 - 0 = 1$ Therefore, -1 is a solution

Problem: Solve and check $\sqrt{5x - 1} - \sqrt{x + 6} = 3$

Answer: 10

Solution: Given $\sqrt{5x - 1} - \sqrt{x + 6} = 3$

Step 1. $\sqrt{5x - 1} = \sqrt{x + 6} + 3$

Step 2. $(\sqrt{5x - 1})^2 = (\sqrt{x + 6} + 3)^2$

Step 3. $5x - 1 = x + 6 + 6\sqrt{x + 6} + 9$
$4x - 16 = 6\sqrt{x + 6}$
$2x - 8 = 3\sqrt{x + 6}$

Step 4. $(2x - 8)^2 = (3\sqrt{x + 6})^2$

Step 5. $4x^2 - 32x + 64 = 9(x + 6)$
$$4x^2 - 41x + 10 = 0$$
$$(4x - 1)(x - 10) = 0$$
$$x = \tfrac{1}{4}, 10$$

Step 6. *Check:*

For $\tfrac{1}{4}$: $\sqrt{5(\tfrac{1}{4}) - 1} - \sqrt{\tfrac{1}{4} + 6} \overset{?}{=} 3$

$$\tfrac{1}{2} - \tfrac{5}{2} \neq 3$$

Therefore, $\tfrac{1}{4}$ is not a solution

For 10: $\sqrt{5(10) - 1} - \sqrt{10 + 6} \overset{?}{=} 3$

$$7 - 4 = 3$$

Therefore, 10 is a solution

Answers To Self-tests

1 (a) 180°, 0°, $-\frac{1}{2}$ rev, and 1 rev are quadrantal angles. (b) 180° and $-\frac{1}{2}$ rev, $\frac{3}{8}$ rev and $\frac{11}{8}$ rev, 0° and 1 rev are coterminal angles.

2 $\pi/6$ radians.

3 (a) 60° (b) $\frac{5\pi}{6}$ (c) $\frac{5\pi}{4}$ (d) 330° (e) $\frac{500\pi}{9}$ (f) $-1,260°$.

4 57.3°

5 4 in.

6 $\frac{9\pi}{8}$

7

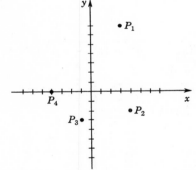

8 (a) $\sin\theta$ = ordinate of P, $\cos\theta$ = abscissa of P
   (b) $\sin\theta = \frac{y}{r}$, $\cos\theta = \frac{x}{r}$

9 (a) III or IV   (b) II or III

10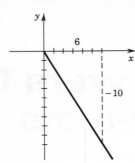

$$\sin \theta = -\frac{5}{\sqrt{34}}, \quad \cos \theta = \frac{3}{\sqrt{34}}$$

11 (a) $1^2 = (-\frac{4}{5})^2 + \sin^2 \theta$

$\frac{9}{25} = \sin^2 \theta$

$\frac{3}{5} = \sin \theta$

(b) $\tan \theta = \dfrac{\sin \theta}{\cos \theta} = \dfrac{3/5}{-4/5} = \dfrac{-3}{4}$

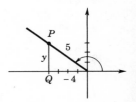

Another solution:

(a) $5^2 = (-4)^2 + y^2$

$3 = y$ (y is positive in quadrant II)

$\sin \theta = \dfrac{y}{r} = \dfrac{3}{5}$

(b) $\tan \theta = \dfrac{x}{y} = \dfrac{+3}{-4} = \dfrac{-3}{4}$

12 $x = r \cos \theta, y = r \sin \theta, d = \sqrt{(x_2 - x_1)^2 + (x_2 - y_1)^2}$

$d = \sqrt{(r \cos \theta - r)^2 + (r \sin \theta - 0)^2}$

$= \sqrt{r^2 \cos^2 \theta - 2r^2 \cos \theta + r^2 + r^2 \sin^2 \theta}$

$= r\sqrt{(\cos^2 \theta + \sin^2 \theta) + 1 - 2 \cos \theta}$

$= r\sqrt{1 + 1 - 2 \cos \theta}$

$= r\sqrt{2 - 2 \cos \theta}$

13

θ, radians	Degrees	$\sin \theta$	$\cos \theta$	$\tan \theta$
$\pi/6$	$30°$	$1/2$	$\sqrt{3}/2$	$1/\sqrt{3}$ or $\sqrt{3}/3$
$\pi/4$	$45°$	$1/\sqrt{2}$ or $\sqrt{2}/2$	$1/\sqrt{2}$ or $\sqrt{2}/2$	1
$\pi/2$	$90°$	1	0	undefined

14 (a)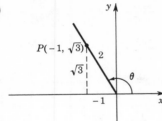

$P(-1, \sqrt{3})$

(b) $\theta = \dfrac{2\pi}{3}$ radians

(c) $\sin \theta = \dfrac{\sqrt{3}}{2}$

$\cos \theta = \dfrac{-1}{2}$

$\tan \theta = \dfrac{\sqrt{3}}{-1}$ or $-\sqrt{3}$

15 $\dfrac{-\sqrt{3}}{2} + \dfrac{\sqrt{3}}{2} \cdot \dfrac{1}{2} = \dfrac{-\sqrt{3}}{2} + \dfrac{\sqrt{3}}{4} = \dfrac{-2\sqrt{3} + \sqrt{3}}{4} = \dfrac{-\sqrt{3}}{4}$

16 (1)(a) $60°$,   (b) $\tan 240° = \dfrac{\sqrt{3}}{1} = \sqrt{3}$

(2)(a) $45°$,   (b) $\tan 315° = -1$

(3)(a) $60°$,   (b) $\tan 120° = \dfrac{-\sqrt{3}}{1} = -\sqrt{3}$

17 (a) $C = 40°$

(b) $AC \approx 15.7$ *Solution:* $\sin 50° = \dfrac{12}{AC}, AC = \dfrac{12}{0.766}, \approx 15.7$

18 $x \approx 9.32$ ft
Solution: $\tan 25° = \dfrac{x}{20}$

$9.32 \approx x$

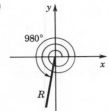

19 (a) $45°$ (b) $240°$ (c) $270°$ (d) $120°$

20 $\alpha = \dfrac{2\pi}{3}$ *Solution:* $\dfrac{14\pi}{3} = (\alpha + 2 \cdot 2\pi), \dfrac{2\pi}{3} = \alpha$

21 (a)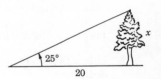

(b) $R = 80°$

(c) $\sin 980° = -0.985$
$\cos 980° = -0.174$
$\tan 980° = 5.671$

22 (a) $\theta = \pi$ (b) $\theta = 180°$

23 $\sin \theta$ decreases from 0 to -1

SELF-TEST 2

1 (a) III   (b) II   (c) IV

2 (a)

θ	$\pi/4$	$\pi/2$	$3\pi/4$	π	$5\pi/4$	$3\pi/2$	$7\pi/4$	2π
$\cos\theta$	$1/\sqrt{2}$	0	$-1/\sqrt{2}$	-1	$-1/\sqrt{2}$	0	$1/2$	1

(b)

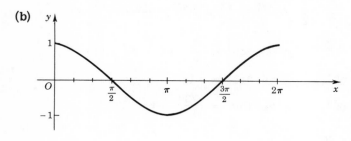

3 (a) 1   (b) -1   (c) 2π

4 (a) π or $180°$ (b) There are no maximum or minimum values for this function. At $-\pi/2$, $\pi/2$, $3\pi/2$, $5\pi/2$, etc., the function is undefined. As we approach these points, $|\tan\theta|$ becomes larger and larger without limit.

5 $c = \sqrt{151} \approx 12.3$
Solution:

$$c^2 = a^2 + b^2 - 2ab\,\cos\gamma$$
$$= 14^2 + 9^2 - 2(14\cdot 9)\,\cos\frac{\pi}{3}$$
$$= 196 + 81 - 126$$
$$c = \sqrt{151} \approx 12.3$$

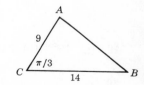

6 $\alpha \approx 23°$
Solution:

7, 10, 15 respectively

$$a^2 = b^2 + c^2 - 2bc\,\cos\alpha$$

$$\cos\alpha = \frac{b^2 + c^2 - a^2}{2bc}$$

$$= \frac{100 + 225 - 49}{2(10\cdot 15)}$$

$$= 0.920$$

$$\alpha \approx 23°$$

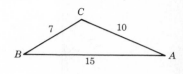

7 (a) $\gamma = \dfrac{7\pi}{12}$ *Solution:* $\gamma = \pi - \left(\dfrac{\pi}{4} + \dfrac{\pi}{6}\right) = \dfrac{7\pi}{12}$

(b) $a \approx 6.6$

Solution:

$$\frac{\sin \alpha}{a} = \frac{\sin \gamma}{c}$$

$$a = \frac{c \sin \alpha}{\sin \gamma} \approx \frac{9 \cdot 0.707}{0.970} \approx 6.6$$

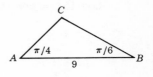

8 (a) $b \approx 18$ (b) area ≈ 125 square units

9 two triangles

10

11 (a) $d_1 \approx 25$ cm   (b) area ≈ 236.4 sq cm

12 (a) 1

(b) $\cos \theta = \dfrac{+ 2\sqrt{6}}{7}$

Solution: $\left(-\tfrac{5}{7}\right)^2 + \cos^2 \theta = 1,\ \cos^2 \theta = 1 - \tfrac{25}{49} = \tfrac{24}{49}$,

$$\cos \theta = \frac{\pm 2\sqrt{6}}{7}$$

If θ is between $3\pi/2$ and 2π, then $\cos \theta = \dfrac{+ 2\sqrt{6}}{7}$.

13 (a) 33
(b) $\sin^2 x + 2 \sin x \cos x + \cos^2 x = 1 + 2 \sin x \cos x$
(c) $3b - 6b \sin x + 3b \sin^2 x$ (d) $\sqrt{1 - \sin^2 \alpha} = \sqrt{\cos^2 \alpha} = \cos \alpha$

14 (a) $(1 - \sin \theta)(1 + \sin \theta)$
(b) $\sin x (\cos x - \sin x)(\cos x + \sin x)$
(c) $r(\cos \theta + i \sin \theta)$

15 (a) $\dfrac{r}{\cos \theta + \sin \theta}$ (b) $\dfrac{\sqrt{a} + \sqrt{b}}{a - b}$

16 $\dfrac{1}{1 - \sin^2 \theta}$ or $\dfrac{1}{\cos^2 \theta}$

17 cos 15° = 0.966

Solution:

cos 15° = cos (60° - 45°) = cos 60° cos 45° + sin 60° sin 45°

$$= \frac{1}{2} \cdot \frac{1}{\sqrt{2}} + \frac{\sqrt{3}}{2} \cdot \frac{1}{\sqrt{2}}$$

$$= \frac{\sqrt{2}}{4} + \frac{\sqrt{6}}{4} = \frac{3.863}{4} \approx 0.966$$

18 $\sin \left(\alpha - \frac{\pi}{2} \right) = \sin \alpha \cos \frac{\pi}{2} - \cos \alpha \sin \frac{\pi}{2}$

$$= \sin \alpha \cdot 0 - \cos \alpha \cdot 1 = -\cos \alpha$$

19 cos (α - β) = cos α cos β + sin α sin β

$$= -\tfrac{4}{5} \cdot \tfrac{5}{13} + \tfrac{3}{5} \cdot \tfrac{12}{13} = -\tfrac{16}{65}$$

20 Let α = β, then sin (α + β) = sin α cos β + cos α sin β

becomes sin (α + α) = sin α cos α + cos α sin α or

$$\sin 2\alpha = 2 \sin \alpha \cos \alpha$$

21 (a) $\sin 2\theta = \tfrac{24}{25}$ (b) $\cos 2\theta = \tfrac{7}{25}$ (c) $\tan 2\theta = \tfrac{24}{7}$

22 (a) $\sin \frac{\theta}{2} = \sqrt{\frac{1}{10}}$ or $\frac{\sqrt{10}}{10}$ (b) $\cos \frac{\theta}{2} = \sqrt{\frac{9}{10}}$ or $\frac{3\sqrt{10}}{10}$

(c) $\tan \frac{\theta}{2} = \frac{1}{3}$

(Sign of each answer is positive; i.e., if θ terminates in the first quadrant, then θ/2 also terminates in the first quadrant.)

23 (a) $\sin \frac{7\pi}{12} = \sqrt{\frac{1 + \sqrt{3}/2}{2}} = \tfrac{1}{2}\sqrt{2 + \sqrt{3}}$

(b) $\cos \frac{7\pi}{12} = -\sqrt{\frac{1 - \sqrt{3}/2}{2}} = -\tfrac{1}{2}\sqrt{2 - \sqrt{3}}$

(7π/12 is an angle terminating in quadrant II; hence, cos (7π/12) is negative.)

24 (a) $\frac{1}{\sqrt{2}}$ or $\frac{\sqrt{2}}{2}$ (b) $-\frac{1}{\sqrt{2}}$ or $\frac{-\sqrt{2}}{2}$ (c) -1   (d) -1   (e) $-\sqrt{2}$ (f) $\sqrt{2}$

SELF-TEST 3

1 (a) $\dfrac{1}{\sin \theta}$ (b) $\pm\sqrt{1 - \sin^2 \theta}$ (c) $\pm\dfrac{1}{\sqrt{1 - \sin^2 \theta}}$

(d) $\pm\dfrac{\sin \theta}{\sqrt{1 - \sin^2 \theta}}$ (e) $\pm\sqrt{\dfrac{1 - \sin^2 \theta}{\sin \theta}}$

2 Here is one possible solution: Working on the left member
$$1 - 2 \sin^2 \theta = 1 - 2(1 - \cos^2 \theta) = 1 - 2 + 2 \cos^2 \theta$$
$$= -1 + 2 \cos^2 \theta$$

3 $\sin^2 x + \cos^2 x = 1$, $(x^2 - 1) = (x - 1)(x + 1)$, $\tan \theta = \dfrac{\sin \theta}{\cos \theta}$

4 $\sin \theta \left(\dfrac{1}{\sin \theta} - \sin \theta \right) = 1 - \sin^2 \theta = \cos^2 \theta$

5 Here is one possible solution.

$$\cos^2 \theta - \sin^2 \theta = \dfrac{1 - \tan^2 \theta}{1 + \tan^2 \theta}$$

$$= \dfrac{1 - \sin^2 \theta/\cos^2 \theta}{\boxed{\sec^2 \theta}} \qquad \text{(work on right member)}$$

$$= \dfrac{(\cos^2 \theta - \sin^2 \theta)/\cos^2 \theta}{1/\cos^2 \theta}$$

$$= \dfrac{\cos^2 \theta - \sin^2 \theta}{\cos^2 \theta} \cdot \dfrac{\cos^2 \theta}{1}$$

$$= \cos^2 \theta - \sin^2 \theta$$

6 Here is one possible solution:
Working on the left member
$$1 - 2 \sin^2 \theta + \sin^4 \theta = \cos^4 \theta$$
$$(1 - \sin^2 \theta)^2 =$$
$$(\cos^2 \theta)^2 =$$
$$\cos^4 \theta =$$

7 $\dfrac{\sin^2 (x/2) + \cos x}{\cos^2 (x/2)} = \dfrac{(1 - \cos x)/2 + \cos x}{(1 + \cos x)/2} = \dfrac{(1 + \cos x)/2}{(1 + \cos x)/2} = 1$

8 $\dfrac{1 - \cos 2\theta}{\sin 2\theta} = \dfrac{1 - (2 \cos^2 \theta - 1)}{2 \sin \theta \cos \theta} = \dfrac{2 - 2 \cos^2 \theta}{2 \sin \theta \cos \theta} = \dfrac{2(1 - \cos^2 \theta)}{2 \sin \theta \cos \theta}$

$$= \dfrac{\sin^2 \theta}{\sin \theta \cos \theta} = \dfrac{\sin \theta}{\cos \theta} = \tan \theta$$

9 (a) $\cos 90° \sin 45° = \frac{1}{2}(\sin 135° - \sin 45°)$

$$= \frac{1}{2}\left[\frac{\sqrt{2}}{2} - \frac{\sqrt{2}}{2}\right]$$

   (b) 0

10 (a) $\cos \frac{\pi}{3} + \cos \frac{\pi}{6} = 2 \cos \frac{\pi}{4} \cos \frac{\pi}{12}$

   (b) $\dfrac{\sin 100° - \sin 40°}{\cos 100° + \cos 40°} = \dfrac{2 \cos 70° \sin 30°}{2 \cos 70° \cos 30°} = \tan 30°$

11 $\sin(270° + \theta) = \sin 270° \cos \theta + \cos 270° \sin \theta$

$$= -1 \cos \theta + 0 \sin \theta = -\cos \theta$$

12 (a) $-\sin 50°$ (b) $-\cos 50°$ (c) $-\tan 48°$

13 $\dfrac{\pi}{3}, \dfrac{5\pi}{3}$ or $(60°, 300°)$

14 $\dfrac{\pi}{2}, \dfrac{7\pi}{6}, \dfrac{11\pi}{6}$ or $(90°, 210°, 330°)$

15 $8\left(\dfrac{\sqrt{2}}{2}\right)^4 - 6\left(\dfrac{\sqrt{2}}{2}\right)^2 + 1 = 0$

$$8\left(\frac{4}{16}\right) - 6\left(\frac{2}{4}\right) + 1 = 0$$

$$2 - 3 + 1 = 0$$

16 $90°, 270°$

17 $\sin(x + 60°) - \cos(x + 30°) = \sin x \cos 60° + \cos x \sin 60°$

$$- (\cos x \cos 30° - \sin x \sin 30°)$$

$$= \sin x \cdot \frac{1}{2} + \cos x \cdot \frac{\sqrt{3}}{2}$$

$$- \left(\cos x \cdot \frac{\sqrt{3}}{2} - \sin x \cdot \frac{1}{2}\right)$$

$$= \frac{1}{2} \sin x + \frac{\sqrt{3}}{2} \cos x - \frac{\sqrt{3}}{2} \cos x$$

$$+ \frac{1}{2} \sin x$$

$$= \sin x$$

18 $\cos(180° + x) = \cos(180° - x)$, $\tan(90° + x) = \cot(180° - x)$

$\cos(x - 180°) = -\cos x$

19 $2 \sin 45° = 2 \cdot \dfrac{\sqrt{2}}{2} = \sqrt{2}$, $\sin 2(45°) = \sin 90° = 1$

$2 \sin \theta > \sin 2\theta$

20 (a) $\dfrac{8\pi}{6} = \dfrac{4\pi}{3}$ radians   (b) 24π

21 (a) 2   (b) $\dfrac{\pi}{2}$

22 approximately $35°$

SELF-TEST 4

1 (a) $\sin 9\pi = \sin \pi = 0$ (b) $\cos 9\pi = \cos \pi = -1$

2 (a) 2π (b) 2π

3 (a) $f(2)$ (b) $f(1)$ (c) $f(1.2)$

4 $x = \pi$, 4π

5 (a) π (b) 4π (c) $\dfrac{2\pi}{a}$

6 (a) $A\left(\dfrac{\sqrt{3}}{2}, \dfrac{1}{2}\right)$ (b) $B\left(\dfrac{1}{\sqrt{2}}, \dfrac{1}{\sqrt{2}}\right)$ (c) $C\left(\dfrac{1}{2}, \dfrac{\sqrt{3}}{2}\right)$

   (d) $D\ (0, 1)$ (e) $E\left(-\dfrac{1}{2}, \dfrac{\sqrt{3}}{2}\right)$ (f) $F\left(-\dfrac{1}{\sqrt{2}}, \dfrac{1}{\sqrt{2}}\right)$

   (g) $G\left(-\dfrac{\sqrt{3}}{2}, \dfrac{1}{2}\right)$ (h) $H(-1, 0)$

7 Each value of $\sin x$ is multiplied by 3. (The amplitude for $y = 3 \sin x$ is 3; for $y = \sin x$ the amplitude is 1.)

8

x	0	$\pi/2$	π	$3\pi/2$	2π	$5\pi/2$	3π	$7\pi/2$	4π
$\frac{1}{2}x$	0	$\pi/4$	$\pi/2$	$3\pi/4$	π	$5\pi/4$	$3\pi/2$	$7\pi/4$	2π
$\sin \frac{1}{2}x$	0	$\sqrt{2}/2$	1	$\sqrt{2}/2$	0	$-\sqrt{2}/2$	-1	$-\sqrt{2}/2$	0

9 (a) π (b) 6π (c) $\dfrac{2\pi}{a}$

10 The graph of $y = \sin x$ is shifted $\pi/2$ units to the left.

11

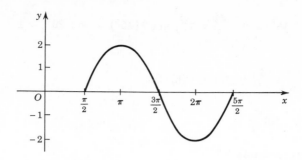

12

Formula	Amplitude	Period	Phase shift
$y = \cos x$	1	2π	0
$y = 3 \sin 4x$	3	$\pi/2$	0
$y = 2 \sin (3x + \pi/2)$	2	$2\pi/3$	$-\pi/6$

13 (a) false (b) true (c) false (d) false (e) true

14

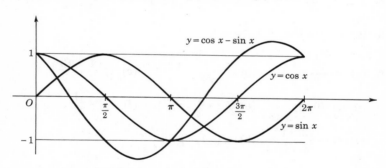

15

x	0	$\pi/6$	$\pi/4$	$\pi/3$	$\pi/2$
$\cot x$	undefined	$\sqrt{3}$	1	$1/\sqrt{3}$	0

16 $\sqrt{3} - \dfrac{1}{\sqrt{3}} + 1 = \dfrac{2 + \sqrt{3}}{\sqrt{3}} \approx 2.15$

17 $\frac{1}{7}$ *Solution:* $\tan (A - B) = \dfrac{\tan A - \tan B}{1 + \tan A \tan B} = \dfrac{3 - 2}{1 + (3)(2)} = \dfrac{1}{7}$

18 (a) $\sin 2A (\sec A + \csc A) = 2 \sin A \cos A \left(\dfrac{1}{\cos A} + \dfrac{1}{\sin A} \right)$

$$= 2(\cos A + \sin A)$$

(b) $\sin(x+y) \sin(x-y) + \cos(x+y) \cos(x-y)$

$= \cos[(x+y)-(x-y)] = \cos 2y$

SELF-TEST 5

1 (a)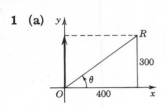

(b) $r = \sqrt{(300)^2 + (400)^2} = 500$ lb

$\tan \theta = \frac{300}{400} = \frac{3}{4} = 0.75$

$\theta \approx 37°$

2 $x = 6$ lb $y \approx 10.4$ lb

Solution:

$\sin 60° = \dfrac{y}{12}$

$y = 6\sqrt{3} \approx 10.4$ lb

$\cos 60° = \dfrac{x}{12}$

$x = 6$ lb

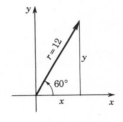

3 $r = \sqrt{10^2 + 8^2 - 2\cdot8\cdot10 \cos 135}$

$= \sqrt{275.12}$

≈ 16.6

$\dfrac{\sin \alpha}{8} = \dfrac{\sin 135°}{16.6}$

$\sin \alpha = \dfrac{8\cdot(0.707)}{16.6} \approx 0.341$

$\alpha \approx 20°$

Note: Answer may be angle $CAD \approx 25°$

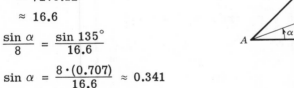

4 (a)

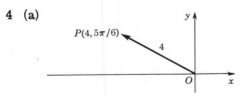

(b) $(-2\sqrt{3}, 2)$

(c) $P\left(4, \dfrac{-7\pi}{6}\right)$ or $P\left(4, \dfrac{17\pi}{6}\right)$

(d) There is no other set of rectangular coordinates corresponding to P.

5 $(13, 247°)$

Solution:
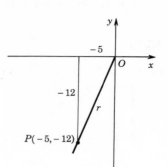

$$r = \sqrt{(15)^2 + (-12)^2} = 13$$

$$\tan \theta = \frac{-12}{-5}$$

$$\theta \approx 67° + 180 \approx 247°$$

6 $d \approx 12$

Solution:
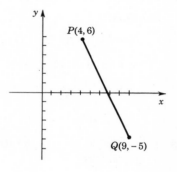

$$d = \sqrt{(4 - 9)^2 + [6 - (-5)]^2}$$
$$= \sqrt{146}$$
$$\approx 12$$

7 (a) $A + B = 5 - i$ (b) $A - B = 3 - 5i$

(c)
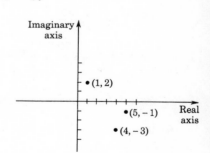

8 $10 + 5i$

9 $\dfrac{-2}{5} - \dfrac{11i}{5}$

10 $4 + 3i$

$(4 - 3i) + (4 + 3i) = 8 + 0i$

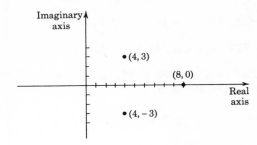

11 (a) -1 (b) $-i$ (c) 1 (d) $-i$ (e) -1

12 (a) $x = 4, y = 7$ (b) $x = 2, y = 1$

13 (a) $\dfrac{-8 + 6i}{10} = \dfrac{-4}{5} + \dfrac{3i}{5}$

(b) $\dfrac{-6 - 3i}{5}$ or $-\frac{6}{5} - \frac{3}{5}i$

14 $z = 2 - 5i$

15 (a) $5(\cos 53° + i \sin 53°)$ (b) $5(\cos 243° + i \sin 243°)$

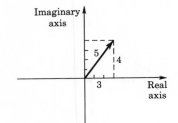   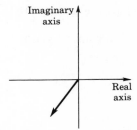

16 (a) $2\sqrt{3} + 2i$ (b) $0 + 5i$ or $5i$

17 (a) $\sqrt{2}\left(\cos \dfrac{5\pi}{4} + i \sin \dfrac{5\pi}{4}\right)$ (b)

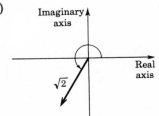

18 $27(\cos 60° + i \sin 60°)$

19 $4(\cos 120° + i \sin 120°) = -2 + i2\sqrt{3}$

20 $(4/\sqrt{2})(\cos 195° + i \sin 159°)$

21 $2^8(\cos 240° + i \sin 240°)$ or $256(\cos 240° + i \sin 240°)$

22 $3(\cos 200° + i \sin 200°), 3(\cos 320° + i \sin 320°),$
$3(\cos 80° + i \sin 80°)$

23 $\cos 225° + i \sin 225° = -\dfrac{1}{\sqrt{2}} - \dfrac{1}{\sqrt{2}} i$

$\cos 45° + i \sin 45° = \dfrac{1}{\sqrt{2}} + \dfrac{1}{\sqrt{2}} i$

24 $R_1 = \cos 72° + \sin 72°,$ $R_2 = \cos 144° + i \sin 144°,$
$R_3 = \cos 216° + i \sin 216°,$ $R_4 = \cos 288° + i \sin 288°,$
$R_5 = \cos 360° + i \sin 360°$

25   (a) real number   (b) real number   (c) pure imaginary

SELF-TEST 6

1   (a) 5   (b) 7   (c) 2

2 $f^{-1}(x) = y = 2x - 10$

3   (a) Quadrants I and II   (d)
(b) 30°
(c) $\dfrac{\pi}{6}$

4   (a) Quadrants I and IV   (d)
(b) 45°
(c) $\dfrac{\pi}{4}$

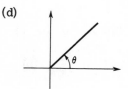

5   (a) Quadrants II and IV   (d)
(b) - 60°
(c) $-\dfrac{\pi}{3}$

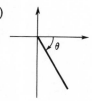

6

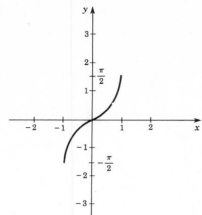

7 $\dfrac{\sqrt{3}}{2}$

8 $\dfrac{-\pi}{4}$

9 $\text{Sin}^{-1}\ \tfrac{1}{2} = 30°,\ \text{Cos}^{-1}\ \tfrac{1}{2} = 60°,\ 2(30°) = 60°$
or
Let $\text{Sin}^{-1}\ \tfrac{1}{2} = \alpha,\ \text{Cos}^{-1}\ \tfrac{1}{2} = \beta$, then we must prove that $2\alpha = \beta$.
We can prove this if we can show that $\cos 2\alpha = \cos \beta$.

$$\begin{aligned}
\cos 2\alpha &= 1 - 2 \sin^2 \alpha & &\text{Panel 8III}\\
&= 1 - 2(\tfrac{1}{2})^2 & &\text{substituting from given}\\
&= 1 - \tfrac{2}{4} = \tfrac{1}{2} & &\text{simplifying}\\
\cos \beta &= \tfrac{1}{2} & &\text{given}
\end{aligned}$$

Therefore, $2\alpha = \beta$ $\quad$ and $\quad$ $2\ \text{Sin}^{-1}\ \tfrac{1}{2} = \text{Cos}^{-1}\ \tfrac{1}{2}$

10 $-\dfrac{2}{\sqrt{5}}$ or $-\dfrac{2\sqrt{5}}{5}$

11 Let $\alpha = \text{Tan}^{-1}\ 1,\ \beta = \text{Tan}^{-1}\ \tfrac{1}{2},\ \gamma = \text{Tan}^{-1}\ 3$. We can show that
$\alpha + \beta = \gamma$ by proving that $\tan(\alpha + \beta) = \tan \gamma$. Using 8II(5):
$$\frac{\tan \alpha + \tan \beta}{1 - \tan \alpha \cdot \tan \beta} = \frac{1 + 1/2}{1 - 1 \cdot 1/2} = \frac{3}{2} \cdot \frac{2}{1} = 3$$
Also $\tan \gamma = 3$; therefore, $\alpha + \beta = \gamma$ and $\text{Tan}^{-1}\ 1 + \text{Tan}^{-1}\ \tfrac{1}{2} = \text{Tan}^{-1}\ 3$

12 0

13 0

14 $\dfrac{8\sqrt{2} + 3}{15}$

PANEL 1

Degrees	Radians	Sine	Cosine	Tangent	Degrees	Radians	Sine	Cosine	Tangent
0	0.000	0.000	1.000	0.000					
1	0.017	0.018	1.000	0.018	46	0.803	0.719	0.695	1.036
2	0.035	0.035	0.999	0.035	47	0.820	0.731	0.682	1.072
3	0.052	0.052	0.999	0.052	48	0.838	0.743	0.669	1.111
4	0.070	0.070	0.998	0.070	49	0.855	0.755	0.656	1.150
5	0.087	0.087	0.996	0.088	50	0.873	0.766	0.643	1.192
6	0.105	0.105	0.995	0.105	51	0.890	0.777	0.629	1.235
7	0.122	0.122	0.993	0.123	52	0.908	0.788	0.616	1.280
8	0.140	0.139	0.990	0.141	53	0.925	0.799	0.602	1.327
9	0.157	0.156	0.988	0.158	54	0.942	0.809	0.588	1.376
10	0.175	0.174	0.985	0.176	55	0.960	0.819	0.574	1.428
11	0.192	0.191	0.982	0.194	56	0.977	0.829	0.559	1.483
12	0.209	0.208	0.978	0.213	57	0.995	0.839	0.545	1.540
13	0.227	0.225	0.974	0.231	58	1.012	0.848	0.530	1.600
14	0.244	0.242	0.970	0.249	59	1.030	0.857	0.515	1.664
15	0.262	0.259	0.966	0.268	60	1.047	0.866	0.500	1.732
16	0.279	0.276	0.961	0.287	61	1.065	0.875	0.485	1.804
17	0.297	0.292	0.956	0.306	62	1.082	0.883	0.470	1.881
18	0.314	0.309	0.951	0.325	63	1.100	0.891	0.454	1.963
19	0.332	0.326	0.946	0.344	64	1.117	0.899	0.438	2.050
20	0.349	0.342	0.940	0.364	65	1.134	0.906	0.423	2.145
21	0.367	0.358	0.934	0.384	66	1.152	0.914	0.407	2.246
22	0.384	0.375	0.927	0.404	67	1.169	0.921	0.391	2.356
23	0.401	0.391	0.921	0.425	68	1.187	0.927	0.375	2.475
24	0.419	0.407	0.914	0.445	69	1.204	0.934	0.358	2.605
25	0.436	0.423	0.906	0.466	70	1.222	0.940	0.342	2.747
26	0.454	0.438	0.899	0.488	71	1.239	0.946	0.326	2.904
27	0.471	0.454	0.891	0.510	72	1.257	0.951	0.309	3.078
28	0.489	0.470	0.883	0.532	73	1.274	0.956	0.292	3.271
29	0.506	0.485	0.875	0.554	74	1.292	0.961	0.276	3.487
30	0.524	0.500	0.866	0.577	75	1.309	0.966	0.259	3.732
31	0.541	0.515	0.857	0.601	76	1.326	0.970	0.242	4.011
32	0.559	0.530	0.848	0.625	77	1.344	0.974	0.225	4.331
33	0.576	0.545	0.839	0.649	78	1.361	0.978	0.208	4.705
34	0.593	0.559	0.829	0.675	79	1.379	0.982	0.191	5.145
35	0.611	0.574	0.819	0.700	80	1.396	0.985	0.174	5.671
36	0.628	0.588	0.809	0.727	81	1.414	0.988	0.156	6.314
37	0.646	0.602	0.799	0.754	82	1.431	0.990	0.139	7.115
38	0.663	0.616	0.788	0.781	83	1.449	0.993	0.122	8.144
39	0.681	0.629	0.777	0.810	84	1.466	0.995	0.105	9.514
40	0.698	0.643	0.766	0.839	85	1.484	0.996	0.087	11.43
41	0.716	0.658	0.755	0.869	86	1.501	0.998	0.070	14.30
42	0.733	0.669	0.743	0.900	87	1.518	0.999	0.052	19.08
43	0.751	0.682	0.731	0.933	88	1.536	0.999	0.035	28.64
44	0.768	0.695	0.719	0.966	89	1.553	1.000	0.018	57.29
45	0.785	0.707	0.707	1.000	90	1.571	1.000	0.000	0.00

ANEL 2

θ	0	$\pi/6$	$\pi/4$	$\pi/3$	$\pi/2$	$2\pi/3$	$3\pi/4$	$5\pi/6$	π
$\sin\theta$	0	1/2	$1/\sqrt{2}$	$\sqrt{3}/2$	1	$\sqrt{3}/2$	$1/\sqrt{2}$	1/2	0

θ	$7\pi/6$	$5\pi/4$	$4\pi/3$	$3\pi/2$	$5\pi/3$	$7\pi/4$	$11\pi/6$	2π
$\sin\theta$	$-1/2$	$-1/\sqrt{2}$	$-\sqrt{3}/2$	-1	$-\sqrt{3}/2$	$-1/\sqrt{2}$	$-1/2$	0

PANEL 3

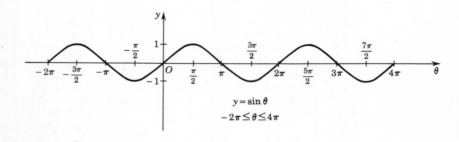

$$y = \sin\theta$$
$$-2\pi \leq \theta \leq 4\pi$$

PANEL 4

θ	0	$\pi/6$	$\pi/4$	$\pi/3$	$\pi/2$	$2\pi/3$	$3\pi/4$	$5\pi/6$	π
$\cos\theta$	1	$\sqrt{3}/2$	$1/\sqrt{2}$	1/2	0	$-1/2$	$-1/\sqrt{2}$	$-\sqrt{3}/2$	-1

θ	$7\pi/6$	$5\pi/6$	$4\pi/3$	$3\pi/2$	$5\pi/3$	$7\pi/4$	$11\pi/6$	2π
$\cos\theta$	$-\sqrt{3}/2$	$-1/\sqrt{2}$	$-1/2$	0	1/2	$1/\sqrt{2}$	$\sqrt{3}/2$	1

PANEL 5

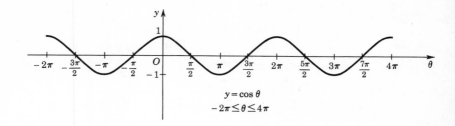

$$y = \cos\theta$$
$$-2\pi \leq \theta \leq 4\pi$$

PANEL 6

θ	0	$\pi/6$	$\pi/4$	$\pi/3$	$\pi/2$	$2\pi/3$	$3\pi/4$	$5\pi/6$
$\tan\theta$	0	$1/\sqrt{3}$	1	$\sqrt{3}$	undefined	$-\sqrt{3}$	-1	$-1/\sqrt{3}$

θ	π	$7\pi/6$	$5\pi/4$	$4\pi/3$	$3\pi/2$	$5\pi/3$	$7\pi/4$	$11\pi/6$
$\tan\theta$	0	$1/\sqrt{3}$	1	$\sqrt{3}$	undefined	$-\sqrt{3}$	-1	$-1/\sqrt{3}$

PANEL 7

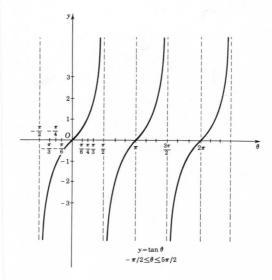

$$y = \tan\theta$$
$$-\pi/2 \leq \theta \leq 5\pi/2$$

PANEL 8

I Identities

  A. Pythagorean relations

    (1) $\sin^2 \alpha + \cos^2 \alpha = 1$ (for α any real number)

    (2) $\tan^2 \alpha + 1 = \sec^2 \alpha$

    (3) $1 + \cot^2 \alpha = \csc^2 \alpha$

  B. Tangent and cotangent relations

    (1) $\tan \alpha = \dfrac{\sin \alpha}{\cos \alpha}$

    (2) $\cot \alpha = \dfrac{\cos \alpha}{\sin \alpha}$

  C. Reciprocal relations

    (1) $\sin \alpha = \dfrac{1}{\csc \alpha}$, $\csc \alpha = \dfrac{1}{\sin \alpha}$

    (2) $\cos \alpha = \dfrac{1}{\sec \alpha}$, $\sec \alpha = \dfrac{1}{\cos \alpha}$

    (3) $\tan \alpha = \dfrac{1}{\cot \alpha}$, $\cot \alpha = \dfrac{1}{\tan \alpha}$

  D. Reduction formulas

$$\cos(-\alpha) = \cos \alpha$$
$$\sin(-\alpha) = -\sin \alpha$$

    (1) $\cos\left(\dfrac{\pi}{2} - \alpha\right) = \sin \alpha$ (7) $\sin(\pi - \alpha) = \sin \alpha$

                                          (8) $\cos(\pi - \alpha) = -\cos \alpha$

    (2) $\sin\left(\dfrac{\pi}{2} - \alpha\right) = \cos \alpha$ (9) $\tan(\pi - \alpha) = -\tan \alpha$

                                          (10) $\sin(\pi + \alpha) = -\sin \alpha$

    (3) $\tan\left(\dfrac{\pi}{2} - \alpha\right) = \cot \alpha$ (11) $\cos(\pi + \alpha) = -\cos \alpha$

                                          (12) $\tan(\pi + \alpha) = \tan \alpha$

    (4) $\cos\left(\dfrac{\pi}{2} + \alpha\right) = -\sin \alpha$ (13) $\sin(2\pi - \alpha) = -\sin \alpha$

                                          (14) $\cos(2\pi - \alpha) = \cos \alpha$

    (5) $\sin\left(\dfrac{\pi}{2} + \alpha\right) = \cos \alpha$ (15) $\tan(2\pi - \alpha) = -\tan \alpha$

    (6) $\tan\left(\dfrac{\pi}{2} + \alpha\right) = -\cot \alpha$

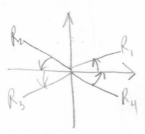

II Addition formulas

(1) $\sin(\alpha + \beta) = \sin\alpha\cos\beta + \cos\alpha\sin\beta$

(2) $\sin(\alpha - \beta) = \sin\alpha\cos\beta - \cos\alpha\sin\beta$

(3) $\cos(\alpha + \beta) = \cos\alpha\cos\beta - \sin\alpha\sin\beta$

(4) $\cos(\alpha - \beta) = \cos\alpha\cos\beta + \sin\alpha\sin\beta$

(5) $\tan(\alpha + \beta) = \dfrac{\tan\alpha + \tan\beta}{1 - \tan\alpha\tan\beta}$

(6) $\tan(\alpha - \beta) = \dfrac{\tan\alpha - \tan\beta}{1 + \tan\alpha\tan\beta}$

III Double-angle formulas

(1) $\sin 2\alpha = 2\sin\alpha\cos\alpha$

(2) $\cos 2\alpha = \cos^2\alpha - \sin^2\alpha = 1 - 2\sin^2\alpha = 2\cos^2\alpha - 1$

(3) $\tan 2\alpha = \dfrac{2\tan\alpha}{1 - \tan^2\alpha}$

IV Half-angle formulas

(1) $\cos \tfrac{1}{2}\alpha = \pm\sqrt{\dfrac{1 + \cos\alpha}{2}}$

(2) $\sin \tfrac{1}{2}\alpha = \pm\sqrt{\dfrac{1 - \cos\alpha}{2}}$

(3) $\tan \tfrac{1}{2}\alpha = \pm\sqrt{\dfrac{1 - \cos\alpha}{1 + \cos\alpha}} = \dfrac{1 - \cos\alpha}{\sin\alpha} = \dfrac{\sin\alpha}{1 + \cos\alpha}$

V A. Products to sums or differences

(1) $\sin\alpha\cos\beta = \tfrac{1}{2}[\sin(\alpha + \beta) + \sin(\alpha - \beta)]$

(2) $\cos\alpha\sin\beta = \tfrac{1}{2}[\sin(\alpha + \beta) - \sin(\alpha - \beta)]$

(3) $\cos\alpha\cos\beta = \tfrac{1}{2}[\cos(\alpha + \beta) + \cos(\alpha - \beta)]$

(4) $\sin\alpha\sin\beta = \tfrac{-1}{2}[\cos(\alpha + \beta) - \cos(\alpha - \beta)]$

alternate form $= \tfrac{1}{2}[\cos(\alpha - \beta) - \cos(\alpha + \beta)]$

B. Sums or differences to products

(1) $\sin\theta + \sin\phi = 2\sin\tfrac{1}{2}(\theta + \phi)\cos\tfrac{1}{2}(\theta - \phi)$

(2) $\sin\theta - \sin\phi = 2\cos\tfrac{1}{2}(\theta + \phi)\sin\tfrac{1}{2}(\theta - \phi)$

(3) $\cos\theta + \cos\phi = 2\cos\tfrac{1}{2}(\theta + \phi)\cos\tfrac{1}{2}(\theta - \phi)$

(4) $\cos\theta - \cos\phi = -2\sin\tfrac{1}{2}(\theta + \phi)\sin\tfrac{1}{2}(\theta - \phi)$

Quadratic formula for finding the roots of an equation of the form $ax^2 + bx + c = 0$:

$$x = \frac{-b \pm \sqrt{b^2 - 4ac}}{2a}$$

Given triangle ABC with angles α, β, and γ and sides a, b, and c respectively.

A. Law of cosines

  (1) $a^2 = b^2 + c^2 - 2bc \cos \alpha$
  (2) $b^2 = a^2 + c^2 - 2ac \cos \beta$
  (3) $c^2 = a^2 + b^2 - 2ab \cos \gamma$

B. Law of sines

$$\frac{a}{\sin \alpha} = \frac{b}{\sin \beta} = \frac{c}{\sin \gamma}$$

C. Law of tangents

  (1) $\dfrac{a - b}{a + b} = \dfrac{\tan \frac{1}{2}(\alpha - \beta)}{\tan \frac{1}{2}(\alpha + \beta)}$

  (2) $\dfrac{a - c}{a + c} = \dfrac{\tan \frac{1}{2}(\alpha - \gamma)}{\tan \frac{1}{2}(\alpha + \gamma)}$

  (3) $\dfrac{b - c}{b + c} = \dfrac{\tan \frac{1}{2}(\beta - \gamma)}{\tan \frac{1}{2}(\beta + \gamma)}$

D. Area of triangle

  (1) area $= \frac{1}{2}$ base $\times$ height

  (2) area $= \frac{1}{2} bc \sin \alpha = \frac{1}{2} ab \sin \gamma = \frac{1}{2} ac \sin \beta$

  (3) area $= \sqrt{s(s - a)(a - b)(s - c)}$, where $s = \frac{1}{2}(a + b + c)$

  (4) area $= rs$, where r is the radius of the circle inscribed in the triangle and s is the semiperimeter given in D(3) above.

E. Radius r of circle inscribed in a triangle

$$r = \sqrt{\frac{(s - a)(s - b)(s - c)}{s}}$$

De Moivre's Theorem: If n is any positive integer, then

  $[r(\cos \theta + i \sin \theta)]^n = r^n(\cos n\theta + i \sin n\theta)$

The theorem also holds for all rational values of n. Hence, if $n = 1/m$,

  $[r(\cos \theta + i \sin \theta)]^{1/m} = r^{1/m}\left(\cos \dfrac{\theta}{m} + i \sin \dfrac{\theta}{m}\right)$

To find the m mth roots of a complex number, use

  $[r(\cos \theta + i \sin \theta)]^{1/m} = r^{1/m}\cos\left(\dfrac{\theta}{m} + \dfrac{360k}{m}\right) + \sin\left(\dfrac{\theta}{m} + \dfrac{360k}{m}\right)$

where m is a positive integer and $k = 1, 2, \ldots, m$.

PANEL 10

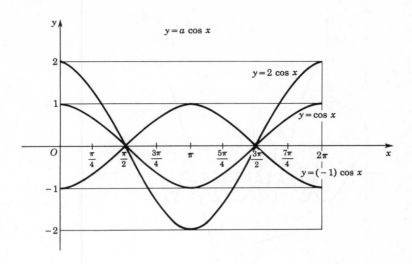

PANEL 11

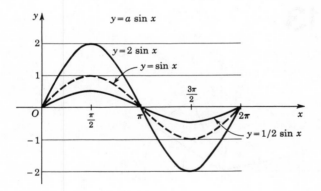

PANEL 12

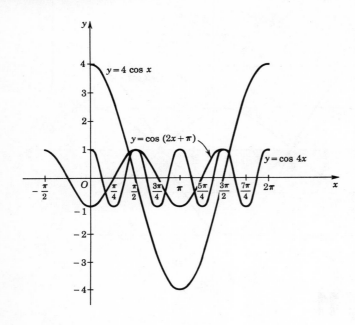

PANEL 13

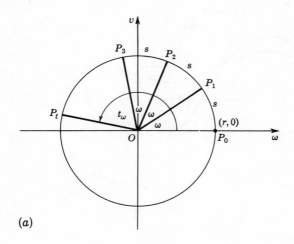

(a)

PANEL **13** *(continued)*

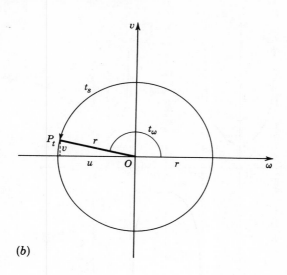

(b)

PANEL **14**

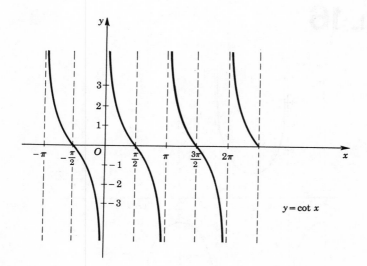

$y = \cot x$

PANEL 15

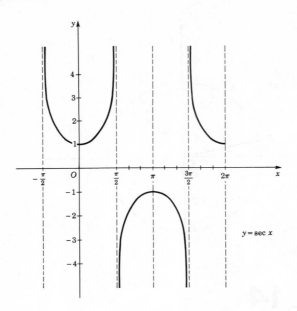

$y = \sec x$

PANEL 16

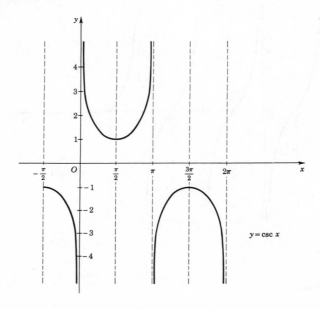

$y = \csc x$

PANEL 17

$y = \arcsin x$

The principal-value branch, $y = \arcsin x$ is indicated by the heavy line.

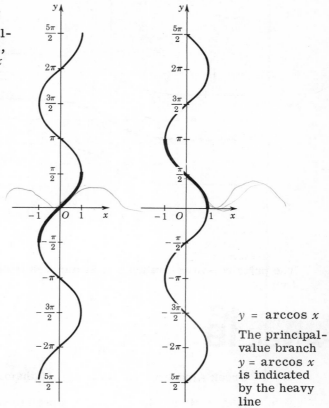

$y = \arccos x$

The principal-value branch $y = \arccos x$ is indicated by the heavy line

PANEL 18

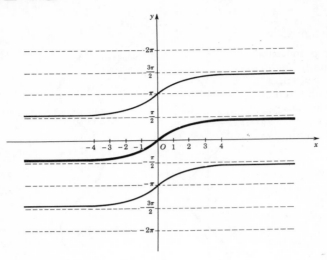

$y = \arctan x$
The principal-value branch $y = \text{Arctan } x$ is indicated by the heavy line.

PANEL 19

Greek Alphabet

A	α	Alpha	N	ν	Nu
B	β	Beta	Ξ	ξ	Xi
Γ	γ	Gamma	O	o	Omicron
Δ	δ	Delta	Π	π	Pi
E	ϵ	Epsilon	P	ρ	Rho
Z	ζ	Zeta	Σ	σ	Sigma
H	η	Eta	T	τ	Tau
Θ	θ	Theta	Υ	υ	Upsilon
I	ι	Iota	Φ	ϕ	Phi
K	κ	Kappa	X	χ	Chi
Λ	λ	Lambda	Ψ	ψ	Psi
M	μ	Mu	Ω	ω	Omega

Mathematical Symbols

$\vert\ \vert$	absolute value
$\triangle$	triangle
$\angle$	angle
$\approx$	is approximately equal to
$<$	is less than
$\leq$	is less than or equal to
$>$	is greater than
$\geq$	is greater than or equal to
$=$	is equal to
$\neq$	is not equal to
$\cong$	is congruent to
$\sim$	is similar to
$\pm$	plus or minus

$x = \arcsin y$
$x = \sin^{-1} y$
$\left\{\begin{array}{l}\text{read "}x\text{ is an angle}\\\text{whose sine is }y\text{"}\\\text{or "}x\text{ is an arc sine}\\\text{of }y\text{" or "}x\text{ is an in-}\\\text{verse sine of }y\text{"}\end{array}\right.$

INDEX

Numbers following entries refer to frames

Absolute value, 1418
  of a complex number, 1680
Amplitude, complex number, 1684
  of sine function, 589, 1230
Angle, 1
  coterminal, 38
    elevation and depression, 277
  equal, 34
  initial and terminal sides, 5
  measure of, 6, 18
  positive and negative, 8
  quadrantal, 33
  reference angle, 363
  special angles, 225
  standard position, 11
  vertex, 1
Applications, 269, 1297
Area, sector of a circle, 102
Asymptotes, vertical, 1370

Circle, unit, 105, 176, 1135
Circular functions, 1125
  magnitude, 1155
Circumference of a circle, 55
Commutative property, 1412, 1602
Complex numbers, 1529
  absolute value (modulus), 1680
  addition and subtraction, 1586
  amplitude (argument), 1684
  conjugate, 1580
  definition, 1551
  DeMoivre's theorem, 1756
  division, 1611
  division polar form, 1745
  geometric addition, 1635
  geometric representation, 1628
  imaginary part, 1558
  multiplication, 1592
    in polar form, 1724
  ordered-pair notation, 1585
  trigonometric form (polar), 1673

Composition of ordinates, 1297,
    1358
Coordinates, 108
  ordinate, abscissa, 297
  polar, 1456, 1458, 1459
  rectangular, 1477
Cycle (vibration), 1225, 1317

DeMoivre's theorem, 1756
Discontinuous function, 430, 591
Distance between two points, 133

Equation, conditional, 775
  radical, Appendix B
  trigonometric, 981

Formulas (derivation), addition,
    622
  double-angle, 672
  half-angle, 694
  law, of cosines, 447
    of sines, 482
  products to sums, 701
  sums to products, 711
  three theorems from geometry,
    766
Frequency, 1318
Function, 113, 288, 1126
  addition, 1179
  composition, 1200
  domain, range, 416, 1128, 1947
  inverse, 1897
  multiplication, 1198
  periodic, 1179
  single-valued, 1936

Graphs, circular functions, 1204
  composition of ordinates, 1297
  cosecant function, 1378
  cosine function, 417
  cotangent function, 1371

Graphs (Continued)
  inverse trigonometric function,
    1942
  secant function, 1378
  sine function, 399
  tangent function, 426, 1366
Greek letter symbols, 8, Panel 19

Half line, 1
Heron's formula, 766

Identity, 775
  proofs, 833
  suggestions for solving, 832
Interpolation, 1174, Appendix A
Inverse trigonometric function,
  1897
  domain and range, 1948
  evaluation, 1980
  graphs, 1942, 2040
  notation, 1925, 1958
  principal value, 1914, 1952

Measure of an angle, 6
  change, 57
  degree, 18
  radian, 44
  revolutions, 6
Modulus, 1680
Motion, clockwise and counter-
    clockwise, 9
  periodic, 1178
  simple harmonic, 1315
  uniform circular, 1315, 1343

Parallelogram law, 1641
Perimeter, 1069
Permissible values, 788
Polar coordinates, 1456
  axis, 1458
  pole, 1458
  radius vector, 1459
Pythagorean relations, 781

Quadrant, 30

Radian, 44, 444, 1170
Radius vector, 1459
Ray, 1
Real numbers, 1130
  integers, 1532

Real Numbers (Continued)
  irrational numbers, 1541
  rational numbers, 1539
Reciprocal relations, 791
Reduction formulas, 283
Resultant, 1417, 1509
Review of algebra, 605

Scalar, 1392
Series, 262
Shift (phase shift), 1247, 1321
Sides of an angle, 1
  initial and terminal, 5
Solution of triangles, 447
  ambiguous case, 506, 1119
Special angles, complementary,
  758
  coterminal, 325
  functions, 225, 568

Tangent and cotangent relations,
    (quotient relations), 781
Trigonometric equations, 981
Trigonometric functions, approxi-
    mate values, 263
  cosine θ, 119
  cotangent θ, cosecant θ,
    secant θ, 721
  domain and range, 416, 422, 433
  graphs, 399
  period, cosine, 421
    sine, 405, 586, 1179, 1236
    tangent, 429
  range of values, 391
  sine θ, 113
  special angles, 225
  tangent θ, 187
Trigonometric identities, 198, 742

Unit circle, 105, 176, 1135

Vectors, 1385, 1633
  addition of, 1397
  centered, 1415
  components of, 1417
  equivalent, 1387
  radius, 1459
  resultant, 1417
  scalar, 1392
  zero, 1395